Latin American Tokens

Catalog and Guide Book

by Russell Rulau

An illustrated, priced catalog of the unofficial coinage of
Latin America – used in plantation, mine, mill
and dock – from 1700 to the 20th century.

Special Consultants

David E. Henkle

George Lill III	Jorge Ortiz Murias
Efrain Archilla-Diez	Wes Scharlow
Clyde Hubbard	Gregory G. Brunk

Arthur Garnett

First Edition

This book is dedicated to my wife,
Darlene,
without whose support and encouragement
this project would have remained a dream.

Published by

krause
publications
700 E State St., Iola, WI 54990-0001

Library of Congress Catalog Number: 92-71454
ISBN: 0-87341-200-1

Printed in the United States of America

Introduction

Collectors who are drawn to Latin American tokens have always faced daunting obstacles. What is available? What is it worth? Where does it come from? When was it made, and why? Why are some pieces seen so frequently?

Why is it that I can't seem to find anyone who can answer my questions? Am I in a collecting field that will prove a waste of time, and money?

Such questions plagued collectors in the 19th century and continue to cause unease today. The road maps available to collectors of many other token series have not been available to guide them through the obstacles to collecting satisfaction in the Latin series.

A few Europeans such as Josef Neuman, Jules Fonrobert, Georg von Ulex-Hamburg, Adolf Weyl, Jacques Schulman I and Adolph Hess spent years recording the series. A few Americans such as the Guttag Brothers, Ole P. Eklund, Howard Gibbs, John W. Scott, Henry A. Ramsden and Howland Wood devoted enormous energies in the same direction.

Yet only a few countries ever enjoyed the kind of coverage that the hobby needs: An illustrated, priced catalog arranged in a user-friendly manner, with such niceties as a glossary, triple-subject index, diesinker list and background history. Since 1960 catalogs have appeared which detail Puerto Rico, Guatemala, Danish West Indies, British Caribbean, Chile nitrate, Dutch Caribbean, Colombia mitads, and other areas, but nothing whatever to serve as a road map to the whole interconnected series of hacienda, mine, industry and store tokens.

Latin American Tokens: A Guide Book and Catalog serves as that blueprint to the series for collector, dealer, student or historian. It took about four years to complete, but would have taken far longer were it not for the existence of the Henkle manuscript, about which we'll write more inside.

Your author had been collecting coins about two years when, in 1941, I purchased an 1882 Puerto Rico almud token. It was my first Latin token. A long time later, about 1965, I acquired a dozen Danish West Indies tokens, and this began a more serious inquiry into the whole expanse of tokens from south of the Rio Grande.

That this catalog may be more than its user had hoped is my wish.

Russell Rulau
Iola, Wisconsin
August, 1992

Preface

This guide book and catalog of Latin American tokens is intended to identify and value those tokens in the hands of the average collector, and to reveal the historical setting for their existence.

It is also intended as a guide to the entire field for the specialist. Copious footnotes and multiple cross-references to published works should aid even the advanced numismatist.

The heart and soul of Latin American token collecting is the workplace tally used in lieu of money on agricultural and stock raising estates and in the mines, mills, and docks. These so-called hacienda or tienda de raya (company store) tokens were outlawed in most of the republics in the 1902-1925 period, but their use was an integral part of the culture of North and South America and their roots as *moneda del pueblo* (money of the people) go back to 16th century Mexico and 17th century Chile and Peru.

In selecting tokens for inclusion in this catalog, we were guided by three premises: (1) If the token is common and is likely to fall into the hands of novice collectors, it will be included. (2) If the token is "classic" — that is, cataloged by Fonrobert, Ulex, Eklund or Scott and thus exposed for many years to hobbyists, it will be included. (3) If the token has achieved a high price at public auction or is otherwise historic, it will be included. The third category includes each nation's first token coinage.

A pioneering international catalog such as this cannot substitute for the specialized catalogs of each individual country which are in existence, nor is it so intended. An extensive bibliography refers the collector to published works in those areas. As advanced collectors know, alas, many countries have no specialized catalog even today, and many catalogs that do exist lack those all-important ingredients: Prices and photographs!

Arrangement of the Catalog

Latin American tokens are divided geographically into the nation in which they were issued. *as that nation's borders exist today.*

A token issued in a part of Bolivia or Peru lost to Chile after the War of the Pacific will be found under Chile. One issued in a part of Colombia lost to Panama in 1903 will be found under Panama. One issued in Danish West Indies, Curacao or Essequebo will be found under U.S. Virgin Islands, Netherlands Antilles or Guyana, respectively.

Nations or colonies are arranged alphabetically within their area (South America, Central America, West Indies). Each nation's major divisions (state, province, department, municipio) are then arranged alphabetically, and under each division is arranged alphabetically the specific location, usually municipality but sometimes county, parish or district. Where state or department is known but locale is not, the token will be found under an Uncertain grouping at the division's end.

Each nation has some tokens which are known to be from that country but which have not been sited. These are gathered in an Unattributed section at the end of each nation's listing.

Tokens are arranged alphabetically within each city or municipality by the *surname of the issuer* or the *first word of a title* where these are given on a token. Where the token states merely J.S. or H. y Cia., it is placed under 'S' or 'H' respec-

tively. A great deal of flexibility has been exercised here.

Many tokens give the name of the estate or mine as well as the name of the owner. Sometimes only a hacienda name appears. Hacienda (finca, fazenda, cafetal, estancia) names usually are given under surnames in title heads.

To find where your token is listed, use the index. Locate family name, hacienda name or locality name on the token, and check this out. The triple-indexing used in this reference should aid collectors. Attributing tokens which bear no words will be more difficult, but devices are also indexed.

Every token cataloged is given a line listing followed by a complete description. The line listing consists of a token number, date, metal, size and value in up to four condition grades. The description includes catalog numbers assigned by others. Background notes follow many issuers' tokens.

Dates given in the clear such as 1828 are those appearing on the token. Dates in parentheses such as (1828) are our estimates of issue date.

Where the token's "metal" is vulcanite, celluloid, cardboard or plastic, the description includes color. Under size, an entry such as 22mm means round, 22 millimeters in diameter. If a shape other than round is described, an abbreviation such as Scal or Oct appears before the diameter.

Attributing Latin America Tokens

The majority of the tokens cataloged inside are attributed to their nation of origin. About 125 years of published attributions — and errors — were considered in making our own judgements.

Still, this book contains errata in attributions. We are not satisfied with many of the conclusions in the catalog. The Las Palmas tokens of Mexico/Panama, the Pilar and Belen and F.C. tokens of Mexico/Cuba/Costa Rica and many other quixotic pieces need more research.

Where there has been a dispute that seems reasonable, the footnotes record this, so the catalog's user may exercise his own judgement.

A small Maverick section appears at the catalog's end. This contains tokens about which we could not hazard an estimate as to their origin (other than Latin America).

The great Ole P. Eklund spent the years 1911-1936 recording the existence of Latin American tokens and his unpublished manuscript details his own conclusions on attribution. The Eklund ms. contains many errors, but his latter-day admirers have corrected most of them.

Collectors who wish to provide information for subsequent editions of this catalog may write: Russell Rulau, Krause Publications, Iola, Wis. 54990.

The Henkle Manuscript

Hobbyists, it is said, generate devotion.

Nothing except love of hobby could account for the existence of the unpublished (and probably unpublishable) Henkle manuscript.

For 12 years Chicagoan David E. Henkle placed into his computer every bit of data known or guessed about every token issued in or for every Latin American nation. This includes such modern pieces as gambling chips, food stamp tokens, parking and vending machine and amusement tokens, and everything issued earlier that could be traced.

Every published work in every language, plus thousands of fixed price lists and auction catalogs, are being fed systematically into the work. The cross-referencing achieved has caused observers to marvel, because specialists in one country's tokens seldom get the opportunity to compare conclusions that stretch across frontiers.

A full description of each side of every token is included, and only paper money is excluded. (Cardboard chits are included, as are tokens in plastic, bakelite, vulcanite, leather, bone and many other substances, as well as all metals.)

In early 1988 Henkle agreed to collaborate on the reference work before you now. It has provided us with the best possible answer to "What's out there?" that plagues every pioneering cataloger. Every project must start somewhere, but the Henkle manuscript served as a trampouline to get us jump-started.

Will the Henkle work ever be published? We'd guess no in its present form because it would need critical editing and compacting to make it usable for the collecting public. As a working tool, however, it demonstrates better than anything I've ever seen how the magic of the computer has enhanced numismatic research.

Lest someone conclude that the computer will replace research in numismatics, we hasten to add that only human persistence driven by devotion matters. There is no monetary or fame award for such work as the Henkle manuscript, only personal satisfaction.

Our deepest gratitude is extended to David Henkle for his collaboration in making *Latin American Tokens* better!

Valuations

What is it worth? is almost as important as What is it? in numismatics. Our long experience as a numismatic editor and author taught us one salient fact: Never produce a catalog without prices. An unpriced catalog may be respected, but it will not be an essential tool.

The tokens of a few countries such as Puerto Rico, Guatemala and Trinidad are well-evaluated, but these are the exception. The prices given herein are our best estimates of what these pieces are worth in the 1990's.

The Henkle manuscript lists almost every published price in auction catalog or fixed price list since about 1980, a tremendous resource in estimating values. It also records what its compiler and others paid privately for pieces, back to 1963.

Our panel of contributors set estimates on many other pieces which are not known to have sold in recent years.

The pricing of Latin American tokens is in its infancy. Except for hoard material which surfaces occasionally, the pieces are rather scarce — probably too scarce to keep today's price levels low as new collectors and dealers are brought into the field by this general reference and what will follow.

Just a word of warning to novice collectors: Dealer price lists may say "not in Rulau" as an indication of scarcity. We have done our best to include everything that is truly common, but this catalog is *representative* rather than complete, by design.

Many numismatic dealer firms have collaborated in our price estimates, but in each case the final decision has been our own.

Metals

Aluminum	pure aluminum, silvery △△	Nickel	pure nickel, silvery, magnetic *
Brass	copper-zinc alloy, yellowish	Pewter	copper-tin alloy, gray-white **
Bronze	copper-tin alloy, brownish	Pot Metal	lead-based alloy, dark
Copper	pure copper, reddish	Silver	silver-copper alloy
Cupronickel	copper-nickel alloy *	Steel	iron alloy, silvery, magnetic
Galvanized Iron	zinc on iron, grayish	Tin	pure tin ***
German Silver	copper-nickel-zinc alloy *	Vulcanite	hardened rubber + +
Gold	gold-copper alloy	White Metal	lead-tin alloy, grayish-white
Goldine	gilt brass alloy	Zinc	pure zinc, grayish
Iron	pure iron, grayish, magnetic		

* It is frequently difficult to tell nickel and its principal alloys apart. New, they all resemble silver and look much alike. Pure nickel is magnetic, however, and only a small amount of impurity removes the magnetic quality. Cupronickel resists tarnish, while German silver (also called nickel-silver, argentan and other names) tarnishes much like silver. The catalog may well be in error in describing some of these nickel-alloy pieces.

** The best pewters are made of 90% tin and 10% copper, but in the 19th century antimony and bismuth partly replaced copper. In the cheapest pewters, lead replaces part of the tin. All these pewters look much alike.

*** Pure tin is seldom used in token manufacture. Old catalogs refer to "tin" pieces; what is meant is generally silvered white metal, a silver-gilt-surfaced lead-tin alloy, which is beautiful.

+ + Vulcanite is, and was, expensive to use for token manufacture, but it had the happy facility of resisting airborne contaminants such as those encountered in the Chilean deserts. Molded vulcanite tokens are almost always attractively colored, and this catalog lists known colorations.

△△ Very few trade tokens, store cards or medals were made of aluminum prior to 1890. It was too expensive for such use. But its price dropped to U.S. $1.50 a pound in 1891 and to 75 cents in 1893. In the Latin American series, most aluminum tokens appeared in the 1893-1920 period, and again since 1950.

NOTE: Certain other substances are cataloged herein, namely Leather, Cardboard, Celluloid, Bone, Ivory, Wood, Mother-of-Pearl, Bakelite, Plastic, etc. These terms are self-explanatory and should cause the reader little trouble.

Items Included

Hacienda Tokens
Tlacos
Tokens for Value
Currency Tokens
Advertising Checks
Work Checks or Talleys
Vulcanite Tokens
Selected Medalets (under 33mm)

Membership Medals

Items Excluded

Transportation Tokens
Telephone Tokens
Car Wash Tokens
Military Tokens
Shell & Mirror Cards
Plastic Tokens
Amusement Tokens
Leprosaria Tokens

Modern Tokens ("modern" means after a certain date in each country; e.g. 1902 in Cuba, 1917 in Mexico, 1920 in Guatemala, etc.)

Geography Included

All Western Hemisphere except:
United States (continental)
Canada
Alaska
Bermuda
Greenland

HISTORY OF THE TLACO IN MEXICO

Mexico was the first area in the New World to produce private token coinage, much earlier than the United States and Canada.

The reason it did boils down to one inescapable fact: Mexico had the most advanced civilization in the New World, wrested from the Aztec and Mayan and Europeanized by the Spaniard.

There seemed an aversion on the part of Spanish authorities to produce small change coins of legal tender status in copper. Viceroy Antonio de Mendoza struck some copper coins in 4 and 2-maravedi denominations in 1542, but only in the amount of 200,000 pesos.

Then the great copper hiatus began and it was not until 1814 that Viceroy Felix Maria Calleja del Rey finally caused copper coins to be struck at the Mexico City Mint, and these were in the denominations of pilon (1/16 real), tlaco (1/8 real) and double tlaco (1/4 real) — all units quite familiar to the citizenry who had long used copper tokens.

Where and when did the private issuance of tlacos and pilones begin? Various authorities have concluded that it began in Mexico City and, more precisely, within the plan area made by the architect Garcia Bravo who had been commissioned by Hernan Cortes to build a modern city over the ruins of destroyed Aztec Tenochtitlan.

Miguel L. Muñoz wrote in 1976: "We have little doubt that it was precisely in this location (the Traza, or plan area) that were born the tlacos and pilones; first the viceregal (1542) and a little later (1550-52) the private."

When the Spaniards came to Tenochtitlan in 1519 it was the most important city in Mexico. So much so that it merited the name Great Tenochtitlan. In 1550, as a Spanish city, it became the most important city on the North American continent.

It was in Mexico City that there was a need for copper coins and it was in Mexico City that there were the means for their fabrication.

A number of tlacos emanating from the city refer in their legends to certain sites, such as Puentes (bridges), Esquinas (corners) and other locales.

The second part of the question — When did this begin — requires more investigation. In his 1935 numismatic essay, Manuel Romero de Terreros wrote:

"During much of two centuries the commerce of New Spain was in need of copper coins for small transactions, and due to the lack of change for specie (silver), beans of cacao were used in their place.

"By the middle of the 18th century, storekeepers had recourse to the use of tokens or jetons in the style of fractional coins, resulting in each merchant making, for his account and under his own responsibility, cuartillas and tlacos that equaled respectively the royal cuartos and octavos — 3 and 1 1/2 centavos (hundredths) of a peso."

Another researcher, Roman Beltran Martinez, wrote:

"The storekeepers continued the use of cacao as money, but since the beginning of the 18th century invented and circulated tokens known by the name of tlacos or clacos, Mexican words which signified La Mitad (the half). The cuarto and cuartillo, transformed by the people to 'cuartilla,' divided it into two parts called TLACO and this was subdivided into two parts called PILON.

"Since the middle of the 18th century this pernicious custom extended to the mining centers and the haciendas of the viceroyalty, until it permeated all of (Spanish) America — leading to the origin of the 'tienda de raya' (company store) and to the consequent disgrace of the abuse of labor."

Dr. Alberto F. Pradeau, in 1963, wrote:

"During the first quarter of the 18th century, storekeepers issued tokens or chits which circulated as tlacos and pilones known as necessity pieces, while the smallest coin minted by the colonial government was the half real of silver."

The oldest *dated* tokens found by the American Numismatic Society study in 1949 bore the dates 1750 and 1767.

Miguel L. Muñoz summed up in 1976: "If the first viceregal tlacos and pilones disappeared from circulation in 1550 and no private tlaco could be found before 1750, but there still remained the great necessity for fractional coins, why did not the Europeans who preferred metal coins of low value produce them in place of cacao?

"We conclude that in the 16th and 17th centuries tokens circulated in all of (Spanish) America just as small coins did in Europe. The custom of making tokens intensified little by little until the 18th century...Before 1700 there apparently were no private tokens bearing dates."

Humberto Burzio found in the archives in Lima, Peru, a clear reference to "tlacos" used in butcher shops as substitutes for regal coins in June, 1570.

The most irrefutable proof that private tokens came into use in Mexico City soon after the Spanish conquest — and definitely by 1550 — was the 1768 official report of the investigation into monetary matters by Agustin de Coronas y Paredes, who noted that tokens had been in use at that time "for 2 1/2 centuries."

Beginning in Mexico City about 1550, the practice of issuing tokens gradually reached the interior of the country. This greatly increased the money supply available to the common people of Mexico; a discussion of that occurs elsewhere in this catalog.

The word TLACO comes from the Nahuatl word TLAHCO, meaning "half."

In reality tlaco means much more than a token for 1/8 real. It was a word of the common people for money itself. Even today it is common to hear a person say "No tengo ni tlaco" (I have no tlaco) when he means "I have no money."

Classification of tlacos and pilones may be divided into three convenient groups:

Colonial tlacos: 1550 - 1821.

Independence tlacos: 1822 - 1867.

Modern tlacos (tokens): 1868 - 1917.

The issue and circulation of private token coinages was prohibited by the Constitution of 1917.

Abbreviations

abt	about	ms.	manuscript
A-D	Archilla-Diez	no.	number
alum	aluminum	N/Steel	nickel-plated steel
ANA	American Numismatic Association	obv.	obverse
ANS	American Numismatic Society	oct	octagonal
Bol.	Bolivian	PF	proof
Bs As	Buenos Aires	pl.	plated
cia.	compania	P-L	proof-like
CN	cupronickel	poss.	possibly
co.	company	prob.	probably
coll.	collection	prov.	province
cop	copper	P.R.	Puerto Rico
ctsp	counterstamped	R.	rarity (number)
dept.	department	r.	right
diff.	different	rect	rectangular
EF	extremely fine	rev.	reverse
Ek.	Eklund	R-F	Rulau-Fuld
ex-	out of (collection)	Rv:	reverse
F	fine	S/Br	silvered brass
Fon.	Fonrobert	S/Brass	silvered brass
G	good	sc	scalloped
G/Br	gilt brass	scal	scalloped
G-Cop	gilt copper	Schiaf.	Schiaffino
G-H	Gould-Higgie	S/Cop	silvered copper
Gilt/B	gilt brass	scrc	scarce
Gilt/C	gilt copper	silv.	silver
GS	German silver	SNdeM	Sociedad Numismatica de Mexico
G/WM	gilt white metal	Span.-Am.	Spanish-American
hcda	hacienda	sq	square
hex	hexagonal	svd.	silvered
hexag	hexagonal	S/WM	silvered white metal
HT	Hard Times	TAMS	Token and Medal Society
HTT	Hard Times token	triang	triangular
hno.	hermano (brother)	U.	Ulex
hnos.	hermanos	Unc	uncirculated
irreg	irregular	VF	very fine
Jam.	Jamaican	VG	very good
KM	Krause-Mishler	W.	Weyl
l.	left	w/	with (whatever)
L.	Leslie	w/o	without
L&P	Leslie-Pradeau	WM	white metal
Mex.	Mexican	Y	Yeoman
mfr. no.	manufacturer's number	Yeo.	Yeoman
mm	millimeters		

CONTRIBUTORS TO LATIN AMERICAN TOKENS

David T. Alexander
Alcedo Almanzar
Efrain Archilla-Diez
Dr. Luis A. Asbun-Karmy
Don Bailey
Gonzalo Barinaga
Ralph W. Behringer
Enrique Bernal M.
Herman Blanton
Frederick Borgmann
Paul Bosco
Colin R. Bruce
Dr. Gregory Brunk
Lester Burzinsky
Carl W. A. Carlson
William B. Christensen
Roberto E. Diaz
Dr. Richard Doty
Roland Elie
L. B. Fauver
Georg Förster
Victor Gadoury
James Garner
Arthur Garnett
Cory Gillilland
Eugene E. Hamlin
Dick Hanscom
Rich Hartzog
David E. Henkle
Serge Huard

Clyde Hubbard
Louis Hudson
Jorge A. Janson
Charles L. Jason
William M. Judd
David A. King
James D. King
Charles E. Kirtley
Dr. John Kleeberg
Kurt R. Krueger
Elwin C. Leslie
George Lill III
Dulce Ludolf C.
Alan Luedeking
Thomas Michael
Soheyla Nojumi
Numismatica Independencia SRL
Francisco Ordonez C.
Jorge Ortiz Murias
Jaime Otero M.
Charles K. Panish
Antonio E. Pedraza
Pe$os Numismatica Profesional
Carol Plante
Miguel A. Pratt Mayans
Dr. Noemi A. Prieto
Carlos A. Pusineri Scala
Toby Qualls
William Randel
Fred L. Reed III

Dana Roberts
Richard Rossa
Wes Scharlow
David E. Schenkman
Dale A. Seppa
Jim Shipley
Kenneth Smith
Juan Socias Lopez
James O. Sweeny
Steve Tanenbaum
Hank Thoele
David Thompson
Ana Maria Cross de Torres
Sergio Torres Martinez
James A. Warmus
Mickey Yablan
Dr. Alan York
Joseph H. Zaffern
Al Zaika

American Numismatic Association
American Numismatic Society
Amos Press Inc.
Asociacion Numismatica Española
Casa Independencia Museo, Asuncion
Fomento Cultural Banamex A.C.
Smithsonian Institution
Sociedad Numismatica de Mexico
Token and Medal Society

Gratitude is extended to these pioneer catalogers of the past...

Raymond Byrne
Henry Christensen
Ole P. Eklund
Jules Fonrobert
Guttag Brothers
Adolph Hess
Lyman H. Low
Miguel L. Muñoz
Josef Neumann
Sydney P. Noe
Roberto Pesant
Jess Peters
Dr. Alberto F. Pradeau
Kurt Prober
Henry A. Ramsden
Manuel Romero de Terreros
Friedrich, Freiherr von Schrötter
Hans M. F. Schulman
Jacques Schulman
John W. Scott
Erma C. Stevens
Georg F. Ulex-Hamburg
Adolf Weyl
P. H. Wittlin
Howland Wood

BIBLIOGRAPHY

GENERAL REFERENCE WORKS

Assay Offices of Great Britain, "Hallmarks on Gold, Silver and Platinum." (London, 1988)

Banister, Judith, ed., "English Silver Hall-marks." (London, 1970, New edition, 1990)

Britten, F. J., "Old Clocks and their Makers." 4th ed. (London, 1919) Lists 11,000+ European and American makers of watches and clocks before 1850.

Encyclopedia Britannica.

Gil-Montero, Martha, "Through the Portals of Stately Ranches." In *America* magazine. (History of Argentine estancias)

Gonzales Moscoso, Rene, "Diccionario Geografico Boliviano." (La Paz, Bolivia, 1984)

Jackson, Sir Charles J., "English Goldsmiths and their Marks." 2nd ed. (London, 1921; reprinted 1964). Lists 13,000+ marks of British and Irish gold and silversmiths.

Langer, William L., "An Encyclopedia of World History." (Boston, 1968)

Lavine, Harold, "Central America." Life World Library. (New York, 1964)

McBride, George McC., "The Land Systems of Mexico." (New York, 1923)

National Assoc. of Coffee, "The Directory of the National Association of Coffee." (Guatemala City, 1963)

U.S. Department of Commerce, "Commercial Directory of the American Republics." (Washington, D.C., 1898)

Vergara, J.R. & Baena, F.E., "Barranquilla su Pasado y su Presente." (Barranquilla, Colombia, 1922)

Wyler, Seymour B., "The Book of Old Silver." (New York, 1937)

GENERAL NUMISMATIC WORKS

Bergsoe. Sale of the Bergsoe collection by Jacques Schulman, Amsterdam, 1903.

Berry, George, "Ralph Heaton & Sons, Coiners." In *Coin News* of England for Sept. 1990.

Brunk, Gregory G., "American and Canadian Countermarked Coins." (Rockford, Ill., 1987)

Brunk, Gregory G., "Merchant Countermarks on World Coins." (Rockford, Ill., 1989)

Byrne, Ray, "Coins, Tokens & Medals from the West Indies." (Decatur, Ill., 1975)

Christensen, Henry Inc. Various auction catalogs, 1975-89.

Christensen, Chriss, "Fake — Die Trial — Fantasy & Restrikes." in *TAMS Journal* for Feb. 1972. (Anillo Industries strikings from Los Angeles Rubber Stamp Co. dies)

Eklund, Ole P., "Catalogue of Tokens of Mexico, Central and South America and the West Indies." Unpublished manuscript, Spokane, Wash., 1936. (Original Eklund ms. presented to ANS was handwritten. Typed copy prepared 1979 by Jerry Schimmel.)

Fauver, L. B., "American Counters, Part 6, Latin America and Canada." (Menlo Park, Calif., 1990)

Fonrobert, Jules, "Die Jules Fonrobertsche Sammlung Mittel-und Sudamerikanischer Munzen und Medaillen." (Berlin, 1878)

Forrer, Leonard S., "Biographical Dictionary of Medallists." (London, 1904-30; 8 volumes)

Furber, E. A. (ed.), "The Coinages of Latin America and the Caribbean." In *The Numismatist* for 1911 to 1971. Reprint 1984 from *The Numismatist*.

Gadoury, V. & Elie R., "Monnaies de Necessite Francaises." (Monte Carlo, 1990)

Guttag. Catalog of the Julius Guttag collection by Edgar H. Adams, New York, 1929.

Hawkins, Roy N. P., "Catalogue of the Advertisement Imitations of 'Spade' Guineas and their Halves." In *British Numismatic Journal* for 1964. (Reprint ca 1966)

Henkle, David E., "Checklist of Latin American Tokens." Unpublished manuscript, Chicago, 1986-91.

Hudson, Louis. Mail bid sale 49 of April 30, 1990. (Greensboro, N.C.)

Krause, C. L. & Mishler, C., "Standard Catalog of World Coins." (Iola, Wis., 1990)

Krueger, Kurt R., Mammoth auction sale of April 16, 1991. (Iola, Wis.) 6125 lots.

Low, Lyman H. Sales of the Fisher collection, 1891; Betts collection, 1898, and Cutting collection, 1898. (New York)

Lyall, Bob, "The Tokens, Checks, Metallic Tickets, Passes and Tallies of the British Caribbean & Bermuda." (Lake Mary, Fla., 1988)

Medina, Jose T., "Las Monedas Obsidionales Hispano-Americanas." (Santiago, 1919; Reprint San Juan, P.R. 1984)

Neumann, Josef, "Beschreibung der Bekanntesten Kupfermunzen." Volume III. (Prague, 1863). Pgs. 21-62. Reprint, Leipzig, 1965.

Peters, Jess. Various auction catalogs.

Rulau Russell, "Discovering America: The Coin Collecting Connection." (Iola, Wis., 1989)

Rulau, Russell, "Latin American Token Finder." In *Numismatic Scrapbook Magazine* for Dec. 1970, Jan. 1971, Feb. 1971, April 1971 and May 1972. (Sidney, Ohio)

Rulau, Russell, "United States Merchant Tokens 1845-1860." 3rd ed. (Iola, Wis., 1990)

Rulau, Russell, "United States Trade Tokens 1866-1889." 2nd ed. (Iola, Wis., 1988)

Salbach, Sale of the Salbach collection by Jacques Schulman, Amsterdam, 1911.

Schimmel, Jerry F., "Worldwide Tokens." In *TAMS Journal* for Aug. 1985, Feb. 1986, Dec. 1986.

Schimmel, Jerry F., "German Tokens Part II: Colonial Issues Austria, Luxembourg, Switzerland and Other Areas." (San Francisco, 1988). Includes german-language tokens used in Brazil, Costa Rica, Guatemala and Venezuela.

Scott, John W., "J. W. Scott's Standard Catalogue No. 2, The Copper Coins of the World." (New York, 1913; reprint Oakdale, N.Y. 1963)

Smith, Kenneth E., "Catalogue of World Transportation Tokens and Passes, except North America." (Redondo Beach, Calif., 1967)

Smith, Kenneth E., "Catalogue of World Ferry, Ship and Canal Transportation Tokens and Passes." (Redondo Beach, Calif. 1981)

Ulex-Hamburg, Georg F., "Munzen und Medaillen von Nord, Central und Sud-Amerika." (Frankfurt/Main, 1908)

Weyl, Adolph, "Sammlung Amerikanischer Munzen & Medaillen." (Berlin, 1899). 4,032 lots; an important dating resource.

Weyl, Adolph, "Westindische Privatmunzen." In *Berliner (Munzblatter)* for July-Aug. 1882.

World Coins for Nov. 1972, pg. 1510. (Aneurol token)

Zay, Ernest, "Historire Monetaire des Colonies Francaises." (Paris, 1892). Supplement (Paris, 1904)

ARGENTINA

Bidone, Concepcion de, "'Pataqua', Una Moneda Privada en la Historia Pampa." In *Cuadernos de Numismatica y Ciencias Historicas* for Aug. 1986)

Catena, Teobaldo, "Medallistica del Instituto de Numismatica e Historia." (San Nicolas de los Arroyos, Argentina, 1986)

Rosa, Alejandro, "Medallas y Monedas de la Republica Argentina." (Buenos Aires, 1898)

Rosa, Alejandro, "Monetario Americano (Ilustrado) Clasificado por su Proprietario." (Buenos Aires, 1892)

Sanz, L.S. & Sanchez Caballero, H.A., "Catalogo de las Collecciones Medallisticas de la Academia Nacional de la Historia." (Buenos Aires, 1987). This 389-page tome is the best source on works of the Argentine diesinking firms. Only 1,500 copies were printed, dedicated to America's 500th anniv.

Woodside, William W., "Argentine Vineyard Tokens." In *TAMS Journal* for June 1972.

BAHAMAS

Leslie, Elwin, C., "Cat Cay Tokens of the Bahamas." In *The Numismatist* for Jan. 1964.

BELIZE

Craig, Dr., Alan K., "Coinage of British Honduras." In *The Numismatist* for Jul. & Aug. 1947.

BOLIVIA

Asbun-Karmy, Luis A., "Monedas Medallas Billetes Acciones y Documentos Bancarios de Bolivia." (Oruro, Bolivia, 1977)

Burnett, LTC Davis. "Bolivian Proclamation Coinage." (Virginia, Minn., 1987)

Leslie, Elwin C., "Bolivian Rubber Plantation Tokens from the Territory of Colonias." In *TAMS Journal* for April 1973.

Leslie, Elwin C., "Bolivian Silver Mine Tokens of the Huanchaca Company." In *TAMS Journal* for June 1972.

Lill, George III, "An Update for the Tokens of Antonio Vaca Diez." In *TAMS Journal* for Aug. 1988.

BRAZIL

De Barros, A.O.F., "Introduction to Brazilian Maverick Tokens." In *Numismatics International Bulletin* for 1989, pp. 29-43.

Ludolf, C., Dulce, "Estudo das Moedas Particulares no Brasil." In *Revista Numismatica* for Year XVI. (Sao Paulo, 1948)

Ludolf C., Dulce, "Moedas Particulares e Vales Metalicos do Brasil." (Rio de Janeiro, 1968)

Meili, Julius, "Das Brasilianische Geldwesen. II Theil. Die Munzen des Unabhangigen Brasilien 1822 bis 1900." (Zurich, 1905)

Rocha, Francisco Dias da, "Gabinete de Historia Natural e Archeologia." (Ceara, Brazil, 1911). Private tokens and counterstamps are listed on pp. 2-3, 66-111.

Scharlow, Wesley E., "A Brief History of the Ferry Boat Tokens of Rio de Janeiro." In *TAMS Journal* for Dec. 1987.

CHILE

Alaskan Token Collector & Polar Numismatist. Various issues dealing with Tierra el Fuego. (Fairbanks, Alaska, 1984-89)

Almanzar, Alcedo F., "Railroad Medals of the World, Part II: Chile." In El Dorado Coin Galleries auction catalog of Aug. 12, 1985.

Chanique B., Dagoberto, "Catalog Simplificado de las Fichas Salitreras." (Santiago, ND)

Christensen, William, "Paper Money of the Chilean Revolution of 1891." In *Numismatic Commentary* for Oct. 1987 and June 1988. (Catalogs the round cardboard tokens of the 1891 revolt)

Judd, William M. Fixed price sale list for 1989. (192 Chile lots)

Leslie, Elwin C., "Chilean Nitrate Mine and Related Tokens." In *TAMS Journal* for April 1980.

Leslie, Elwin C., "The Lota and Schwager Coal Mine Tokens of Central Chile." In *TAMS Journal* for Dec. 1972.

Leslie, Elwin C., "The Braden Copper Company of Chile Mine Store Tokens." (In *TAMS Journal* for 1973, pp. 91-95.

Wells, L. T., "Water, Bread and Meat: Payment for Work in the Atacama Desert." IN *TAMS Journal* for June 1988.

COLOMBIA

Anon., "Fichas de Colombia." In *Boletin Numismatico* number 19, for 1974. (Numismaticos Colombianos, Bogota)

Barriga del Diestro, Fernando, "Senas y Billetes Particulares." In *Boletin Numismatico* number 50, for 1990. (Bogota)

Bernal M., Enrique, "Fichas de Colombia Numismalia." (Caracas, 1988)

Leslie, Elwin C., "Colombia, South America Merchant Tokens struck over United States Hard Times Tokens." In *TAMS Journal* for Aug. 1973.

Sweeny, James O. & Bernal M., Enrique, "The MITAD Tokens of Latin America." (Lake Mary, Fla., 1991)

COSTA RICA

Schimmel, Jerry F., "Costa Rica Tokens." (San Francisco, 1984)

CUBA

Moreno Fraginals, Manuel, "El Token Azucarero Cubano." (Havana)

Pesant, Roberto, "Tokens of Some of Havana's Old Coffee Houses." In *Numismatic Scrapbook Magazine* for July 1965.

Pesant, Roberto, "The Sugar Estate Tokens of Cuba." In auction catalogs of Henry Christensen Inc., Spring 1968 thru Jan. 25, 1974.

Ramsden, Henry A., "A List of Tokens and Paper Notes Issued for the use of Sugar Estates on the Island of Cuba." (Barcelona, 1904)

ECUADOR

Bognoly, J. A. & Espinosa, J.M., "Las Islas Encantadas o el Archipielago de Colon." (Guayaquil, 1905)

Ortuno Carlos, "Historia Numismatica del Ecuador." Published by Banco Central de Ecuador.

Seppa, Dale, "Coins and Paper Money of the Galapagos Islands." (Unpublished manuscript, 1990)

EL SALVADOR

Ulloa Llach, Roberto, "The Tokens of El Salvador." Unpublished manuscript. (Santiago de Maria, El Salvador, 1980)

FALKLAND ISLANDS

Hanscom, Dick, "The Whaling Company Tokens of South Georgia Island." (In *Coin News* of England for Sept. 1991.

GUADELOUPE

Eckardt, K. V., "A West Indian Salt Tally." In *TAMS Journal* for Dec. 1987. Token of St. Barthelemy, Guadeloupe dependency.

GUATEMALA

Clark, Odis H. Jr., "The Token Coinage of Guatemala." (San Antonio, Texas, 1974)

Jason, Charles L., "Plantation & Merchant Tokens of Guatemala." (Shalimar, Fla., 1973)

Leslie, Elwin C., "The 'Pochuta' Coffee Plantation Tokens Belong to Guatemala." In *TAMS Journal* for April 1967. Supplement in *TAMS Journal* for Aug. 1967.

Mohler, Harry A., "Present Day Authorized Medals of Guatemala." (*In Medal Collector* for Feb. 1957.

Prober, Kurt, "Historia Numismatica de Guatemala." (Guatemala City, 1957; 2nd edition 1973)

Wallace, Holland, "Central American Coinage since 1821." (Weslaco, Texas, 1966). Counterstamped Guatemala centavos.

Weyl, Adolf, Catalog of the sale of April 11, 1899. (Berlin)

HONDURAS

Mabbott, Thomas, O., "Coinage of Tela, Honduras." In *The Numismatist* for May 1942.

JAMAICA

Byrne, Ray, "Banana Stem Money-Jamaican Hoard Uncovers New Tokens." In *World Coins* for Nov. 1972.

Thompson, David. "Chronic Shortage of Coins Dogged Jamaica through Most of its Existence." In *World Coin News* for Sept. 3, 1990.

MEXICO

Almanzar, Alcedo F., "Mexican Tokens from the 'Guatimoc' Coffee Plantation of L. R. Brewer." In *TAMS Journal* for June 1973.

Alpert, Stephen P., "A Preliminary Listing of Mexican Marriage Tokens." In *TAMS Journal* for 1974, pp. 182-184.

Bordenave, Vicente O., "Colima Coins Span Six Decades." In *World Coins* for Jan. 1970.

Brunk, Gregory G., "Some Apparently Unlisted Mexican Hacienda Tokens." In *TAMS Journal* for Aug. 1978.

Castaneda Rico, Jose, "Hacienda de Estipac." In *Plus Ultra* for Winter 1981, pgs. 4-8.

Castaneda Rico, Jose, "Tijuana and its Numismatics." In *Boletin de Sociedad Numismatica de Mexico* for Jan. 1982.

Deana Salmeron, Antonio, "Las Contrasenas del Cafetal 'Guatimoc'." In *Monedas* for March 1967.

Eklund, O. P. & Noe, S. P., "Hacienda Tokens of Mexico." (New York, 1949)

Fernandez, Garza, Mauricio, "Las Monedas Municipales Mexicanas." (Mexico City, 1979)

Gabriel, Don, "Too Tough To Die." In *World Coins* for May 1975. (Mexicali bar tokens)

Gomez Saborio, Gabriel, "Las Monedas de Hacienda de Mexico." In *Boletin de Sociedad Numismatica de Mexico* for June 1984 and Sept. 1984.

Grove, Frank W., "Tokens of Mexico." (Ontario, Calif., 1989)

Hattersley, Frank, "Anillo Patterns of Possible Mexican Usage." (In *Plus Ultra* for Autumn 1981, pgs. 3-6)

Leslie, Elwin C., "Santa Juliana Mining Co. Tokens." In *TAMS Journal* for Aug. 1971.

Leslie, E. C. & Pradeau, A. F., "Henequen Plantation Tokens of the Yucatan Peninsula." (Los Angeles, 1972)

Mosser Barendun, Oswaldo, "Monedas, Medallas y Fichas de Aguascalientes." In *Boletin de Sociedad Numismatica de Mexico* for Sept. 1956.

Munoz, Miguel L., "Tlacos y Pilones, La Moneda del Pueblo de Mexico." (Mexico City, 1976)

Olmedo, Benito, "Bolos." In *Boletin de Sociedad Numismatica de Mexico* for 1972, pp. 340-359.

Pedraza, Francisco J., "Los Tlacos y Pilones Mexicanos." (Puebla, Mexico, 1963)

Pradeau, Alberto F., "Store-Cards or Tokens of Mexico." In *Centennial Publication of the American Numismatic Society.* (New York, 1958). Pgs. 563-576, ed. by Harald Ingholt.

Romero de Terreros, Manuel, "Los Tlacos Coloniales de Mexico." (Mexico City, 1935)

Schrotter, Friedrich Freiherr von, "Mexikanische Haciendamarken." (Spandau, Germany, 1932)

Stevens, Erma C., "Privately Issued Storecards and Tokens-State of Sonora, Mexico." (Calif., 1970)

Utberg, Neil S., "Numismatic Sidelines of Mexico." (Texas, 1965)

Verrey, Claudio, "Monedas Municipales de Zamora Michoacan." In *Boletin de Sociedad Numismatica de Mexico* for Dec. 1976.

Verrey, Claudio, "Monedas Emitidas en la Villa de Lagos." In *Boletin de Sociedad Numismatica de Mexico* for Dec. 1977.

Verrey, Claudio, "Fichas de la Fabrica de Metepec." In *Boletin de Sociedad Numismatica de Mexico* for Dec. 1982.

NETHERLANDS ANTILLES

Byrne, Ray, "The Dutch Colonial Coins and Tokens of America (1645 to 1900)". In *The Numismatist* for June & July 1972.

Roehrs, Edward, "The Jinks of St. Eustatius-A Tentative Attribution." In *TAMS Journal* for Dec. 1983.

NICARAGUA

Lamb, Robert A., "A Check List of the Coins of Nicaragua." (1965)

Lamb, Robert A., "Nicaragua Token Dates from 1885." In *Numismatic Scrapbook Magazine* for July 1969.

PANAMA

Conte Porras, J., "Colleccion Numismatic Panamena." (Panama, 1982)

Grigore, Capt. Julius, "Coins & Currency of Panama." Iola, Wis., 1972. Contains valuable information on San Blas Indians.

Hamlin, Eugene E., "Canal Zone Brass Checks." In *The Panama Collector* for Sept. 1985.

Majilton, E. A., "Introduction to the Tokens of Panama." In *Journal of International Numismatics* for 1970, pp. 17-24.

Plumer, Warren L., "Panama & C. Z. Tokens, A Trial Listing." 2nd ed. (Doswell, Va., 1975)

Rose, Harvey I., "Palo Seco (Leper Colony) Tokens." In *Whitman Numismatic Journal* for 1967, pp. 542-543.

PARAGUAY

Pena, Enrique, "Monedas y Medallas Paraguayas." (Asuncion, 1900)

PERU

Aliaga Derteano, Luis, "Las Fichas Peruanas." In *Numismatica de la Sociedad Numismatica del Peru* for 1969-70.

Schiaffino, Jose A., "Las Fichas Peruanas." (Lima, 1984)

PUERTO RICO

Archilla-Diez, Efrain, "Catalogo Numismatico de Puerto Rico." (San Juan, P.R., 1990)

Banco Popular de Puerto Rico, "The Banco Popular de Puerto Rico Numismatic Collection." (San Juan, 1989)

Fernandez, Alexis O., "Some Errors in Puerto Rican Coins and Tokens." In *The Numismatist* for 1986, pp. 433-443.

Gonzales, Mariano A., "The Puerto Rican Coffee Plantation Tokens." In *The Numismatist* for Jan. 1951.

Gould, M. M. and Higgie, L. W., "The Money of Puerto Rico." (Racine, Wis., 1962)

Vaia, Dulio, "Plantation Tokens of Puerto Rico." (New York, 1980)

ST. LUCIA

Byrne, Ray, "Some Unlisted St. Lucia Coaling Tokens." In *Coins Magazine* for May, 1973.
Deveaux, Robert J., "A Century of Coaling in St. Lucia, including a Description of the Coaling Tokens." In *Numismatic Circular* for 1975, pp. 2-4, 50-54, 105.
McDowell, J. K., "St. Lucia Used Coaling Tokens." In *World Coins* for Aug. 1966.

SPAIN

Ministerio de Economia y Hacienda, "Carlos III y La Casa de la Moneda." 296 pgs. (Madrid, 1988)

TORTOLA

Pridmore, Fred, "Notes on Colonial Coins: The Virgin Islands, Tortola." In *Numismatic Circular* for 1959, pp. 116-117, 139-141, 179.

TURKS & CAICOS ISLANDS

Peterson, Mendel L., "Turks and Caicos Islands Currency." In *The Numismatist* for Oct. 1942.

VENEZUELA

Garriga, Gorgias R., "Fichas, Senas y Napas de Venezuela." (Caracas ?, 1979 ?). Part of the Cuadernos Lagoven series.
Landaeta R., Manuel, "Colleccion de Medallas, Monedas y Fichas de Manuel Landaeta Rosales." (Caracas, 1911)
Stohr, Tomas, "Table of the Best Known Tokens." (Maracaibo, 1965)

VIRGIN ISLANDS (U.S.)

Higgie, Lincoln W., "The Colonial Coinage of the U.S. Virgin Islands." (Racine, Wis., 1962)

TABLE OF CONTENTS

PART I

MEXICO

MEXICO

Mexican Hacienda Tokens

An excellent overview of Mexican haciendas and their place in Mexican life appeared in the 1923 book by George McC. McBride, *The Land Systems of Mexico*, published by the American Geographical Society.

The hacienda system Dr. McBride describes has not existed in Mexico, however, for about 70 years. The Mexican Revolution of 1911-17 cracked the entire structure and during and since the 1920's large estates have been broken up into much smaller units.

But the system of haciendas existed from Colonial times to the Revolution and must be considered by anyone collecting the tokens of Mexico.

Dr. McBride wrote:

"The haciendas of Mexico are the most conspicuous feature of the land system of the country. They give agricultural Mexico its distinctive cast, and, by their great size, create the impression that the entire land is divided into vast rural estates. These properties, indeed, are the only type of agricultural holding immediately visible to the traveler in many parts of Mexico, just as the *haciendado* is the only type of agriculturist whose interests reach beyond the immediate neighborhood of his home.

"Many of the haciendas are of very great extent; it is estimated that 300 of them contain at least 25,000 acres each; 116 have not less than 62,500 acres; 51 have approximately 75,000 acres; while 11 are believed to have 250,000 acres apiece.

"The Mexican hacienda seldom contains less than 25,000 acres — whether situated in the arid plains of the north, where land is worth little or nothing, or in the densely settled areas of the Mesa Central, where the price of land is high even in comparison with that of agricultural lands in other countries.

"The great size of these holdings is due, in part, to the fact that the typical hacienda aspires to be self-sustaining, and the variety of a countryside is taxed to render it independent. Hence, for the many different products required, different kinds of land must be included within its limits. In the first place, a large acreage of valley land is needed for the production of grain. These hundreds of thousands of acres of arable land form the nucleus of the estate.

"An *hacendado* would not, however, be satisfied to hold valley lands alone; for, in his economy, the products of the hills are only less important than those of the lowlands. Thus, the farm requires a supply of water, for irrigation as well as for the livestock; the hacienda must, therefore, include some stream, which should be controlled up to its headwaters in order to insure the undisputed use of the supply. Again, grazing land is needed for herds of cattle, horse, sheep and goats; this is found upon the parklike mountain sides and the alpine meadows.

"Timber is a prime necessity and is derived either from the deciduous trees that grow along the lower mountain slopes or from the pine forests that clothe the tops of the higher ridges. The products even of the wasteland are likewise essential, since from this are obtained stone and lime for building purposes, clay for adobe huts, coarse grass for thatched roofs, salt, and the wild fruits and herbs which are gathered for household use. The administration of such extensive properties necessarily present great difficulties.

"The haciendas are settlements complete in themselves. Indeed, few of these estates have less than 100, while many of them have as many as 1,000 inhabitants.

"In Michoacan there are two haciendas, Huaracha and Buenavista, each of which maintains over 2,000 persons; while in Morelos, Mexico, Puebla, Durango, Veracruz, Queretaro and Chihuahua there are others in which the number is not much smaller.

"The haciendas are all named; they appear on the maps, and they are important units of public administration, often being incorporated as *municipios*. They include all the customary accessories of an independent community, such as church, a store, a post office, a burying ground and sometimes a school or a hospital. Workshops are maintained, not only for repair but even for the manufacture of machinery and of the numerous implements required upon the estate. Over this aggregation the owner presides in a more or less patriarchal manner, the degree of paternal care or of tyranny varying with the character of the individual and with that of his superior employees."

Dr. McBride explains that tillable soil is chiefly to be found in the tableland section of Mexico, known as the *Mesa Central*, and that, with relatively unimportant exceptions, the exigencies of rainfall and soil impose conditions which made haciendas impossible elsewhere. In more modern times irrigation has somewhat affected these conditions. The Mesa Central is the most thickly populated section of Mexico. It surrounds the capital city, and its climatic conditions are admirable, since "altitude counteracts latitude with such nicety that the mean temperature over the entire plateau is nearly uniform."

Most of the haciendas are to be found in this section, and they provide the agricultural supplies not only for themselves but for the remainder of the country, where climatic conditions are less favorable. Something of the independent nature of these huge land holdings has been shown, and it will be apparent that conditions favorable to the untroubled operation of such large units encouraged conservatism on the part of the owners. The employment of native laborers and the faults of the peonage system led to occasional insurrections and explain some of the happenings in Mexico's history.

It is not surprising to find, under such conditions, that the owners of the haciendas found it necessary to have a circulating medium of low denomination, and that this medium should vary widely in form and reflect some of the independence that marks the life of the hacienda. It is this very diversity which has attracted the attention of numismatists to these tokens.

Circulation of the tokens was forbidden in 1917, and a provision that all salary payments must be made in legal tender was written into the Constitution of 1924. These tokens are rarely to be found in Mexico now, and there seems strong probability that most of them have been melted down or have disappeared for other reasons.

The many and great changes in Mexico during the period of their circulation are reflected in these substitutes for coin.

After 1871 the growth in commercial prosperity brought about the introduction of modern business tokens, machine made, which are quite different from the earlier pieces issued by the haciendas. While their legends are more explicit, the later issues have none of the appeal of the Colonial and Early Republican pieces.

Mexico City

Ciudad de Mexico, capital of Estados Unidos de Mexico, is the world's largest city, with a 1990 estimated population of 16 million. Located in the southern part of the Valley of Mexico, it occupies an ancient plain that once was a lake surrounded by mountains.

The city proper covers 147 square miles, but the greater metropolitan area covers 779 square miles.

The center of the powerful Aztec empire in the 14th, 15th and early 16th centuries, its name derives from *mexliapan* (lake of the moon) and *xitli* (center) — "city at center of the lake of the moon."

Aztec Indians arrived in the Valle de Mexico about 1221. In 1325 they built their city on a small island in Lake Texcoco, calling it Tenochtitlan ("place of the high priest Tenoch"). The city spread over the island's marshes and swamps, and was divided into *calpullis*, self-governed districts.

When Cortes and the Spaniards arrived in 1519, some 500,000 persons lived in Tenochtitlan. All the lake's islands had been united to form one large oval island connected to the mainland by three causeways — Tepeyac (north), Ixtapalapa (south) and Tacuba (west). The main temple and palace were located on a plaza called Zocalo (now Plaza de la Constitucion, hub of the modern city).

Cortes razed Tenochtitlan to the ground after its conquest in 1521, and by 1530 built a Spanish city on its ruins. The city was chartered in 1522 and became the capital of all Spanish America from Panama to Oregon.

The lakes of the Valle de Mexico floor were gradually filled and, in the 17th century, it became a well-laid-out city.

In 1824 the Distrito Federal was created, and the city was separated from the Estado de Mexico around it. In 1865 the city limits were expanded, and *colonias*, or *barrios*, began to grow up on the city's fringes.

Mexico City's altitude is 7350 feet. The Sierra de Pachuca range walls it in to the north, Serrania del Ajusco south, Sierra de las Cruces west, and Sierra Nevada east. Sierra Nevada contains the extinct volcanos Iztacihuatl (17,340 feet) and Popocatepetl (17,887 feet).

In 1971 the metropolitan area covered all of the Distrito Federal (except the rural area of Milpa Alta and its 10 municipios), plus 10 municipios in Estado de Mexico.

Counterfeit Colonial Tokens

There has been some limited forgery of Mexican Colonial copper tokens. Genuine pieces known to have been imitated are mentioned in the text. Fantasies are also pointed out where known.

We believe most bogus pieces were made in Mexico in the 1970's.

In most instances they are easy to detect because they differ from originals in noticeable respects.

Genuine specimens have been examined by the author in the American Numismatic Society, Smithsonian Institution and private collections, and bogus pieces have been noted by Gregory G. Brunk, Frank Grove, Arthur Garnett, William Judd, Clyde Hubbard and others.

The greatest danger is simply lack of knowledge. Few dealers or collectors have ever examined more than a few Colonial tokens. Buyer beware! Compare offered specimens with illustrations in this book; if they differ too much in size, motif or lettering, they are best avoided.

A Guadalajara, Mexico metalsmith made forgeries and fantasies of early (pre-1840) Mexican hacienda tokens in the 1970's. At first this workman had little knowledge of numismatics, apparently copying designs from *Numismatic Sidelines of Mexico* and from line drawings of genuine tokens.

Not knowing what sizes they should be, he chose U.S. half dollar size or larger for most of his products, which were made of red copper, artificially 'aged' after stamping. Most were round, but he also produced square, rectangular, diamond-shaped, triangular and heart-shaped pieces.

In addition to copper, the workman prepared tokens of base silver and of a white metal alloy containing tin. He was apparently unaware that genuine pieces were made of copper, brass or iron — seldom of other materials.

The Guadalajara metalsmith sold a large number of his bogus pieces to a major U.S. coin dealer about 1978. This dealer in turn sold groups of the forgeries and fantasies to other American coin dealers in Texas, Iowa, California etc. *as forgeries* for about $1.50 to $2 each, and these were resold by the secondary dealers *again as forgeries* to collectors and others at up to $3.50 each.

Several dishonest U.S. dealers sold them as genuine early Mexican tokens to collectors at prices ranging from $15 to $40 or more each.

We have isolated some 70 varieties, thanks to precautions taken in 1980 by specialist Art Garnett of California, in keeping back one of every type he saw.

The Guadalajara counterfeiter is reportedly dead. Not content with forging numismatic items, he also counterfeited Mexican coin of the realm and was arrested by Mexican police. He may have died in custody. The U.S. dealer who first distributed these concoctions, and several rogue dealers who resold them as genuine, are still active in 1991.

This warning should not be taken by collectors as indicating that counterfeit Latin American tokens are a significant problem. The field only recently attained sufficient popularity to merit the attention of forgers. The Guadalajara pieces are clumsy imitations, with lettering and designs as shown in the clear photographs in this book.

Tlacos in Circulation in 1768
Special Section

Don Agustin Coronas y Paredes was a Spaniard who came to Mexico in 1753, at age 46, and spent 10 years there. In his visits to Puebla, Queretaro, Celaya, Leon, San Miguel Allende, Guanajuato, Mexico City etc., he was impressed by the use — but even more by the abuse — of tlacos and pilones, private issue 1/8 and 1/16-real tokens.

On his return to Spain in 1763, he decided to report the matter. He made a formal presentation to the Holy Office of the Inquisition in Seville in 1764, and a second presentation in Madrid in 1766. On Oct. 21, 1767, King Carlos III appointed Coronas to investigate the matter of abuse of the regal currency and directed the Viceroy of New Spain to provide all assistance.

The superintendent of the mint in Mexico City, Pedro Nuñez de Villavicencio, sensing a rival and an intruder in Don Agustin, did what he could to block the project.

Written in Mexico City in the summer of 1768, Coronas' report consists of 16 printed pages, 317 manuscript pages and one page of illustrations. Written in the antique Spanish of the 18th century, it provides the best contemporary insight into the utilization of small private copper coins all over Mexico.

The page of line drawings provides the only certain documentary evidence of the existence of specific tlacos as early as 1768. Thirty pieces are illustrated, including 20 of non-round shapes, some of which are quite exotic. Perhaps he chose an inordinate number of exotic-shaped tokens for visual effect.

Coronas' text on the illustration page translates:

"These are a few of the many coins which are in the mestizo stores of the city of Mexico, and of the other parts of the kingdom; there are ones of metal, others of copper, and some of wood, and each one of these has a name, or is called by which-ever sound, each one being worth one claco, which is two fourths, comprising a fourth of those half reals of silver, etc."

Mestizo is an Indian-Spanish halfbreed. Claco = Tlaco. By "two fourths" Coronas meant a "half fourth," or an eighth.

In his voluminous, detailed report, Don Agustin wrote that tlacos and pilones had been in use in Mexico *since the 16th century!*

Nothing was ever done about Coronas' report to suppress the circulation of tlacos. Coronas well understood that the excess purchasing power of so many copper coins of no more backing than their metallic content greatly increased the "float" of money in Mexico — to the detriment of the common people.

The report of Don Agustin was rescued from obscurity by Manuel Romero de Terreros in 1935 in his *Los Tlacos Coloniales*. It was later (in 1976) commented upon in detail by Miguel L. Muñoz in his book *Tlacos y Pilones, La Moneda del Pueblo de Mexico* (1/8 and 1/16 Real Tokens, the Money of the People of Mexico).

Some of the 30 illustrated pieces in Coronas' 1768 report are not known today, and it must be surmised that an enormous number of private tokens from the late 1500's to the late 1700's have been destroyed entirely, or are awaiting the onslaught of metal detectors and other sophisticated search equipment. Copper was copper, and the peasantry and urban poor would have used them up as metal.

Copper does not survive well in the ground unless it is alloyed.

The illustrations are presented here in alphabetical order with our own descriptions, rather than in the form offered by Don Agustin Coronas y Paredes.

Juan Alvarez

Toribio Blas

Julian Cruz
on 8-point star

D
on moonface

D
on crowned double eagle

Juan de Diego
on tambourine

Granados
on pomegranate

D L
on human head

D C M L

M

M.

M.
on scallop flan

B M
on bishop's mitre

B L V M

N

C A N
on begging dog

R. P.
on crown

D V R
on sunface

P R
on winged heart

Z A R
on boot

**Julian Ramos
on semicircle**

**Julia Rasura
on three united
rings**

Toribio Rosa

**Juan Rubio
on scallop flan**

R S V T

P Y S V

**L . Y
on scallop flan**

**Star of David
on Star of David**

8-pointed Star

Turtle

Some of the pre-1768 tlacos of the Coronas y Paredes report have survived in the Mexican National collection, in the American Numismatic Society holdings, and in other holdings.

Illustrated below are anepigraphic specimens which match or closely resemble the 1768 illustrations. The numbers are those "anepigrafas" numbers assigned by Miguel L. Munoz.

(All tokens shown below are in actual size.

 8

 3

 2

 6

 1

 4

 7

AGUASCALIENTES STATE

Aguascalientes
V. B.
Hacienda El Saucillo

Rulau	Date	Metal		Size	VG	F	VF	Unc
Agu 5	ND	Brass	Oct	31mm	—	—	15.00	—

HACIENDA EL SAUCILLO / VB monogram / * AGUASCALIENTES *. Rv: BUENO POR / 50 / CENTAVOS / EN EFECTOS. Plain edge. (Paul Bosco Nov. 1985 sale)

| Agu 6 | ND | Brass | Oct | 25.5mm | — | 5.00 | — | — |

As last, but 10 / CENTAVOS. (Utberg report). Specimens are known holed for used as a tag, and a number incused, such as 69.

| Agu 7 | ND | Brass | Oct | 22mm | 5.50 | 10.00 | — | — |

As last, but 1 / CENTAVO. (Zaika coll.)

MESQUITE

Rulau	Date	Metal	Size	VG	F	VF	EF
Agu 11	ND	Copper	21.5mm	—	45.00	—	—

Tree on ground. * MESQUITE. * above. Rv: Rosette at center. Plain edge. (Eklund 379; Guttag 3905; Utberg H11; Fischer 565)

| Agu 12 | ND | Copper | 21.5mm | — | 40.00 | 55.00 | — |

As last, but counterstamped with ampersand (&) sign. (Rulau coll.)

D. VELASCO
Washington Hotel

Rulau	Date	Metal	Size	VG	F	VF	Unc
Agu 19	ND	CN	25mm	—	—	10.00	—

WASHINGTON HOTEL / (radiant star) / AGUASCALIENTES. / (radiant star) / D. VELASCO. Rv: Large 25. Incised beaded rim on each side. Plain edge. (Zaffern coll.; Eklund 2192)

A 10-centavos, brass, 21mm, brings $15 in EF.

(Bunch of Grapes)

Rulau	Date	Metal	Size	VG	F	VF	EF
Agu 25	1820	Copper	21mm	—	—	—	—

Within beaded border: (Bunch of grapes) / 23804 (stamped). Rv: Within beaded border: 1/8 / 1820. (Grove 'Tokens' 407)

| Agu 26 | 1824 | Copper | 20mm | 8.00 | 20.00 | — | — |

Similar, but stamped number is 23480 and date 1824. (Almanzar 1980 sale; Eklund 767). Other numbers known: 1578, 6119, 28417.

Nickel-plated brass pieces dated 1824 with large bunch of grapes separating B — T are fantasy concoctions!

(Brand mark) / 2
Hacienda La Troje

Rulau	Date	Metal	Size	VG	F	VF	Unc
Agu 28	1888	Iron	—mm	—	—	—	—

Brand mark / 2 (incused). Rv: 1888 / 2 (incused). Plain edge. (*Boletin de S.N. de M.* for July 1956, pg. 7)

Sheep shearing token of Hacienda La Troje.

JR Monogram
(Jacobo Romo)

Rulau	Date	Metal	Size	VG	F	VF	Unc
Agu 30	ND	Iron	—mm	—	—	—	—

JR monogram. Rv: R. Plain edge. (*Boletin de S.N. de M.* for July 1956, pg. 6)

Sheep shearing token for 100 sheep, of Jacobo Romo at Hacienda Chinampas.

CM Monogram
Hacienda Cienega de Mata

Rulau	Date	Metal	Size	VG	F	VF	Unc
Agu 32	ND	Sheet Iron	—mm	—	—	—	—

CM monogram / rosette. Rv: Intaglio of obverse.

Varieties are known, including one without rosette.

BAJA CALIFORNIA NORTE STATE

El Arco
CALMALLI

Rulau	Date	Metal	Size	VG	F	VF	Unc
BCN 1	(1890-95)	Brass	37mm	—	—	55.00	—

TIENDA DE RAYA / Y (in diamond) / * CALMALLI *. Rv: 1 / PESO in laurel wreath. Below: (tiny) C. A. KLINKNER S.F. Plain edge. (Eklund 2082)

| BCN 2 | (1890-95) | Brass | 31mm | — | — | — | — |

As last, but 4 / REALES. (*TAMS Journal* for Feb. 1986, pg. 12)

| BCN 3 | (1890-95) | Brass | 21mm | — | — | — | 60.00 |

As last, but 1/2 / REAL. (Eklund 2081)

Struck by Charles A. Klinkner & Co. of San Francisco, Calif. This was a gold mine, according to Jerry Schimmel. Tienda de raya = Company store.

Ensenada
A. PERPICH
Reform Saloon

Rulau	Date	Metal	Size	VG	F	VF	Unc
BCN 10	(1883-91)	Brass	24mm	—		—	55.00	—

Billiard table at center. Above: JACOB STRAHLE & CO / BILLIARD MFRS. Below: 515 MARKET ST / SAN FRANCISCO, CAL. Rv: GOOD FOR ONE DRINK / A. PERPICH / REFORM / SALOON / * ENSENADA, MEX *. Plain edge. Rare. (George Hosek coll.; Hank Thoele report)

The Jacob Strahle firm supplied tokens to its billiard table customers only in the 1883-1891 period.

CAMPECHE STATE

Campeche
MUNICIPIO DE CAMPECHE

Municipios

Rulau	Date	Metal	Size	VG	F	VF	Unc
Cam 3	1861	Brass	21mm	17.50	25.00	40.00	60.00

MUNICIPIO / -.- / DE / -.- / CAMPECHE. Rv: * UN * / -*- / CENTAVO / -*- / * 1861 *. Plain edge. (L&P AD-12; KM Mexico L27; Eklund 104; Ulex 1916)

Cam 4	1861	Brass	21mm	—	25.00	—	—

As last, but counterstamped C. (L&P AD-13)

Cam 5	1861	Brass	21mm	—	15.00	—	—

As first, but ctsp CV.

CASINO CAMPECHANO

Rulau	Date	Metal	Size	VG	F	VF	Unc
Cam 8	ND	Vulcanite*	28mm	—	—	35.00	—

* Black hard rubber.
CASINO CAMPECHANO / CAMPECHE / *. Rv: Large numeral 5. (L&P AD-2)

Gambling chip.

Carmen
B. A. & C.
Polvoxal

Rulau	Date	Metal	Size	VG	F	VF	Unc
Cam 10	ND	CN	26.5mm	—	—	—	—

POLVOXAL / B. A. & C. / (ornament) / * 1888 *. Rv: 2 / DOS REALES / (ornament) - all within laurel wreath. Plain edge. (L&P P-6)

Cam 11	ND	CN	20mm	—	10.00	20.00	—

As last, but 1 / UN REAL. (L&P P-5; Eklund 482)

Cam 12	ND	CN	14mm	—	—	12.00	—

As last, but . 1888 . and only the fraction 1/2 in wreath on reverse. (L&P P-4)

Benito Aznar & Co. raised vegetables and corn as the principal products on Hacienda Polvoxal in Carmen, Carmen County, Campeche.

B. A. & C.
(Benito Aznar & Co.)

Rulau	Date	Metal	Size	VG	F	VF	Unc
Cam 14	1886	CN	26.5mm	20.00	35.00	—	—

SANTA MARIA DE O. / B. A. & C. / (ornaments) / * 1886 *. Rv: Within laurel wreath: 2 / DOS REALES / (ornaments). (L&P S-56)

Cam 15	1886	CN	22.5mm	20.00	30.00	—	—

As last, but 1 / UN REAL / (ornaments). (Schimmel report)

Carmen County
LANZ
Hacienda Marentes

Rulau	Date	Metal	Size	VG	F	VF	Unc
Cam 18	1891	Brass	36mm	—	—	—	V. Scarce

(All incused): HDA / MARENTES / CONTRASEÑA. Rv: 4 / LANZ / 1891. Plain edge. (L&P M-4)

Cam 19	1891	Brass	29mm	—	—	10.00	—

As last, but 2.

Cam 20	1891	Brass	22mm	5.00	7.00	12.50	—

As last, but 1.

Cam 21	1891	Brass	18mm	—	5.00	8.00	20.00

As last, but 1/2. (L&P M-1; Rulau coll.)

Contraseña = Check or Token. All denominations are in Reales.

Luisa Galera de Lanz was the owner circa 1891-1905 of Marentes and these other Campeche plantations: Haltunchen, Niop and Sihoplaya.

Marentes hacienda here is attributed to Carmen County, detached from the other Lanz holdings. But Pradeau pointed out that the plantation which issued these tokens could have been located in Seybaplaya, Champoton County, near the other three.

Mexico numismatic specialist Neil Utberg tried to collect as many Lanz tokens as he could since his stepfather's name was Lanz. In 1965 he noted that the smaller tokens of Marentes and Haltunchen were common, but that the 4-reales pieces were very scarce.

Only Marentes and Haltunchen issued tokens. The others presumably used tokens of the other Lanz interests. The 4 and 2-real tokens occur ctsp radiant M or plain M.

Champoton
HACIENDA SACAKAL

Rulau	Date	Metal	Size	VG	F	VF	Unc
Cam 25	ND	Aluminum Oct	32mm	—	10.00	—	—

HACIENDA SACAKAL / 1 / CHAMPOTON. Rv: Blank.

Cam 26	ND	Aluminum Oct	29mm	—	—	12.00	—

As last, but 1/2. (L&P S-1)

These tokens are found ctsp C S O incuse, possibly for a new owner.

HACIENDA ULUMAL

Rulau	Date	Metal	Size	VG	F	VF	Unc
Cam 28	1892	CN	39mm	—	—	—	—

(All incused): HACIENDA ULUMAL / 1892. Rv: EL PORTADOR / TRABAJO / UN PESO. No borders. Plain edge. (L&P U-7)

Cam 29	1892	CN	32mm	—	—	—	—

As last, but 50 / CENTAVOS. (L&P U-6)

Cam 30	1892	CN	22mm	—	—	—	—

As last, but 25 / CENTAVOS. (L&P U-4). There is a variety measuring 24mm.

Cam 31	1892	CN	20mm	—	15.00	20.00	—

As last, but 12 / CENTAVOS. (L&P U-3; Sobrino 513)

Cam 32	1892	CN	18mm	—	—	—	—

As last, but 6 / CENTAVOS. (L&P U-2)

Rulau	Date	Metal	Size	VG	F	VF	Unc
Cam 33	1892	CN	14mm	—	10.00	15.00	—

as last, but 3 / CENTAVOS. (L&P U-1; Rulau coll.)

| Cam 34 | 1892 | CN | 28.5mm | — | 22.00 | — | — |

(All incused, beaded border around each side): HACI-
ENDA ULUMAL . 1892. Rv: EL PORTADOR / TRA-
BAJO / 25 / CENTAVOS.

| Cam 35 | 1892 | CN | 25mm | — | 11.00 | — | — |

As last, but 12 / CENTAVOS.

Nunkini
SISTO GARCIA
Hacienda Santa Cruz

Rulau	Date	Metal	Size	VG	F	VF	Unc
Cam 40	ND	WM	25mm	—	—	—	—

HACIENDA SANTA CRUZ / (radiant star) / SISTO
GARCIA. Rv: 1/2. Plain edge. (Eklund 1912b; Utberg
H-11/42; L&P S-50)

| Cam 41 | ND | WM | 23mm | — | — | 8.00 | — |

As last, but 1/4. (Eklund 1912a; Utbert H11/43; L&P
S-49)

| Cam 42 | ND | WM | 20mm | — | — | — | — |

As last, but 1/8 (real). (L&P S-48; Eklund 1912)

Palizada
H. J. M. DE PALIZADA

Municipios

Rulau	Date	Metal	Size	VG	F	VF	EF
Cam 44	1872	Copper	24mm	—	—	—	—

(Crude) H J M / DE / PALIZADA / -*-. Rv: Within circle of large beads: 1/4 between sprays / 1872. Plain
edge. (Eklund 375; Fernandez 161)

| Cam 45 | 1873 | Copper | 23mm | — | — | — | — |

As last, but 1873. (Eklund 2211)

| Cam 46 | 1875 | Copper | 23mm | — | — | — | — |

(Crude) H. J. M. / DE / PAILZAD / -*-. Rv: As last, but
1875. (L&P P-1; Guttag 3924; Fernandez 162)

| Cam 48 | 1881 | Copper | 25mm | 30.00 | 38.50 | — | — |

(Crude) H J M . / DE - / PALIZADA / -*- / . 1881 . Rv: .
VALE . / o 1/4 o / . REAL. Plain edge. (Eklund 376;
Fernandez 164; L&P P-2)

For some reason, these tokens have had difficulty in acceptance. Eklund attributed them to Merida. Elwin Leslie said their attribution to Campeche State was
tentative; he was disturbed that their style and fabric were unlike most of the
henequen tokens listed in his book on Yucatan.

Yet Palizada is clearly a municipio in Carmen County, Campeche, and Fernandez and other authorities accept them.

SAN AGUSTIN OLA

Rulau	Date	Metal	Size	VG	F	VF	Unc
Cam 50	(1893-97)	CN	31mm	—	5.00	8.00	15.00

HACIENDA / SAN AGUSTIN OLA / CAMPECHE /
(tiny) L.H. MOISE, S.F. Rv: large shaded numeral 50.
Plain edge. (L&P S-10; Eklund 105)

| Cam 52 | ND | CN | 23mm | — | 3.50 | 5.00 | 12.50 |

As last, but 5 (centavos). Maker's name appears as:
MOISE, S.F. (L&P S-9)

Corn was the principal product raised on San Agustin Ola hacienda in the
municipio of Palizada, Carmen County, Campeche. These tokens were struck by
L. H. Moise Co., San Francisco, Calif.

Grove reports a 10-centavo token, CN, 29mm.

Pocyaxum
FRANco SAN ROMAN
Nohakal

Rulau	Date	Metal	Size	VG	F	VF	Unc
Cam 55	ND	Brass	29mm	6.00	11.00	20.00	35.00

CONTRASEÑA / EN NOHAKAL. Rv: 2 / FRANco
SAN ROMAN. (L&P N-7)

| Cam 56 | ND | Brass | 22mm | — | 20.00 | — | — |

As last, but 1 (real). (L&P N-6; Grove 'Tokens' 1783)

Francisco San Roman's Nohakal hacienda, devoted mainly to raising sugar
cane, was in the municipio of Pocyaxum, Campeche County, Campeche.

San Pablo
B. A. & C.
(Benito Aznar & Co.)

Rulau	Date	Metal	Size	VG	F	VF	Unc
Cam 60	1886	CN	26mm	—	—	15.00	35.00

SAN PABLO / B. A. & C. / -.- / @ 1886 @. Rv: 2 /
REALES in wreath. (L&P S-41)

| Cam 61 | 1886 | CN | 20mm | — | — | — | — |

As last, but 1 (real). (L&P S-40)

| Cam 62 | 1886 | CN | 14mm | — | — | — | — |

As last, but 1/2 (real). (L&P S-39)

San Pedro
FELIPE BELTRAMO
Sahcabchen

Rulau	Date	Metal	Size	VG	F	VF	Unc
Cam 65	ND	Aluminum	23mm	—	20.00	—	—

FELIPE BELTRAMO / - / CONTRATISTA / - / SAH-
CABCHEN. S.P. Rv: EL PORTADOR TRABAJO / 1/8
/ (crossed laurel sprays). Plain edge. (L&P S-5)

Contratista = Contractor. Work on some haciendas was farmed out to private
contractors, and some of these apparently issued tokens to pay off their workers.
Henkle assigns this piece to Yucatan State.

Seybaplaya
LANZ
Hacienda Haltunchen

Rulau	Date	Metal	Size	VG	F	VF	Unc
Cam 70	1891	Brass	37mm	—	—	30.00	—
		HDA / HALTUNCHEN / CONTRASENA. Rv: 4 / LANZ / - / 1891. Plain edge. (L&P H-4)					
Cam 71	1891	Brass	29mm	—	8.00	14.00	
		As last, but 2. (L&P H-3)					
Cam 72	1891	Brass	22mm	—	5.00	6.50	—
		As last, but 1. (L&P H-2; Rulau coll.)					
Cam 73	1891	Brass	18mm	—	5.00	6.50	—
		As last, but 1/2. (L&P H-1; Rulau coll.)					

Haltunchen, devoted to raising sugar cane, was owned in 1905 by Luisa Galera de Lanz. She also owned Niop and Sehoplaya haciendas in the municipio of Seybaplaya, and Hacienda Marentes (which see in this catalog).

Seybaplaya is in Champoton County, Campeche.

Tixmucuy
HEREDIA HNOS.
Hacienda Cuyukak (Dzuyukak)

Rulau	Date	Metal	Size	VG	F	VF	Unc
Cam 78	(1889-96)	CN	24mm	—	—	18.00	—
		HEREDIA Hnos. / (ornament) / HACIENDA / (5-point star) / CUYUKAK. (C backward). Rv: Large shaded 10 in circle of 8 stars. At bottom: (tiny) C. A. KLINKNER CO., S.F. Plain edge. ((L&P C-10)					
Cam 80	(1889-96)	CN	32mm	—	10.00	20.00	—
		Similar to last, but 50 and no circle of stars. (L&P C-11)					

The C. A. Klinkner Co. of San Francisco, Calif. made tokens only 1889-96. They were bought out in 1897 by L. H. Moise, who made many tokens for Latin American enterprises.

Tixmucuy is in Campeche County, Campeche.

A 25-centavos is known.

B. A. & C.
San Geronmito

Rulau	Date	Metal	Size	VG	F	VF	Unc
Cam 85	1886	CN	26mm	—	8.00	—	—
		SAN GERONMITO / B. A. & C. -.- / . 1886 . Rv: Within laurel wreath: 2 / DOS REALES / (ornament). (Limarc report)					
Cam 86	1886	CN	20mm	—	—	11.00	—
		As last, but 1 / UN REAL / (ornament).					
Cam 87	1886	CN	14mm	—	—	7.50	—
		Obverse as last. Rv: Within laurel wreath: 1/2.					

B. A. & C. = Benito Aznar & Co.

CHIAPAS STATE

Cacahoaton
MANUEL T. ESPADAS
Hacienda El Rosario

Rulau	Date	Metal	Size	VG	F	VF	Unc
Chp 1	(1893-97)	Brass	22.5mm	—	—	15.00	25.00
		MANUEL T. ESPADAS / -*- / EL ROSARIO / *-* / CACAHUATAN. Rv: UNA / -*- / TAREA / (tiny) L. H. MOISE. S.F. Plain edge. (ANS coll.; Grove 'Tokens' 1856)					

Huixtla
JOAQUIN GARCIA
Finca Santa Julia

Rulau	Date	Metal	Size	VG	F	VF	Unc
Chp 5	ND	Aluminum	28mm	—	8.50	—	—
		JOAQUIN GARCIA / (ornament) / FINCA STA JULIA. Rv: HUIXTLA CHIS. / 50 / CENTAVOS. Plain edge.					
Chp 7	ND	Aluminum	39mm	—	—	—	—
		JOAQUIN GARCIA / FINCA STA JULIA. Rv: HUIXTLA CHIS / 2 50 / DOS PESOS CINCUENTA CENTS. Plain edge. (Verrey S-17; Grove 1408)					

Soconusco
FINCA MEXICO

Rulau	Date	Metal	Size	F	VF	EF	Unc
Chp 20	1895	Aluminum	**	—	—	12.50	—
		** Rectangular with clipped corners, 28x18 mm. FINCA MEXICO / SOCONUSCO / 1895 / (tiny) L. H. MOISE S.F. Rv: VALE / 1/2 / TAREA. (Grove 1375; Eklund 2219)					
Chp 21	1895	Aluminum	xx	—	—	—	—
		xx Rect. with clipped corners, 35x20mm. As last, but -1- / TAREA. (Eklund 2220)					

These have been claimed for Guatemala's San Marcos Dept.

Tapachula
L. R. BREWER
Cafetal Guatimoc

FIRST ISSUE - ALL INCUSED

Rulau	Date	Metal	Size	VG	F	VF	Unc
Chp 30	ND	Brass	Oct 27mm	—	4.00	7.00	—
		(All incused): CAFETAL GUATIMOC / 2 / L. R. BREWER. Rv: Blank. Incised beaded rim on each side. Plain edge. Scarce. (Verrey G-4; Garriga pg. 45; *TAMS Journal* for June 1973, pg. 99). Die varieties exist.					

Rulau	Date	Metal	Size	VG	F	VF	Unc
Chp 31	ND	Brass	Scal 25mm	—	—	7.00	—

As last, but 1. Scarce. (Verrey G-4)

FIRST ISSUE - COUNTERSTAMPS

Rulau	Date	Metal	Size	VG	F	VF	EF
Chp 33	ND	Brass	Scal 25mm	3.00	—	10.00	—

As last (numeral 1), ctsp R on obverse; I on reverse. Rare.

Chp 34	(1941)	Brass	Scal 25mm	—	—	—	—

As last (numeral 1), ctsp M. Used in 1941 in Venezuela; see special note below.

SECOND ISSUE - ALL RELIEF

Rulau	Date	Metal	Size	VG	F	VF	Unc
Chp 36	(1893-97)	Aluminum	29mm	—	3.00	6.00	8.00

L. R. BREWER / (Cruciform ornament) / * GUATI-MOC *. Rv: Numeral 3 (large,shaded) within wreath. Tiny L. H. MOISE. S.F. at bottom. Plain edge. (Utberg report; Eklund 2114)

Chp 37	(1893-97)	Aluminum	Oct 27mm	—	—	—	8.00

Obverse as last. Rv: Large 1 1/2 / (tiny) L.H. MOISE. S.F. Plain edge.

SECOND ISSUE - COUNTERSTAMPS

Rulau	Date	Metal	Size	VF	F	VF	EF
Chp 39	ND	Aluminum	29mm	—	—	—	—

As first token (numeral 3), ctsp R on obverse; D on reverse. Rare.

Chp 40	(1941)	Aluminum	29mm	—	—	—	—

As first token (numeral 3), ctsp S on obverse; M on reverse. Used in 1941 in Venezuela; see special note below.

Chp 41	(1941)	Aluminum	29mm	—	—	6.00	—

Same as last (ctsp S and M), but with 0 gouged into center of obverse. Used in Venezuela; see note below. Scarce.

Chp 42	ND	Aluminum	Oct 27mm	—	4.00	8.00	—

As second token (numeral 1 1/2), ctsp A.

Chp 43	ND	Aluminum	Oct 27mm	—	4.00	8.00	—

As second token (numeral 1 1/2), ctsp T.

1911 SERIES

Rulau	Date	Metal	Size	VG	F	VF	Unc
Chp 45	1911	Brass	31mm	—	4.00	7.00	9.00

Coffee tree on ground. Rv: GUATIMOC / * * * / 1911 / * * * / MOISE S.F. Plain edge. Common. (Verrey G-11)

Chp 46	1911	Nic/Bs	31mm	—	—	8.00	—

As last, but plated with CN. Scarce.

Chp 47	1911	Brass	Oct 27mm	—	—	—	—

Maltese cross. Rv: As last. Common

Chp 48	1911	Brass	Sq 24mm	—	—	5.00	8.00

Crescent moon and X. Rv: As last.

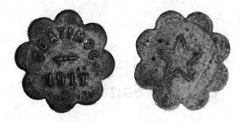

Chp 49	1911	Brass	Scal 28mm	—	—	8.00	—

Outlined 5-pointed star. Rv: As last. (Verrey G-8)

Chp 50	1911	Brass	Scal 28mm	—	—	—	—

Large house left. Rv: As last.

Chp 51	1911	Brass	24mm	—	—	6.00	—

Small house right, a tree at the right. Rv: As last.

None of the 1911 series of tokens bears any marks of value, yet each depicts a different object which must have been recognizable to the plantation's workers as representing some valuation.

1911 SERIES - COUNTERSTAMPS

Rulau	Date	Metal	Size	VG	F	VF	EF
Chp 53	1911	Brass	31mm	—	2.50	7.00	8.00

Coffee tree token, ctsp A. Common.

Chp 54	1911	Brass	Oct 27mm	—	3.50	6.50	9.50

Maltese cross token, ctsp G. Scarce.

Chp 55	1911	Brass	Scal 28mm	—	—	—	—

Star token, ctsp A on obverse. Rare.

Chp 56	1911	Brass	Scal 28mm	—	—	—	—

Star token, ctsp A on reverse.

Chp 57	1911	Brass	Scal 28mm	—	—	—	—

Large house left token, ctsp A. Rare.

Chp 58	1911	Brass	24mm	—	—	—	—

Small house right token, ctsp A. Rare.

There are more counterstamp varieties of these tokens. Many of the basic tokens were made by L. H. Moise & Co., San Francisco, Calif., for the coffee plantation's owner, L. R. Brewer.

A large hoard of some of these tokens came on the market in late 1972, depressing their price for years to come.

Chiapas is the southernmost of the Mexican states, bordering on Guatemala.

See Alcedo Almanzar's "Mexican Tokens from the 'Guatimoc' Coffee Plantation of L. R. Brewer" in *TAMS Journal* for June, 1973.

NOTE: Guatimoc estates tokens bearing a counterstamped letter M were used long after their need in Chiapas State. All such hacienda tokens were outlawed by the Mexican constitution in 1917.

In 1941, Simon Medone de Motatan imported a quantity of the remainders of the Guatimoc pieces into Venezuela, and applied the incuse stamp M to them for use on his hacienda in Trujillo State.

FINCA LAS NUBES

Rulau	Date	Metal	Size	VG	F	VF	Unc
Chp 62	ND	CN	30mm	—	—	—	—

Tree at center. Around: FINCA LAS NUBES / * TAPACHULA *. Rv: As next, but 1. (Utberg report)

Chp 63	ND	CN	24mm	—	—	—	—

Obverse as last. Rv: CHIAPAS / 1/2 / - MEXICO -. Plain edge. (Grove 1386)

Chp 64	ND	CN	18mm	—	—	—	—

As last, but 1/4. (Verrey; Grove 1385)

HIND Y COMPANIA

Rulau	Date	Metal	Size	VG	F	VF	Unc
Chp 66	ND	Brass	30.5mm	—	—	12.50	—

HIND Y COMPANIA / 1 / (cruciform ornament) / DIA / TAPACHULA. Rv: Same as obverse. (Utberg report)

| Chp 67 | ND | Brass | 26mm | — | — | 10.00 | — |

As last, but 1/10 / DIA at center, no ornament. (Grove 1662)

Dia = Day's work.

TEOFILO PALACIOS
Cafetal Santa Maria

Rulau	Date	Metal	Size	VG	F	VF	Unc
Chp 69	ND	Aluminum	29mm	—	—	—	—

Coffee tree at center. Around: CAFETAL SANTA MARIA / * SOCONUSCO *. Rv: TEOFILO PALACIOS / 1 / * TAPACHULA MEXICO *. Plain edge. (Eklund 621)

| Chp 70 | ND | — | 23mm | — | — | — | — |

As last, but 1/2. (Grove 1218)

Grove reports the 1-real piece in bronze.

LUIS THOMALEN
La Estrella

Rulau	Date	Metal	Size	VG	F	VF	Unc
Chp 72	(1893-97)	Aluminum	Oct 34x20mm	—	—	—	45.00

LA ESTRELLA / -*- / LUIS THOMALEN / * / TAPACHULA / (tiny) L. H. MOISE. S. F. Rv: VALE / + 1/2 + / REAL / AL PORTADOR. Plain edge. (Zaffern coll.)

| Chp 73 | (1893-97) | Aluminum | Oct 28x18mm | — | — | — | 45.00 |

As last, but 1/4 REAL. (Grove 1338)

Vale 1/2 real al portador = worth 1/2 real to the bearer.

Uncertain
INES AUYUN
San Bartolome

Rulau	Date	Metal	Size	VG	F	VF	Unc
Chp 80	ND	Brass	—mm	—	—	—	—

INES AUYUN. SAN BARTOLOME. 2 R. (Ulex 1696)

Ulex also reported a brass 1-real token of this issuer.

ENRIQUE BRAUN
Cafetales La Trinidad

Rulau	Date	Metal	Size	VG	F	VF	Unc
Chp 83	ND	Aluminum	Scal 29mm	—	6.00	8.25	—

CAFETALES LA TRINIDAD / UNA / TAREA / ENRIQUE BRAUN. Rv: Same as obverse. (Grove 1222; TAMS Maverick 12066)

| Chp 84 | ND | Aluminum | Scal 29mm | — | — | — | — |

As last, but UNA / CAJA.

| Chp 85 | ND | Aluminum | Scal 25mm | — | — | 10.00 | — |

As last, but MEDIA / CAJA.

| Chp 86 | ND | Brass | Oct 27mm | — | 6.00 | 7.50 | 12.50 |

C in beaded circle. Around: CAFETALES DE / * E. BRAUN *. Rv: C in beaded octagon. Plain edge. (Henkle coll.)

| Chp 87 | ND | Brass | Oct 24mm | — | 5.00 | 6.50 | — |

As last, but L on each side. (Henkle coll.) Also occurs in CN.

Tarea = Task. Caja = Box. Media caja = Half box. C = 100 centavos. L = 50.

The Braun pieces have been assigned, erroneously to Guatemala.

Tokens denominated XX (20) and X (10) are reported. Die varieties exist.

CHITALON

Rulau	Date	Metal	Size	VG	F	VF	Unc
Chp 90	(1893-97)	Aluminum	28.5mm	—	—	15.00	—

(Ornament) / CHITALON / (ornament). Rv: *** / SEIS / (ornament) / JORNALES / *** / (tiny) L. H. MOISE S. F. Plain edge. (Rulau coll.; Henkle N/L; Eklund 2290)

| Chp 92 | (1893-97) | Aluminum | 25mm | — | — | 10.00 | — |

As last, but UN / JORNAL.

F. DE C.
Cafetal Acapulco

Rulau	Date	Metal	Size	VG	F	VF	Unc
Chp 94	(1891-97)	Brass	27mm	—	—	—	—

CAFETAL ACAPULCO / F DE C. / +. Rv: 1 / CAJA within wreath, tiny C. A. KLINKNER & CO. S.F. below. Plain edge. (Verrey; Grove 'Tokens' 1165)

KORTUM HERMANOS

Rulau	Date	Metal	Size	VG	F	VF	Unc
Chp 96	(1870)	Bronze	19mm	—	—	10.00	—

KORTUM HERMANOS / 1/4 R within dentilated circle. Rv: FINCA MUMUNIL / CHIAPAS. Plain edge. (Eklund 2195; Verrey; Grove 1377)

Rulau	Date	Metal	Size	VG	F	VF	Unc
Chp 97	ND	Brass	38mm	—	—	80.00	—

KORTUM HERMANOS / 2oo / PESOS (lst two lines in dentilated circle). Rv: FINCA MUMUNIL / CHIAPAS. Plain edge. (Utberg report; Grove 1383)

Rulau	Date	Metal	Size	VG	F	VF	Unc
Chp 98	ND	Brass	36.5mm	—	—	45.00	—

As last, but 1oo / PESO. (Utberg report)

Rulau	Date	Metal	Size	VG	F	VF	Unc
Chp 99	ND	Brass	29mm	—	—	8.00	—

As last, but large 25 within dentilated circle (for 25 centavos). (Grove 1380)

Ole P. Eklund assigned the 1870 date to the first token above; we do know his source. The last three pieces would be later emissions.

These tokens also occur in CN and aluminum.

LAS PALMAS

Rulau	Date	Metal	Size	VG	F	VF	Unc
Chp 102	ND	Brass	20mm	—	—	15.00	—

LAS / PALMAS. Rv: 50 / MEX. Plain edge. Centrally holed flan. (Grove 1805)

Rulau	Date	Metal	Size	VG	F	VF	Unc
Chp 103	ND	Brass	15mm	—	—	15.00	—

As last, but 25. (Grove 1804)

Rulau	Date	Metal	Size	VG	F	VF	Unc
Chp 104	ND	Gilt/Bs	Sq 15mm	—	—	12.50	20.00

As last, but 5. (Rulau coll.)

Rulau	Date	Metal	Size	VG	F	VF	Unc
Chp 105	ND	Gilt/Bs	Triang 22x18mm	—	—	12.50	20.00

As last, but 2. (Rulau coll.)

Rulau	Date	Metal	Size	VG	F	VF	Unc
Chp 106	ND	Gilt/Bs	Triang 19x14mm	—	—	12.50	20.00

As last, but 1 / MEX. (Rulau coll.; Grove 1801)

Claudio Verrey attributed these attractive scarce tokens to Chiapas. Almanzar says they were issued by the Firestone Rubber plantation.

They have also been claimed for U.S. Virgin Islands, Panama and the United States.

Charles K. Panish, chairman of the Attribution committee of Numismatics International, assigned these tokens to the "Las Palmas Plantation in Panama" in an Aug. 19, 1982 letter to dealer Dale A. Seppa.

In February, 1963 a small hoard of these tokens, including some Unc. specimens, surfaced. They are still inexpensive as a result, though too scarce to satisfy demand.

The conflicting claims of experts David King, Warren Plumer and Charles Panish who favor Panama, and Claudio Verrey and Alcedo Almanzar, who prefer Chiapas, Mexico, are impossible to settle without provenance. We need to know if indeed there was a Las Palmas estate and just where it was.

We admit leaning toward Panama though placing them under Chiapas for now. The reason is the choice of the term 50 MEX (etc.) on the token. This phrase is common on Danish West Indies 19th century tokens, because the cent tokens used there were not based on the Danish krone but on the Mexican silver dollar. This phrase also was used on some U.S. 1933 tokens prepared for the Chicago World's Fair (Century of Progress Exposition).

It could make sense also for Panama which used (and still uses) the U.S. dollar as legal tender, so that a token based on the Mexican dollar should be so inscribed. But it makes little sense to us to use the phrase on a Mexican token, when the Mexican silver peso is implied in any centavo (hundredth) denomination. Unless, of course, the *users of the tokens were not Mexicans.*

Please write to us if you *know* where the Las Palmas pieces were used!

M. MARTINEZ
La Aurora

Rulau	Date	Metal	Size	VG	F	VF	Unc
Chp 110	ND	Brass	25mm	—	—	—	—

(All incused): M. MARTINEZ / 3 . - "LA AURORA" -. Rv: Blank. Plain edge. (Grove 'Tokens' 1143; Verrey)

Rulau	Date	Metal	Size	VG	F	VF	Unc
Chp 111	ND	Brass	25mm	—	—	—	—

As last, but 2.

RAFAEL ORTEGA
Cafetal Las Chicharras

Rulau	Date	Metal	Size	VG	F	VF	Unc
Chp 113	ND	Brass	27mm	—	—	—	—

RAFAEL ORTEGA / (radiant ornament) / ... Rv: CAFETAL LAS CHICHARRAS / 1 / CAJON / *. (Grove 'Tokens' 1172)

Rulau	Date	Metal	Size	VG	F	VF	Unc
Chp 114	ND	Brass	23mm	—	—	—	—

As last, but 1/2 / CAJON.

Rulau	Date	Metal	Size	VG	F	VF	Unc
Chp 116	(1891-97)	Brass	28mm	—	—	—	—

CAFETAL LAS CHICHARRAS / R. O. / *. Rv: 1 / CAJA in wreath, tiny C. A. KLINKNER & CO. S.F. below. (Grove 'Tokens' 1174)

Rulau	Date	Metal	Size	VG	F	VF	Unc
Chp 117	(1891-97)	Brass	24mm	—	—	—	—

As last but 1/2 / CAJA.

JOSE REVUELTO
La Alianza

Rulau	Date	Metal	Size	VG	F	VF	Unc
Chp 120	ND	Aluminum	Oct 30mm	—	—	—	—

LA ALIANZA / 1 (shaded) / * TAREA *. Rv: JOSE REVUELTO / (ornament) / * LA ALIANZA *. (Grove 'Tokens' 1132)

Rulau	Date	Metal	Size	VG	F	VF	Unc
Chp 121	ND	Aluminum	Oct 30mm	—	—	—	—

As last, but 1 / * CAJA *.

Rulau	Date	Metal	Size	VG	F	VF	Unc
Chp 122	ND	Aluminum	Oct 23mm	—	—	—	—

As last, but 1/2 / . CAJA.

Rulau	Date	Metal	Size	VG	F	VF	Unc
Chp 124	ND	Aluminum	29mm	—	—	—	—

LA ALIANZA / 1 (ornate, shaded) / + TAREA +. Rv: JOSE REVUELTO / -+- / * LA ALIANZA *. (Grove 'Tokens' 1135)

Rulau	Date	Metal	Size	VG	F	VF	Unc
Chp 125	ND	Aluminum	31mm	—	—	—	—

Similar to last, but 1 / - CAJA -.

Rulau	Date	Metal	Size	VG	F	VF	Unc
Chp 126	ND	Aluminum	24mm	—	—	—	—

As last, but 1/2 / - CAJA -. Letter A ctsp next to numeral 1/2. (Grove 'Tokens' 1133)

CHIHUAHUA STATE

Almoloya
CIA. MINERA IGNACIO RODRIGUEZ RAMOS S.A.

Rulau	Date	Metal	Size	VG	F	VF	Unc
Chh 3	ND	Brass	31mm	—	—	20.00	27.50

CIA. MINERA IGNACIO RODRIGUEZ RAMOS S.A. / - / ALMOLOYA / — CHIH. MEX. / *. Rv: COMPROBANTE DE / 1 / DIA / DE TRABAJO. Plain edge. (Jerry Schimmel report)

Comprobante de 1 dia de trabajo = Voucher for one day of work.

Barranca del Cobre
MENDOZA & NESBITT

Rulau	Date	Metal	Size	VG	F	VF	Unc
Chh 7	ND	Brass	33mm	—	—	10.00	—

MENDOZA & NESBITT / BARRANCA / DE COBRE / CHIH., MEX. Rv: VALE POR / 25 / CARNE. Plain edge.

Carne = Meat. For use in a railroad store.

Batopilas
BATOPILAS

Municipio ?

Rulau	Date	Metal	Size	VG	F	VF	Unc
Chh 10	1887	**	23mm	—	—	—	—

** Black vulcanite.
BATOPILAS / ESTADO / DE / CHIHUAHUA / 1887. Rv: VALE POR / UN / REAL. Plain edge. (Utberg report; Artes 103; *ANS Centennial Publications*, plate XXXVII / 8)

Dr. Pradeau in the 1958 ANS centennial publication reported this as 13mm, probably an error. All mining companies in the Batopilas area combined in 1887.

MINES OF SAN MIGUEL

Rulau	Date	Metal	Size	F	VF	EF	Unc
Chh 13	1869	Silver	38mm	—	—	90.00	—

Intricate monogram (BMSC ?) at center. Around: MINES OF SAN MIGUEL / BATOPILAS MEXICO. Rv: All within wreath: 1861 / FINIS / CORONAT / OPUS / 1869. Plain edge. (Grove 184a; Christensen Oct. 1987 sale, lot 831)

Chihuahua
L. EMILIO LAFON

Rulau	Date	Metal	Size	VG	F	VF	Unc
Chh 18	ND	Brass	28.5mm	10.00	22.50	—	—

BOTICA DEL AGUILA / L. EMILIO / LAFON / FARMACEUTICO /CHIHUAHUA. Rv: BUENA POR / UN VASO DE / AGUA GASEOSA / 12 POR $1.-. Plain edge. (Eklund 134)

Un vaso de agua gaseosa = One glass of soda water.

SOCIEDAD RECREATIVA

Rulau	Date	Metal	Size	VG	F	VF	Unc
Chh 25	ND	CN	34mm	—	25.00	—	—

Clasped hands at center. Around: SOCIEDAD RECREATIVA. / CHIHUAHUA. Rv: - 1 - / UN PESO. Plain edge. (Eklund 133; *World Coin News* for Dec. 30, 1986, page 4)

Chh 26	ND	CN	—mm	—	—	—	—

As last, but 50 / CENTAVOS. (Eklund 132)

Also in this series are 10 C, 24mm; 5 C, 21mm, and 1 C, 16mm, all in cupronickel alloy. Prices range from $17 to $23 each in VF.

Corralitos
TIENDA DE CORRALITOS

Rulau	Date	Metal	Size	VG	F	VF	Unc
Chh 30	ND	Brass	32mm	—	—	8.00	—

TIENDA DE CORRALITOS / (floral design in circle) / *. Large Y-shaped brand mark ctsp on floral design. Rv: Blank. Plain edge. (TAMS Maverick 3068)

Chh 31	ND	Brass	31mm	—	—	15.00	—

Obverse as last, without ctsp. Rv: VALE UNA COPA / * / COGNAC / * / (ornament). Plain edge. (Eklund 172)

F. J. Bingen of the Netherlands attributed the first token to Corralitos, near Mendoza, Argentina (see *TAMS Journal* for April 1973, pg. 64)
Attributed tentatively to Mexico.

Cusihuiriachic
M. Co.

Rulau	Date	Metal	Size	VG	F	VF	Unc
Chh 33	1880	Brass	29mm	—	50.00	—	—

TIENDA DE RAYA / M. Co. in Gothic script / COSIHUIRIACHIC. Rv: 1880 / 1/2 / DE REAL EN EFECTOS. (Eklund 174)

Chh 34	1880	Brass	25mm	—	50.00	—	—

As last, but 1/4 (Eklund 173)

Chh 35	1880	Brass	35mm	12.00	25.00	50.00	—

As last, but 1. (Eklund 2202)

Chh 36	1880	Brass	34mm	—	—	70.00	—

Obverse as last. Rv: 1880 / 1 / PESO EN EFECTOS. Reeded edge. Scarce.

The municipality spells its name as Cusihuiriachic, though the tokens spell it Cosihuiriachic.

Jesus Maria
L. DE LA VEGA
Hacienda de Jesus Maria

Rulau	Date	Metal	Size	VG	F	VF	Unc
Chh 40	(1897-99)	Brass	32mm	—	—	—	—

HACIENDA DE JESUS / MARIA / * 1 * / DIA / L. DE LA VEGA / (tiny) MOISE, KLINKNER. CO. S.F. Rv: As obverse, but no maker's mark. Plain edge. (Eklund 2124)

SANTA JULIANA MINING CO.

Rulau	Date	Metal	Size	VG	F	VF	Unc
Chh 45	1893	CN	25mm	15.00	18.00	25.00	35.00

Pack mule left. Rv: SANTA JULIANA MINING CO. / JESUS / MARIA / * 1893 *. Plain edge. (*TAMS Journal*, Aug. 1971 issue)

Chh 46	1893	CN	22mm	—	17.00	22.00	30.00

Miner with pick walking left. Rv: As last.

Chh 47	1893	CN	19mm	—	17.00	22.00	30.00

Crossed miners' tools (sledgehammer, pickaxe and spade). Rv: As last. (Eklund 2125; Rulau coll.)

Rulau	Date	Metal	Size	VG	F	VF	Unc
Chh 48	1893	CN	16mm	15.00	18.00	—	—

Mine car on tracks. Rv: As last.

Rulau	Date	Metal	Size	VG	F	VF	Unc
Chh 49	1893	CN	13mm	—	—	27.00	35.00

Coiled rope. Rv: As last.

In 1883 Matras Alsua and some relatives, and B. Phelps of New York, took over the silver-gold mines of Santa Juliana near the source of the river Mayo in the Sierras in western Chihuahua State. These mines had been worked in colonial times but had been abandoned about 1810. They were pumped dry by some others and the Alsuas in the 1870's. Between 1828-1840 some $35 million in silver and gold had been taken from the mines around Jesus Maria.

No denomination are stated on the Santa Juliana tokens, so they must have passed for some specified value represented by their decreasing size.

Parral
LA BOLSA

Rulau	Date	Metal	Size	VG	F	VF	Unc
Chh 55	(1890's)	Brass	38mm	—	—	30.00	—

(Ornament) / LA BOLSA (script) above crossed laurel branches, tiny L. H. MOISE S.F. below. Rv: (Ornament) / Parral (script) / (crossed laurel branches). Plain edge. (Eklund 452)

Chh 56	(1890's)	Aluminum	25mm	—	—	—	10.00

As last, smaller and in aluminum. Plain edge. (Eklund 451; TAMS Maverick 9108; *TAMS Journal* for April 1980, pg. 66)

JOAQUIN SALDANA
La Mascota Cantina

Rulau	Date	Metal	Size	VG	F	VF	Unc
Chh 58	ND	Brass	21mm	—	—	40.00	—

JOAQUIN SALDANA / * / PARRAL / CHIa - / - MEX. Rv: LA MASCOTA CANTINA. / 10. Plain edge. (Eklund 450)

SANCHEZ Y GARCIA

Rulau	Date	Metal	Size	VG	F	VF	Unc
Chh 60	1899	Alum	Rect 35x20mm	—	—	—	—

(All in script lettering): 1899. / Sanchez y Garcia / Parral / (crossed laurel branches). Rv: (All in script lettering): Baños / Regadera / "El Diamante". Rectangular flan has cut corners. Plain edge. (Eklund 453)

1 V.

Rulau	Date	Metal	Size	VG	F	VF	Unc
Chh 62	ND	Copper	28mm	—	—	—	—

1 v. / Parral (all in script, within ornamental border). Rv: Blank. (Eklund 449)

Santa Clara
TIENDA DE RAYA

Rulau	Date	Metal	Size	VG	F	VF	Unc
Chh 70	ND	Brass	28mm	—	25.00	—	—

TIENDA DE RAYA / CHIHUAHUA / -+- / MEX. / SANTA CLARA. Rv: BUENO POR / 20 / EN MERCANCIAS. Plain edge. (Eklund 540)

Sierra de Naica
MIGUEL OCADIZ

Rulau	Date	Metal	Size	VG	F	VF	Unc
Chh 73	ND	Brass	30mm	—	18.00	30.00	—

MIGUEL OCADIZ / 50 / SIERRA DE NAICA. Rv: CONTRASENA / 50 / LITROS / AGUA. Plain edge.

Sierra de Naica was a small town near the city of Chihuahua which could be reached only by burro trail. Water had to be packed into the community, and Ocadiz apparently provided this service. The 'contraseña' (check) was good for 50 liters of water. Probably rare.

Uruachic
N. Y F. RASCON HERMANOS
Mineral de Uruachic

Rulau	Date	Metal	Size	VG	F	VF	Unc
Chh 80	1873	Brass	35mm	—	—	60.00	—

MINERAL DE URUACHIC / (Eagle on cactus, serpent in its beak) / * MEXICO *. Rv: N. Y F. RASCON HERMANOS / 100 / CENTAVOS / * 1873 *. (Fonrobert 6745; Eklund 662)

Chh 81	1873	Brass	31mm	—	—	40.00	—

As last, but 50 / CENTAVOS. (Eklund 661)

Chh 82	1873	Brass	28.5mm	—	—	40.00	—

As last, but 25 / CENTAVOS. (Fonrobert 6746; Eklund 660)

Chh 83	1873	Brass	26mm	10.00	30.00	50.00	—

As last, but 12 1/2 / CENTAVOS. (Eklund 659)

Uncertain

A. M. / C. A.

Rulau	Date	Metal	Size	VG	F	VF	EF
Chh 90	ND	Brass	29mm	—	13.00	—	—

A . M (in square) ctsp on cast copy of Chihuahua State 1/4 real. C A (incuse) ctsp on opposite side of the coin. (*TAMS Journal* for Aug. 1978, pg. 153)

F. O.

Rulau	Date	Metal	Size	VG	F	VF	Unc
Chh 92	ND	Copper	28.5mm	12.00	—	—	—

F . O (relief, in 13mm serrated oval depression) ctsp on Chihuahua State 1/4 real. (*TAMS Journal* for Aug. 1978, pg 148)

A. S.

Rulau	Date	Metal	Size	VG	F	VF	Unc
Chh 94	ND	Copper	28.5mm	—	10.00	—	—

A S (relief, in 8mm square depression) ctsp on Chihuahua State 1/4 real. (*TAMS Journal* for Aug. 1978, pg. 148)

M. S.

Rulau	Date	Metal	Size	VG	F	VF	EF
Chh 96	ND	Copper	28mm	—	—	25.00	—

M. S. within wreath, in relief within shaped depression, ctsp on Chihuahua State 1860 cuartilla, KM-344. A large incuse V had been ctsp before the M. S. punch partially covered it. (Brunk coll.)

| Chh 98 | ND | Copper | 27mm | — | — | 35.00 | — |

M. S. (in relief, within floreate irregularly rect. depression) ctsp on Mexico Chihuahua State cuartilla of 1860-66 type, KM-344. (Krueger 1991 sale, lot 1741; Eklund 283)

Eklund says Jalisco State.

12-Pointed Star

Rulau	Date	Metal	Size	VG	F	VF	EF
Chh 100	ND	Copper	28.5mm	8.50	—	—	—

12-pointed star with circular center ctsp incuse on Chihuahua State 1865 1/4-real.

46

Rulau	Date	Metal	Size	VG	F	VF	Unc
Chh 102	ND	Copper	29mm	—	3.00	—	—

Large numeral 46 ctsp on pierced Chihuahua State 1861 1/4-real. Possibly used as a tool check.

COAHUILA STATE

Jimenez
CIA. AGRICOLA Y GANADERA DEL RIO DE SAN DIEGO S.A.

Rulau	Date	Metal	Size	F	VF	EF	Unc
Coa 8	1910	Aluminum	29mm	20.00	—	—	—

CIA AGRICOLA Y GANADERA / DEL RIO DE / SAN DIEGO S.A. / 1910 SAN CARLOS / —RAYA 50-. Rv: Same as obverse. Ctsp T on reverse.

| Coa 9 | 1910 | Aluminum | 26mm | — | — | — | — |

As last, but -RAYA 10-. No ctsp.

| Coa 10 | 1910 | Aluminum | 29mm | 20.00 | — | — | — |

As last, but -RAYA 5-. Ctsp H on reverse.

The lengthy company name means: Agricultural and Cattle Company of the River of San Diego Inc. There is a municipality of San Carlos in Coahuila State.

Monclova
A. F. CANEL

Rulau	Date	Metal	Size	VG	F	VF	Unc
Coa 15	ND	Copper	23mm	—	2.00	—	—

A. F. CANEL / MONCLOVA, MEX. Rv: VALE POR UNA COPA.

Saltillo
AGUILA DE ORO

Rulau	Date	Metal	Size	VG	F	VF	Unc
Coa 20	ND	Brass	23mm	—	—	6.00	—

Mexican eagle. Around: AGUILA DE ORO / SALTILLO, MEX. Rv: BUENO POR UNA COPA.

Aguila de oro = Golden eagle.

GUSTAVO H. F. GARCIA

Rulau	Date	Metal	Size	VG	F	VF	Unc
Coa 23	(18) 88	Silver	20mm	—	—	—	—

Mexican eagle, GUSTAVO H. F. GARCIA around. Rv: SALTILLO. AGOSTO 4. 88. (Fernandez 188)

Sierra Mojada
MIGUEL BERNARDININ

Rulau	Date	Metal	Size	VG	F	VF	Unc
Coa 30	(1890's)	Brass	24mm	—	—	—	—

MIGUEL BERNARDININ / SIERRA / -.- / MOJADA / GUARDA RAYA / *** / COAH. MEX. Rv: Large 10 (pebbled) in circle of 10 stars / (tiny) C. A. KLINKNER S.F. — all within beaded circle. Plain edge. (Eklund 2197)

| Coa 31 | (1890's) | Brass | 24mm | — | — | — | — |

As last, but 20. (Eklund 2198)

COLIMA STATE

COLIMA

Municipios

Rulau	Date	Metal	Size	VG	F	VF	EF
Col 10	1813	Copper	24mm	25.00	35.00	50.00	—

VILLA DE (monogram) COLIMA / 1813. Rv: Blank. (ANS 106; KM L41)

| Col 11 | 1814 | Copper | Sq 16mm | 25.00 | 35.00 | 50.00 | — |

VILLA de / Colima 1814. Rv: Blank. (ANS 107; KM L42)

| Col 12 | 1816 | Copper | 26mm | 25.00 | 35.00 | 50.00 | — |

QVART. / COLIMA / 1816. within wreath. Rv: COLIMA monogram within wreath. (ANS 108; KM L43)

| Col 14 | 1819 | Copper | 23mm | 30.00 | 42.50 | 60.00 | — |

+ / OCT.o. / DE / COL Ia. Rv: ANO / DE / 1819. (KM L44)

Rulau	Date	Metal	Size	VG	F	VF	EF
Col 16	1824	Copper	24mm	30.00	42.50	60.00	—

OCTO DE COLIMA / 1824. Rv: OCTAVO / (branch). (ANS 109; KM L45)

Rulau	Date	Metal	Size	VG	F	VF	EF
Col 18	1824	Copper	22mm	30.00	42.50	60.00	—

OCTO / DE / COLA. Rv: ANO / DE / 1824. Wide dentilated rim on each side. (ANS 110; KM L47). Also known with date 1828.

Rulau	Date	Metal	Size	VG	F	VF	EF
Col 20	1824	Copper	24mm	30.00	42.50	60.00	—

Cuarto de Colima. Rv: MA script monogram. (ANS 111; KM L45)

Rulau	Date	Metal	Size	VG	F	VF	EF
Col 21	1828	Copper	22mm	30.00	42.50	60.00	—

OCTo. / DE / COL.a. Rv: ANO / DE/ 1828.

Rulau	Date	Metal	Size	VG	F	VF	EF
Col 23	1830	Copper	23mm	30.00	42.50	60.00	—

OCT.o / DE / COLIMA. Rv: ANO (N retrograde) / DE / 1830. Wide dentilated rim on each side. (ANS 112; KM L48)

Eklund and others also list Colima municipal tokens dated 1798, 1811, 1812, 1815, 1818, 1822, 1826, 1833, 1834, 1835, 1836, 1853, 1855 and 1858.

Caution: Counterfeit!

Rulau	Date	Metal	Size	VG	F	VF	EF
Col 25F	1830	Copper	33mm	—	—	1.75	—

OCT.o. / DE monogram. / COLIMA. Rv: AÑO / . DE monogram . / 1830. Wide dentilated border on each side. Plain edge. Thick (6.3mm) heavy flan forgery.

Tecoman
TECOMAN

Rulau	Date	Metal	Size	VG	F	VF	Unc
Col 40	ND	Copper	25mm	—	—	30.00	—

TECOMAN ctsp on Mexico 1880-Ho 1-centavo, KM 391.5. Reeded edge. (Fernandez 235)

DISTRITO FEDERAL

Azcapotzalco
ESCAT. PUSALCO

Municipio

Rulau	Date	Metal	Size	VG	F	VF	Unc
DF 1	ND	Copper	24mm	—	—	—	—

ESCAT. PUSALCO + in circular legend around a sun. All within a laurel wreath. Rv: Blank. (Munoz PVM 1; ANS 156)

Ixtacalco
ISTACALCO

Municipio

Rulau	Date	Metal	Size	VG	F	VF	Unc
DF 4	ND	Copper	Oct 27mm	—	40.00	65.00	—

ISTA / CAL / * CO *. within octagonal frame. Rv: Blank. (Muñoz PVM 3; Eklund 252; Fernandez 128; ANS 202)

This is four miles southeast of the capital's center today.

Panzacola
PANZACOLA

Municipio

Rulau	Date	Metal	Size	VG	F	VF	Unc
DF 9	ND	Copper	Rect 22x19mm	—	—	—	—

PANZA / COLA within rectangular frame. Rv: Blank. (Muñoz PVM 5; ANS 302)

The village of Panzacola no longer exists, but the chapel of Panzacola stands between Coyoacan and San Angel.

Santa Maria Hastahuacan
SANTA MARIA

Municipio

Rulau	Date	Metal	Size	VG	F	VF	EF
DF 15	1852	Copper	22mm	—	—	—	—

SANTA MARIA / 1/8 / 1852. Rv: M monogram (possibly crowned). (Fernandez 205)

The municipio of S. M. Hastahuacan is now part of the Distrito Federal.

Santiago Tlasilpa
ESQINA DE TLASILPA

Rulau	Date	Metal	Size	VG	F	VF	Unc
DF 18	ND	Copper	Irreg 25mm	—	—	—	—

ESQINA / DE TLA / SILPA. Rv: Blank. (Muñoz ESQ 26)

The barrio (ward) of Santiago Tlasilpa is today on Avenida Morelos in Mexico City, between Paseo Nuevo de Bucareli and Callejon del Sapo.

Tacuba
TIENDA DE CARDENA

Rulau	Date	Metal	Size	VG	F	VF	Unc
DF 22	ND	Copper	28mm	—	—	—	—

Fleur-de-lis at center. Circular legends around: TIENDA DE CARDENA / TACUBA. Rv: Blank. (Muñoz COM 47)

Xoloc
XOLALCO

Municipio

Rulau	Date	Metal	Size	VG	F	VF	Unc
DF 25	1810	Copper	25mm	—	—	—	—

Within laurel wreath: XOLALCO / 1810. Rv: Blank. (Muñoz PVM 14; ANS 487)

Possibly Xoloc junction, in the source of the causeway of Tlalpan and Xola.

Uncertain

V. DE S. FRANCISCO

Municipio

Rulau	Date	Metal	Size	VG	F	VF	Unc
DF 30	ND	Copper	Sq 21mm	—	—	400.	—

V. DE S. / FRAN / CISCO within square frame. Rv: Blank. (Muñoz PVM 13; ANS 483; Fernandez 193)

The Villa de San Francisco has been absorbed somewhere in the Valley of Mexico. There are today several barrios of San Francisco in Mexico City and in the State of Mexico.

Caution: Fantasy!

Rulau	Date	Metal	Size	VG	F	VF	EF
DF 32F	1878	Copper	Sq 33mm	—	—	1.75	—

V. DE S. / FRAN / CISCO. Rv: MEDIA / ANEGA / MAIZ / 1878.

A rather clumsy concoction. Anega should have been Fanega, the date 1878 should have been closer to 1778, and the size much smaller, to be a believable fantasy. Media fanega is a dry measure of about 7 1/2 bushels, in this case of maiz (corn).

MEXICO CITY, D.F.

D. F. = Distrito Federal, Federal District.

Mexico City has become the largest city in the world. It is thus not surprising that it has a great many tokens, and that the history of these tokens goes back some three centuries.

'Puentes'

Puentes (bridges) were originally the Aztec causeways across Lake Texcoco connecting Tenochtitlan with its surrounding areas. Puentes became sections of the old Spanish city of Mexico after Tenochtitlan had been razed to the ground by the Spaniards after its capture in 1521.

Tenochtitlan was built on the puente of Cozotlan, later called La Leña and surviving today in the puentes of Tezontlale and Tepito.

The Avenida del Puente de Alvarado is built along the site of the famous fighting retreat across the causeway on the Noche Triste (June 30, 1520); Pedro de Alvarado had been Cortes' governor of the Aztec capital.

Many tlacos name puentes on them, so they may be attributed to Mexico City.

ARQUITO

Rulau	Date	Metal	Size	VG	F	VF	EF
DF 50	ND	Copper	20mm	—	—	—	—

ARQUITO curved, in script letters. Rv: Blank. Crude. (Munoz COM 2; ANS 39)

Rulau	Date	Metal	Size	VG	F	VF	EF
DF 51	ND	Copper	24mm	—	—	—	—

Same, in larger size.

In the 19th century there was a Callejon del Arquillo (Arquillo Alley), now under the Avenida 5 de Mayo.

ASOCIACION INT. MEXICANA DE CAZA

Rulau	Date	Metal	Size	VG	F	VF	Unc
DF 53	ND	Brass	24mm	7.00	12.00	—	—

Greyhound right, standing on ground. Around: ASOCIACION INT. MEXICANA / * DE CAZA *. Rv: HIPODROMO DE LA INDIANILLA / 15 C / * MEXICO *. (Eklund 2347; Zaika coll.)

Asociacion Int. Mexicana de Caza = Mexican International Association of the Hunt.

A. B.
(at Esquina de la Calle de SantoDomingo)

Rulau	Date	Metal	Size	VG	F	VF	EF
DF 55	ND	Copper	22mm	—	—	—	—

Monogram AB under the arms of a balance scale, all presented in pyramidal form. Rv: (E) SQVIN / DE LA CA / DE So DO / MINGO. Plain edge. (Muñoz ESQ 25)

A. B. did business at the esquina (corner) of Santo Domingo Street, probably referring to the church there.

The plaza of the church of Santo Domingo still exists with the same name. The street itself today is called Calle de Republica de Brasil.

C. O. V. E.
(Cooperativa Obrera de Vestuario y Equipo)

Rulau	Date	Metal	Size	VG	F	VF	Unc
DF 57	ND	Brass	32mm	—	10.00	—	—

Nude male half torso facing rear, his raised hands handcuffed. Background shaded. Rv: C. O. V. E. / (scroll) / 50 (in wreath) / ** CONSUMO **.

Rulau	Date	Metal	Size	VG	F	VF	Unc
DF 59	ND	Brass	26mm	—	10.00	—	—

Obverse as last. Rv: C. O. V. E. / -o- / 10 (radiant) / -o- / * CONSUMO *. (TAMS Maverick 13034: Schimmel report; Grove 'Tokens' 1317)

There are similar 5 and 20-centavo tokens in brass. Cooperative Obrera de Vestuario y Equipo = Workers Cooperative for Uniforms and Equipment.

CALLE DE LAS DAM

Rulau	Date	Metal	Size	VG	F	VF	EF
DF 63	ND	Copper	25mm	—	—	—	—

Within square cartouche: CALLE / DE LAS / DAM. Rv: Blank. Plain edge. (Smithsonian coll.)

The Smithsonian accession ticket says "brothel token," but this may be guesswork. This token escaped notice by Noe-Eklund, Munoz and other catalogers.

CALLE DE OLMEDO

Rulau	Date	Metal	Size	VG	F	VF	EF
DF 65	ND	Copper	24mm	—	—	—	—

Running horse left in beaded central circle. Around: CALUE DE OLMEDO +. Rv: Blank. (Munoz COM 4; ANS 288)

Calle de Olmedo today makes up part of the 6a Calle del Correo Mayor.

C DE STA CLARA
(Calle de Santa Clara)

Rulau	Date	Metal	Size	VG	F	VF	EF
DF 68	ND	Copper	26mm	—	—	—	—

C / DE STA / CLARA. Rv: Blank. (Munoz COM 5)

Calle de Santa Clara was another name for Calle de Tacuba, in front of Santa Clara Convent.

CHABES
(Chavez)

Rulau	Date	Metal	Size	VG	F	VF	EF
DF 69	ND	Copper	21mm	—	—	35.00	—

Running greyhound left at center. Sa. CALLE DE MESONES + / CHABES around. All within a laurel wreath. Rv: Blank. (Munoz NOM 155; Eklund 548)

Calle de Mesones = Street of the Inns, or Taverns. Chabes is an archaic way of rendering the surname Chavez. This is in downtown Mexico City. It runs into Calle Bolivar, says Clyde Hubbard.

CHIVATO

Rulau	Date	Metal	Size	VG	F	VF	Unc
DF 70	ND	Copper	+ +	—	—	—	—

+ + Goat shaped flan, to right, 33x25mm. CHI / UATO in relief within toothed depression. Rv: Blank. (Munoz COM 15; ANS 100)

There was a panaderia (bakery) named Chivato in Mexico City in 1799. The name Chivato is reflected in the goat design of the tlaco, as CHIVO = Goat.

COLEGIO DE NIÑAS

Rulau	Date	Metal	Size	VG	F	VF	EF
DF 72	ND	Copper	Scal 28mm	—	—	—	—

Fountain at center, COLEGIO DE NIÑAS around. Crude. Rv: Blank. (Munoz COM 8)

Rulau	Date	Metal	Size	VG	F	VF	EF
DF 73	ND	Copper	Rect 29x26mm	—	—	—	—

Similar to last. (Munoz COM 8)

El Colegio de Niñas (Girls' Colege) is known today as El Colegio de Bolivar y Venustiano Carranza.

COLICEO
(Coliseo)

Rulau	Date	Metal	Size	VG	F	VF	EF
DF 75	ND	Copper	Oval 28x21mm	—	—	—	—

COLIC / cEO. Rv: Blank. (Munoz COM 10; ANS 105)

There are two Coliseos (Coliseums) in Mexico City, one on 16 de Septiembre and the other on 2a Calle de Donceles.

CRUZ DEL FACTOR

Rulau	Date	Metal	Size	VG	F	VF	EF
DF 77	ND	Copper	24mm	—	—	—	—

Circle of letters S surrounds: CRUZ (Z inverted) / DEL / FACTOR. Rv: Blank. (Munoz COM 12; ANS 124)

Calle Cruz del Factor is today known as Calle de Allende in Mexico City. Romero de Terreros had noted that Cruz del Factor was the name of a hacienda.
This might be a bakery token. There was a panaderia (bakery) on Cruz del Factor in the 1790's, Miguel L. Munoz pointed out.

DE LA PLAZA

Rulau	Date	Metal	Size	VG	F	VF	Unc
DF 80	ND	Copper	27mm	—	—	—	—

DELA / PLAZA. Rv: Blank. Cast. (Munoz COM 33)

Rulau	Date	Metal	Size	VG	F	VF	Unc
DF 81	ND	Iron	27mm				

As last. Cast. (Eklund 321; ANS 217).

There are varieties in copper, including one measuring 25mm.

DEL PUENTE

Rulau	Date	Metal	Size	VG	F	VF	Unc
DF 83	ND	Copper	26mm	—	—	—	—

del / PueNte / (cross on a hill, between sections of causeway). Rv: Blank. (Muñoz PUE 2; ANS 351)

Miguel L. Muñoz, after careful study, attributed this piece to the Puente of Santa Cruz built over the Aztec canal of Mexicaltzingo.

DUBOILLE E HIJOS

Rulau	Date	Metal	Size	VG	F	VF	Unc
DF 88	ND	Brass	25mm	—	—	—	—

DUBOILLE E HIJOS / GRABAN / SELLOS / TARJETAS / LAPIDAS / (three symbols) / MEXICO. Rv: 2a. CALLE DE PLATEROS No. 9 / - / GRABADOR / DEL SUPmo. / GOBIERNO / (ornament) / * MEXICO *. Plain edge. (Grove 'Tokens' 1332)

There is a scalloped border on each side. This is probably an important die-sinker card for Duboille & Sons.

EL CAMBIO

Rulau	Date	Metal	Size	VG	F	VF	EF
DF 90	ND	Copper	—mm	—	15.00	—	—

EL CAMBIO. Rv: Blank. Cast. (Muñoz COM 6; Eklund 211)

El Cambio = The (Money) Exchange.

EL MIRADOR
Chapultepec

Rulau	Date	Metal	Size	VG	F	VF	Unc
DF 95	ND	Brass	25mm	—	—	—	—

EL / MIRADOR / -o- / CHAPULTEPEC (tall slim letters). Rv: 5 / C within beaded circle. Thin flan. (Eklund 126; ANS coll.)

ESQUINA DE BASQUEZ

Rulau	Date	Metal	Size	VG	F	VF	Unc
DF 98	ND	Copper	24mm	—	—	—	—

Ducally crowned double eagle. Around: * ESQUINA DE BASQUEZ. Rv: Blank. (Muñoz ESQ 5)

Esquina de Basquez = Basque Corner.

ESQVIA DE BOLA
(Esquina de Bola)

Rulau	Date	Metal	Size	VG	F	VF	EF
DF 100	(17) 98	Copper	24mm	—	—	75.00	—

ESQVIA / DE . BOLA. / ANO 98. Rv: Monogram within a circle of leaves. (Muñoz ESQ 6; ANS 67)

Rulau	Date	Metal	Size	VG	F	VF	EF
DF 101	(17) 98	Copper	25mm	—	—	100.	—

ESQUIa. DE LA BOLA ANO (curved) / (script monogram) / 98. Rv: Blank. Plain edge. (Smithsonian coll.)

Warning: Counterfeit!

Rulau	Date	Metal	Size	VG	F	VF	EF
DF 102F	1798	Copper	30mm	—	—	1.50	—

ESQVIA / DE . BOLA / ANO. DE / 1798. Rv: Blank. Plain edge. This is a fairly plentiful counterfeit.

Esquina de Bola means, literally, Corner of the Ball (sphere).

ESQUIa DE CHISs
(Esquina de Chiquis)

Rulau	Date	Metal	Size	VG	F	VF	EF
DF 105	ND	Copper	25mm	—	—	—	—

Hook left, at center. Around: ESQUIa DE CHISs. Rv: Blank. (Muñoz ESQ 10: ANS collection)

Calle de Chiquis is today known as Calle de la Academia, behind the National Palace.

ESQVINA DE CORDOBANES

Rulau	Date	Metal	Size	VG	F	VF	Unc
DF 110	ND	Copper	25mm	—	—	—	—

ESQVI / NADE / CORDO / BANES. Rv: Blank. Cast. Plain edge. (Muñoz ESQ 8)

Calle de Cordobanes today is 4a Calle de Donceles.

ESQa DE DECUNA
(Esquina de Cuna)

Rulau	Date	Metal	Size	VG	F	VF	EF
DF 112	ND	Copper	23mm	—	—	—	—

ESQa DE / (Rosette of 7 points) / DECUNA. Rv: Blank. (Muñoz ESQ 9)

La Casa de Cuna (House of Ancestry) was located on the Acequia del Apartado (Secluded Ditch), by El Carmen. Cuna = Cradle, so Esquina de Cuna means literally Cradle Corner.

ESQVINA DE LACAY
(Esquina de Lacayo)

Rulau	Date	Metal	Size	VG	F	VF	Unc
DF 114	ND	Copper	Irreg 30x21mm	—	—	—	—

ESQVINA (N retrograde) / DE LACAY. Rv: Blank. (Muñoz ESQ 14)

Not localized to a site. Esquina de Lacayo = Corner of the Lackey.

ESQ DE LA ENCARNACION
(Esquina de la Encarnacion)

Rulau	Date	Metal	Size	VG	F	VF	Unc
DF 116	ND	Copper	27mm	—	—	—	—

ESQ / DELA / ENCAR / NACI / ON. Rv: Blank. (Muñoz ESQ 12)

Corner of the Incarnation. Not localized to a site.

ESQI DE PERPETUA
(Esquina de la Perpetua)

Rulau	Date	Metal	Size	VG	F	VF	EF
DF 118	ND	Copper	Irreg 25x31mm	22.50	—	—	—

Rosette within beaded central circle. Around: ESQI DE' PERPETUA. All within octagonal depression. Rv: Blank. Pomegranate-shaped flan. (Muñoz ESQ 18; ANS 327)

La Calle de la Perpetua is today 1a Calle de la Republica Venezuela.

A VG specimen appeared as lot 1506 in the Henry Christensen sale of April 23, 1976.

ESQVINA DE LARBL
(Esquina del Arbol)

Illustration reduced

Rulau	Date	Metal	Size	VG	F	VF	EF
DF 120	ND	Copper	28mm	—	—	—	—

Within 17x20mm rect. depression: ESQVINA (monogram) / dE (monogram) LAR (monogram). Rv: Blank. (Muñoz ESQ 1)

Esquina del Arbol (Corner of the Tree) has not been located. Muñoz opined that this could be a bakery tlaco from Mexico City.

At the end of the 18th century there was registered with the government a Mexico City panaderia (bakery) at Plazuela del Arbol (Little Plaza of the Tree), a place not yet localized.

This token provides a good example of the "shorthand" used by token-makers to create early 19th century tlacos, compressing words into logical (or illogical) monograms to save space on the die or the mold. Miguel L. Muñoz has done a masterful job of translating many of these monogram-shortened words so that attribution can be possible.

ESQVINA DELARCO
(Esquina del Arco)

Rulau	Date	Metal	Size	VG	F	VF	EF
DF 122	ND	Copper	23mm	—	—	—	—

Stone archway above: ESQVINA / DELAR / CO. Rv: Blank. (Muñoz ESQ 2)

Possibly this was the Arch of San Agustin, today Calle de la Republica del Salvador.

ESQ. DEL COLICEO
(Esquina del Coliseo)

Rulau	Date	Metal	Size	VG	F	VF	EF
DF 124	ND	Copper	25mm	—	—	—	—

ESQ + DELCO / LICEO within irregular circular frame. Rv: Blank. (Muñoz ESQ 7)

El Coliseo Viejo stood on Calles de las Canoas, now 2a Calle de Donceles. Esquina del Coliseo = Coliseum Corner.

ESQ DEL FAROLITO
(Esquina del Farolito)

Rulau	Date	Metal	Size	VG	F	VF	EF
DF 126	ND	Copper	27mm	—	—	—	—

Rosette at center within beaded circle. Around: ESQ + DEL . FAROLITO. Rv: Blank. (Muñoz ESQ 13; ANS collection; Hubbard coll.)

Muñoz reports this piece has been classified erroneously as a sheep shearing token (ficha de esquila) for a Mexican sheep ranch.

Esquina del Farolito = Corner of the Little Street Lamp.

ESqVIN DE LOS DOLORES
(Esquina de los Dolores)

Rulau	Date	Metal	Size	VG	F	VF	EF
DF 130	ND	Copper	**	—	—	—	—

** Fruit-shaped flan, 25x22mm.

ESqVIN / DE LOS D / OLORES. Rv: Blank. (Muñoz ESQ 11)

The barrio (ward) or pueblo (village) of Los Dolores is today Calle de Dolores. The chapel of the same name was at the intersection of Dolores and Calle de Independencia; it was torn down in the 19th century.

Los Dolores = The Sorrows.

ESQNA DE LOS REVELDES
(Esquina de los Rebeldes)

Rulau	Date	Metal	Size	VG	F	VF	EF
DF 132	ND	Copper	25mm	—	—	—	—

Within beaded central circle: ESQNA / DE LOSR EVELDES / (4-petaled flower). Rv: Blank. (Muñoz ESQ 20)

Esquina de los Rebeldes (Corner of the Rebellious) was where later was built 1a Calle de Nuevo Mexico and is today 3a Calle del Articulo 123.

ESQ. .S. FELPE NERI
(Esquina de San Felipe Neri)

Rulau	Date	Metal	Size	VG	F	VF	EF
DF 134	ND	Copper	24mm	—	—	—	—

ESQ. / .S. FEL / PE NE / RI. Rv: Blank. (Muñoz ESQ 28)

San Felipe Neri Street today is called Calle de Uruguay.

ESQ. DE S. RAMON
(Esquina de San Ramon)

Rulau	Date	Metal	Size	VG	F	VF	EF
DF 136	1785	Copper	27mm	—	—	—	—

ESQ / DESRA / MON ANO (monogram) DE (monogram) / 1785 / (colonial rubric). Rv: Blank. (Muñoz ESQ 22)

La Calle de San Ramon (San Ramon Street) was renamed San Agustin and today is 7a Calle de Uruguay.

(ESQ)A SANT(A) CRVS
(Esquina Santa Cruz)

Rulau	Date	Metal	Size	VG	F	VF	EF
DF 138	ND	Copper	Irreg 22x31mm	—	—	—	—

A / ANT / CRVS within irregular shaped depression. Rv: Blank. (Muñoz ESQ 23)

The barrio of Santa Cruz.

CARLOS FELIX Y CA.

Rulau	Date	Metal	Size	VG	F	VF	Unc
DF 140	ND	Brass	28mm	—	4.00	7.50	—

ANTIGUA DROGUERIA DE LA PALMA * / CARLOS / FELIX Y Ca / 4 Profesa 4 / MEXICO. Rv: DROGAS / PRODs QUIMs / PERFUMERIA / MEDICINAS / DE / PATENTE / *. (Eklund 398; Schimmel June 1989 sale, lot 271)

Drogas prods. quims. perfumeria medicinas de patente = Drugs, chemical products, perfumery, patent medicines.

FLUGGER AND MANCHESTER

Rulau	Date	Metal	Size	VG	F	VF	EF
DF 144	ND	CN	21mm	—	11.00	19.00	—

FLUGGER / - AND - / MANCHESTER / MEXICO. Rv: Ornate monogram F&M. (Eklund 401)

Used as a 5-centavos coin in trade. (See Manchester y Carriles under Mexico City)

GALBAN PERZ
(Galvan Perez)

Esquina de Abraham

Rulau	Date	Metal	Size	VG	F	VF	EF
DF 147	ND	Copper	25mm	—	—	—	—

ESQIa DE ABRAHAM (fleur-de-lis) around: GAL / BAN / PERz. Rv: Blank. (Muñoz ESQ 3)

Esquina de Ave Maria

Rulau	Date	Metal	Size	VG	F	VF	Unc
DF 149	ND	Copper	26mm	—	—	—	—

Within 19mm octagonal depression: . ESQUIa. DE ABE MARIA / GAL / BAN / PERz. Laurel wreath around all. Rv: Blank. (Muñoz ESQ 4; Hubbard coll.)

GOMEZ
(Esquina de Santa Ines)

Rulau	Date	Metal	Size	VG	F	VF	Unc
DF 151	ND	Copper	21mm	—	—	—	—

GO- / MEZ within central beaded circle. Around: ESQUINA . DE . SANTA . YNES. Rv: Blank. (Muñoz ESQ 24)

This tlaco is well made in comparison with others of this type. Santa Inez is between the Calle de Moneda and Calle de Santisima.

GRANADITAS

Rulau	Date	Metal	Size	VG	F	VF	EF
DF 160	ND	Copper	25mm	—	—	—	—

GRA / NADI / TAS in crude letters. Rv: Blank. Cast. (Muñoz COM 19; ANS 189)

The pulqueria (tavern serving pulque, fermented spirits made from juice of the maguey plant) of Las Granaditas was located in the barrio (ward) of San Francisco, Tepito, from about 1752 on.

JUNTA DE LOS NOTABLES

Rulau	Date	Metal	Size	VG	F	VF	Unc
DF 162	1863	Brass	20.5mm	5.00	7.00	11.00	30.00

Bust left. Around: MAXIMILIANO DE AUSTRIA. Rv: JUNTA DE LOS NOTABLES / MEXICO / 6 DE JULIO / 1863. Reeded edge. (Grove 110b; Fauver Maxim 1; Hubbard coll.)

These occur ctsp 2 or 3, probably for use as counters, Clyde Hubbard reports. The ctsp pieces bring about 20% premium.

G. LOHSE Y CA. SUCS.

Rulau	Date	Metal	Size	F	VF	EF	Unc
DF 165	1892	Brass	24mm	—	7.50	11.00	

Statue of Columbus on a pedestal, in a park. Around: CRISTOBAL COLON DESCUBRIDOR DE AMERICA / * 1492 - 1892 *. Rv: G. LOHSE Y Ca SUCs / ANTIGUA / FERRETERIA / Y / MERCERIA / DE LA / PALMA / * MEXICO *. Plain edge. (H. Christensen March 1973 sale, lot 2195)

Ferreteria y merceria = Hardware and notions store. Sucs = Sucursales (branches).

SANTIAGO C. LOHSE

Rulau	Date	Metal	Size	VG	F	VF	Unc
DF 167	ND	Brass	30mm	—	—	—	—

Head left. Around: SANTIAGO C. LOHSE * COMISIONISTA * / PENA. Rv: CALLE DE D'JUAN MANUEL No. 4 MEXICO around a portable engine. (Eklund 400)

E. M.
Cercle Francaise de Mexico

Rulau	Date	Metal	Size	VG	F	VF	Unc
DF 169	ND	Lead	26mm	—	15.00	25.00	—

CERCLE FRANCAISE / DE / MEXICO / (large) E. M. - all within beaded border. Rv: 50 / .C. within beaded border. (Eklund 397)

| DF 170 | ND | Lead | 25mm | — | 15.00 | 25.00 | — |

As last, but 20. (Eklund 396)

MANCHESTER Y CARRILES

Rulau	Date	Metal	Size	F	VF	EF	Unc
DF 180	ND	CN	21mm	5.50	9.50	12.50	—

Ornate monogram MyC. Rv: MANCHESTER / -Y- / CARRILES (one L) / MEXICO. Plain edge. (Eklund 402; Brunk coll.; Hubbard coll.)

| DF 181 | ND | CN | 21mm | — | 12.00 | 18.00 | — |

Obverse as last. Rv: Similar to last, but with extra line inserted between CARRILLES (two L's) and MEXICO: -.- (Eklund 403; Brunk coll.). Error token.

The first token above was offered frequently in the 1973-83 period, usually at the $3 to $5 range in Fine and occasionally at the $6 to $8 range in EF.

Possibly because "carriles" means rails (ferrocarriles is railroads), some collectors say MyC was a railway. This needs checking.

IGNATIO MARTINEZ

Rulau	Date	Metal	Size	VG	F	VF	Unc
DF 183	ND	Brass	39mm	—	—	—	—

Pallet and artist's materials above crossed branches. Rv: IGNATIO MARTINEZ. (Eklund 399; Fischer 348)

MESQUITE
(Plazuela Mezquite)

Rulau	Date	Metal	Size	VG	F	VF	EF
DF 185	ND	Copper	20mm	—	—	60.00	

MES / QUITE / (ornaments). Rv: Blank. (Munoz COM 22)

Plazuela del Mezquite appears in the list of plazas, etc. compiled for Mexico City by Miguel L. Muñoz in his *Tlacos y Pilones).*

Issued for Gomez Saborio.

CAYETANO OCAMPO

Rulau	Date	Metal	Size	F	VF	EF	Unc
DF 190	1885	Silver	26mm	—	—	20.00	—

Aztec calendar stone. Rv: Wreath at center. Around: CAYETANO OCAMPO GRABO EN MEXICO / * 1885 *. Plain edge. (Grove 231a)

| DF 191 | ND | Silver | 25.5mm | — | — | 15.00 | — |

Obverse as last. Rv: Around blank center: CALENDARIO AZTECA / (tiny) C. OCAMPO G. / MEXICO. Plain edge. Weight 5.97 grams. (Grove 232a)

| DF 193 | ND | Silver | 26.6mm | — | — | 15.00 | — |

Obverse as last. Rv: Around blank center: CAYETANO OCAMPO / MEXICO. Plain edge. (Grove N/L; Rulau coll.; Grinolds Aug. 1989 sale, lot 317)

Cayetano Ocampo was a skilled engraver who signed a number of medals of the period, including the beautiful 60mm silver Columbus Monument medallion of 1892 (Rulau B80; Eglit 83). His first name has been given erroneously in literature as Cargetano.

He signed some of his works C.O.G. (Cayetano Ocampo, Grabador = Engraver).

The Aztec calendar stone is a huge stone weighing 24½ tons discovered in El Zocalo (the Mexico City public square) in 1790. It was constructed by the Aztecs 1427-1479 and served as an inspiration for their art and science. As the centenary of its discovery in 1890 approached, Ocampo prepared dies for a number of silver medalets to be sold in Mexico City.

There are many later imitations sold to tourists, but they do not bear his name.

In 1890 a beautiful silver medal of 64mm diameter was struck by another engraver, Jose Jimenez Gomez, which also uses the Aztec calendar stone as its obverse. This was catalogued by Grove as number 233a. It gives a brief history of the stone on its reverse.

This author has examined medals bearing Cayetano Ocampo's signature dated from 1865 through 1910. The signature of his successor S. Ocampo appears at least 1906-1912. His first medals seem to have been portrait pieces of Emperor Maximilian dated 1865 to commemorate the restoration of the Order of Guadalupe (Grove 117).

J. OLLIVIER Y CIA.

Rulau	Date	Metal	Size	VG	F	VF	Unc
DF 197	1893	Aluminum	36.5mm	—	—	11.00	—

Building. Above: CIUDAD DE LONDRES / J. OLLIVIER / Y Cia. Below: 1a MONTERILLA Nos 5 y 6 / MEXICO. Rv: GRAN REALIZACION / DE / MERCANCIAS / CASTIGADAS EN EL BALANCE / PRECIOS SIN IGUAL / MEXICO / 1o DE AGOSTO 1893. Plain edge.

1 PAN (One Loaf Bread)

Rulau	Date	Metal	Size	VG	F	VF	EF
DF 200	ND	Copper	23mm	—	—	—	—

1 PAN (the PAN in monogram form), ornaments on all four sides. (Rv: Blank. (Munoz COM 30)

1 PAN = One loaf of bread. Panaderias (bakeries) were a substantial issuer of tlacos in the early 19th and late 18th centuries.

Bread was always regulated in Mexico. To prevent unscrupulous merchants from abusing the poor on such vital staples as bread and meat, a tribunal — Fiel Ejecutoria — was created Oct. 3, 1539, just 18 years after the conquest of Tenochtitlan. Ordinances for the bakers' guilds set forth these prices (other rules governed meat and some other foods):

Common bread - 20 ounces for 1/2 real.

Pan floreado - 15 ounces for 1/2 real.

By a decree of May 12, 1796, there was established for the poor a second class of bread of greater weight than the floreado bread.

ORTEGA
Colegio de Santo Barios

Rulau	Date	Metal	Size	VG	F	VF	EF
DF 203	ND	Copper	21mm	—	—	—	—

Within a garland: Monogram in a circle. Around: DEL (monogram) COLEGIO DE (monogram) SANTO BARIOS. An impressed rectangular resello reads: ORTEGA. Rv: Blank. (Munoz COM 9; ANS 417)

PA. CE. DE BANEG
(Panaderia Calle de Banegas)

Rulau	Date	Metal	Size	VG	F	VF	EF
DF 205	ND	Copper	22mm	—	—	—	—

Pa. Ce. DE (monogram) BANEG around an 8-petaled rosette. Stylized laurel border. Rv: Blank. (Munoz COM 25)

Panaderia Calle de Banegas = Banegas Street Bakery. Present location uncertain.

PA ESQVINA DE LORETO
(Panaderia Esquina de Loreto)

Rulau	Date	Metal	Size	VG	F	VF	Unc
DF 207	ND	Copper	25mm	—	—	—	—

PA / ESQVINA (QV in monogram) / DEL (monogram) ORETO. Rayed border. Rv: Blank. (Munoz COM 27; Eklund 448)

| DF 208 | ND | Copper | 25mm | — | — | — | — |

PA / ESQVINA (QV monogram) / DE (monogram) (L) ORETO. Rv: Blank. Plain border. (Munoz ESQ 16)

Panaderia Esquina de Loreto = Bakery Corner of Loreto. Early 19th century.

There was a Plazuela de Loreto which probably was the locale of the "bakery corner."

BERNARDO PEREZ

Rulau	Date	Metal	Size	VG	F	VF	Unc
DF 210	ND	Brass	30mm	—	—	—	—

Wine bottle and glass. Around: SALON BERNARDO PEREZ / (ornament) CANTINA (ornament). Rv: LOS MEJORES LUNCHS DE LA CAPITAL / JOYA Y / ARCO DE SAN / AGUSTIN / * MEXICO *. Plain edge. (Paul Bosco sale of Nov. 1985)

PLATEROS

Rulau	Date	Metal	Size	VG	F	VF	EF
DF 212	ND	Copper	23mm	—	—	—	—

PLATE (TE in monogram) / ROS / AB monogram. Rv: Blank. (Muñoz COM 32; Eklund 481)

Plateros Streets are now called Francisco I. Madero and San Francisco Streets.

PLAZA DEL MERCADO

Rulau	Date	Metal	Size	VG	F	VF	EF
DF 215	ND	Copper	22mm	—	—	—	—

* PLAZA DEL MERCADO / 1/8. Monogram AV incused in field. Rv: Blank. (Ulex 1819; Eklund 381; Muñoz COM 35)

Plaza del Mercado = Market Square. Ulex assigned this piece to Ahualulco de Piños in San Luis Potosi State, but he was unware of the tokens which follow. Ulex also assigned a date of 1813 to this token, which seems too early.

The monogram AV resembles :

Rulau	Date	Metal	Size	VG	F	VF	EF
DF 217	1824	Copper	24mm	—	—	—	—

Radiant Liberty cap, PLAZA DEL MERCADO. ANO / DE / 1824. Rv: Blank. (Eklund 385)

| DF 218 | 1824 | Copper | 29mm | — | — | — | — |

Within radiant circle: PLAZA DEL MERCADO /ANO / DE / 1824. Rv: Blank. (Eklund 386, from a Jacques Schulman catalog)

| DF 219 | 1825 | Copper | 21mm | — | — | — | — |

PLAZA DEL MERCADO / (star) / (monogram AV in relief) / (flower) / * 1825 *. Rv: Blank. (Eklund 382)

| DF 220 | 1826 | Copper | 22mm | 15.00 | 25.00 | — | — |

Similar to last, but 1826. (Eklund 383)

| DF 225 | 1841 | Copper | 29mm | — | — | — | — |

Radiant Liberty cap. PLAZA DEL MERCADO / 1/16 (real) 1841. Rv: Blank. (Eklund 387)

| DF 227 | ND | Copper | 25mm | — | — | — | — |

2 in relief within 14mm toothed circular depression ctsp on Mexico centavo. (Eklund 388)

| DF 228 | ND | Copper | 25mm | — | — | — | — |

As last, but 3 ctsp. (Eklund 389)

| DF 229 | ND | Copper | 25mm | — | — | — | — |

As last, but 4.

Rulau	Date	Metal	Size	VG	F	VF	EF
DF 230	ND	Copper	25mm	—	—	—	—

As last, but 5.

| DF 231 | ND | Copper | 25mm | — | — | — | — |

As last, but 6. (Eklund 392)

The last five counterstamped centavos are said to have been used at the city market. The numerals signify 'almudes' or measures of corn.

| DF 233 | ND | Copper | 25mm | — | — | — | — |

Mexico centavo cut in half. (Eklund 393)

These pieces were used as change at the city market and other places. A worn specimen in the Eklund collection was ink-marked 1864 by a previous collector.

The Plaza del Mercado (market square) was known as City Market in Mexico City. There are probably other tokens used there which have not been reported.

PORTAL DE PRADO

Rulau	Date	Metal	Size	VG	F	VF	EF
DF 240	ND	Copper	19mm	—	—	—	—

Male bust left in central circle. Around: PORTAL . DE . PRADO. Tiny fleurs-de-lis are around all. Rv: Blank. (Muñoz NOM 37)

| DF 241 | ND | Silver | 21mm | — | — | — | — |

As last. (Fonrobert 7170)

Portal = Entrance.

PUENTE

Rulau	Date	Metal	Size	VG	F	VF	EF
DF 243	ND	Copper	21mm	—	—	—	—

Fountain divides PUE — NTE. Dentilated (rayed) border all around rim. Rv: Blank. (Muñoz PUE 1)

Munoz reported great difficulty in localizing this piece. Puente de Salto del Agua near the acqueduct of Chapultepec is possible. Also known in 23mm size.

PUENTE BLANCO

Rulau	Date	Metal	Size	VG	F	VF	EF
DF 245	ND	Copper	21mm	—	—	—	—

PVeNte / BLaNCO above bridge, within circular frame. Rv: Blank. (Muñoz PUE 3)

Puente Blanco was over Tezontlale canal and part of Lake Texcoco.

BUENTE COLEORADO
(Puente Colorado)

Rulau	Date	Metal	Size	VG	F	VF	EF
DF 247	(1812)	Copper	Oct 24mm	—	—	—	—

Within octagonal depression: BUEN / TE / COLEORADO (in arc) - all amid flowers. Rv: Blank. (Muñoz PUE 5; ANS 352)

Puente Colorado was built over Mexicaltzingo canal, between the puentes of Blanquillo and Santiaguito. Puente Colorado = Red Bridge.

Rulau	Date	Metal	Size			
DF 249	ND	Copper	24mm	—	—	—

8-pointed star at center. Around: PVENTE COLORADA. Rv: Blank. (Schimmel June 1989 sale, lot 191)

Schimmel says the token above was issued by a shop located at the bridge.

P. DE JS. MA.
(Puente de Jesus Maria)

Rulau	Date	Metal	Size	VG	F	VF	Unc
DF 260	ND	Copper	20mm	—	—	—	—

TE / P. DE (monogram) / JS. MA. (monogram). Rv: Blank. (Muñoz PUE 9; ANS 443)

Puente de Jesus Maria was over the Royal Canal, now Calle de la Corregidora at the National Palace.

LEÑA
(Puente de La Leña)

Rulau	Date	Metal	Size			
DF 262	1773	Copper	28mm	—	—	—	—

Two cartouches depressed in flan. In uper: A 1773. In lower: LE / ÑA. Bridge between. Rv: Blank. (Muñoz PUE 7; Eklund 331; ANS 360)

| DF 264 | 1793 | Copper | 25mm | — | — | — | — |

Similar, but better executed. Upper: A 1793. Lower: LE / ÑA, Rv: Blank. (Muñoz PUE 6; ANS 360)

Puente de La Lena was built over the Royal Canal at the end of Mexicaltzingo acqueduct, today 4a Calle de la Soledad in Mexico City. It is the heart of the old Aztec city.

PUENTE DE LA MARISCALA

Rulau	Date	Metal	Size	VG	F	VF	EF
DF 266	ND	Copper	Oval 28x22mm	—	—	—	—

PUENTE / DELA . MAR / ISCALA GA / ONA. Rv: Blank. (Muñoz PUE 8; Eklund 357; ANS 359)

Puente de la Mariscala was over Santa Ana canal, in what is today 1a Calle de Aquiles Serdan.

P D MONZON
(Puente de Monzon)

Rulau	Date	Metal	Size	VG	F	VF	EF
DF 268	ND	Copper	Oct 24mm	—	—	—	—

Within octagonal frame: P D / MON / ZON. Rv: Blank. (Muñoz PUE 10; ANS 268)

Puente de Monzon today would be at the crossing of Calles de Isabel la Catolica and San Jeronimo.

PUent De PiPis
(Puente de Pipis)

Rulau	Date	Metal	Size	VG	F	VF	EF
DF 270	ND	Copper	Sq 25mm	—	—	—	—

puent / De / PiPis within rect. depression. Rv: Two rectangular counterstamps are impressed. Each of them reads the same: LASO DE / LA BEGA. (Muñoz PUE 13; ANS 353)

Puente de Pipis was over Mexicaltzingo canal, between Santo Tomas and San Pablo.

Who or what Laso de la Bega (possibily Lazaro de la Vega) was has not been explained.

Uniface specimens with PUENT/DE/PiPiS in large letters are counterfeit!

PUENTE DE SAN YNACIO
(Puente de San Ignacio)

Rulau	Date	Metal	Size	VG	F	VF	EF
DF 272	ND	Copper *	23mm	—	—	—	—

* Copper, with a plug of white metal (silver ?). Triple-arched structure at center. Above it: BAY. Below: EJO (inverted). Around: (Sun) PUENTE DE. SAN YNA-CIO. Rv: Blank. (Muñoz PUE 15)

| DF 274 | ND | Copper | 21mm | — | — | — | — |

Triple-arched structure at center. Around: PUENTE DE SAN YNACIO. Rv: Counterstamp of flowers and lis joined at base. (Muñoz PUE 16; ANS 357)

Puente de San Ignacio was named after the School of San Ignacio de las Vizcainas, still preserved.

PUENTE DE SAN PABLO

Rulau	Date	Metal	Size	VG	F	VF	EF
DF 276	ND	Copper	26mm	—	—	—	—

puente / de sn / pablo within irregular depression. Rv: Blank. (Muñoz PUE 18)

Puente de San Pablo was over the canal of Mexicaltzingo.

Pt DE Sn P. I Sn. P.
(Puente de San Pedro y San Pablo)

Rulau	Date	Metal	Size	VG	F	VF	EF
DF 278	ND	Copper	Oval 25x19mm	—	—	—	—

Pt DE (monogram) Sn. / P. I Sn. P. within toothed rect. depression. Rv: Blank. (ANS 355; Muñoz PUE 19)

The Bridge of Saints Peter and Paul stood where today is 2a Calle del Carmen.

Pt DE STA ANA
(Puente de Santa Ana)

Rulau	Date	Metal	Size	VG	F	VF	EF
DF 280	ND	Copper	Oct 18mm	—	—	—	—

Pt DE (monogram) / + STA + ? ANA. Rv: Blank. (Muñoz PUE 20; ANS 356; Ulex 2285; Schrotter 25)

This area was in front of the Church of Santa Ana in Peralvillo.
The Clyde Hubbard specimen measures 21mm and has a variant legend.

P DE Sn TISmo
(Puente de Santisimo)

Rulau	Date	Metal	Size	VG	F	VF	EF
DF 282	ND	Copper	Sq 22mm	—	—	—	—

P DE (monogram) S / nTISmo. Rv: Blank. (Muñoz PUE 21)

Puente de Santisimo (Holiest Bridge) was located at what is today 3a Calle de Dolores.

PUENTE (D)E S. S. IOSE
(Puente de Señor San Jose)

Rulau	Date	Metal	Size	VG	F	VF	EF
DF 284	ND	Copper	24mm	—	—	—	—

In rectangular depression: PVENTE / DE (monogram) SS. IOSE. Rv: Blank. (Muñoz PUE 17; ANS 354)

Puente de San Jose el Real stood where today is the Calle de Isabel la Catolica.

PUENTE MORA
(Puente Morado)

Rulau	Date	Metal	Size	VG	F	VF	EF
DF 286	ND	Copper	23mm	—	—	—	—

In center: PUENTE / (line) / MORA. / * A *. Around: TIB(URCIO) - SANCHO * PANZA. Beaded border around all. Rv: Blank. (Muñoz PUE 11)

Probably Puente Morado.

PUEN NUEV
(Puente Nuevo)

Rulau	Date	Metal	Size	VG	F	VF	EF
DF 288	ND	Copper	Irreg 27x25mm	—	—	—	—

PUEN / NUEV within rectangular depression on an irregular copper flan shaped a little like a claw. (Muñoz PUE 12; ANS 349)

Puente Nuevo was over Merced canal. Tentative attribution possibly reads PUL / NIO.

PVERT DE S. SABEL
(Puerta de Santa Isabel)

Rulau	Date	Metal	Size	VG	F	VF	Unc
DF 291	ND	Copper	22mm	—	—	—	—

Tower at center. Around: PVERT DE S. SABEL . Rv: Blank. Cast. (Muñoz COM 39)

Calle de Santa Isabel today is Calle Juan Ruiz de Alarcon.

QVEMADA
(Quemada)

Rulau	Date	Metal	Size	VG	F	VF	EF
DF 293	ND	Copper	24mm	—	—	—	—

qve / MA (monogram) DA. Rv: Blank. (Muñoz COM 40)

Quemada was between Puente del Fierro and Calle de las Ratas.

TIENDA DE LA CAMPA
(Tienda de la Campana)

Rulau	Date	Metal	Size	VG	F	VF	Unc
DF 300	1798	Copper	22mm	—	—	Rare	—

Bell between branches central circle. Around: TIENDA DE LA CAMPA / 1798 (crude). Rv: OCTAVO. (Muñoz COM 45; Schrotter 70)

Tienda de la Campana = Store of the bell.

TIENDA DE LA VICTORIA

Rulau	Date	Metal	Size	VG	F	VF	EF
DF 302	1812	Copper	**	—	—	—	—

** Rabbit-shaped flan (to right), 28x23mm. Legend in circular (oval) form: TIENDA DE LA VICTORIA. In field: ANO / DE / 1812 between rosettes above and below. Rv: Blank. (Muñoz COM 48; Schrotter 23; Eklund 330)

NOTE: Most of the inscription does not show on the illustration.

TIENDA NUEVA

Rulau	Date	Metal	Size	VG	F	VF	EF
DF 303	ND	Copper	27mm	—	—	—	—

DE (monogram) LA TI / ENDAN / UEVA. Rv: Blank. Cast. (Muñoz COM 52)

Tienda Nueva = New Store. Doubtful attribution.

TORRE LATINOAMERICANA

Rulau	Date	Metal	Size	F	VF	EF	Unc
DF 306	ND	Brass	22mm	—	—	1.00	2.00

Tall modern building, TORRE LATINOAMERICANA (Latin American Tower) around. Rv: MIRADOR / MEXICO D. F. Plain edge. (Grove 'Tokens' 1971)

Rulau	Date	Metal	Size	F	VF	EF	Unc
DF 306A	ND	Aluminum	22mm	—	—	1.00	1.50

As last.

Very common modern telescope activator token. The telescopes are atop the tower. Mirador = Viewer.

BUTRON Y MUXICA
Distrito Federal

Rulau specimen

ANS specimen

Rulau	Date	Metal	Size	VG	F	VF	EF
DF 325	1806	Copper	31.7mm	—	30.00	40.00	50.00

BUTRON / Y. / MUXICA. / (ornaments). Rv: ANO / DE / 1806 / . (Muñoz NOM 99; Ulex 1493; Eklund 80; ANS 72; Rulau coll.)

Genuine tokens are known measuring 29mm.
Somewhat similar tokens in copper, 32mm, dated 1805, are counterfeits!

Caution: Forgery!

Rulau	Date	Metal	Size	VG	F	VF	EF
DF 326F	1806	Copper	35mm	—	—	1.75	—

⊿ . ⊿ / BUTRON / ⊿ Y ⊿ / MUXICA / ⊿ . ⊿. Rv: ⊿⊿ / ANO / ⊿ DE ⊿ / 1806 / ⊿⊿. Plain edge.

BUTRON

Rulau	Date	Metal	Size	VG	F	VF	EF
DF 328	ND	Copper	34mm	—	35.00	50.00	70.00

BVTRON across center, surrounded by a field filled with ornamentation. Rv: Blank. (Muñoz NOM 98)

A relationship between Butron and Butron y Muxica may be inferred. Also see VAQUEDANO in Unattributed Mexico section!

ESTADO DE MEXICO
Apasco de Ocampo
APASCO DE OCAMPO

Rulau	Date	Metal	Size	VG	F	VF	EF
EDM 1	1878	Copper	26mm	—	—	30.00	—

APASCO DE OCAMPO / (ornament) ctsp on Mexico 1-centavo coin. Rv: FEBRERO 2, 1878 ctsp on opposite side of the coin. Reeded edge. (Fernandez 11)

Chalco
..... DE CHALCO

Rulau	Date	Metal	Size	VG	F	VF	Unc
EDM 4	ND	Lead	25mm	—	—	—	—

.... DE CHALCO / (arms of Mexico) — all in border of stars. Rv: Blank. (Fernandez 91)

Nexquipayac
NESQUIPAYA

Municipio

Rulau	Date	Metal	Size	VG	F	VF	Unc
EDM 8	1806	Copper	26mm	—	—	—	—

NESQUIPAYA 1806 in circular legend around monogram at center. (Muñoz PVM 4)

San Mateo Atenco
SMA Monogram

Rulau	Date	Metal	Size	VG	F	VF	EF
EDM 15	ND	Copper	25mm	—	—	—	—

MA monogram, tiny S above, in 16mm square indent. Rv: Blank. (Eklund 730)

Used in San Mateo Atenco, Estado de Mexico. A similar 21mm piece, dated 1817, 2/4 real, is listed by Eklund as 729.

Tenancingo
TENANCINGO

Rulau	Date	Metal	Size	VG	F	VF	Unc
EDM 20	ND	Copper	22mm	—	—	—	—

TENANCINGO curved above flowers on stem, crossed branches below. Rv: Blank. (Fernandez 237)

TEOFILO HERNANDEZ

Rulau	Date	Metal	Size	VG	F	VF	EF
EDM 22	ND	Copper	22mm	—	—	—	—

Dog left. Around: TENANCINGO / 1/16. Rv: TEO-FILO HERNANDEZ / (flowers). (Fernandez 238; Grove 'Tokens' 966)

Tetlizpac
TETLCPAC

Rulau	Date	Metal	Size	VG	F	VF	EF
EDM 25	ND	Copper	20mm	—	—	—	—

TETL / CPAC. Rv: Blank. (Muñoz PVM 9)

Tetlizpac is a village near the old city of Guadalupe.

Texcoco
TEZCUCO

Municipio

Rulau	Date	Metal	Size	VG	F	VF	Unc
EDM 29	ND	Copper	24mm	—	85.00	125.	—

.R. / TEZ / CUCO. Rv: Blank. (Muñoz PVM 10; Duffield 1695; Eklund 511; ANS 446; Fernandez 246)

Variations are known in 25 and 26mm size with flat-top Z and with S in second line.

CUEBAS Y COMPANIA

Rulau	Date	Metal	Size	VG	F	VF	Unc
EDM 31	ND	Copper	22mm	—	—	—	—

CUEBAS Y COMPANIA / TES. / CUCO. Rv: Blank. (Muñoz NOM 150; Fernandez 247)

Cuevas and Co., Texcoco, near Mexico City.

HACIENDA DE FOCUILA

Rulau	Date	Metal	Size	VG	F	VF	EF
EDM 35	1898	Bone *	34mm	—	—	65.00	—

(All script): Hacienda De Focuila / 12 1/2 / Centavos / Carne. Rv: (All script): F.L. / 1898. (Muñoz PVM 12; Grove 'Tokens' 1492)

*Made of a polished animal bone, probably sheep. Text is darkened. All hand work.

This token was good for 12 1/2 centavos (1/8 peso, or one real) worth of meat (carne). Neil Utberg reported about 1965 that one collector owned 40 of these pieces.

Miguel L. Muñoz read this as Tocuila, and Frank Grove as Focula. Focuila seems the proper reading.

Toluca
TOLUCA

Municipio

Rulau	Date	Metal	Size	VG	F	VF	Unc
EDM 40	1915	+ +	28.5mm	—	30.00	—	50.00

Toluca arms at center. Around: ESTADO LIBRE Y SOBERANO DE MEXICO / TOLUCA (all impressed incuse). Rv: CIRCULARA CONFORME AL DECRETO No. 4 DE / 5 (large) / CENTAVOS (on scroll across 5) / + III. 1 . 1915 +. (all impressed incuse). (G/B 263)
+ + Grey cardboard round.

Revolutionary issue of emergency small change.

Uncertain
THE SOLORZANO FAMILY
SOLORSANO

Rulau	Date	Metal	Size	VG	F	VF	Unc
EDM 50	1807	Copper	30mm	—	—	—	—

Dentilated object in central circle. Around: SOLOR-SANO . ANO DE 1807. Rv: Blank. (Muñoz NOM 555; Hubbard coll.)

Varieties exist.

RAMON SOLORZANO

Rulau	Date	Metal	Size	VG	F	VF	Unc
EDM 52	ND	Copper	28mm	—	—	—	—

RAMON . SOLORZANO in circular legend around stylized radiant sun. Around all is an ornate border. Rv: Blank. (Muñoz NOM 557)

Varieties exist.

AGAPITO SOLORZANO

Rulau	Date	Metal	Size	VG	F	VF	Unc
EDM 54	ND	Copper	31mm	—	—	—	—

Concentric lines form center; at center is an illegible abbreviation. Around: AGAPITO SOLORZANO / MEXICO. (Muñoz 556)

DURANGO STATE

Ciudad Lerdo
HOTEL MADRID

Rulau	Date	Metal	Size	VG	F	VF	Unc
Dur 11	(1893-97)	CN	32mm	—	—	15.00	25.00

HOTEL MADRID / (radiant cross) / C. LERDO / DGO / (tiny) L.H. MOISE. Rv: -+- / UNA / COPA . -+-. Leaf border. Plain edge. (Eklund 205)

Una copa – One cup. Struck by L. H. Moise Co., San Francisco, Calif.

Gomez Palacio
JUAN N. N. MENDOZA

Rulau	Date	Metal	Size	VG	F	VF	Unc
Dur 18	ND	Brass	24mm	—	—	—	—

"EL GLOBO" / JUAN H. H. / MENDOZA / .*. / GOMEZ PALACIO. Rv: Ornate numeral 15. Plain edge. (Eklund 2099)

PRINCE TORRES Y PRINCE

Rulau	Date	Metal	Size	VG	F	VF	Unc
Dur 21	ND	CN	25mm	—	—	—	—

PRINCE TORRES Y PRINCE / (6-pointed star) / UNA PIEZA. Rv: Clasped hands. Around: LA AMISTAD GOMEZ PALACIO / DURANGO. Plain edge. (Eklund 204)

Una pieza – One piece.

GOMES
(Hacienda Gomez?)

Rulau	Date	Metal	Size	VG	F	VF	Unc
Dur 30	ND	Copper	++	—	—	—	—

++ 7-sided flan, 26mm.
GOMES (ME united) in irregular rect. depression ctsp on blank flan. Uniface. (Muñoz NOM 239; Eklund 726)

Muleros
MULEROS

Rulau	Date	Metal	Size	VG	F	VF	Unc
Dur 35	ND	Lead	21mm	—	—	—	—

MULEROS ADI — I —O. / XX (in circle). Rv: Blank. (Fernandez 158)

S. JOSE DE AVINO
(San Jose de Avino Mines Administration)

Rulau	Date	Metal	Size	VG	F	VF	Unc
Dur 40	1864	Copper	20mm	6.00	10.00	—	—

Within wreath: S. JOSE / DE / AVINO. Rv: ADMINISTRACION / 1/4 / DE MINAS 1864. Plain edge. (ANS 412; Eklund 525)

Rulau	Date	Metal	Size	VG	F	VF	Unc
Dur 41	1864	Copper	21mm	10.00	15.00	25.00	—

As last. Reeded edge. (Smithsonian coll.)

Administracion de Minas – Mines administration. The reeding is: .).) repeated over and over.

Rulau	Date	Metal	Size	VG	F	VF	Unc
Dur 42	1864	Copper	38mm	—	—	80.00	Rare

Rv: ADMINISTRACION / 1 PESO. / * DE MINAS . 1864 . *. Obv: As last. (Utberg report; Eklund 526)

The three S's in the inscription are all retrograde!

Velardeña
CA. M. DE LA VELARDEÑA

Rulau	Date	Metal	Size	VG	F	VF	Unc
Dur 50	(1885-95)	CN	Scal 29mm	—	15.00	—	—

CA. M. DE La / VELARDEÑA / -o- / (tiny) HEIDEMANN MFG CO. S.A. TEX. Rv: 50¢ C / EN MERCANICIAS.

Rulau	Date	Metal	Size	VG	F	VF	Unc
Dur 52	ND	CN	25mm	8.00	9.50	—	—

CA. M. DE LA / * / VELARDEÑA / -.-. Rv: BUENO POR / 10 C / * EN MERCANCIAS *. Plain edge.

Rulau	Date	Metal	Size	VG	F	VF	Unc
Dur 53	ND	CN	19.5mm	4.00	5.50	—	—

As last, but 5 C.

Compania Minera de la Velardeña – mining tokens?
Heidemann Mfg. Co. of San Antonio, Texas struck many of the beautiful cupronickel Texas pictorial tokens of the 1880's and 1890's. The 25-centavo CN octagonal 25mm token was TAMS Maverick 13058 in the Feb. 1991 journal.

GUANAJUATO STATE

Acambaro
R. O. T. (Monogram)
(Romero de Terreros)
Hacienda de San Cristobal Acambaro

Rulau	Date	Metal	Size	VG	F	VF	EF
Guj 1	ND	Copper	Rect 26x37mm	—	—	Rare	—

8 RS / distinctive ROT monogram. Rv: Blank. (Thickness 5mm. (Muñoz NOM 509; ANS 391; Eklund 2367)

<table>
<tr><th>Rulau</th><th>Date</th><th>Metal</th><th>Size</th><th>VG</th><th>F</th><th>VF</th><th>Unc</th></tr>
<tr><td>Guj 2</td><td>ND</td><td>Copper</td><td>Rect 25x26mm</td><td>—</td><td>—</td><td>Rare</td><td>—</td></tr>
</table>

ROT mongram R (tiny) 4. Rv: Blank. 2mm thick. (Muñoz NOM 510; ANS 392)

Guj 3	ND	Copper	28mm	—	—	Rare	—

Modified ROT monogram and 2, small R above the 2. 2mm thick. Rv: Blank. (Muñoz NOM 511; Eklund 2365; ANS 393)

Guj 4	ND	Copper	Rect 23x18mm	—	—	Rare	—

RO monogram and small R over 1. Rv: Blank. (Muñoz NOM 512; ANS 394)

Guj 5	ND	Copper	Triang 18mm	—	—	Rare	—

RO monogram. Rv: ½. (Muñoz NOM 513; ANS 395; Eklund 2363)

Guj 6	ND	Copper	Rect 33x29mm	—	—	Rare	—

Large monogram JTRo similar to preceding but small tails added to the monogram; at left: 2. Rv: Blank. (ANS 396; Muñoz N/L)

Hacienda de San Cristobal Acambaro, in Guanajuato State, was in Colonial times one of the most important haciendas in Mexico. It belonged to Doña Micaela Romero de Terreros, second Marquesa de San Francisco, eldest daughter of Don Pedro Romero de Terreros, Conde de Regla.

The marquesa issued extremely limited numbers of copper tokens in 8, 4, 2, 1 and ½-real denominations for use in her holdings and all are extremely rare. These were used in San Cristobal Acambaro hacienda and its annexes.

The issuer was an ancestor of Manuel Romero de Terreros, the well-known Mexican numismatist and author.

Caution: Forgery

Rulau	Date	Metal	Size	VG	F	VF	EF
Guj 7F	1750	Copper	40mm	—	—	1.75	—

JTRo monogram / 1750. Border of alternating dots and balls. Rv: . V . / REAL / . 8 Rs. Plain edge. Thick (4.7mm) heavy flan.

In his haste to imitate the Terreros tokens, among Mexico's most desirable, the forger made a number of clumsy errors. Users of this catalog may study the photos provided to see the differences between real and fake.

Celaya
JOSE ANTONIO DE PRADO

Rulau	Date	Metal	Size	VG	F	VF	EF
Guj 10	ND	Copper	32mm	—	—	—	—

Ornament at center. Around: JOSE ANTONIO. Rv: DE PRADO CELAIA. (Muñoz NOM 456; ANS 343)

LUIS VASQUES

Rulau	Date	Metal	Size	VG	F	VF	EF
Guj 13	1803	Copper	32mm	37.50	52.50	75.00	—

(Flower) / * / LVIS / VASQUE / S (crossed palm branches). Rv: EN / CELAYA / DE / 1803 within palm branches. Plain edge. (Muñoz NOM 596; KM L33; Eklund 121; ANS 470)

Luis Vasquez. Larger (34mm) pieces reading EN / CELAYA / 1803 on reverse are counterfeits!

Frank Grove claims the date on the genuine token is 1805.

VIDERIQUE

Rulau	Date	Metal	Size	VG	F	VF	Unc
Guj 15	1808	Copper	24-28mm	25.00	35.00	50.00	—

VIDER / iquE / (CELAYA / 1808. Rv: Blank. (Muñoz NOM 610; KM L34; Eklund 122; ANS 476; Hubbard coll.)

Guj 16	1808	Copper	24-26mm	30.00	40.00	60.00	—

Videri / que / CELAllA / 1808. Rv: Blank. Well made. (Banco de Mexico coll.)

Guj 18	1814	Copper	24mm	25.00	35.00	50.00	—

VIDER. / QUE / CEAYA / 1814. Rv: Blank. (Muñoz NOM 611; KM L35 var.; ANS 477)

There are additional die varieties of the 1808 tokens.

VISCARA

Rulau	Date	Metal	Size	VG	F	VF	EF
Guj 20	1814	Copper	25mm	25.00	—	—	—

(Ornament) / VISCARA / CELAYA / 1814. Rv: Blank. (Fernandez 36; Muñoz NOM 618; KM L35)

Chamacuero
CHAMACUERO

Rulau	Date	Metal	Size	VG	F	VF	EF
Guj 25	ND	Copper	26mm	—	25.00	—	—

CHAMACUERO (circular) within ornate circular border. Rv: Blank. (Fernandez 92)

Guj 26	ND	Copper	24mm	11.00	25.00	—	—

CHAMACUERO / (cross) - all in ornamental border. Rv: Blank. (Fernandez 93)

Guj 27	ND	Copper	28mm	—	30.00	—	—

CHAMACVERO / (monogram) - all in circle. Rv: Blank. (ANS 95; Fernandez 94)

Chamacuero was founded by Viceroy Luis de Velasco about 1561. In 1874 its name was changed to Comonfort.

Dolores Hidalgo
PUEBLO DE LOS DOLORES

Municipios

Rulau	Date	Metal	Size	VG	F	VF	Unc
Guj 29	ND	Copper	25mm	—	—	—	—

PVEBLO / DE / LOS / DOLORES. Rv: Blank. (Eklund 341; Muñoz PVM 7). A specimen measuring 22mm is reported.

A variety has VALE on reverse.

Guj 31	(1810)	Copper	29mm	15.00	—	—	—

o / PVEBLO / DE LOS / DOLO / RES. Rv: Blank. (Eklund 342; MuñozPVM 6; ANS 237; Scott)

Guj 33	ND	Copper	33mm	—	—	—	—

(Branches) / PVEBLO / DE LOS / DOLO / RES. Rv: Blank. (Fernandez 115)

Guj 34	ND	Copper	Oval 28x33mm	—	—	—	—

(Ornaments) / PVEBL / DE . LOS / DOLO / RES. Rv: Blank. (Grove 'Tokens' 744)

The pueblo (village) of Los Dolores is now called Dolores Hidalgo.

Irapuato
YRAPUATO

Rulau	Date	Metal	Size	VG	F	VF	EF
Guj 39	1813	Copper	Sq 20mm	—	—	—	—

(Flower with leaves) / YRAPUATO / 1813 / (crossed branches). Rv: G FP-monogam D / (crossed branches). (Fernandez 127)

Penjamo
PENJAMO

Municipios

Rulau	Date	Metal	Size	VG	F	VF	Unc
Guj 50	1814	Copper	20mm	—	—	—	—

OCTAVO / DE / PENJAMO. / ANO . 1814. Rv: VIVA / LA / NACION / (rosette) -- all in wreath border. (Fernandez 176)

Guj 55	1859	Copper	22mm	—	—	—	—

⅛ / (radiant Liberty cap) / PENJAMO 1859. Rv: ARVITRIO PUBLICO, PENJAMO, GTO. 1859 ⅛ DE REAL. (Description uncertain)

Guj 53	1852	Copper	22mm	15.00	25.00	50.00	100.

Radiant Liberty cap. Around: PENJAMO / ⅛ / 1852. Rv: Eagle on cactus. Around: ARVITRIO PUBLICO.

Salvatierra
ALLER

Rulau	Date	Metal	Size	VG	F	VF	Unc
Guj 58	1805	Copper	31mm	—	—	90.00	—

Crowned shield of arms, male figure stands at left, trophies around. In exergue: ALLER. Rv: E. Cv DE (monogram) / SALVATIER / RA - i ENERO 1o / DE 1805. (Muñoz NOM 29; Fernandez 189; ANS 23)

Frank Grove reads the date as 1803. The Hubbard specimen measures 29mm.

San Felipe
VILLA DE SAN FELIPE

Municipio

Rulau	Date	Metal	Size	VG	F	VF	Unc
Guj 60	ND	Copper	31mm	—	—	—	—

VILLA. DE. SAN FELIPE. / (Maltese cross) -- all in a beaded circle. Rv: Blank. (Fernandez 192; Eklund 556; ANS 482)

F. C. O. DE G.

Rulau	Date	Metal	Size	F	VF	EF	Unc
Guj 62	1892	Silver	22.5mm	—	—	25.00	—

Locomotive left. In exergue: F. C. O. DE G. Rv: RECUERDO / ENTRADA / SAN FELIPE / 1892 on panel and on 11-pointed star. Plain edge. (Dick Grinolds collection; Grove 276a)

F. C. O. DE G. stands for Ferro Carril Oriental de Guanajuato. (Eastern Railway of G.). San Felipe in Guanajuato State, is near but not on a railway.
Recuerdo entrada San Felipe 1892 = Souvenir entry (into) San Felipe 1892.
Claimed for Guatemala.

San Luis de La Paz
SN. LS. DE LA PAZ

Rulau	Date	Metal	Size	VG	F	VF	EF
Guj 65	1790	Copper	28mm	—	—	—	—

Sn. Ls. / DE LA PAZ / 1790 As. / ACOSTA. Rv: GUERERO in rectangle ctsp on blank reverse (Fernandez 197)

San Miguel Allende
MIGUEL GONZALEZ RIVADENEYRA

Rulau	Date	Metal	Size	VG	F	VF	EF
Guj 69	1813	Copper	26.5mm	—	—	—	—

Within wreath: MIGUEL / GONZALEZ / RIVADE / NEYRA. Rv: Within wreath: S. MIGUEL / EL GRE. A / DE 1813 / ⅛. (Grove 'Tokens' 404; Muñoz NOM 247; ANS 188)

San Miguel El Grande (S. Miguel El Gre.) is now the town of San Miguel Allende.

Muñoz reports a slightly different arrangement for the last name: RIVADEN / EIRA.

Valle de Santiago
BALLE DE SANTIAGO

Rulau	Date	Metal	Size	VG	F	VF	EF
Guj 71	1814	Copper	24mm	—	—	—	—

BALLE / DE SAN / TIAGO / 1814 / NS in rectangle ctsp. Rv: Blank. (Fernandez 274; Sobrino 488)

Varieties in 21-22mm diameter are known. There are also die varieties of the 24mm piece.

Uncertain
Mo.

Rulau	Date	Metal	Size	VG	F	VF	Unc
Guj 80	ND	Brass	32.3mm	20.00	—	40.00	—

Mo. ctsp in center of reverse of Guanajuato State cuartilla of 1856, KM-352a. (Eklund 241; Duffield 574; Rulau coll.)

Same ctsp known on Guanajuato State 1875 octavo, 27mm brass.

ANTONO MENDOZA

Rulau	Date	Metal	Size	VG	F	VF	EF
Guj 83	1801	Copper	33mm	—	—	55.00	85.00

Within wreath: Q / ANTONO / MENDOZA / 1801 / (Basket of flowers). Rv: Blank. (James Shipley coll.)

Shipley assigns this token to Spanish General Antonio Mendoza's hacienda in Guanajuato State. Francisco Agular of Guadalajara discovered this piece in 1964; Agular was an antiquarian.

REGLA

Rulau	Date	Metal	Size	VG	F	VF	EF
Guj 85	ND	Copper	24mm	—	—	100.	—

REG / LA in toothed circle. Rv: Blank. (ANS 371)

The Conde de Regla was a wealthy landowner of the Colonial period. His daughter, the Marquesa de San Francisco, also issued hacienda tokens.

Don Pedro Romero de Terreros, Conde de Regla, was an ancestor of Manuel Romero de Terreros, the famed Mexican numismatist.

GUERRERO STATE

Campo Morado
TIENDA LA REFORMA

Rulau	Date	Metal	Size	VG	F	VF	Unc
Gur 8	ND	Aluminum	Sq 16.5mm	—	10.50	—	—

TIENDA LA REFORMA / -.- / CAMPO MORADO. Rv: 1 / UN LITRO / MAIZ.

Un litro maiz = One liter of corn.

Cuautepec
QUAUTEPEC

Municipios

Rulau	Date	Metal	Size	VG	F	VF	EF
Gur 12	(1810)	Copper	Oct 23mm	—	—	—	—
		QUAU / TEPEC within serrated oct. depression. The first letter E is tiny. Rv: Blank. (Muñoz PVM 2)					
Gur 13	(1810)	Copper	Oct 22x26mm	—	—	—	—
		As last, but larger. (ANS 125; Fernandez 90)					
Gur 16	1869	Copper	21mm	—	15.00	—	—
		Large tree. Around: QUATEPEC / 1869. Rv: Blank.					

Huitzuco
HUITZUCO

Warning! Possible fantasy

Rulau	Date	Metal	Size	VG	F	VF	EF
Gur 19	ND	Silver	23mm	—	—	—	—

Large cross. Rv: HUITZUCO . above a flower. Cast in a mold. (Fernandez 126)

Fernandez says this could be a fantasy piece.

Tlapa
TLAPA

Rulau	Date	Metal	Size	VG	F	VF	EF
Gur 25	1874	Wood	54mm	—	—	100.	150.

(All incused) M.D. / TLAPA / 1874 / (laurel branch).
Translates: Moneda (coin) de Tlapa. 7mm thick.
(Muñoz MAD 15; Eklund 792; Hubbard coll.)

Tlapa de Comonfort is in the municipio of Tlapa.

Uncertain
ZAPATA OROZCO

Rulau	Date	Metal	Size	VG	F	VF	EF
Gur 40	1913	Copper	25mm	—	Unique	—	—

ZAPATA 19-13 OROZCO / $ $ *engraved* on obverse of
Mexico 1906-Mo 2-centavo coin, KM-419. Rv:
ZAPATA R MOS 1913 in circle around many small letters (including PAZ 6), serrated border around all —
engraved on coin's reverse. Plain edge. (Smithsonian
coll., ex-Bureau of Customs)

Apparently engraved by a supporter of Pascual Orozco.

HIDALGO STATE

Huasca
HUASCA

Rulau	Date	Metal	Size	VG	F	VF	EF
Hid 5	ND	Copper	27.5mm	—	—	25.00	—

HUASCA in relief in 13x3mm oval depression, ctsp on
Mexico 1834-Mo-A cuartilla, K-M 358. (Utberg H6/22;
Fernandez 125)

There is some doubt about the reading of this stamp, which appears to be gar-
bled as HUASCluom.

Pachuca
F. DE P. CASTREJON

Rulau	Date	Metal	Size	VG	F	VF	Unc
Hid 10	(1893-97)	Aluminum	24.5mm	—	10.00	35.00	50.00

PELUQUERIA / * / "EL BUEN TONO" / -DE- / F. DE
P. CASTREJON / * / PACHUCA, MEX. / (tiny) L. H.
MOISE. S.F. Rv: Large 4 within wreath. Plain edge.
(Zaffern coll.)

4 Reales ? Peluqueria = Barber shop. "El Buen Tono" = "The Good Taste."

JALISCO STATE

AHUALULCO

Municipios

Rulau	Date	Metal	Size	VG	F	VF	EF
Jal 3	1813	Copper	21mm	25.00	35.00	50.00	—

⅛ on raised boss at center. Around: 1813 / AHUA-
LULCO. Rv: Blank. (ANS 14; KM L1)

Jal 5	ND	Copper	18mm	17.50	25.00	35.00	—

AHO (script) / ⅛. Milled border. Rv: Blank. Plain edge.
(ANS 13; KM L2; Eklund 11)

Jal 7	1830	--	20mm	—	—	—	—

MUNICIPALIDAD DE AHUALULCO / ⅛ (Mexican
eagle) ⅛ / 1830. Rv: Blank. (Eklund 12)

Ahualulco today is known as Ahualulco de Mercado. It is near Ameca, another
issuer of municipio coinage in Jalisco State.

Amajac
P. L.
(Pedro Lazaro)

Rulau	Date	Metal	Size	VG	F	VF	Unc
Jal 9	1886	Copper	20mm	—	—	—	—

(Radiant star) / P. L. (Gothic script) / AMAJAC.
Branches either side of P.L. Rv: 1 / REAL / 1886 /
(crossed branches). Plain edge. (Eklund 25)

Ameca
AMECA

Municipios

Rulau	Date	Metal	Size	VG	F	VF	EF
Jal 12	(1)806	Copper	23mm	—	50.00	—	—

Monogram. 806. Rv: Blank. (Ulex 1644)

Jal 13	(1)806	Copper	20mm	—	45.00	—	—

Similar to last, but smaller. (U. 1644)

The 1908 Ulex sale in Berlin contained four of these pieces.

Rulau	Date	Metal	Size	VG	F	VF	Unc
Jal 15	(1)1811	Copper	24mm	25.00	35.00	50.00	—

AME (E inverted) . CA 811 within circle of points. Rv:
Blank. Thick planchet. (ANS 27; KM L8)

Rulau	Date	Metal	Size	VG	F	VF	Unc
Jal 16	(1)811	Copper	Oct 25x22mm	25.00	35.00	50.00	—

As last. (ANS 28; KM L9)

P. D. AMECA QUITILLA

Rulau	Date	Metal	Size	VG	F	VF	EF
Jal 18	1824	Copper	22mm	—	—	—	—

Facade of a church, trees (?) on either side. 3 at left,
inverted G at right. Around: P. D. AMECA QUI-
TILLA. D 1824. Rv: Blank. (ANS 25)

V. F.
(Vicente Figarosa)

Rulau	Date	Metal	Size	VG	F	VF	EF
Jal 20	1826	Copper	--mm	—	—	—	—

V. F. ¼ R. 1826. (U. 1645)

Rulau	Date	Metal	Size	VG	F	VF	EF
Jal 22	1858	Copper	23mm	—	17.50	25.00	35.00

(Branches) ⅛ / V. F. AMECA 1858. Plain edge. (U.
1645; KM Mexico L12; ANS 31)

The 1908 Ulex sale contained five Figarosa tokens. The Brunk Collection contains an 1858 measuring 25mm which is bogus.
There are 1836, 1855, 1853 pieces listed in Eklund.

Brunk specimen, 1858
25mm
Counterfeit!

Q. T. G.

Rulau	Date	Metal	Size	VG	F	VF	EF
Jal 24	ND	Copper	20mm	25.00	50.00	70.00	—

Monogram QTG and two rosettes within central
toothed circle. Around: TLACO DE AMEC *. Border
of leaves. Rv: Blank. (Muñoz TPM 106; ANS 26; KM
L7)

F. Z.
(F. Zamora)

Rulau	Date	Metal	Size	VG	F	VF	EF
Jal 26	ND	Copper	20mm	25.00	35.00	50.00	—

Within border of wavy lines: F ⅛ Z. Rv: Blank. (ANS
29; Brunk pg. 146; KM L10)

T. Z.
(Teobaldo Zamora)

Rulau	Date	Metal	Size	VG	F	VF	EF
Jal 28	1833	Copper	22mm	17.50	25.00	35.00	—

T. Z. AMECA 1833 / ⅛. (ANS. 30; Duffield 1678; KM
L11)

Also 1855 in Eklund.

Atotonilco
ATOTONILCO

Municipios

Rulau	Date	Metal	Size	VG	F	VF	EF
Jal 31	1808	Copper	25mm	37.50	52.50	75.00	—

In beaded central circle: L. S. S. / JUSU / ESES.
Around: ATOTONILCO ANO. DE. 1808. Rv: Blank.
(ANS 44; KM L22; Fonrobert 6737)

Fonrobert reported this piece struck in silver, weight 6.7 grams.

Rulau	Date	Metal	Size	VG	F	VF	EF
Jal 33	1821	Copper	24mm	25.00	35.00	50.00	—

1821 at center, ATOTONILCO ANO DE around. Rv:
V. F7. 9. D. G ¼ Z around rim. (KM L23)

Rulau	Date	Metal	Size	VG	F	VF	EF
Jal 35	1826	Copper	22mm	25.00	35.00	50.00	—

1826 at center, VILL.ATOTONILCO around. Rv: ⅛ at
center, SOTO MAIOR above, stars around. (KM L24;
Fernandez 28)

The legend on the 1826 token probably indicates Villa (city) Atotonilco, inferring a municipio character to the piece. The abbreviations on the 1808 and 1821 tokens have not been deciphered.
Clyde Hubbard reads the reverse legend on Jal 33 as meaning: Viva Fernando VII que Dios guarde (en paz).
We have assigned this issuer as Atotonilco el Alto in Jalisco. Jalisco was the site for a number of other token issuers in this period: Ahualulco, Ameca and Tlajomulco, for example.
Other Atotonilcos are located in Durango and Zacatecas States. There was also Atotonilco el Grande in Hidalgo (see Fonrobert 6737).

Cocula
COCULA

Municipio

Rulau	Date	Metal	Size	VG	F	VF	EF
Jal 40	1808	Copper	23mm				

(Crown) / Cocula / Ao 1808 / VANDINO in rect.
depression counterstamped. Rv: Blank. (ANS 103;
Guttag 3895)

HACIENDA DE LEDO

Warning! Fantasies!

Rulau	Date	Metal		Size	VG	F	VF	EF
Jal 44F	1833	Copper	**		—	—	—	3.00

** Triangular copper planchet, irregular, 30x46mm. Three circular depressions bearing relief letters ctsp across token. At left: 1 / - * - / 8 in dentilated circle. At center: HACIENDA / DE / . LEDO . in dentilated circle. At right: COCULA / ⅛ in dentilated circle. Rv: UN / OCTAVO / 1833 in relief within circular depression ctsp on reverse of token. Plain edge. (Brunk coll.)

Rulau	Date	Metal		Size	VG	F	VF	EF
Jal 45F	1833	Copper	++		—	—	—	3.00

++ Irregular triangular planchet, 30x41mm.
Similar to last, but order of the three obverse ctsp is: (from left) COCULA - ⅛ - LEDO. *TAMS Journal* for Aug. 1978, pg. 147)

There are genuine LEDO tokens listed in the Mexican unattributed section, which see.

Contla
A. O.
(Apoloni Ochoa)

Rulau	Date	Metal	Size	VG	F	VF	EF
Jal 48	ND	Copper	25mm				

CONTLA (the N retrograde) within beaded rectangle across center, branches above and below. Rv: A. O. / 1 within wreath. Crudely reeded edge. (Eklund 163)

Rulau	Date	Metal	Size	VG	F	VF	EF
Jal 49	ND	Copper	25mm				

As last, but 2 within wreath. (Eklund 164)

Jal 50	ND	Copper	25mm				

As last, but 3. (Eklund 165)

Jal 51	ND	Copper	25mm				

As last, but 4. (Eklund 166)

Jal 52	ND	Copper	25mm				

As last, but 5. (Eklund 167; Smithsonian coll.)

Jal 53	ND	Copper	25mm				

As last, but 6. (Eklund 168)

Eklund says this series was emitted before 1890. 1 = 1 almud of corn; 2 = 2 almudes, etc. The 5-almudes at Smithsonian is part red Unc.

Corona
CORONA

Municipios

Rulau	Date	Metal	Size	VG	F	VF	Unc
Jal 56	ND	Copper	21mm				

J. / CORONA / (rosette). Beaded circle around. Rv: ⅛ within laurel wreath, rosette in opening. (Eklund 170; Muñoz NOM 138)

Jal 57	(1)807	Copper	19mm				

C O monogram 807 / (ornament). Rv: Blank. Cast. (Eklund 171)

Guadalajara
M. ALVAREZ Y CA.

Rulau	Date	Metal	Size	VG	F	VF	Unc
Jal 62	1873	Copper	20mm	—	—	—	—

* M. ALVAREZ * / Y Ca. / (ornate bar) / 1873. Rv: Beehive and bees, star in exergue. Reeded edge. (Eklund 237; Ulex 1677)

CIRCULO MERCANTIL

Rulau	Date	Metal	Size	VG	F	VF	Unc
Jal 64	ND	Brass	24mm	—	—	—	—

CIRCULO MERCANTIL / * GUADALAJARA * between beaded circles. Rv: Large 2 within beaded border. (Eklund 240; Ulex 1678)

Jal 65	ND	Brass	24mm	—	—	—	—

As last, but 1 (real). (Eklund 239)

Jal 66	ND	Brass	24mm	—	—	—	—

As last, but ½ (real). (Eklund 237)

Circulo mercantil = Mecantile club.

B. Y. P.

Rulau	Date	Metal	Size	VG	F	VF	Unc
Jal 68	ND	Copper	29mm	—	—	—	—

B. Y. P. / GUADALAJARA (small) / (star). Milled border. Rv: Blank. Machine-made token (Eklund 236; Brunk 50295)

INDUSTRIA DEL CALZADO

Rulau	Date	Metal	Size	VG	VF	EF	Unc
Jal 70	1959	CN	29mm	—	—	7.50	9.00

Head right. Around: 50 ANOS EN LA INDUSTRIA DEL CALZADO. Below: 1909 1959 / AURELIO LOPEZ NUNEZ. Rv: Upper facade of a building at lower right. GUADALAJARA / CUNA DEL / CALZADO / CANADA / Y SEDE DE LA / III EXHIBICION / NACIONAL / DEL CALZADO / NOVIEMBRE / 1959. Plain edge. (Rulau coll.)

Calzado = Footwear.

Jalostotitlan
XALOS TOTITLAN

Municipio

Rulau	Date	Metal	Size	VG	F	VF	EF
Jal 74	1820	Copper	24mm	37.50	52.50	75.00	—

Crown at center, ILVSTRE AYVNTAMIENTO around. Rv: Numeral 4 at center. Around: DE XALOS . TOTITAN / .1820. (ANS 136; KM L54)

Ilustre Ayuntamiento de Xalos Totitan = Illustrious municipal government of Xalos Totitan. The numeral 4 indicates this token is a cuartilla, or one fourth real.

Jalostotitlan is located 135 km. northeast of Guadalajara on the Guadalajara-San Luis Potosi highway.

Mascota
DEL AYUNTO. MASCOTA

Municipio

Rulau	Date	Metal	Size	VG	F	VF	EF
Jal 80	1814	Copper	25mm	—	—	Rare	—

Within ornamental border; DEL / AYUNTo. / MASCOTa / 2 R. Rv: Within ornamental border: VIVA / F. VII / 1814. Plain edge. (Fernandez 152; Grove 'Tokens' 548)

Fernandez reports this token at 28mm. It is a nice late Royalist issue. Del Ayunt(amient)o Mascota 2 R. = Two reales of the municipal government of Mascota.

MINA DE SANTA CRUZ
Duraznito

Rulau	Date	Metal	Size	VG	F	VF	Unc
Jal 82	(1893-97)	Brass	24mm	—	—	25.00	35.00

MINA DE / -+- / SANTA CRUZ -+- / DURAZNITO. / (tiny) L. H. MOISE. S.F. Rv: VALE / * 25 * / EN LA TIENDA / -+- / DE RAYA. Plain edge. (Zaffern coll.)

Rulau	Date	Metal	Size	VG	F	VF	Unc
Jal 85	(1893-97)	Brass	20.5mm	—	7.50	15.00	25.00

As last, but * 5 *. (Henkle report)

Rulau	Date	Metal	Size	VG	F	VF	Unc
Jal 83	(1893-97)	Brass	32mm	—	—	35.00	60.00

As last, but * 100 *. Die varieties.

Tienda de Raya = Company store. Duraznito = Little Peach. Numerals are centavos.

Mazamitla
MAZAMITLA

Municipio

Rulau	Date	Metal	Size	VG	F	VF	EF
Jal 89	185.	Copper	22mm	15.00	—	—	—

Radiant Liberty cap. Rv: MAZAMITLA / ⅛ / 185. (Fernandez 155; Eklund 361)

Mazamitla is near Ciudad Guzman.

Quitupan
YGNACIO BUENROSTRO

Rulau	Date	Metal	Size	VG	F	VF	EF
Jal 94	1854	Copper	22mm	25.00	35.00	50.00	Rare

Bow and two arrows crossed. Around: QUITUPAN (N retrograde) / ** 1854 **. Rv: YGNACIO BUENROS-TRO / ⅛. A resello with letters YB in it is counterstamped. (ANS 364; KM L69; Ulex 1680; Eklund 497; Scott; Grove 'Tokens' 773)

The YB in the resello would seem to be reenforcement that this is an issue of Ygnacio Buenrosto in octavo denomination for (possibly) Quitupan hacienda. Both Noe-Eklund in 1949 and the editors of the *Standard Catalog of World Coins* in 1988 considered it a municipal issue, however.

Quitupan on the Jalisco-Michoacan border has 1,800 inhabitants and is the capital of a municipality of the same name.

Clyde Hubbard owns 5 of these tokens, of which 3 bear the YB resello.

Rulau	Date	Metal	Size	VG	F	VF	Unc
Jal 96	ND	Copper	20mm	—	—	—	—

Bow and two arrows crossed. Around: *** QUITUPAN *** . Rv: IGNACIO / ⅛. (Grove 'Tokens' 772)

Rulau	Date	Metal	Size	VG	F	VF	Unc
Jal 97	ND	Copper	20mm	—	—	—	—

Bow and crossed arrows at center, *** QUITUPAN (N retrograde) *** around. Rv: IGNACIO (N retrograde) / ⅛. (Grove 'Tokens' 772)

Rulau	Date	Metal	Size	VG	F	VF	Unc
Jal 99	1854	Copper	22mm	—	—	—	—

First Quitupan token above (YGNACIO BUENROSTO), but ctsp E. M. / TEXADA in two lines. Both the YB and Texada ctsps are present. (Eklund 498)

Apparently Texada was a later owner of the hacienda.

YGNACIO RAMOS

Caution: Counterfeits exist!

Rulau	Date	Metal	Size	VG	F	VF	EF
Jal 101F	1858	Copper	Rect 32x22mm	—	—	—	65.00

YGNACIO / RAMOS within scalloped border. Rv: QUITUPAN / 1858 ⅛ within scalloped border. Plain edge. Thick flan. (Brunk coll.; ANS 364)

Worth ⅛ real, about 1.6 U.S. cents. The copper weight alone would be worth more than that.

Counterfeit copies are common: the illustrated specimen is bogus!

HACIENDA DE SAN BLAS

Rulau	Date	Metal	Size	VG	F	VF	EF
Jal 111	ND	Copper	--mm	—	—	—	—

SAN BLAS. 5 CENTAVOS. (Ulex 1681)

A. P. (ingora)
Hacienda de San Gabriel

Rulau	Date	Metal	Size	VG	F	VF	EF
Jal 114	ND	Copper	--mm	—	—	—	—

HACIENDA DE SAN GABRIEL. CENTAVO. Counterstamped A. P. for A. Pingora. (Ulex 1681)

Sayula
A. C. D. SAYULA

Municipios

Rulau	Date	Metal	Size	VG	F	VF	EF
Jal 120	1814	Copper	26mm	9.00	14.00		

A. C. D. SAYULA / Q / 1814. Rv: Blank. (Scott; ANS 419; Garza 208; Fernandez 206)

Rulau	Date	Metal	Size	VG	F	VF	EF
Jal 121	1814	Copper	21mm	—	—	—	—

C. D. SAYULA / 1./4 / 1814 / R---. Rv: Blank. (Fernandez 207)

Rulau	Date	Metal	Size	VG	F	VF	EF
Jal 122	1814	Copper	21mm	—	—	—	—

Lion (or dog ?). Around: CD SAYULA QUARTYLLA / . 1814 . Rv: Blank. (Fernandez 208)

Rulau	Date	Metal	Size	VG	F	VF	EF
Jal 123	1815	Copper	19mm	—	—	—	—

SAYULA / Q / 1815. Rv: Blank. (Fernandez 209)

Q = Cuartilla, or ¼ real. Sayula is on the Laguna de Sayula and is a station on the Guadalajara-Manzanillo railway. A = Ayuntamiento.

Tecalitlan
MENDOZA HERMANOS

Rulau	Date	Metal	Size	VG	F	VF	Unc
Jal 125	ND	Aluminum	32mm	—	11.00	20.00	35.00

MENDOZA HNOS. / TECALITLAN / JAL. / HDA. DE SANTIAGO -. Rv: 10 Litros MAIZ.

This token also comes in the 36mm size, denomination 1.00 (peso), and the 25mm size, denomination not known.

Teocaltiche
TEOCALTICHE

Municipio

Rulau	Date	Metal	Size	VG	F	VF	EF
Jal 127	1807	Copper	19mm	—	—	60.00	—

1807 / TEOCAL / TICHE. Rv: Blank. (ANS 442; Romero de Terreros report)

TEPEC

Rulau	Date	Metal	Size	VG	F	VF	EF
Jal 130	ND	Copper	28mm	—	25.00	—	40.00

TEPEC ctsp on Jalisco State cuartilla of the 1828-36 type, KM 353. Rv: TI.N / PN ctsp on the other side of the coin. (ANS 444; Ulex 1685; Muñoz PVM 8)

No place exists now or has existed named Tepec. Hubbard believes this word means something other than a site.
Tepec is a corruption of Tepetl (mountain).
The TiN stamp resembles Tinguidin in Michoacan.

Tequila
TEQUILA

Municipio

Rulau	Date	Metal	Size	VG	F	VF	EF
Jal 132	1814	Copper	19mm	—	—	—	—

PBO / DE TEQUILA / 4. / 1814. Beaded border. Rv: Blank. (ANS 445; Eklund 635; Scott; Fernandez 245)

PBO = Pueblo (village or Indian communal holding)

LAZARO J. GALLARDO
Hacienda Camichines

(**NOTE:** This is an extremely confusing series, complicated by multiple counterstamps, about which little background is known. Most of these tokens are known in perfect, unworn condition, which may indicate restriking for collector use or may simply indicate that many new pieces were never used as money.)

HALF REAL SIZE (30mm)

Rulau	Date	Metal	Size	F	VF	EF	Unc
Jal 140	1857	Copper	30mm	13.00	25.00	40.00	50.00

Century plant (or maguey), LAZARO J. GALLARDO curved above. Rv: Barrels and bottles on a table top across lower center. CAMICHINES curved above, 1857 in exergue. Plain edge. (Ulex 1651; Scott; Eklund 95)

QUARTER REAL SIZE (26-28mm)

Rulau	Date	Metal	Size	F	VF	EF	Unc
Jal 141	1857	Copper	27mm	3.00	4.00	6.50	11.00

As last, in smaller size. (Eklund 96)

Rulau	Date	Metal	Size	F	VF	EF	Unc
Jal 142	1857	Brass	27mm	3.00	4.00	6.50	11.00

As last. (Eklund 97)

Rulau	Date	Metal	Size	F	VF	EF	Unc
Jal 143	1857	Copper	28mm	3.00	4.00	6.50	11.00

As last, but Spread Eagle ctsp in field above table. (Ulex 1651; Duffield 1673; Eklund 99)

| Jal 144 | 1857 | Brass | 27mm | 3.00 | 4.00 | 6.50 | 11.00 |

As last (Spread Eagle ctsp). (Eklund 100)

| Jal 145 | 1857 | Copper | 27mm | — | 8.00 | 14.00 | |

Similar, but Dog ctsp. (Ulex 1651; Duffield 1667 to 1669)

| Jal 146 | 1857 | Copper | 27mm | 3.00 | 4.00 | 6.50 | 11.00 |

Similar, but Horse left ctsp. (Duffield 1674; Eklund 98)

| Jal 147 | 1857 | Brass | 27mm | — | — | — | — |

Similar, but Mexican Eagle with serpent ctsp. (Eklund 101)

| Jal 148 | 1857 | Brass | 27mm | — | — | — | — |

Similar, but Horse left and Rooster ctsps. (Eklund 102)

Rulau	Date	Metal	Size	VG	F	VF	Unc
Jal 151	1857	Brass	27mm	2.50	4.00	7.00	14.00

Similar to Eklund 96 (basic quarter real), but L J G in rectangle ctsp above table. Eklund said this variety was the only one he'd seen which occurred worn from circulation. (Duffield 1672 & 1677; Eklund 103)

In 1919, Frank Duffield reported these additional counterstamps on Camichines tokens: Dog and Horse (D. 1669); Dog and Cactus (D. 1670); Eagle and Rooster (D. 1675; Spread Eagle and Mexican Eagle with snake (D. 1676). Also, A C T in ANS collection.

EIGHTH REAL SIZE (20-21mm)

Rulau	Date	Metal	Size	F	VF	EF	Unc
Jal 154	1857	Copper	21mm	30.00	—	—	—
		Two trees on ground, LAZARO J. GALLARDO above. Rv: S. A. DEL POTRERO / 1857. Border on each side made up of leaves and pellets. Thick flan. Plain edge. (Eklund 87)					
Jal 155	1857	Brass	20mm	—	—	—	—
		As last. (Eklund 88)					
Jal 156	1857	Copper	20mm	—	—	—	—
		As last, but small Cow ctsp on reverse. (Eklund 89)					
Jal 157	1857	Copper	20mm	—	22.00	33.00	—
		As last, but small Goat left ctsp. (Eklund 90)					
Jal 158	1857	Brass	20mm	—	—	—	—
		As last (Goat ctsp). (Eklund 91)					
Jal 159	1857	Brass	20mm	—	—	—	—
		Similar, but small Goat left ctsp at left of 1857, and Cactus plant ctsp at right. (Eklund 92)					
Jal 160	1857	Brass	20mm	—	—	—	—
		Similar, but small Goat left ctsp at left of 1857, and small Horse ctsp at right. (Utberg H11/24)					
Jal 161	1857	Brass	20mm	—	—	—	—
		Similr, but small Horse left ctsp on reverse. (Eklund 93)					
Jal 162	1857	Copper	20mm	—	—	—	—
		Similar, but L J G in rectangle ctsp on reverse. Stands for Lazaro J. Gallardo. (Eklund 94)					

Reports of sizes and of metallic content are based upon the best information we have, but most of these pieces have not been examined by the author or his contributors.

These attractive cuartillas and octavos (if indeed that is what they were intended to be) occur without counterstamp or with counterstamped Spread Eagle, Horse or L J G in rectangle about equally. The Ulex sale in 1908 contained 10 Gallardo pieces. In the 1950's several small hoards were discovered in Mexico and were soon dispersed among collectors.

Potrero = Grazing field of horses.

Tizapan el Alto
TIZAPAN

Municipio

Rulau	Date	Metal	Size	VG	F	VF	Unc
Jal 170	1828	Copper	21mm	15.00	35.00	—	—
		+ TIZAPAN 1828 / ⅛ / (laurel spray). Beaded border. Rv: Blank. (Muñoz PVM 11). An 1826 occurs.					

Warning: ¼ tokens dated 1831 are fantasies!

C. G.
La Violeta

Rulau	Date	Metal	Size	VG	F	VF	Unc
Jal 172	ND	Brass	25mm	—	—	12.50	—
		LA VIOLETA / UN LITRO / TIZAPAN. Rv: CG monogram.					

Tlajomulco de Zuniga
CAVEZERA DE TLAJOMVLCO

Municipio

Rulau	Date	Metal	Size	VG	F	VF	EF
Jal 174	ND	Copper	Oct 24mm	—	—	—	—
		CAVEZ / ERADE / TLAJO / MVLCO. Rv: Blank. (ANS 451)					

Cavezera is an archaic spelling for Cabecera, or county seat.

Turja
TURJA

Municipios

Rulau	Date	Metal	Size	VG	F	VF	Unc
Jal 176	ND	Copper	20mm	—	50.00	—	—
		TURJA / 8 / (branches). Rv: Blank. (Fernandez 260)					
Jal 178	ND	Copper	28mm	—	60.00	—	—
		On a 20mm punch: Rayed Liberty cap within branches. Around: TURJA / 1851. Rv: Blank. Struck on an oversized blank. (Fernandez 262)					
Jal 179	ND	Copper	20mm	—	50.00	—	—
		As last, struck on a 20mm blank. (Fernandez 261)					

Zacoalco
ZACOALCO

Municipio

Rulau	Date	Metal	Size	VG	F	VF	EF
Jal 181	ND	Copper	24mm	—	—	—	—
		(Crude script lettering): ZA / COAL / CO. Rv: Blank. Cast. (ANS 488; Eklund 685)					

Zacoalco de Torres.

Zapotlan
ZAPOTAN

Rulau	Date	Metal	Size	VG	F	VF	Unc
Jal 183	ND	Wood	36mm	—	—	100.	150.
		Zapo / tan Jo. Rv: Blank. (Muñoz MAD 18)					

Jo. = Jalisco.

Zapotlan Barrio
ZAPOTLAN

Municipios

Rulau	Date	Metal	Size	VG	F	VF	Unc
Jal 185	1813	Copper	20mm	30.00	42.50	60.00	—

ZAPO / TLAN / 1813. Rv: Blank. (ANS 489; Muñoz PVM 15; KM L84)

Warning: Fantasy!

Rulau	Date	Metal	Size	VG	F	VF	Unc
Jal 186F	1814	Copper	21mm	—	—	1.50	—

ZAPOTLAM / A / DE / 1814. Rv: Blank. (KM L85; Brunk coll.)

Zapotlan
BENITO VISCARRA

Caution: Fantasy!

Rulau	Date	Metal	Size	VG	F	VF	EF
Jal 187F	1813	Copper	Sq 33mm	—	—	1.75	—

ZAPOTLAN / * 1813 * / BENITO / VISCARRA / (ornament). Rv: VALE UNA / CARGA DE / LEÑA / (ornaments).

Vale una carga de leña = Worth one load of firewood.

Uncertain
R. A.

Rulau	Date	Metal	Size	VG	F	VF	EF
Jal 189	ND	Copper	21mm	—	—	35.00	—

Script R. A. in relief within rectangular depression ctsp on Jalisco State 1860 half-octavo (1/16 real), KM-316. (ANS coll.)

This is also known with additional ctsp script PDN in rect. punch.

EL CAMBIO

Rulau	Date	Metal	Size	VG	F	VF	Unc
Jal 190	(ca 1858-60)	Copper	29mm	20.00	—	30.00	—

EL CAMBIO in relief ctsp on Jalisco Quarto coins of 1828-36 type. (Ulex 1652; Brunk 50800)

Rulau	Date	Metal	Size	VG	F	VF	Unc
Jal 191	(ca 1858-60)	Copper	34mm	20.00	—	30.00	—

Same ctsp on Jalisco Cuartilla coins of 1858-62 type.

Rulau	Date	Metal	Size	VG	F	VF	Unc
Jal 192	(ca 1858-60)	Copper	29mm	40.00	—	60.00	—

∆ EL ∆ / CAMBIO in rect. cartouche ctsp on Jalisco State 1862 cuartilla. Rv: ++ ELCAMBIO circular within circle frame ctsp on opposite side of coin. (ANS coll.)

EL CAMBIO = The (Money) Exchange. Jalisco changed over its coinage size in 1858; this may have been a private validation.

JAO - C

Rulau	Date	Metal	Size	VG	F	VF	Unc
Jal 194	1842	Copper	17.5mm	—	—	35.00	—

-o- / J A O / :: C. :: Rv: -o- / ¼ / 1842. Reeded edge. (Fonrobert 6900; Eklund 257)

Rulau	Date	Metal	Size	VG	F	VF	Unc
Jal 195	1842	Silver	17.5mm	—	—	—	Rare

As last. Reeded edge. (F. 6900)

PEDRO CUELLAR
Hacienda Del Cuiz

Rulau	Date	Metal	Size	VG	F	VF	EF
Jal 59	(1)806	Iron	20mm	—	—	—	—

Viper. DEL CUIZ PEDRO CUELLAR. A resello is stamped below: 806. Rv: Blank. Cast iron planchet. (Muñoz NOM 157); ANS 132)

NICOLAS REMAS
Hacienda del Plan

Rulau	Date	Metal	Size	VG	F	VF	Unc
Jal 71	ND	Copper	--mm	—	—	—	—

NIC. REMAS. HAC. DEL PLAN. 1 BARRIL HARINA. (Ulex 1679; Eklund 197)

Good for one barrel of flour.

DE PRIETO

Rulau	Date	Metal	Size	VG	F	VF	EF
Jal 198	ND	Copper	27mm	—	—	—	—

de / pxieto / (rope in five loops). Rv: Blank. Cast. (Muñoz NOM 457; ANS 344; Ulex 1680)

| Jal 199 | ND | Copper | 27mm | — | — | — | — |

Similar to last, but spelled **prieto** (r for x), and rosette added below rope ornament. (Muñoz NOM 458; ANS 345)

| Jal 200 | ND | Copper | 27mm | — | — | — | — |

As last, but small cross before de (+ **de**). (Muñoz NOM 459; ANS 346)

The attribution to Jalisco was by Ulex in 1908.

J. D. V.

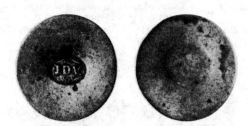

Rulau	Date	Metal	Size	VG	F	VF	EF
Jal 205	ND	Copper	30mm	—	25.00	—	35.00

J D V (relief, within oval depression) ctsp on Mexican state copper cuartillas. Rv: ⅛ (relief, in toothed oval depression) ctsp on opposite side of coin. (ANS coll.; Brunk pg. 146; Eklund 273)

The ANS collection contains 30 specimens of this counterstamp! It is probably a municipal issue.

MICHOACAN STATE

Acuitzio
AQUIJZIO

Rulau	Date	Metal	Size	VG	F	VF	EF
Mic 1	ND	Copper	20mm	—	—	—	—

In 11mm square depression: AQUIJ / ZIO / MOre / lia. Rv: Blank. (Fernandez 1)

Acuitzio is a district of Morelia. Henkle reports this in 18mm size.

Angamacutiro
ANGAMACUTIRO

Municipios

Rulau	Date	Metal	Size	VG	F	VF	Unc
Mic 6	1855	Copper	24mm	—	—	—	—

Eagle on cactus. Around: ANGAMACUTIRO. / 1855. Rv: Quiver with arrows. Around. FONDO MUNICI-PAL / UN OCTAVO.

| Mic 8 | 1858 | Copper | 25mm | — | — | — | — |

Eagle on arrow. Around: ANGAMACUTIRO / 1858. All within wreath. Rv: ARBITRIO MUNICIPAL / P. (Quiver) V. / UN OCTAVO. (Eklund 2371; Fernandez 10; Hubbard coll.)

Ario
ARIO

Municipios

Rulau	Date	Metal	Size	VG	F	VF	EF
Mic 11	ND	Copper	23-25mm	—	—	—	—

ARIO / 1/8 / (wreath). Rv: Blank. (Fonrobert 6926; Ulex 1697; Hubbard coll.)

| Mic 12 | ND | Silver | 22.5mm | — | — | — | — |

As last. 5.05 grams. (Fonrobert 6926)

| Mic 13 | ND | Copper | 24mm | — | — | — | — |

ARIO / 8 (large). Rv: Blank. (Eklund 44)

| Mic 14 | 1843 | Copper | 25mm | — | — | — | — |

Flag and cornucopia crossed above branches. ARIO 1843. Rv: Blank. (Eklund 43; Hubbard coll.)

| Mic 15 | (18)14 | Copper | 21mm | — | — | — | — |

A / 14 within wreath of lilies. Rv: Blank. Also in silver? (Fonrobert 6927)

| Mic 16 | (18)14 | Silver | 21mm | — | — | — | — |

As last. (Fonrobert 6927)

| Mic 18 | (1)1824 | Copper | 20mm | — | — | — | — |

ARo. monogram / 824 (incuse). Rv' Blank. (Eklund 45)

| Mic 23 | 1866 | Copper | 23mm | 10.00 | 15.00 | 25.00 | — |

Fountain (or monument). Around: MUNICIPALIDAD DE ARIO / 1866. Rv: 1/8 within wreath. (Eklund 47)

| Mic 21 | 1858 | Copper | 20mm | 10.00 | 15.00 | 25.00 | — |

Indian head right. Around: MUNICIPALIDAD DE ARIO / 1858. Rv: 1/8 in wreath. Reeded edge. (Ulex 1699; Eklund 46)

PADILLA

Rulau	Date	Metal	Size	VG	F	VF	EF
Mic 25	ND	Copper	20mm	—	—	—	—

PADI / LLA. Rv: Blank. Thin planchet. (Muñoz NOM 403)

| Mic 27 | 1826 | Copper | 20mm | — | — | — | — |

Within a circle of palm leaves: PADILLA / 1/8 / A. D. 1826. Rv: Monogram IMR within double circle. Thin planchet. (Muñoz Nom 404)

| Mic 28 | 1827 | Copper | 20mm | — | — | — | — |

Within closed wreath: PADILLA / 1/8 / A.D. 1827. Rv: JMR monogram within double circle. (Eklund 446)

| Mic 30 | 1830 | Copper | 20mm | — | — | — | — |

Similar to last. (Eklund 447)

IMR or JMR = IMARIO (Illustre Municipio de Ario)

HDA. DEL TEJAMANIL

Rulau	Date	Metal	Size	VG	F	VF	Unc
Mic 32	1858	Copper	19mm	—	—	—	—

HDA . DE . TEJAMANIL . / (Volcano with half moon to left). Rv: VALOR DE MEDIO REAL. / (Palm tree) / 1858. Utberg H12, 13, 16)

Rulau	Date	Metal	Size	VG	F	VF	Unc
Mic 33	1858	Brass	19mm	—	—	—	—

HDA. DEL TEJAMANIL. / 1/4 in laurel wreath. Rv: 1/4 / - / 1858 -- all in laurel wreath. (Eklund 2355)

Rulau	Date	Metal	Size	VG	F	VF	Unc
Mic 34	1858	Brass	18mm	—	—	—	—

As last, but 1/8. (Utberg H12)

Balencia
COMERCIO DE BALENCIA

Municipios

Rulau	Date	Metal	Size	VG	F	VF	EF
Mic 37	ND	Copper	18mm	—	—	—	—

Large 6-pointed star at center, COMERCIO DE BALENCIA around. Rv: Blank. (Muñoz COM 11; Eklund 61)

Comercio = Trade or Business.

Rulau	Date	Metal	Size	VG	F	VF	EF
Mic 38	ND	Copper	19mm	—	—	—	—

Large pentagram. Around: MUNICIPIO . DE . BALENCIA. Two oval resellos ctsp: RR and BC. Rv: Blank. (Fernandez 31)

Chabinda
RAFAEL TAMALLO

Rulau	Date	Metal	Size	VG	F	VF	EF
Mic 40	1848	Copper	20mm	—	—	—	—

Woman seated. Around: CHABA. — 1848. Rv: COM. DE R. TAM.

Rulau	Date	Metal	Size	VG	F	VF	EF
Mic 42	1858	Brass	21mm	—	—	—	—

Mexican eagle. RAFAEL TAMALLO around. Rv: Seated Liberty. Around: CHABINDA AÑO DE 1858 / ***. (Fernandez 101)

Co. de R. Tam. = Comercio de Rafael Tamallo.

Charo
CAR(O)

Rulau	Date	Metal	Size	VG	F	VF	EF
Mic 44	ND	Copper	22mm	—	—	—	—

Fraction 1/8 in center, CAR+ around. Rv: Blank. (Muñoz NOM 108; Fernandez 100)

Attribution by Romero de Terreros.

Rulau	Date	Metal	Size	VG	F	VF	EF
Mic 45	ND	Copper	19mm	—	—	—	—

1 / CARO /. Rv: Blank. (Fernandez 99)

Rulau	Date	Metal	Size	VG	F	VF	EF
Mic 46	ND	Copper	25mm	—	—	—	—

CARO in 12mm oval / CARO in 8mm oval — both ctsp on unidentified copper coin. Rv: No stamps. (Fernandez 98)

Chilchota
CHILCHOTA

Municipio

Rulau	Date	Metal	Size	VG	F	VF	EF
Mic 50	1858	Copper	20mm	25.00	35.00	50.00	—

Head right. Around: CHILCHOTA UN OCTAVO / 1858. Rv: Wreath at center. Around: RESPONSAVIDAD (sic) DE MURGVIA. (ANS 98; KM L38)

A. MORFIN

Rulau	Date	Metal	Size	VG	F	VF	Unc
Mic 51	1854	Copper	21mm	—	—	—	—

Bow and two arrows, crossed. Around: A MORFIN / 1854. Rv: CHILCHOTA / 1/8 / (wreath). (Grove 'Tokens' 62; Hubbard coll.)

Clyde Hubbard owns 3 pieces measuring, respectively, 20, 21 and 22mm.

Coalcoman
ANTONIO VALLARES ?

Rulau	Date	Metal	Size	VG	F	VF	Unc
Mic 52	1868	Copper	25mm	—	—	—	—

Eagle on cactus, etc. Around: ANTONIO VALLARES (surname partly illegible) / COALCOMAN. Rv: Un / OCTAVO / 1868 within laurel wreath. (Eklund 142; Fernandez 38)

Cotija de la Paz
D. JOSE NUÑES

Rulau	Date	Metal	Size	VG	F	VF	EF
Mic 54	1852	Copper	19mm	20.00	28.50	40.00	—

Liberty seated right, holding a staff. Around: DE-D.-JOSE NUÑES. Rv: 1/8 and 1852 at center, COMERCIO. D. COTIJA around. (ANS 121; KM L51)

Rulau	Date	Metal	Size	VG	F	VF	EF
Mic 55	1856	Brass	20mm	7.50	—	—	—

TANTEO DE COTIJA / (eagle on cactus) / 1/8 between branches / 1856 * (inverted). Rv: Radiant Liberty cap between branches. Above: JOSE NUÑES. (Eklund 176)

Struck in imitation of the Mexican Republic coins in circulation.

Huerta
ACIENDA DE LA HUERTA

Rulau	Date	Metal	Size	VG	F	VF	Unc
Mic 60	1830	Copper	28mm	—	—	—	—

2. R. / ACIENDA / DE LA / HUERTA / AN. D. 1830. Rv: Brand mark between oak branches. (Utberg H11/17)

Ixtlan
J. M. G.
Hacienda de Buenavista

Rulau	Date	Metal	Size	VG	F	VF	EF
Mic 62	1848	Copper	24mm	—	—	22.00	—

HACIENDA DE / JMG script monogram / * BUENAVISTA *. Rv: 1848 in oval. Plain edge. (Eklund 74; Utberg H11/5 etc.; Smithsonian coll.)

In 1984, Gomez Saborio attributed this to the municipio of Vistahermosa de Negrete in Michoacan. The monogram has also been read as JEMC.

J. F. V.
(Jose Francisco Velarde)
Hacienda de Buena Vista

Rulau	Date	Metal	Size	VG	F	VF	Unc
Mic 64	—1855	Copper	29mm				

HACIENDA / JFV (script monogram) / DE / BUENA VISTA. Rv: RACIONES DE MAIZ / 1855 (in brand mark) / . VALE POR 1 ALMUD. Plain edge. (Eklund 75; Fischer 391; Utberg H11)

Rulau	Date	Metal	Size	VG	F	VF	Unc
Mic 65	1855	Copper	22mm	6.00	—	—	—

JFV (script monogram). Rv: HACIENDA DE BUENA VISTA / 1855 (in brand mark). (Scott; *Boletin de Sociedad Numismatica de Mexico* for Jan. 1955)

Rulau	Date	Metal	Size	VG	F	VF	Unc
Mic 66	1855	Brass	23mm	—	20.00	—	—

(Scrollwork) / JFV (script monogram) / (scrollwork). Rv: * TIENDA * / 1855 (in brand mark) / DE * BUENAVISTA. (Eklund 77)

Rulau	Date	Metal	Size	VG	F	VF	Unc
Mic 68	1857	Brass	—mm	—	—	—	—

No description available. (Ulex 1677)

Rulau	Date	Metal	Size	VG	F	VF	Unc
Mic 70	1861	Brass	23mm	—	20.00	—	—

(Scrollwork) / JFV (script monogram) / (scrollwork). TIENDA DE BUENA VISTA / 1861 (in brand mark). Also reported in copper. (Eklund 78; Utberg H11)

Manuel Romero de Terreros assigned these to Jose Francisco Velarde of Ixtlan, Michoacan. Raciones de maiz, vale por 1 almud = Rations of corn, worth one measure.

Jiquilpan
J. S. G.
(Jiquilpan, Sahuayo & Guarachita)

Rulau	Date	Metal	Size	VG	F	VF	EF
Mic 72	ND	Copper	32mm	—	—	—	—

J. S. G. in relief within oval depression ctsp on Jalisco State 1/4-real, date worn, KM-355. (Brunk pg. 146; Fernandez 138; Grove 'Tokens' pg 64; *Boletin de S.N. de M.* for Jan. 1955. no. JI1)

Jiquilpan, Sahuayo and Guarachita are neighboring Michoacan towns.

La Piedad
PIEDAD

Rulau	Date	Metal	Size	VG	F	VF	EF
Mic 74	1871	Brass	26mm	—	—	15.00	—

PIEDAD / 1871 ctsp on worn-smooth Mexican brass coin. (Fernandez 142; Brunk 53585; Rulau coll.)

Rulau	Date	Metal	Size	VG	F	VF	EF
Mic 75	1871	Brass	26.3mm	—	—	15.00	—

Similar ctsp on brass disc. (Smithsonian coll.; ANS coll. has 8 pieces)

Rulau	Date	Metal	Size	VG	F	VF	EF
Mic 76	1871	Brass	26.3mm	—	—	50.00	—

PIEDAD / 1871 cstp on brass disc. PROVICIONAL ctsp on opposite side. (ANS coll.)

Rulau	Date	Metal	Size	VG	F	VF	EF
Mic 77	1871	Copper	27mm	—	—	—	—

PIEDAD in wreath ctsp on Mexico coin. Rv: EL AVE FENIX / LEONES / (ornament) ctsp on opposite side of coin. (Fernandez 143)

Various Mexican copper coins in at least three sizes: 1/8 R, small 1/4 R and large 1/4 R, are found with this counterstamp, PIEDAD / 1871. Each is worth about $15 in VF.

The PROVICIONAL stamp on Mic 76 listed above is associated with Zacatecas State. In 1908, Ulex assigned the PIEDAD / 1871 stamp to Guadalajara in Jalisco State.

Los Reyes
V. C.

Rulau	Date	Metal	Size	VG	F	VF	EF
Mic 78	ND	Copper	27mm	—	—	—	—

V. C. in relief within 12mm punch ctsp on Jalisco State 1/4-real. (Fernandez 151; Brunk pg 146)

* R S *

Rulau	Date	Metal	Size	VG	F	VF	EF
Mic 80	ND	Copper	32mm	—	—	—	—

* R S * within 19x8mm oval dentilated depression ctsp on Jalisco State cuartilla of 1858-62 type, KM-355 or 356.

Rulau	Date	Metal	Size	VG	F	VF	EF
Mic 81	ND	Copper	27mm	—	—	—	—

Similar ctsp on Jalisco State octavo of 1857-62 type, KM-330 or 331. (Fernandez 150)

Rulau	Date	Metal	Size	VG	F	VF	EF
Mic 83	ND	Copper	30mm	—	—	—	—

* R S * within diagonally dentilated oval depression ctsp on Mexican Republic cuartilla of indeterminate type. Rv: D ctsp on opposite side.

Rulau	Date	Metal	Size	VG	F	VF	EF
Mic 84	ND	Copper	32mm	—	—	—	—

Similar ctsp on Jalisco State cuartilla (?), with added ctsp M. D. H. Rv: Po ctsp on opposite side. (Po = Penjamillo)

Rulau	Date	Metal	Size	VG	F	VF	EF
Mic 85	ND	Copper	28mm	18.00	—	—	—

Similar ctsp on Sinaloa State cuartilla of 1847-66 type, KM-363. There is an added ctsp P. (script) A. (block letter). (*TAMS Journal* for Aug. 1978, pg. 153)

AGAPITO ROJAS

Rulau	Date	Metal	Size	VG	F	VF	EF
Mic 87	1842	Copper	20mm	—	—	—	—

Mexican eagle, REYEZ 1842 around. Rv: Man walking right. Around: AGAPITO ROJAS * UN OCTAVO. (Grove 'Tokens' 800)

RAMON TORRES Y COMPA.

Rulau	Date	Metal	Size	VG	F	VF	EF
Mic 89	1845	Brass	20mm	—	—	—	—

Radiant Liberty cap above Mexican eagle. Around: TANTEO DE LOS REYES 1845. Rv: Within oak and olive wreath: RAMON TORRES Y COMPA. (Eklund 343; Fernandez 149)

Pazcuaro
PATZCUARO

Municipio

Rulau	Date	Metal	Size	VG	F	VF	Unc
Mic 93	ND	Copper	23mm	17.50	25.00	35.00	—

* Also struck in brass and cast in bronze. Woman fish peddler walking right, carrying a bag over her shoulder, a fishing net and string of fish. Rv: Three mountains in Lake Pazcuaro; a church and buildings at foot of the largest mountain. Man in boat fishes on the lake. Above: MUNICIPd DE PAZTCUARO. Plain edge or Reeded edge. (ANS 309; KM L63; Eklund 458; Fernandez 171)

PAZCUARO

Municipios

Rulau	Date	Metal	Size	VG	F	VF	EF
Mic 95	ND	Copper	20.4mm	17.50	25.00	—	—

Mountains and lake. Rv: 1/8 / PAZCUARO. Plain edge. (Fonrobert 6931; Scott: Eklund 456; Fernandez 169-170; KM L64)

This token is known ctsp VALE in rectangle.

Rulau	Date	Metal	Size	VG	F	VF	EF
Mic 97	1856	Copper	32mm	—	—	—	—

Mexican eagle, MUNICIPIO DE PAZCUARO above. Rv: 1/8 / A. 1856 within palm and oak wreath. Plain edge. (Fernandez 173)

Purepero
MUNICIPALIDAD DE PUREPERO

Municipios

Rulau	Date	Metal	Size	VG	F	VF	EF
Mic 99	1851	Brass	23mm	—	—	—	—

Radiant Liberty cap. MUNICIPALIDAD. above. Rv: Island in lake. Around: DE PUREPERO. UN OCTAVO. / 1/8 / 1851. Border of stars on each side. Reeded edge. (Fernandez 183; Smithsonian coll.)

The reeding is: .I.I.I repeated over and over.

Rulau	Date	Metal	Size	VG	F	VF	EF
Mic 100	1851	Brass	23mm	12.50	—	—	—

As last, but error PURERO. (Eklund 787; Fernandez 182)

Qviroga
QVIROGA

Rulau	Date	Metal	Size	VG	F	VF	EF
Mic 103	ND	Copper	20mm	—	—	—	—

QVIRO / GA within toothed rect. depression. Rv: Blank. (Grove 'Tokens' 771)

Sahuayo
ZAHUAYO

Rulau	Date	Metal	Size	VG	F	VF	EF
Mic 104	1856	Copper	23mm	—	35.00	50.00	—

Coyote left, ZAHUAYO above. Rv: (Branches) / scrip monogram JMA / AÑO DE 1856. (Grove 'Tokens' 1088; Eklund 687; Fernandez 187)

JMA = Jose Maria Arregui.

Santa Clara
COMERCIO DE STA. CLARA

Rulau	Date	Metal	Size	VG	F	VF	EF
Mic 105	ND	Copper	26mm	—	—	—	—

L. V. T. / - / & within circle. Around: COMERCIO . DE . STA CLARA . Rv: Blank. Crude. (Smithsonian coll.)

A 1/8-real of Santa Clara, Michoacan, bordering on Patzcuaro, Tacambaro, Ario and Taretan, all coin issuers.

J. A.
(Jose Aspero)
Hacienda de Santa Efigenia

Rulau	Date	Metal	Size	VG	F	VF	EF
Mic 108	ND	Copper	24mm	—	—	—	—

STA / EFYG in toothed octagonal depression. Rv: Blank. (ANS 415)

Rulau	Date	Metal	Size	VG	F	VF	EF
Mic 110	1846	Copper	25mm	—	—	65.00	100.

Monogram JA at center, HACIENDA DE Sa EFIGENIA * around. Rv: Large numeral 1/4, hand with balance scales above, 1846 * below. Plain edge. (Schrotter 67; Ulex 1712; Hubbard coll.)

Tacambaro
TACAMBARO

Municipios

Rulau	Date	Metal	Size	VG	F	VF	EF
Mic 115	1843	Copper	27mm	18.00	25.00	40.00	—

Mercury's staff at center, scrollwork below. Rv: TACAMBARO / 1/8 / 1843 within wreath. (Ulex 1712; Eklund 615; Scott)

The token is also reported in 21mm size. Date given as 1842 or 1848.

Rulau	Date	Metal	Size	VG	F	VF	EF
Mic 117	ND	Copper	21mm	—	—	—	—

Within laurel wreath: 1/8. Below: TACAMBARO. Rv: A rock.

Tacambaro now appears on maps as Tacambaro de Codallos.

Taretan
TARETAN

Municipios

Rulau	Date	Metal	Size	VG	F	VF	EF
Mic 119	1837	Copper	19mm	30.00	42.50	60.00	—

TARETAN / 1837 / 1/8. Cast. (Ulex 1712)

Rulau	Date	Metal	Size	VG	F	VF	EF
Mic 121	1840	Copper	25mm	35.00	50.00	—	—

Similar, but 1840. (Hubbard coll.)

| Mic 123 | 1851 | Copper | 19mm | 30.00 | 42.50 | 60.00 | — |

Liberty cap amid rays. Around: TARETAN UN OCTAVO / 1851. Cast. (U. 1712)

| Mic 125 | 1858 | Brass | 18mm | 30.00 | 42.50 | 60.00 | — |

Male bust right. Around: TARETAN UN OCTAVO / 1858. Rv: FONDO MUNICIPAL around a tree. Cast. (U. 1712; KM Mexico L75; ANS 440)

| Mic 126 | 1858 | Copper | 18mm | 30.00 | 42.50 | 60.00 | — |

As last, but MUNICIPIA.

The Banco de Mexico collection contained at least 16 variations of the Taretan pieces in 1965. The workmanship was crude.

Tipitaro
FLORES
Hacienda de Tipitaro

Rulau	Date	Metal	Size	VG	F	VF	Unc
Mic 130	1846	Copper	23mm	20.00	—	—	—

Mountain between two flowers. HACIENDA DE TIPITARO around. Rv: Vase of flowers. Around: MEDIO REAL AÑO DE 1846. (Schrotter 68; Ulex 1713 var.; Eklund 637)

Rulau	Date	Metal	Size	VG	F	VF	EF
Mic 132	ND	Copper	24mm	22.50	45.00	60.00	85.00

Building. HACIENDA DE TIPITARO. Rv: Laurel wreath. UN REAL / DESE EN EFECTOS / FLORES. (Schrotter 69; ANS 449)

EFECTOS = Goods. Señor Flores (Flowers) used flowers as ornamentation on his Tipitaro tokens.

TLAZASALCA

Municipio

Rulau	Date	Metal	Size	VG	F	VF	EF
Mic 134	1853	Copper	22mm	25.00	35.00	50.00	—

Two wooded mountains, TLAZASALCA / 1853 around. Rv: 1/8 within wreath. (ANS 452; KM L78)

URUAPAN

Municipio

Rulau	Date	Metal	Size	VG	F	VF	EF
Mic 136	1839	Copper	21mm	—	15.00	25.00	—

Eagle on cactus, serpent in its beak. Around: URUAPAN / 1839. Rv: Blank. (ANS 464; Eklund 663)

This large city is known officially as Uruapan del Progreso.

Zamora
MUNICIPIO DE ZAMORA

Municipios

Rulau	Date	Metal	Size	VG	F	VF	EF
Mic 140	(ca 1857)	Copper	21mm	—	25.00	—	70.00

Za in relief within 9mm dentilated depression ctsp on various Zamora tokens dated 1843 to 1857, K-M Mexico L81. (Brunk coll.; Smithsonian coll.)

Rulau	Date	Metal	Size	VG	F	VF	Unc
Mic 141	(ca 1858)	Brass	21mm	—	25.00	—	70.00

Similar ctsp on Zamora token dated 1858, K-M L81. (Brunk coll.; Guttag 3909)

The city token issues of Zamora are dated 1842-58 (Seated Libertad type) and 1853-58 (Liberty cap above bow and arrow type), respectively cataloged in the *Standard Catalog of World Coins* as L80 and L81. All occur without counterstamps. Some occur with official ctsp 1/8 in circle, and some other markings.

PEDRO RODRIGUZ FERNANDEZ

Rulau	Date	Metal	Size	VG	F	VF	EF
Mic 143	ND	Copper	29mm	15.00	20.00	27.50	50.00

Rosette within double circle of leaves at center. Around: PEDRO. RODRIGUZ. FERNANDEZ. Ornate frame around all. Rv: Blank. (Muñoz NOM 197; ANS 159; Eklund 465)

Pedro Rodriguez Fernandez.

M. D. A.
(Municipio de A....?)

Rulau	Date	Metal	Size	VG	F	VF	EF
Mic 145	ND	Copper	26.4mm	—	—	—	—

M. D. A. in relief within beaded oval depression ctsp on worn Jalisco State octavo of 1828-34 type, KM-329. (Smithsonian coll.)

In the Michoacan series, counterstamp M.D.H. stands for Municipio de Huarachita and M.D.T. stands for Municipio de Tinguiden. We believe the piece above represents an unpublished stamp.

MORELOS STATE

Ayala
HACIENDA CUAHUISTLA

Rulau	Date	Metal	Size	VG	F	VF	Unc
Mor 3	ND	Copper SQ 28x30mm		—	—	—	—

Ve. Pa. EFos. DE LA TIENDA DE LA HACa. DE / 1/2 / CUAHUISTLA. All within circle. Rv: F M C monogram in circle. Circular die 21mm. Square planchet has cut corners. (Eklund 128)

Rulau	Date	Metal	Size	VG	F	VF	Unc
Mor 4	ND	Copper	34mm	—	—	—	—

F M C monogram in circle (from die above) struck uniface on blank planchet. (Eklund 129)

Ve. (vale) Pa. (para) EFos. (efectos) de la Tienda de la HACa. (hacienda) de 1/2 = worth half real in goods at the hacienda store.

Rulau	Date	Metal	Size	F	VF	EF	Unc
Mor 8	1880	Silver	27mm	—	—	80.00	—

Angel flies above sugar mill machinery, MENS AGITAT MOLEM above; in exergue: GRABADA EN 48 HORAS / A.H.G. (engraved in 48 hours, A.H. Galaviz). Rv: COAHUIXTLA 25 DE DICIEMBRE / (empty circle) / * 1880 *. Plain edge. (Grove 211a)

In 1880, Hacienda Coahuixtla (or Cuahuistla) in Ayala municipio, Morelos State, was owned by Manuel Mendoza Cortina.

To expand the boundaries of his hacienda, he ordered his workers to destroy the barrio of Olaque, adjacent to Anenecuilco in Morelos state. This area was the birthplace of the revolutionary hero Emiliano Zapata.

The tokens bearing the monogram FMC thus may indicate F. Mendoza Cortina.

The silver medalet is dated on Christmas Day of 1880.

Today the town is spelled Cuahuixtla.

Puente de Ixtla
MOSSO HERMANOS

Rulau	Date	Metal	Size	VG	F	VF	Unc
Mor 15	ND	Copper	28mm	—	—	12.00	—

Ornate border surrounds: MOSSO HERMANOS / 1 RL. Rv: VALE POR EFECTOS DE TIENDA DE LA HACIENa. * / (ornament) / DE SAN / GABRIEL / (ornament). (Eklund 520)

Rulau	Date	Metal	Size	VG	F	VF	Unc
Mor 16	ND	Copper	32mm	—	—	12.00	—

As last, but 2 Rs. (Eklund 521; Utberg report; Grove 'Tokens' 1568)

Rulau	Date	Metal	Size	VG	F	VF	Unc
Mor 17	ND	Copper	25mm	—	—	—	—

As last, but 1/2. (Eklund 519)

Mosso Hermanos y Ca. obtained a concession in 1855 to build a railway from Mexico City toward the Gulf of Mexico. The government concession was granted by President Antonio Lopez de Santa Ana. Construction began in July, 1855.

Rulau	Date	Metal	Size	F	VF	EF	Unc
Mor 19	1855	Svd/Bz	46mm	—	120.	180.	—

Antique locomotive right. Around: PRIVILEGIO DE LOS SRES. MOSSO HERMANOS Y Ca. In exergue: MEXICO / 1855. Rv: 12-line Spanish inscription. (Moyaux 587 (420); Bosco Apr. 1989 sale, lot 414)

Rulau	Date	Metal	Size	F	VF	EF	Unc
Mor 20	1855	Bronze	46mm	—	40.00	65.00	—

As last. (Grove 99)

NAYARIT STATE
Compostela
B. D.
(Bonifacio Dias)

Rulau	Date	Metal	Size	VG	F	VF	EF
Nay 3	ND	Copper	21mm	—	—	—	—

B. D. AUTLAN / (rosette) / COMPAÑIA (incuse on bar) / (rosette). Dentilated border. (ANS coll.)

Rulau	Date	Metal	Size	VG	F	VF	EF
Nay 4	1855	Copper	21mm	11.00	25.00	—	—

Obverse similar to last, but ** 1855 * added below lower rosette. Rv: (Rosette) / 1/8 / (wreath). (Grove 'Tokens' 105; Ulex 1650; Scott; Eklund 53)

Struck in Autlan de Navarro in Jalisco State for Dias' interests in Compostela.

Pitic
PITIC

Municipio

Rulau	Date	Metal	Size	VG	F	VF	Unc
Nay 8	1821	Copper	22mm	—	—	—	—

CUARTO D. R. AYUN / (Crown) / 1821. Rv: PITIC. (Utberg H17/18; Fernandez 177)

Ayuntamiento de Pitic ? This is a late royalist local issue.

Pradeau says Pitic was the native settlement that ultimately became Hermosillo in Sonora State, but Fernandez assigns this to Pitic in Nayarit.

Tepic
B. P.
(Bonifacio Peña)

Rulau	Date	Metal	Size	VG	F	VF	EF
Nay 10	ND	Brass	**	—	20.00	25.00	45.00

(All incused): B (rosette) P / (Spread eagle with serpent in its beak). Rv: Blank. Plain edge. Only 16 known, 6 outside museums. (Ulex 1686; Eklund 633; Muñoz Anepigraphs 40; Fischer 469; Rulau coll.; Smithsonian coll. ex-F. C. C. Boyd)

** Specimens examined have been struck on brass discs measuring 25.5mm to 27.8 mm.

The 1908 Ulex sale catalog attributed this as a cuartilla of Bonifacio Peña, but this German sale was little known in America or Europe until 1981, when Numismatics International reprinted the sale catalog.

Ole P. Eklund (1936) assigned this piece to Tepec in Jalisco State. Fischer, Henkle and others prefer Tepic in Nayarit State. One Rulau specimen (ex-Weinberg) measures 27.8mm; another the same.

The Smithsonian Institution possesses 6 specimens of the B.P. token, three of which are ex-F. C. C. Boyd. One of the Smithsonian pieces is stamped on a gilt brass, thinner planchet measuring 27.8mm.

The ANS collection has 5 specimens on brass discs.

This token was published with photograph as a Mexican Whatzit in *World Coin News* during 1975. Despite the newspaper's 12,000 circulation of foreign-oriented collectors at that time — including a good number in Latin America — no identification was made.

Rulau	Date	Metal	Size	VG	F	VF	EF
Nay 11	ND	Gilt/B	27mm	—	—	35.00	—

As last, but struck on thin gilt planchet. (Smithsonian Institution coll.)

HACIENDA DE PUGA

Rulau	Date	Metal	Size	VG	F	VF	EF
Nay 15	1871	Copper	22mm	—	8.00	—	12.50

HACIENDA DE PUGA / C. T. / 1871. Rv: Spur-like brand mark within laurel wreath. Thick flan. (Ulex 1515; Eklund 490)

Rulau	Date	Metal	Size	VG	F	VF	EF
Nay 16	1871	Copper	—mm	—	—	—	—

Similar. 6 1/4 CENTAVOS. (Eklund 491)

Rulau	Date	Metal	Size	VG	F	VF	Unc
Nay 18	ND	Copper	22mm	—	—	8.00	—

Spur-like brand mark within thick open-top wreath. Rv: Same brand mark on plain field. Plain edge. (Bill Randel coll.)

NUEVO LEON STATE

Guadalupe
MLNL (Monogram)
(Mineral Nuevo Leon)

Rulau	Date	Metal	Size	VG	F	VF	Unc
NL 10	ND	Copper	25mm	—	—	—	—

MLNL monogram within wreath (MineraL Nuevo Leon). Rv: No descr. available. (Eklund 395)

Rulau	Date	Metal	Size	VG	F	VF	Unc
NL 12	1845	Copper	25mm	12.50	20.00	—	—

TNMACL script monogram. Rv: 1/4 / A. 1845 within wreath. (Eklund 394; Scott; Sobrino pg. 279)

The 1845 token above also occurs struck in brass and in iron.

Linares
LINARES

Rulau	Date	Metal	Size	VG	F	VF	EF
NL 20	ND	Copper	30mm	—	—	—	—

LINARES (NAR in monogram) across center, Aztec ornamentation above and bird below. Rv: Blank. (Muñoz NOM 287)

Rulau	Date	Metal	Size	VG	F	VF	EF
NL 21	ND	Copper	24mm	—	—	—	—

LINA / RES. Rv: Blank. (Muñoz NOM 288; Eklund 334)

These two tokens may not be connected.

GOMEZ LINARI
(Gomez Linares)

Rulau	Date	Metal	Size	VG	F	VF	EF
NL 28	ND	Copper	30mm	20.00	—	—	—

(Flower and foliage) / GOMEZ / (bird). Rv: (Snake's head device) / LINARI (NAR in monogram) / (scrollwork). Plain edge. (Muñoz NOM 241; Eklund 324; Hubbard coll.)

OAXACA STATE
San Miguel Peras
CINCO SEÑORES

Rulau	Date	Metal	Size	VG	F	VF	Unc
Oax 20	(1915)	Copper	37mm	—	—	—	—

CINCO SEÑORES / 1 / PESO. Rv: Blank. Flan 3mm thick.

Neuman says this was for Wenceslao Garcia of Hacienda Cinco Señores. 50, 25 and 10-centavo tokens exist, 32, 27 and 22mm.

M V / M M
(Mineral de La Montaña,
Manuel Varela)

Rulau	Date	Metal	Size	VG	F	VF	Unc
Oax 22	(1915)	Iron	10mm	—	—	—	—

M M / M V around central hole. Rv: Blank. Centrally holed flan.

PN Monogram
(Pablo Neuman)

Rulau	Date	Metal	Size	VG	F	VF	Onc
Oax 25	(1915)	Brass	25mm	—	—	—	—

PN monogram / A 59. Rv: SAN MIGUEL PERAS / 50 / CTS.

Rulau	Date	Metal	Size	VG	F	VF	Onc
Oax 26	(1915)	Zinc	20mm	—	—	—	—

PN monogram / A. Rv: SAN MIGUEL PERAS / 20 CTS.

Rulau	Date	Metal	Size	VG	F	VF	Onc
Oax 27	(1915)	Zinc	16mm	—	—	—	—

As last, but 10.

Pablo Neuman, gold mine.

Uncertain
RAMON CASTILLO

Rulau	Date	Metal	Size	VG	F	VF	EF
Oax 30	1843	xx	30mm	—	—	—	—

xx Dark green glass!
RAMON / CASTILLO / 1843. Rv: Blank ? Flan 7mm thick. (Pradeau Tlaco pg. 60/7)

THE OAXACA ASSOCIATION

Rulau	Date	Metal	Size	VG	F	VF	Unc
Oax 33	ND	Brass	21mm	—	—	—	—

THE OAXACA / (ornament) / ASSOCIATION / (ornament) / LA SOLEDAD. Rv: BUENO EN NEGOCIOS SOLO / 3 C. (Eklund 2346)

PUEBLA STATE
Atlixto
FABRICA DE METEPEC

Rulau	Date	Metal	Size	VG	F	VF	Unc
Pue 3	ND	Bronze	25mm	3.00	7.00	10.00	—

FABRICA DE METEPEC / 5 (in beaded circle). Rv: Large 5. Plain edge. (Eklund 380)

Made in France for a textile factory about 1902? Also made in brass and in tin, each of which is worth 2 to 3 times the bronze value. Thread and textile factory in Atlixto, Puebla State.

San Jose Acateno
M. DE S. J. ACATENO

Municipio

Rulau	Date	Metal	Size	VG	F	VF	Unc
Pue 25	1877	Wood	52mm	—	—	100.	150.

+ M. DE S. J. ACATENO / 1877. / -.- / (laurel spray). Rv: Blank. Plain edge. 9mm thick! (Muñoz MAD 1)

The Municipio de San Jose Acateno is located in Teziutlan District in Puebla. This is one of the largest Mexican tokens. M = Moneda.
Muñoz calls this a "tlaco de Madera" (wood token). Tlaco was the native word for 1/8 of a real, but it was also a term for token.
Pilon was the native word for 1/16 of a real. Another term, Señales, was slang for I.O.U. tokens.

Tepeyahualco
TEPEYAHUALCO

Rulau	Date	Metal	Size	VG	F	VF	Unc
Pue 30	ND	Wood	Oval 43x35mm	—	—	125.	

DE in central oval. Around: M. / TEPEYAHUALCO. Rv: Same as obverse. (Muñoz MAD 12)

Tepeyahualco is in a circle of mountains. Wood was plentiful there.

Uncertain
MENDOZA PUEBLA

Rulau	Date	Metal	Size	VG	F	VF	Unc
Pue 35	ND	Copper	24mm	—	—	—	—

MENDOZA. Rv: PUEBLA around a Calatrava cross. Plain edge. (Muñoz NOM 329)

QUERETARO STATE

Cañada
MOTA SUCS.
Hacienda del Lobo

Rulau	Date	Metal	Size	VG	F	VF	Unc
Que4	ND	Brass	30mm	—	—	—	—

(All incused): HDA. DEL LOBO / No. / 6. / o MOTA SUCS. o. Rv: Blank.

Hacienda del Lobo = Ranch of the Wolf. Sucs. = Sucursales (branches). These tokens are also known with No. / 3., No. / 4., No. / 5. and No. / 8.

Queretaro
BAÑOS DE PATEHE

Rulau	Date	Metal	Size	VG	F	VF	Unc
Que 20	(1893-97)	Brass	33.5mm	—	—	18.50	30.00

BAÑOS DE PATEHE / 1 / CLASE / = QUERETARO + / (tiny) MOISE. S. F. Rv: Large numeral 12 1/2. Plain edge. (Rulau coll. ex-Bill Randel; Eklund 494)

Baños = Baths. 1 Clase = First class. Struck by L. H. Moise & Co., San Francisco, Calif. The denomination 12 1/2 centavos was equal to 1/8 of a silver peso, or one real.

Eklund reported this token as nickel, reeded edge.

GRMIO DE PANADEROS

Rulau	Date	Metal	Size	VG	F	VF	EF
Que 25	1801	Copper	29mm	15.00	22.50	35.00	60.00

GRMIO / DE PANA / DEROS. Rv: DE. / QUERET / ARO. DE / 1801. Beaded border on each side. (Muñoz COM 20; ANS 362; Rulau coll.)

Gremio de Panaderos = Guild of Bakers.

JOSE YGNACIO GUTIEREZ

Rulau	Date	Metal	Size	VG	F	VF	EF
Que 27	1801	Copper	35mm	—	—	—	—
Que 28	1801	Copper	23mm	—	—	—	—

Que 27: Canopy over ornaments. Around: JOSE . YGNACIO . GUTIEREZ / . 1801 . Wide beaded border. Rv: Blank. (Grove 'Tokens' 426)

Que 28: JOSE YGNACIO GUTIEREZ / 1/8. Rv: DE. (monogram) LA / CIUDAD / D. QUERE / TARO / 1801. (Muñoz NOM 257; ANS 195; Grove 'Tokens' 425)

The name is misread as Jose Venancio Gutierrez by Eklund-Noe and Muñoz.

BASILIO LOPES Y NIETO

Rulau	Date	Metal	Size	VG	F	VF	EF
Que 30	1805	Copper	32mm	20.00	30.00	50.00	75.00

BASILIO / LOPES Y / NIETO. Rv: QUERE / TARO MA / YO DE / 1805. Leaf border on each side. (Muñoz NOM 297; ANS 363)

This token is dated in May, 1805.

Mineral del Doctor
NEGOCIACION DEL DOCTOR

Rulau	Date	Metal	Size	VG	F	VF	Unc
Que 35	1894	Brass	35mm	12.00	22.50	27.50	—

Saint standing, facing, a pig lying behind him. Around: NEGOCIACION DEL DOCTOR / * 1894 *. Rv: VALE POR / 50 cs / TIENDA. Plain edge. (Eklund 189; Artes 103; Grinolds Aug. 1989 sale, lot 334)

Rulau	Date	Metal	Size	VG	F	VF	Unc
Que 36	1894	Brass	31mm	—	10.00	15.00	—

As last, but 20 cs. (Eklund 188; Sobrino 501)

Rulau	Date	Metal	Size	VG	F	VF	Unc
Que 37	1894	Brass	24mm	—	7.50	12.50	—

As last, but 10 cs. (Eklund 187)

Rulau	Date	Metal	Size	VG	F	VF	Unc
Que 38	1894	Brass	21mm	—	7.50	12.50	—

As last, but 5 cs. (Eklund 186)

Your author was offered a VG-F specimen of the 10-centavo token in Mexico City in 1974 for U.S. $8.50, then a princely sum for a worn token of this type. The offer was rejected, but the price seems more realistic today. This was the only mining or hacienda token in the Mexico City dealer's inventory at the time!

This particular 1974 convention (of Sociedad Numismatica de Mexico) was disappointing from a token collector's standpoint. Not a single token was offered openly on the bourse floor! I had to be content with purchasing a set of the beautiful silver crown-sized annual medals of SNdeM which depict early coins.

Finding accumulations of Latin American tokens is no easy task. In early 1989, while in Dallas, Texas on a business trip, I surveyed every dealer who advertised in the Yellow Pages and not one had even a single token for sale!

The best chance of finding Latin tokens for sale seems to be at selected coin conventions. During 1989, for example, I was able to purchase better material at the A.N.A. gathering in Pittsburgh, the C.I.C.F. event in Chicago, and the February and October Long Beach Expos in California. Oddly enough, the better-known token dealers at these shows had almost nothing for sale, while certain coin dealers had small accumulations.

Negociacion = (Usually) mining enterprise.

Mineral del Doctor is 47 km. north of Cadereyta and has 600 inhabitants. Zinc tokens in 10 and 5-centavos also exist.

SAN LUIS POTOSI STATE

Ahualulco
ELEUTERIO TREJO

Rulau	Date	Metal	Size	VG	F	VF	EF
SLP 2	ND	Copper	20.5mm	—	—	60.00	—

ELEUTERIO TREJO (curved) / AHUALULCO ctsp on worn Jalisco State octavo of 1828-34 type, KM-329. (Smithsonian coll.)

The stamp is neat and professional, from a single punch.

Catorce
BANEGAS

Rulau	Date	Metal	Size	VG	F	VF	EF
SLP 8	ND	Copper	27mm	—	—	65.00	—

BANE / GAS. Rv: Blank. (Muñoz NOM 63; ANS 49; Pedraza page 15)

Issued by Hacienda San Juan de Banegas, before 1827. After 1827 the name was spelled Vanegas.

Real de Catorce
FONDOS PUBLICOS DE CATORCE

Municipio

Rulau	Date	Metal	Size	VG	F	VF	EF
SLP 10	1822	Copper	19mm	20.00	30.00	40.00	—

Flower above raised rectangle at center, FONDOS PUBLICOS around. Rv: Branch at center, DE CATORCE 1822 around. (KM L30)

Fondos Publico = Public funds. This city was known as Real de Catorce in colonial times, but now simply as Catorce.

Charcas
CHARCAS

Municipio

Rulau	Date	Metal	Size	VG	F	VF	EF
SLP 15	1870	Copper	28mm	—	20.00	—	30.00

CHARCAS / 1870 in relief in two separate rectangular depressions ctsp on 1862 or 1867 San Luis Potosi State 1/4-real coin, KM 361 or 362 (quartilla). Reeded edge or plain edge. (Utberg report; Brunk 60190 & 50905; ANS coll.)

Charcas is a town in northern San Luis Potosi near the Monterrey-San Luis Potosi-Celaya rail line and also near the mines at Catorce.

Guadalcazar
FONDOS PUBS. DE GUADALCAZ

Municipio

Rulau	Date	Metal	Size	VG	F	VF	EF
SLP 20	1823	Copper	21mm	—	—	—	—

FONDOS PUBS. DE - GUADALCAZ - / (triangle) / (crossed arrows ?) / 1823 (in rectangle). Rv: Blank. (Fernandez 123)

Lagunillas
BERGARA LA GUNILLA
(Vergara, Lagunilla)

Rulau	Date	Metal	Size	VG	F	VF	Unc
SLP 25	ND	Copper	Rect 25x20mm	—	—	—	—

BER / GARA. LA / GUNILLA. Arc of stars above, horizontal line below. Rv: Blank. (Muñoz NOM 608)

There is a Lagunillas in San Luis Potosi State, but there may be no connection. Lagunilla is a Pond, or Small Lagoon.

Matehuala
EL CABYO. D. MATEHVALA

Municipio ?

Rulau	Date	Metal	Size	VG	F	VF	EF
SLP 27	(ca 1808-21)	Copper	19mm	—	—	—	—

EL CABYo. D. MATEHVALa / (Crown) / POR F. / VIII. Rv: POR EL BYEN COMVN / (Crown) / VIVA / Fo. 7. (Fernandez 154)

MTEJ Monogram?

Rulau	Date	Metal	Size	VG	F	VF	EF
SLP 30	ND	Copper	18mm	—	—	—	—

Script MTEJ monogram within circle. Rv: Blank. (Eklund 753)

Mates Torres at Matehuala, San Luis Potosi State, says Eklund.

Ramos
RAMOS

Rulau	Date	Metal	Size	VG	F	VF	EF
SLP 35	(1821-23)	Copper	28mm	—	—	—	—

1/4 / RAMOS / oooo (Tree ?) oooo. Rv: Blank.

A quarter real for Mineral de Ramos, says Pedraza.

Rio Verde
CHAVES

Rulau	Date	Metal	Size	VG	F	VF	EF
SLP 38	(18..)	Copper	26mm	—	—	—	—

ANO 18-- / RIO VERDE / CHAVES / (ornament). Rv: Blank. (Fernandez 186)

SLP 37	(17)93	Copper	25mm	—	—	—	—

Border of stars around: ANO 93 / RIO BERDE / CHAVES / *. Rv: Blank ? (Grove 'Tokens' 812)

Salinas
E.
Peñon Blanco

Rulau	Date	Metal	Size	VG	F	VF	Unc
SLP 40	ND	Brass	26mm	—	—	—	—

Large script E. Rv: PEÑON / BLANCO in ornamental border. (Fonrobert 8264; Eklund 1129; Schrotter 66; Pedraza pgs. 43-44)

E = Joaquin Maria and Ramon de Errazu, the owners. For a salt mine. Peñon blanco = White rocky prominence. Issued before 1878.

Also known in copper, and reported in sizes from 25 to 28mm. This token was long claimed for Colombia.

San Ciro
S. CIRO

Rulau	Date	Metal	Size	VG	F	VF	Unc
SLP 45	ND	Brass	22mm	—	—	—	—

S. CIRO ctsp on Zacatecas State octavo, type of 1836-46, K-M 339. (Fernandez 190C)

SLP 46	ND	Brass	22mm	—	—	—	—

S. CIRO ctsp on Zacatecas State octavo as last. Rv: SNC script monogram in circle ctsp on opposite side. (Fernandez 190C)

Santo Domingo
HACIENDA DE SIERRA HERMOSA

Rulau	Date	Metal	Size	VG	F	VF	EF
SLP 48	ND	Brass	32mm	—	—	—	—

Sheep walking left, TRASQUILA above, -o- 160 -o- below. Rv: * HACIENDA * / DE / SIERRA HERMOSA. Plain edge. (Boletin de S.N.deM. for July 1984, pgs. 67-69)

SLP 49	ND	Brass	28mm			—Scarce	

As last, but 80. (Weyl 1578; Eklund 601; Utberg H-15-16; Zaika coll.)

SLP 50	ND	Brass	26mm				

As last, but 40. (Eklund 600; Utberg H15/1)

Sierra de Piños
YLUSTRE AYUNTAMIENTO DE SIERRA DE PIÑOS

Municipio

Rulau	Date	Metal	Size	VG	F	VF	EF
SLP 53	1814	Copper	22mm				

Rampant lion between pillars. Around: YLUSTRE. AYUNTAMIENTO. / V (crown) 1/4. Rv: Castle and box between pillars. Around: DE SIERRA. DE PIÑOS / DE (monogram) F P /. 1814. (Utberg J6/12; Fernandez 210E)

Villa de Arriaga
HACIENDA DE SANTIAGO

Rulau	Date	Metal	Size	VG	F	VF	Unc
SLP 57	1868	Copper	27mm	—	—	—	—

Sheep standing right, TRASQUILA above, 1868 below. Rv: HACIENDA DE SANTIAGO / 5 (in circle) / * B. P. *. Plain edge. (Utberg H11/37)

Rulau	Date	Metal	Size	VG	F	VF	Unc
SLP 59	ND	Copper	31mm	—	—	—	—

TG monogram in circle (brand mark ?). Rv: HACIENDA DE SANTIAGO / 50 / S. L. P. Plain edge. (Utberg H14/10)

TG = Teodomiro Garfias ?

TEODOMIRO GARFIAS
Hacienda de Santiago

Rulau	Date	Metal	Size	VG	F	VF	Unc
SLP 61	(1903-05)	Brass	34mm	—	—	—	—

TEODOMIRO GARFIAS / (ornaments) / HACIENDA / DE / SANTIAGO S.L.P. Rv: Large 1oo. Plain edge. (Utberg H16/32)

There are also 50 centavo, 30mm, and 10 centavo, 25mm, brass tokens in this series.

Uncertain
PILAR

Rulau	Date	Metal	Size	F	VF	UNC	Proof
SLP 65	ND	Copper	24mm	—	—	—	100.

PILAR. Rv: Same as obverse. Plain edge. Thick flan (2.5mm). Rare. (Rulau coll.)

Rulau	Date	Metal	Size	F	VF	UNC	Proof
SLP 66	ND	WM	24mm	—	—	—	100.

As last. Thick flan (2.7mm). Rare. (Rulau coll.; Eklund 473)

Both above struck at Scovill Mfg. Co., Waterbury, Conn. before 1880.
Hacienda Pilar's location in S.L.P. State may indicate a connection with the maverick F.C. pieces (Eklund 220) and the Hacienda Belen pieces (Eklund 68), which see —all struck by Scovill in same basic style.
It is possible these are not for Mexico, but for Cuba or another Latin American country.

S.
(Hacienda de San Francisco)

Rulau	Date	Metal	Size	VG	F	VF	EF
SLP 70	ND	Wood	28mm	—	—	—	—

Large S. Rv: Blank. (Grove 'Tokens' 2027)

SINALOA STATE

Los Mochis
SINALOA SUGAR COMPANY

Rulau	Date	Metal	Size	VG	F	VF	Unc
Sin 15	ND	Brass	39mm	—	12.50	—	—

SINALOA SUGAR COMPANY / (ornament) / LOS MOCHIS / (ornament). Rv: COMPROBANTE / (ornament) / DE UN DIA / (ornament) / DE TRABAJO. (Utberg H14/8)

Rulau	Date	Metal	Size	VG	F	VF	Unc
Sin 16	ND	Brass	21mm	—	10.00	—	—

As last, but DE UNA HORA. (Utberg H14/7)

Un dia = One day (of labor). Una hora = One hour.

UNITED SUGAR COMPANIES

Rulau	Date	Metal	Size	VG	F	VF	Unc
Sin 18	1915	Aluminum	21mm	—	9.00	—	—

UNITED SUGAR COMPANIES / LOS / MOCHIS / SIN. / *. Rv: COMPROBANTE (ornament) / DE UNA HORA / 1915 / DE TRABAJO.

Mazatlan
MAZATLAN

Rulau	Date	Metal	Size	VG	F	VF	EF
Sin 20	ND	Copper	23mm				

Anchor in a circular depression, with ADMITIDO - EN MAZATLAN around — all ctsp on Durango State octavo. (Eklund 362 & 363; Lepczyk Sept. 1987 sale, lot 814)

Rulau	Date	Metal	Size	VG	F	VF	EF
Sin 21	ND	Copper	23mm				

Similar ctsp on copper colonial Durango octavo of 1812-18. (ANS 253; Ulex 1849)

Novolato
J. ALMADA Y HNO.
Hacienda La Primavera

Rulau	Date	Metal	Size	VG	F	VF	Unc
Sin 24	ND	Brass	30.5mm	7.00	10.00	—	—

HACIENDA / LA PRIMAVERA / NOVOLATO / SIN. MEX. Rv: BUENO POR / UNO DIA / DE TRABAJO / - / J. ALMADA y HNO. Plain edge.

Rulau	Date	Metal	Size	VG	F	VF	Unc
Sin 25	ND	Brass	27mm	—	—	—	—

As last, but MEDIO DIA. (Utberg H16/28)

Rulau	Date	Metal	Size	VG	F	VF	Unc
Sin 26	ND	Brass	24mm	—	6.00	—	—

As last, but CUARTO DIA. (Zaika coll.)

Rulau	Date	Metal	Size	VG	F	VF	Unc
Sin 27	ND	Brass	19mm	—	25.00	—	Rare

As last, but UN OCTAVO DIA. (Utberg H11/26)

Rulau	Date	Metal	Size	VG	F	VF	Unc
Sin 29	ND	Aluminum	Scal 27mm				

HACIENDA / LA / PRIMAVERA / NOVALATO / SIN. MEX. Rv: BUENO POR UN / DIA DE / TRABAJO / J. ALMADA Y. Hno. (*TAMS Journal* for Dec. 1969, pgs. 170-260)

The last item above may not exist as a token. Irvine & Jachens of San Francisco depicted this design in a trade advertisement of their work. All brass pieces were issued and used.

F. C. DEL P. DE N.

Rulau	Date	Metal	Size	VG	F	VF	Unc
Sin 35	ND	Brass	29mm	—	—	1.50	—

F.C. del . P . de N. (rectangular box). Rv: IDENTIF . ICACION / (rectangular box) / FIERROS. (TAMS Maverick 9104; Jerry Schimmel identif.)

F. C. del P. de N. = Ferrocarril del Pacifico de Norte ? Worker's identity disc? See *Fare Box* for April 1978, pg. 51)

SONORA STATE

Aduana
QUINTERA MG. CO. LD.

Rulau	Date	Metal	Size	VG	F	VF	Unc
Son 1	ND	Brass	23mm	—	—	Scarce	—

Cow's head ctsp on obverse of Ocharan y Ca. "medio pasaje" transportation token of Palmarejo, Chihuahua State, for use as a mining company payment tally. (*Numismatic Scrapbook Magazine* for Nov. 1968, pgs. 1742-43; *Plus Ultra* for June 1969, pg. 6; Robert A. Lamb report)

Rulau	Date	Metal	Size	VG	F	VF	Unc
Son 2	(1905)	Brass	Oct 33mm	—	15.00	20.00	—

Gold miner with pick walking left, small L.H. Moise. S.F. below. Cow's head ctsp on obverse. Rv: QUINTERA / 100 (in beaded circle) / * Mg. Co. Ld. *. Plain edge. (Stevens 4; Artes 103; Sobrino 279)

Rulau	Date	Metal	Size	VG	F	VF	Unc
Son 3	(1905)	Brass	Sq 23.5mm	12.00	20.00	40.00	—

Horse's head left in circular frame, small L. H. MOISE. S.F. at bottom. Cow's head ctsp on obverse. Rv: QUINTERA / 25 / Mg. Co. Ld. (Stevens 3)

Rulau	Date	Metal	Size	VG	F	VF	Unc
Son 4	(1905)	Brass	**			45.00	—

** Pentagonal flan, 23x22mm.
Indian head left, small L. H. MOISE S.F. below. Cow's head ctsp on obverse. Rv: As last, but 10. (Stevens 2)

Rulau	Date	Metal	Size	VG	F	VF	Unc
Son 5	(1905)	Brass	15mm	—	—	60.00	—

Ornamental 6 pointed star, small L.H. MOISE. S.F. below. Rv: As last, but 5. (Stevens 1; *Plus Ultra* for June 1969, pg. 6)

Quintera Mining Co. Ltd. operated a mine 10 miles west of the mining center of Alamos in Sonora State, until 1909. Alamos was the site of a Mexican government mint 1862-1895, and its surrounding area was a rich source of silver.

The first token above shows a cow's (or steer's) head counterstamped on railway transportation tokens of Ocharan y Compania of Palmarejo in neighboring Chihuahua State, on the Chinipas River.

Researcher Elwin Leslie said the bovine head counterstamp, also found on the specially-made tokens for Quintera, could signify use on ranches owned by the mining enterprise.

The regular Quintera tokens were made by L.H. Moise Co. in San Francisco, Calif.

Map by Robert A. Lamb.

Altar
AGUSTIN L. SERNA

Rulau	Date	Metal	Size	VG	F	VF	Unc
Son 7	ND	Aluminum	36mm	—	—	35.00	80.00

Mexican eagle. Around: NEGOCIACION DEL TIRO / * SONORA *. Rv: AGUSTIN L. SERNA / 50 / CVOS. / (ornament).

Rulau	Date	Metal	Size	VG	F	VF	Unc
Son 8	ND	Aluminum	29mm	—	—	35.00	—

As last, but 25. (Eklund 2353; Stevens 8)

Rulau	Date	Metal	Size	VG	F	VF	Unc
Son 9	ND	Aluminum	25mm	—	—	45.00	—

As last, but 12 1/2. (Stevens 7). These are reported ctsp T.

Rulau	Date	Metal	Size	VG	F	VF	Unc
Son 10	ND	Aluminum	21mm	—	—	45.00	—

As last, but 6 1/4. (Stevens 6)

Mines were discovered 1779. In 1910, Llanos Co. had taken over from Serna.

Caborca
BORQUEZ Y GARCIA

Rulau	Date	Metal	Size	VG	F	VF	Unc
Son 14	(1880)	Brass	16mm	—	—	50.00	—

(All incuse): BORQUEZ Y GARCIA / 1/4 RL / (star). Rv: NEGOCIACION DE CABORCA / (star) / SONORA. (Eklund 609; Zaika coll.; Stevens 26)

Rulau	Date	Metal	Size	VG	F	VF	Unc
Son 15	(1880)	Brass	18mm	—	—	30.00	45.00

As last, but 1/2 RL and Mexican eagle replace 1/4 RL on obverse and star on reverse. (Eklund 610)

Rulau	Date	Metal	Size	VG	F	VF	Unc
Son 16	ND	Brass	25mm	—	—	35.00	—

As last, but 1 RL.

Rulau	Date	Metal	Size	VG	F	VF	Unc
Son 17	ND	Brass	31.5mm	—	—	35.00	—

As last, but 2 Rs.

Modesto Borquez and Benigno V. Garcia operated Mina Grande, a gold-silver mine, and were dealers in grain and flour.

MIGUEL PALAFOX

Rulau	Date	Metal	Size	VG	F	VF	Unc
Son 19	ND	CN	Scal 28mm	—	—	15.00	—

LA POBLANA / MIGUEL / PALAFOX / COMERCIANTE / CABORCA / SON, MEX. Rv: 10 / CVS. (Stevens 30)

Campo Lenero
M. P. TORRES

Rulau	Date	Metal	Size	VG	F	VF	Unc
Son 21	ND	Brass	Oct 40mm	—	—	25.00	—

M. P. TORRES / CAMPO / LENERO. Rv: 1 (peso).

Rulau	Date	Metal	Size	VG	F	VF	Unc
Son 22	ND	Brass	Oct 24mm	—	—	25.00	—

As last, but 10 (centavos).

Campo Verde y Seguro
E. B. MUNOZ

Rulau	Date	Metal	Size	VG	F	VF	Unc
Son 24	ND	Brass	30mm	—	12.50	30.00	—

E. B. MUNOZ / CAMPO / VERDE / Y / SEGURO. Rv: 50.

Rulau	Date	Metal	Size	VG	F	VF	Unc
Son 25	ND	Brass	28mm	9.00	20.00	35.00	—

As last, but 25.

Campo Verde y Seguro was near Ures.

Cienega
L. LOAIZA

Rulau	Date	Metal	Size	VG	F	VF	Unc
Son 27	(1891-97)	Brass	27mm	—	20.00	35.00	40.00

L. LOAIZA / CIENEGA, / MEX. Rv: VALE POR UN / DIA / (tiny) KLINKNER & CO. S.F.

Etchojoa
IDELFONSO SALIDO
Hacienda Bacobampo

Rulau	Date	Metal	Size	VG	F	VF	Unc
Son 29	ND	Aluminum	24mm	—	10.00	15.00	22.50

IDELFONSO SALIDO / (scrollwork) / HACIENDA / BACOBAMPO / (scrollwork). Rv: VALE / UN / BOTE. (Stevens 43; Rulau coll.)

Bacobampo is near Navajoa. "Bote" has a number of different meanings, but in the context of this hacienda token it probably indicates "one can" of tallow or lard.

A number of pieces were offered in Oct. 1990 in VF+. These tokens sometimes were enameled red on one side.

"Idelfonso" should have been Ildefonso. Ildefonso Salido resided in Alamos, but the hacienda was in Etchojoa municipio, Navojoa county. He was known to be active 1906-12, but his successors were in charge 1920-22.

Tokens exist with correct spelling ILDEFONSO; same prices.

Guaymas
HOTEL ALMADA CANTINA

Rulau	Date	Metal	Size	VG	F	VF	Unc
Son 32	(1905)	Aluminum	25mm	—	—	7.50	—

HOTEL ALMADA / CANTINA / GUAYMAS, SON., / MEX. Rv: GOOD FOR / C 25 C / IN TRADE.

RAYMONDO MURGA M.

Rulau	Date	Metal	Size	VG	F	VF	Unc
Son 34	ND	Brass	25mm	—	—	50.00	—

RAYMONDO MURGA M / GUAYMAS / SON, MEX. Rv: BUENO POR / UNA COPA. Plain edge. (Stevens 51; Pradeau *Tlaco* pg. 66)

MERCERIA DE LA PAZ

Rulau	Date	Metal	Size	VG	F	VF	Unc
Son 36	ND	Brass	24mm	—	—	35.00	—

MERCERIA DE LA PAZ / SELDNER / Y VON / BORSTEL / GUAYMAS. Rv: V. A. ALMADA / MAGDA / JUAN MARCOR / HERMOSO / AD MARCOR / ALAMOS.

This is a most curious piece, apparently a quadruple store card for a notions store chain in Sonora State. Merceria de la Paz = Peace dry goods store, or possibly notions store in a less literal rendering.

Magda = Magdalena? Hermoso = Hermosillo? Guaymas, Alamos, Hermosillo and Magdalena are cities of unequal size in Sonora.

Hermosillo
HACIENDA EL ZACATON

Rulau	Date	Metal	Size	VG	F	VF	Unc
Son 38	ND	Aluminum	26.5mm	—	—	35.00	—

HACIENDA / EL ZACATON / (Star) / M. G. Rv: 10. (Stevens 13)

M. G. = Miguel Gandara, the owner. This token occurs ctsp with the 8-spoke wheel device of Hermosillo, which see below.

Zacaton hacienda was 16 miles north of Hermosillo city, and just a ½ mile from Zamora railroad station. Before 1910 this 5,000-acre ranch, irrigated by the San Miguel River, was one of the largest and most productive in the state.

AGUSTIN MONTEVERDE

Rulau	Date	Metal	Size	VG	F	VF	Unc
Son 40	(1905)	Brass	29mm	—	—	50.00	—

BUENO POR UN / DIA DE / TRABAJO / AGUSTIN / MONTEVERDE / HERMOSILLO / SONORA, MEX. / (tiny) L. A. RUBBER STAMP CO. Rv: (Incused): MARTES. Plain edge. (Stevens 37)

Martes = Tuesday.

MUNOZ HERMANOS
Y SOBRINO
Hacienda Realito

Rulau	Date	Metal	Size	VG	F	VF	Unc
Son 42	(1905-10)	Aluminum	30mm	—	—	50.00	—

HACIENDA REALITO / (brand mark) / HERMO-SILLO / * / SONORA. Rv: MUNOZ HERMANOS Y SOBRINO / VALE POR / 1/4 DE / JORNAL / *** / (tiny) L. A. RUB. STAMP CO. Plain edge. (Stevens 16)

Munoz Hermanos Y Sobrino = Munoz Brothers and Nephew, who were, respectively, E. D., G. F., M. P., C. E. and E. Munoz. Realito in Hermosillo county contained 5,000 areas and produced sugar cane, cotton, grapes, wheat and corn, and employed 300 men. It was irrigated by Sonora River. 1/4 de Jornal = One fourth day's wages.

A. A. RODRIGUEZ Y HNO.
Hacienda El Tecolote

Rulau	Date	Metal	Size	VG	F	VF	Unc
Son 44	(1905)	Brass	34mm	—	—	50.00	—

A. A. RODRIGUEZ Y HNO / HACIENDA / EL TECOLOTE / (tiny) L. A. RUBBER STAMP CO. Rv: 100.

Rulau	Date	Metal	Size	VG	F	VF	Unc
Son 45	(1905)	Brass	32mm	—	—	50.00	—

As last, but 50.

FELIPE SALIDO

Rulau	Date	Metal	Size	VG	F	VF	Unc
Son 47	(1905)	Brass	35mm	—	—	35.00	—

FELIPE SALIDO / 50 / * HERMOSILLO. * / (tiny) MOISE. S.F. Rv: Same as obverse. Plain edge. (Stevens 36)

Rulau	Date	Metal	Size	VG	F	VF	Unc
Son 48	(1905)	Brass	30mm	—	—	35.00	—

As last, but 25. (Stevens 35)

Felipe Salido, an 1884 graduate of Chapultepec Military Academy, was an architect and teacher, and built Alamos city hall and Hermosillo federal building. The tokens may have been used for workers on his building projects.

(Eight-spoked Wheel)

Rulau	Date	Metal	Size	VG	F	VF	EF
Son 50	(1919 ?)	Bronze	30mm	—	15.00	—	27.50

Eight-spoked wheel device ctsp on reverse of Mexico 1919-Mo 10-centavos, KM-430. (Stevens 15)

Rulau	Date	Metal	Size	VG	F	VF	EF
Son 51	(1891 ?)	Aluminum	31mm	—	—	—	35.00

Similar ctsp on Hacienda de Topahue 50-centavo token of Hermosillo. (Stevens 14)

Rulau	Date	Metal	Size	VG	F	VF	EF
Son 52	(?)	Copper	25mm	—	—	—	35.00

Similar ctsp on Principal Cantina 50-centavo token of Hermosillo. (*ATCO* for Feb. 1985, pg 6)

Rulau	Date	Metal	Size	VG	F	VF	EF
Son 53	(?)	Aluminum	26.5mm	—	—	—	35.00

Similar ctsp on Hacienda El Zacaton 10-centavo token of Hermosillo. (Stevens 13)

This counterstamp may be a Hermosillo municipal validation of some purpose.

Horcasitas
M. YÑIGO

Rulau	Date	Metal	Size	VG	F	VF	Unc
Son 55	(1855)	Brass	24mm	10.00	14.00	18.00	35.00

Eagle on cactus, etc. Around: REPUBLICA MEXICANA / SONORA. Rv: MAQUINARIA / (signature) M. Yñigo / 1 / 0 DE LOS ANGELES o. Plain edge. (Ulex 1858; Eklund 608; Stevens 34)

Rulau	Date	Metal	Size	VG	F	VF	Unc
Son 56	(1855)	Copper	24mm	—	—	—	150.

As last. Trial strike. (Stevens note 34)

Rulau	Date	Metal	Size	VG	F	VF	Unc
Son 57	(1855)	Brass	22mm	10.00	14.00	18.00	35.00

As last, but 1/2 (real). (Pradeau report)

Rulau	Date	Metal	Size	VG	F	VF	Unc
Son 59	(1855)	Copper	19mm	—	—	—	135.

As last, but 1/4. Trial strike in copper. (Stevens 33 note; Rulau coll.)

Rulau	Date	Metal	Size	VG	F	VF	Unc
Son 60	(1855)	Brass	19mm	8.00	12.00	15.00	30.00

As last. Normal circulation strike. (Ulex 1858; Eklund 607; Stevens 33)

The brass 1/4-real token is known counterstamped with numeral 8. These tokens were struck by Scovill Mfg. Co., Waterbury, Conn.; the copper trial strike in the Rulau collection was in the estate of a Scovill executive broken up in 1981.

Smithsonian Institution possesses an Unc 1/2-real in cupronickel, probably a trial strike.

The Maquinaria de Los Angeles referred to on the tokens was the only textile plant that existed in Sonora State. Founded 1834 by M. Yñigo and two partners, it was under Yñigo complete control when the tokens were ordered in 1855 from Scovill Mfg. Co.

The plant was located at (San Miguel de) Horcasitas until 1948, when it was dismantled and erected in Guadalajara (Jalisco State). Though the 1855 token issue (and perhaps some reissues) may have been reasonably large, the pieces are quite rare today.

La Colorada
LA COLORADA / PRIETAS STORES

Rulau	Date	Metal	Size	VG	F	VF	Unc
Son 63	(1905)	+ +	30mm	—	—	125.	—

+ + Maroon vulcanite.
PRIETAS STORES . / 10 C (in circle) / * LA COLORADA . *. Rv: Same as obverse. (Eklund 2128; Stevens 23)

There may be varieties. Made by Moise-Klinkner Co., San Francisco. Issued by La Colorada Mines, which produced gold, copper and sulphur from early Spanish workings called "Real de Tayopa." Later these mines, near Hermosillo, were owned by Minas Prietas and then Creston Colorado Mining Co.

La Labor
HACIENDA DE LA LABOR

Manuel N. Amozurrutia, Owner

Rulau	Date	Metal	Size	VG	F	VF	Unc
Son 65	ND	Brass	30mm	—	—	—	—

HACIENDA / DE LA / LABOR / V ctsp. Rv: MANUEL N. / AMOZURRUTIA.

Juan Y. Luken, Owner

Rulau	Date	Metal	Size	VG	F	VF	Unc
Son 67	(1905-20)	Aluminum	Oct 38mm	—	—	—	—

HACIENDA LABOR / 100 / *. J. Y. L. * / (tiny) L. A. RUB. STAMP CO. Rv: 100. (Stevens 18)

Rulau	Date	Metal	Size	VG	F	VF	Unc
Son 68	(1905-20)	Aluminum	Oct 24mm	—	—	—	—

As last, but 10. (Stevens 17)

Hacienda de la Labor, 500 acres, was 35 miles northeast of Hermosillo. Amozurrutia was an early proprietor. Luken was proprietor in the 1905-1920 period.

La Trinidad
LA TRINIDAD LIMITED

Rulau	Date	Metal	Size	F	VF	EF	Unc
Son 70	ND	Lead	38mm	—	—	100.	—

LA TRINIDAD / 8 / * SONORA, MEXICO *. / TMC monogram ctsp. Rv: Same as obverse. (Stevens 12; Grove 'Tokens' 1985)

Rulau	Date	Metal	Size	F	VF	EF	Unc
Son 71	ND	Lead	31mm	—	—	50.00	—

Similar to last, but 4. No ctsp. (Stevens 11)

WM and aluminum 1-real tokens, 18mm, exist. Also aluminum 2-reales, 25mm. Henkle calls the WM token lead, but they are a zinc-lead alloy.

The mines were in Sahuaripa county.

Mulatos
NEGOCIACION MINERA DE MULATOS

Rulau	Date	Metal	Size	VG	F	VF	Unc
Son 73	(1893-97)	Brass	27.5mm	—	15.00	30.00	—

(All incused): NEGOCIACION MINERA / DE / MULATOS. Rv: 1 / REAL. Plain edge.

Rulau	Date	Metal	Size	VG	F	VF	Unc
Son 74	(1905)	Zinc	29mm	—	—	35.00	—

As last. Plain edge. (Stevens 22; Grove 'Tokens' 1777)

Rulau	Date	Metal	Size	VG	F	VF	Unc
Son 75	(1893-97)	Brass	29mm	—	—	35.00	—

NEGOCIACION / *** / MINERA / DE / * MULATOS * / (tiny) L. H. MOISE. S.F. Rv: SIRVANSE ADELANTAR / *** / AL PORTADOR / 25 / CENTAVOS. Plain edge.

Rulau	Date	Metal	Size	VG	F	VF	Unc
Son 76	ND	**	36mm	—	—	—	—

** Brown bakelite.
As last. (Grove report)

Rulau	Date	Metal	Size	VG	F	VF	Unc
Son 77	(1893-97)	Brass	24mm	—	15.00	30.00	—

As last, but 6 / CENTAVOS. (Stevens 21; Grove 'Tokens' 1775)

REY DEL ORO MINING CO.

Rulau	Date	Metal	Size	VG	F	VF	Unc
Son 79	ND	Aluminum	30mm	—	—	35.00	—

REY DEL ORO MINING CO. / -.- / MULATOS / (tiny) PATRICK & CO. S.F. Rv: VALOR EN MERC'S / 50 (shaded) / . SOLAMENTE . Plain edge. (Stevens 20)

Rulau	Date	Metal	Size	VG	F	VF	Unc
Son 80	(1905)	Aluminum	20mm	—	—	—	—

As last, but 5. (Stevens 19)

See *ATCO* bulletin for Feb. 1985. Gold mine, employed 100 men.

Promontorios
TIENDA DE RAYA

Rulau	Date	Metal	Size	VG	F	VF	Unc
Son 85	(ca 1905)	Brass	29mm	10.00	15.00	35.00	75.00

TIENDA DE / 1/2 / RAYA. Rv: PROMONTORIOS (incused).

Tienda de raya = Company store. Promontorios is near Alamos.

Rastras
A. T. CO.
(Antonio Tellechea Co.)

Rulau	Date	Metal	Size	VG	F	VF	Unc
Son 87	ND	Brass	29mm	—	—	20.00	—

A T Co. Rv: 4.

C. Y.
(Clemente Ybarra)

Rulau	Date	Metal	Size	VG	F	VF	Unc
Son 89	ND	Copper	34mm	—	—	35.00	—

TIENDA DE RAYA / C. Y. / RASTRAS / (tiny) MOISE. S.F. Rv: 4 (reales ?)

Rulau	Date	Metal	Size	VG	F	VF	Unc
Son 90	ND	Copper	28mm	—	15.00	35.00	—

As last, but 2.

Rulau	Date	Metal	Size	VG	F	VF	Unc
Son 91	ND	Copper	22mm	—	—	25.00	—

As last, but 1.

Tonichi
G. TONA

Rulau	Date	Metal	Size	VG	F	VF	Unc
Son 93	ND	Aluminum	Oct 23mm	—	—	—	—

(Ornament) / G. TONA / (ornament). Rv: 25. (Stevens 25)

Gabriel Tona owned a store at Tonichi in a mining area.

Uncertain
J. G. DERBY

Rulau	Date	Metal	Size	VG	F	VF	EF
Son 100	(1863)	Copper	33mm	—	—	50.00	—

J. G. DERBY ctsp on Mexico Sonora State cuartillas (KM Mexico 365). Examined: 1861, 1862; 1863. (Ulex 1853-54)

YAQUI COPPER CO.

Rulau	Date	Metal	Size	VG	F	VF	EF
Son 105	ND	Brass	39mm	—	6.00	15.00	25.00

(All incused): YAQUI / 762 (serial no.) / COPPER CO. Rv: Blank. Issued holed.

Tool check? Garnett coll. contains serial no. 764.

TABASCO STATE

Balancan
B. A. & C.
(Benito Aznar & Co.)
Chinal

Rulau	Date	Metal	Size	VG	F	VF	Unc
Tab 3	1888	CN	20mm	—	—	—	—

CHINAL / B. A. & C. / --.-- / * 1888 *. Rv: 1 / UN REAL / -.- within wreath. Plain edge. (L&P C-5; Eklund 137)

Rulau	Date	Metal	Size	VG	F	VF	Unc
Tab 4	1888	CN	28mm	—	—	—	—

As last, but 2 / DOS REALES. (L&P C-6)

Most of the Benito Aznar & Co. hacienda operations were in neighboring Campeche State. For other Aznar tokens, see under Campeche.

Henkle says Balancan was in Yucatan State. There is also a 1/2-real CN Token, 14mm.

TAMAULIPAS STATE

Tampico
RAMON CAVAZOS

Rulau	Date	Metal	Size	VG	F	VF	Unc
Tam 15	ND	Brass	24mm	—	—	25.00	35.00

CAFE EL BUEN TONO / (sunburst) / RAMON / CAVAZOS / (sunburst) / TAMPICO, MEX. Rv: BUENO POR / .... / -UNA- / ...... / COPA. Plain edge. (Zaffern coll.; Eklund 617)

Bueno por una copa = Good for one cup (coffee). Cafe El Buen Tono = The good taste cafe.

GRAN HOTEL CONTINENTAL

Rulau	Date	Metal	Size	VG	F	VF	Unc
Tam 18	(1893-97)	Aluminum	32mm	—	—	12.50	25.00

GRAN HOTEL / """ / CONTINENTAL / """ / TAMPICO / (tiny) L. H. MOISE S.F. Rv: Large pebbled 50. Plain edge. (Zaffern coll.)

50 centavos.

INDUSTRIA EMPACADORA DE TAMPICO, S.A.

Rulau	Date	Metal	Size	F	VF	EF	Unc
Tam 19	1947	Bronze	Irreg 31mm	—	—	—	4.50

Overhead view of plant in circle. Around: INAUGURADA 1947 . / INDUSTRIA EMPACADORA DE TAMPICO, S.A. Rv: LA PRIMERA INDUSTRIA / INDUSTRIA / EMPACADORA / DE TAMPICO, S.A. / TAMPICO / MEXICO / DE SU CLASE EN MEXICO / (tiny) WHITEHEAD-HOAG. Plain edge. Issued holed.

Empacadora = Packaging. Struck by Whitehead & Hoag Co., Newark, N.J.

Tula
R. V.
(Rafael Villasenor)

Rulau	Date	Metal	Size	VG	F	VF	Unc
Tam 20	ND	Copper	21mm	—	—	40.00	—

R V ctsp on copper octavo. (Ulex 1867)

I. S. TA.

Rulau	Date	Metal	Size	VG	F	VF	Unc
Tam 25	ND	Copper	29mm	—	—	125.	—

I. S. TA in relief within rect. depression ctsp on U.S. 1805 large cent. (Eklund 2227)

Supposely issued at Santa Ana de Tamaulipas.

TLAXCALA STATE

Tlaxco
TLAXCO

Municipio

Rulau	Date	Metal	Size	VG	F	VF	EF
Tlx 5	ND	Copper	19mm	—	—	—	—

Within wreath: TLAX.co / (Flowers). Rv: Within wreath: AYUNto / DE / --- . (Fernandez 255)

VERACRUZ STATE

Alvarado
ALVARADO

Rulau	Date	Metal	Size	VG	F	VF	EF
Ver 4	ND	Copper	27mm	—	—	35.00	50.00
		ALVA / RADO. Rv: Blank. (Munoz NOM 32)					
Ver 5	ND	Copper	17mm	—	—	25.00	40.00
		As last, but smaller. (Eklund 23; ANS 24; Munoz NOM 33)					
Ver 6	ND	Copper	26mm	—	—	35.00	—
		Same die as first tlaco above, struck over Mexico 1/4 real of 1829-37 type. (Eklund 21; Brunk 50180)					
Ver 7	ND	Copper	17mm	—	—	50.00	—
		ALVA / RADO struck over Mexico 1/16 real. Rv: A in circle of dashes struck over the other side. (Eklund 22; Fonrobert 7040)					

Both Eklund and Brunk point out that Alvarado is a city in Veracruz State as well as a common surname. Municipio tokens of the Veracruz Alvarado are a possibility.

Ceactipac
CEATICPA

Rulau	Date	Metal	Size	VG	F	VF	Unc
Ver 11	1877	Wood	39mm	—	—	—	Rare

(All incused) CEATICPA / EGV monogram / (rhomboid) 1877 (rhomboid). Rv: Blank. 8mm thick! (Muñoz MAD 2)

Ceactipac is in the municipio of Zongolica. EGV = Emilio Galvan H.

Coatzacoalcos
HOTEL COLON

Rulau	Date	Metal	Size	VG	F	VF	Unc
Ver 13	ND	CN	29mm	—	—	15.00	—

HOTEL COLON / * / CECILIO ALEGRIA / * / COATZACOALCOS. Rv: Large 25 (centavos). (Eklund 1053)

Rulau	Date	Metal	Size	VG	F	VF	Unc
Ver 14	ND	CN	26mm	—	—	20.00	—

As last, but 13. (Eklund 1052)

The denomination 13 centavos is odd by any measure. This token has been claimed as one of Panama.

Cordova
CORDOBA

Rulau	Date	Metal	Size	VG	F	VF	EF
Ver 16	ND	Copper	24mm	—	—	—	—

COR / DO (small pomegranate) BA / (stylized elaborate coiled lariat begun as the tail of the pomegranate). Rv: Blank. (Muñoz NOM 137; ANS 114; Grove 'Tokens' 273)

Huatusco
HUATUSCO

Municipios

Rulau	Date	Metal	Size	VG	F	VF	EF
Ver 18	ND	Wood	38mm	—	—	100.	150.

(All incused) TLACO / (star) / HUATUSCO, all within circular frame. Rv: Blank. 5mm thick. (Muñoz MAD 6)

Rulau	Date	Metal	Size	VG	F	VF	EF
Ver 20	ND	Wood	Rect 35x48mm	*	—	100.	150.

Within ornate rectangular frame: MONEDA / DE CAMBIO / HUATUSCO. Rv: Blank. 5mm thick. (Muñoz MAD 5)

* Other reported specimens measure 33x47, 35x47 and 36.5x51 millimeters. The workmanship is crude.

TLACO = 1/8 real. MONEDA DE CAMBIO = Exchange Coin (or money).

For a complete explanation of Tlacos de Madera, see Miguel L. Muñoz; "Tokens y Pilones" published in Mexico City in 1976.

Ex. Rare.

Rulau	Date	Metal	Size	VG	F	VF	EF
Ver 22	1846	Wood **	45.5x32.6mm	—	—	150.	200.

Huatusco /Año de 1846 within beaded rect. frame. Rv: Blank. Fonrobert 7041; Muñoz N/L; Smithsonian coll., ex-F.C.C. Boyd)

** Cedar wood plaquette, according to Fonrobert's cataloger, Adolf Weyl of Berlin, in 1878. The Smithsonian specimen has been lacquered.

Ixtaczoquitlan
HACIENDA DE TUXPANGO

Rulau	Date	Metal	Size	VG	F	VF	Unc
Ver 25	ND	Brass	30mm	—	7.50	20.00	35.00

Eagle with serpent in its beak, perched on a cactus. Rv: HACIENDA DE TUXPANGO 10 (in small beaded circle) / * MEXICO *. Plain edge. (Fonrobert 6744; Schrotter 80; Ulex 1526; Eklund 654; Scott catalog; Rulau coll.)

Rulau	Date	Metal	Size	VG	F	VF	Unc
Ver 26	ND	Brass	25mm	10.00	12.50	18.50	25.00

As last, but 5. Plain edge. (Ulex 1526; Scott cat.; Schrotter 81; Eklund 653)

Rulau	Date	Metal	Size	VG	F	VF	Unc
Ver 28	ND	Copper	30mm	—	10.00	30.00	45.00

Obverse similar to Ver 25, but snakehead has different attitude, and plain border on either side. 10 in large rope circle on reverse. Plain edge. (Eklund 655)

These tokens are not round, but are struck on a 25-sided polygonal flan. Struck before 1878, since Fonrobert reported them. They can occasionally be found in Proof or Prooflike Unc. condition.

Jalapa
F. P. D. X.
(Fondo Publico de Xalapa)

Municipios

Rulau	Date	Metal	Size	G	VG	F	EF
Ver 30	1824	Copper	21mm	11.00	15.00	22.00	—

F. P. / D. X. / 1824. Rv: Blank. Plain edge. (Duffield 1690; Eklund 674; Muñoz NOM 203)

| Ver 32 | 1836 | Copper | 21mm | — | — | — | — |

F: P: / D. X. / . 1836 . in laurel wreath. Rv: * UN. / - / + 8 BO. Plain edge. (Eklund 675)

According to Frank Duffield, writing in 1919, F. P. D. X. stands for Fondo Provisional de Xalapa (Xalapa Provisional Fund). Henkle and others attribute it to Jalapa municipality in Veracruz State.

M. R.

Rulau	Date	Metal	Size	VG	F	VF	EF
Ver 34	ND	Copper	28mm	20.00	—	—	—

Within dotted border: MR (large) / JALAPA / (two leaves). Rv: Blank, but numeral 8 incused at top rim. Plain edge. (ANS 205)

Jalapa Enriquez is a medium-sized city in Veracruz State. There is a small city Jalapa in Tabasco and a small city Jalapa de Diaz in Oaxaca.

Naranjal
EMILIO GALVAN H.

Rulau	Date	Metal	Size	VG	F	VF	EF
Ver 37	1877	Wood	40mm	—	—	—	150.

(All incused) NARAN / JAL within central circle. Around: EMILIO GALVAN H. / 1877. Rv: 1/8 at center of wavy circle. 5mm thick. (Muñoz MAD 8)

Orizaba
ORIZAVA

Rulau	Date	Metal	Size	VG	F	VF	EF
Ver 40	1842	Copper	29mm				

(All script): ORIZAVA / Ao 1842 under curved branch. Rv: Spear of wheat upright, above fraction 1/8 flanked by eight rosettes, all within crossed branches. (ANS 291; J. Schulman 1911 sale of Salbach collection, lot 3720; Eklund 438)

HACIENDA DE JAZMIN

Rulau	Date	Metal	Size	VG	F	VF	Unc
Ver 42	ND	Brass	30mm	10.00	30.00	50.00	75.00

HACIENDA DE JAZMIN * / 10 in beaded circle / ORIZABA *. Rv: Large ornate monogram A.E. J.? (Eklund 440)

| Ver 43 | ND | Brass | 25mm | — | 12.50 | — | — |

As last, but 5 (centavos). (Eklund 439)

SALAS

Rulau	Date	Metal	Size	VG	F	VF	EF
Ver 45	ND	Copper	25mm	—	—	—	—

SALAS / ORI / SAUA. Rv: Blank. (Muñoz NOM 522; ANS 403; Grove 859)

Tlanepaquila
TLANEPAQUILA

Rulua	Date	Metal	Size	VG	F	VF	EF
Ver 50	1877	Wood	35mm	—	—	100.	150.

Monogram PER in central circle. Around: TLANEPA-QUILA / 1877. Rv: Blank. 8mm thick. (Muñoz MAD 13)

Tlapacoyan
TLAPACOYAN

Rulau	Date	Metal	Size	VG	F	VF	EF
Ver 52	(1)865	Wood	44mm	—	—	100.	150.

865 at center. TLAPACOYAN around. Rv: Blank. 6.5mm thick. (Muñoz MAD 16)

| Ver 54 | 1872 | Wood | 45mm | — | — | 100. | 150. |

1872 / (Rosette) at center, TLAPACOYAN around. Rv: Blank. (Muñoz MAD 17; Fernandez 254)

Tuzamapan
TUZAMAPAM

Rulau	Date	Metal	Size	VG	F	VF	EF
Ver 57	1914	—	39mm	—	—	15.00	—

(All incused) TUZAMAPAM / 100 / 1914. Rv: no descr. avail.

Veracruz
LONJA MERCANTIL

Rulau	Date	Metal	Size	F	VF	EF	Unc
Ver 58	1868	Svd/WM	32mm	—	—	65.00	100.

LONJA MERCANTIL / - / DE / VERA / CRUZ / - / + 1868 +. Rv: UN / PESO within oak wreath, Liberty cap in opening above. Plain edge. (ANS coll.; ex-J.F. Jones, 1940)

Unpublished anywhere, this well-made token probably has a European origin. Lonja mercantil = Mercantile exchange.

VELASCO HERMANOS

Rulau	Date	Metal	Size	VG	F	VF	Unc
Ver 60	ND	WM	25mm	—	—	45.00	80.00

VELASCO HERMANOS / 1 / . VERA CRUZ . Rv: TIENDA / NOVILLERO / EFECTOS. Plain edge. (Smithsonian coll.)

A beautiful machine-struck token. Tienda novillero efectos = Goods (at) herdsman store. Novillero can also mean bullfighter.

Zapoapan
Z P P n

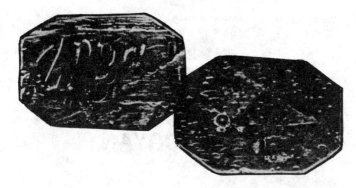

Rulau	Date	Metal	Size	VG	F	VF	Unc
Ver 65	ND	Wood	Rect41x29mm	—	—	100.	150.

Z P P n. Rv: 1/8. (Muñoz MAD 19)

Zapoapan is in the municipio of Cordoba.

YUCATAN STATE
Acanceh County
MONICA CONTRERAS DE CAMPOS
Hacienda Mukuiche

Rulau	Date	Metal	Size	VG	F	VF	Unc
Yuc 1	ND	Aluminum	33mm	—	—	9.50	14.00

Large 5-pointed star at center. Around: MONICA CONTRERAS DE CAMPOS / . HACIENDA MUKUICHE. Rv: ENTREG'O / * 500 * / PENCAS. Plain edge. (L&P M-8)

Rulau	Date	Metal	Size	VG	F	VF	Unc
Yuc 2	ND	Aluminum	Oct 29mm	—	—	9.50	14.00

Obverse as last. Rv: ENTREG'O / 1 / * MECATE CHAPEO. Plain edge. (Rulau coll.)

Entreg(ad)o 500 Pencas - Delivered 500 (henequen) leaves. This was about 1/4 of a day's work for a top laborer, and seemed to be a standard of measurement in the Yucatan henequen plantations.

The 1,000-penca denomination in this series was also issued. Value $25 VF, $50 Unc.

These exist with ctsps J, M or C in circle.

Baca
GAMBOA RIVERO
Kancabchen Hacienda

Rulau	Date	Metal	Size	VG	F	VF	Unc
Yuc 4	1910	CN	30mm	—	—	30.00	40.00

Crossed mattock and axe superimposed over crossed machete and tilling knife. Around: KANCABCHEN DE GAMBOA RIVERO + Rv: 1 / MECATE / - / 1910. (L&P K-6)

Rulau	Date	Metal	Size	VG	F	VF	Unc
Yuc 5	1910	CN	30mm	—	—	—	—

As last, but 2 / MECATES. (L&P K-7)

Rulau	Date	Metal	Size	VG	F	VF	Unc
Yuc 6	1910	CN	30mm	—	—	—	—

As last, but 500 / PENCAS. (L&P K-4)

Rulau	Date	Metal	Size	VG	F	VF	Unc
Yuc 7	1910	CN	30mm	—	—	—	—

As last, but 1000 / PENCAS. (L&P K-5)

Baca is in Motul County, Yucatan. Mecate = 400 square meters cleared. Pencas = Leaves.

GAMBOA RIVERO
Kuche Hacienda

Rulau	Date	Metal	Size	VG	F	VF	Unc
Yuc 9	1910	Aluminum	30mm	—	—	—	—

Crossed mattock and axe superimposed over crossed machete and tilling knife. Around: KUCHE DE GAMBOA RIVERO + Rv: 1000 / PENCAS / - / 1910. Plain edge. (L&P K-10)

This issuer also released 500-penca, 1-mecate and 2-mecate tokens of the same type in aluminum, all 30mm and dated 1910.

Bolon
O. T.
Sacnicte

Rulau	Date	Metal	Size	VG	F	VF	Unc
Yuc 11	ND	CN	25mm	—	—	—	—

SACNICTE / OT monogram. Rv: Four fleurs de lis and four rosettes surround center ornament. Plain edge. (L&P S-4)

Rulau	Date	Metal	Size	VG	F	VF	Unc
Yuc 12	ND	CN	22mm	—	—	—	—
		As last, but smaller. (L&P S-2)					
Yuc 13	ND	CN	22mm	—	—	—	—
		As last, but counterstamped L.C. / 20. (L&P S-3)					

The ornate OT monogram stood for Olegario and Trinidad Molina in the town of Bolon, Hunucma County, Yucatan.

Don Olegario Molina was the infamous governor of Yucatan who by 1909 owned 15,000,000 acres of land—much of it seized from Indians.

Cacalchen
GAMBOA RIVERO
S. Antonio Pua

Rulau	Date	Metal	Size	VG	F	VF	Unc
Yuc 15	1910	Brass	30mm	—	—	—	—
		Crossed mattock, axe, machete and tilling knife. Around: S. ANTONIO PUA DE GAMBOA RIVERO / + . Rv: 1000 / PENCAS / - / 1910. (L&P S-12)					
Yuc 16	1910	Brass	30mm	—	—	—	—
		As last, but ctsp F — L on reverse. (L&P S-13)					
Yuc 17	1910	Brass	30mm	—	—	—	—
		Obverse as last. Rv: 1 / MECATE / - / 1910. (L&P S-14)					

Caucel
J. M. PEON
Tankuche Hacienda

Rulau	Date	Metal	Size	VG	F	VF	Unc
Yuc 19	1888	CN	17mm	—	4.50	7.00	12.00
		Within laurel wreath: TANKUCHE / 1/4 / 1888. Rv: FICHA CONVENCIONAL / PARA LAS / FINCAS / DE / J. M. PEON. Plain edge. (L&P T-2)					
Yuc 20	1888	CN	20mm	—	5.00	7.50	12.00
		As last, but 1/2. (L&P T-3)					

These tokens are denominated in reales - quarter real and half real.

The reverse legend translates: Contractual token for the plantations of Jose Maria Peon. These were henequen (hemp, or sisal) plantations in Merida County.

These pieces are well made, similar to the Camara tokens for Texan Hacienda.

Conkal
J. ANCONA E HIJOS
Hacienda San Jose Kuche

Rulau	Date	Metal	Size	VG	F	VF	Unc
Yuc 22	1874	Copper	23mm	—	—	40.00	50.00
		Farmhouse in circle. Around: EQUIVALENTE A DIEZ CENTAVOS / * J. ANCONA E HIJOS *. Rv: Three henequen plants in circle, 1874 below. Around: HACIENDA SAN JOSE KUCHE / (rosette). (F. 8292; L&P S-33)					
Yuc 23	1874	Copper	18mm	—	—	65.00	
		As last, but 2 Y 1/2 CENTAVOS, and only KUCHE on reverse. (F. 8293; L&P S-32)					

This hemp plantation was in Tixkokob County, Yucatan. Scott in 1913 had attributed this to Panama in Colombia.

EULALIO CASARES
Hacienda Xcuyum

Rulau	Date	Metal	Size	VG	F	VF	Unc
Yuc 25	ND	WM	28mm	—	—	—	40.00
		HACIENDA XCUYUM / (radiant star in beaded circle) / . EULALIO CASARES . Rv: 1 (large, shaded). Reeded edge. (Eklund 2253; Leslie & Pradeau X-5; Randel coll.)					

Rulau	Date	Metal	Size	VG	F	VF	Unc
Yuc 26	ND	WM	25mm	—	—	—	30.00
		As last, but 1/2. Reeded edge. (Randel coll.)					

M. F. C.
(Manuel Fuentes Correa)

Rulau	Date	Metal	Size	VG	F	VF	Unc
Yuc 28	1866	Brass	20mm	—	—	—	—
		SAN SEBASTIAN / 1/2 / 1866. Rv: M. F. C. Plain edge. (L&P S-46)					

Conkal is in Tixkokob County, Yucatan. This is one of the earliest Yucatan hacienda tokens.

Cuzama
RICARDO MOLINA
San Jose Eknacan

Rulau	Date	Metal	Size	VG	F	VF	Unc
Yuc 30	1872	Nic/Bs	24mm	—	15.00	30.00	70.00
		RICARDO MOLINA / (henequen sprig) / * NOVIEMBRE 9 DE 1872 *. Rv: SAN JOSE EKNACAN / AR monogram brand / * YUCATAN *. Plain edge. (L&P S-31; Eklund 527; Rulau coll.)					
Yuc 31	1872	Nic/Bs	20mm	—	10.00	15.00	35.00
		As last, smaller. Plain edge. (L&P S-30; Rulau coll.)					

Ricardo Molina may have been an ancestor of the infamous Yucatan governor and landowner, Olegario Molina.

Espita
CARLOS Y ROBERTO OSORIO
Hacienda San Antonio Holka

Rulau	Date	Metal	Size	VG	F	VF	Unc
Yuc 33	ND	Aluminum	20mm	—	—	—	—
		In concentric circles: HACIENDA SAN ANTONIO HOLKA / CARLOS Y ROBERTO OSORIO. Rv: 500 / PENCAS. Plain edge. (L&P S-11)					

It is possible this hacienda was located in Teya, Temax County, Yucatan, rather than in the municipality of Espita in Espita County.

Hocaba
EVIA
Hacienda Buena-Vista

Rulau	Date	Metal	Size	VG	F	VF	Unc
Yuc 35	ND	Brass	38mm	—	—	—	—
		(All incuse) HDA. BUENA-VISTA / 500 / EVIA. Rv: Blank. Plain edge. (L&P B-4)					

All the 500 (penca) tokens examined by Elwin Leslie had been heavily dented at their exact centers, perhaps to make them stack easily.

Rulau	Date	Metal	Size	VG	F	VF	Unc
Yuc 36	ND	Brass	28.5mm	—	—	—	—
		(All incuse) HDA. BUENA-VISTA / 1 Mte / EVIA. Rv: Blank. Incised beaded border on each side. Plain edge. (L&P B-5)					

Mte - Mecate (400 square meters cleaned of weeds). Hocaba is in Sotuta County, Yucatan.

Hoctun
JOSE N. ARJONA
Hacienda Valix

Rulau	Date	Metal	Size	VG	F	EF	Unc
Yuc 38	1888	CN/Bs	24mm	—	15.00	45.00	—
		Bee. Around: JOSE N. ARJONA / * HOCTUN *. Rv: Cow left. Around: HACIENDA VALIX. / * 1888 *. Reeded edge. (LYP V-7) There are 2 die varieties.					
Yuc 39	1888	CN/Bs	24mm	—	—	—	—
		As last, but plain edge. (Smithsonian coll.)					
Yuc 40	1888	CN/Bs	24mm	—	—	45.00	—
		As first token above (reeded edge), but ctsp 1000 (pencas). (L&P V-8)					
Yuc 41	1888	CN/Bs	21mm	7.00	11.50	—	—
		As last, but smaller. (L&P V-1)					
Yuc 42	1888	CN/Bs	21mm	—	—	Scarce	—
		As last, but ctsp 500 (pencas). (L&P V-2)					
Yuc 43	1888	CN/Bs	21mm	—	—	—	—
		As last, but ctsp 1 (mecate). (L&P V-3)					

MIGUEL ESPINOSA RENDON
Hacienda Chinkila

Rulau	Date	Metal	Size	VG	F	VF	Unc
Yuc 45	1889	CN	28mm	—	—	35.00	45.00
		Worker left cuts henequen leaves. Around: MIGUEL ESPINOSA RENDON / CONVENCIONAL / . * . Rv: HACIENDA CHINKILA / 12 1/2 / YUCATAN / - 1889 -. Plain edge. (L&P C-9)					
Yuc 46	1889	CN	25mm	—	—	—	—
		As last, but 6 1/4 (centavos). (L&P C-8)					
Yuc 47	1889	CN	20mm	—	—	—	—
		As last, but 3 (centavos). (L&P C-7)					

Hoctun is in Izamal County, Yucatan. 12 1/2 centavos equaled 1 real, 6 1/4 centavos was 1/2 real, and 3 centavos was approximately 1/4 real.

JUAN GAMBOA
(Hacienda Dziuche)

Rulau	Date	Metal	Size	VG	F	VF	Unc
Yuc 49	ND	Brass	Oct 38mm	—	10.00	15.00	—
		HDA. CIUCHE (C backward) / Y ANEXAS / 500 / JUAN GAMBOA. Rv: Blank. Issued holed. (L&P C-1 thru C-4)					

This token for 500 pencas (leaves) occurs with blank reverse and with these counterstamps: P, S A and S A / P.

Rulau	Date	Metal	Size	VG	F	VF	Unc
Yuc 50	ND	Brass	39mm	—	10.00	20.00	—
		Similar to last, but on a round flan and with numeral 1000 (pencas). (L&P C-5 thru C-8)					

This check occurs with blank reverse and with these counterstamped: P, S A and S A / P.

Rulau	Date	Metal	Size	VG	F	VF	Unc
Yuc 51	ND	Brass	28mm	—	10.00	15.00	—
		HDA. CIUCHE (C backward) / Y ANEXAS / 1 MTe / JUAN GAMBOA. Rv: Blank. Incused beaded rim on each side. Plain edge. Issued holed. (L&P C-9)					

Hoctun is in Izamal County, Yucatan. The hacienda name CIUCHE has as its initial letter a backward C. This is the Mayan O (pronounced DZ). The name can be rendered as DZIUCHE. The token issuers in this area chose to render the spelling accurately, requiring the use of the Mayan O (a backward C), and their token manufacturers cooperated - producing this quite unique lettering from Mexico.

JUAN GAMBOA
Hacienda San Jose

Rulau	Date	Metal	Size	VG	F	VF	Unc
Yuc 53	ND	Brass	38mm	—	10.00	20.00	—
		HDA. SAN JOSE / 1000 / JUAN GAMBOA. Rv: Blank. Plain edge. Issued holed. (L&P S-29)					
Yuc 54	ND	Brass	Oct 38mm	—	—	—	—
		As last, but 500 (pencas). Issued holed. (L&P S-28)					

Homun
ENRIQUE Y ELIAS ESPINOSA
Hacienda Chichi

Rulau	Date	Metal	Size	VG	F	VF	Unc
Yuc 56	ND	Aluminum	30mm	—	—	—	—
		ENRIQUE Y ELIAS ESPINOSA - HOMUN / CHICHI / *. Rv: 2000 / PENCAS. Plain edge. (L&P C-4)					

2000 Pencas (leaves) was a hard day's labor for one man on this henequen plantation.

Hunucma County
E. E.
Hacienda Hotzuc

Rulau	Date	Metal	Size	VG	F	VF	Unc
Yuc 58	ND	Brass	18mm	—	—	—	—
		E. E. Rv: HOTZUC. Plain edge. (L&P H-6)					

Izamal
A M A (Monogram)

Rulau	Date	Metal	Size	VG	F	VF	Unc
Yuc 60	1879	Lead	25mm	—	—	—	—
		IZAMAL / AMA monogram. Rv: 1879 / 1/8. (L&P AD-7; Guttag 3913; Fernandez 131)					

M B (Monogram)

Rulau	Date	Metal	Size	VG	F	VF	Unc
Yuc 62	1857	Lead	25mm	—	—	Scarce	

Within central circle: 1/16. Around: IZAMAL / (illegible word). Rv: Within laurel wreath: 1857 / MB monogram. (L&P AD-6; Guttag 3911; Fernandez 130)

Kanasin
V. ESCALANTE S.
Hacienda San Pedro

Rulau	Date	Metal	Size	VG	F	VF	Unc
Yuc 64	ND	WM	22mm	—	25.00	40.00	85.00

VE monogram at center. Around: HACIENDA SAN PEDRO / . V . ESCALANTE S . Rv: 1/8. (L&P S-42)

Kanasin is in Merida County, Yucatan.

Maxcanu
A. M. G.
(Antonio Mimenza G.)
Nueva Granada

Rulau	Date	Metal	Size	VG	F	VF	Unc
Yuc 66	1866	Brass	20mm	—	—	—	—

A. M. G. within laurel wreath. Rv: NUEVA GRANADA / 1/2 / 1866. Plain edge. (L&P N-8)

Merida
ACIENDA SOOIL
(Hacienda Dzodzil)

Rulau	Date	Metal	Size	VG	F	VF	EF
Yuc 68	ND	Lead	40mm	—	—	Rare	

ACIENDA SOOIL (crude). Rv: (Ornament) / 1 / PESO. (L&P D-1)

JOSE MARIA CASTRO
San Pedro Chimay

Rulau	Date	Metal	Size	VG	F	VF	Unc
Yuc 70	1889	CN	17mm	—	—	20.00	32.50

(All incused) Large C in center. Around: JOSE MARIA CASTRO / 1889. Stylized henequen sprig at center. Around: SAN PEDRO CHIMAY / -YUCATAN-. Plain edge. Issued holed. (L&P S-43)

Rulau	Date	Metal	Size	VG	F	VF	Unc
Yuc 71	1889	CN	22mm	—	—	12.00	18.00

(All incused) M within 5-pointed star at center. Around: JOSE MARIA CASTRO / 1889. Rv: As last. Plain edge. Issued holed. (L&P S-44; Rulau coll. ex-Charles Wyatt)

Rulau	Date	Metal	Size	VG	F	VF	Unc
Yuc 72	1889	CN	26mm	—	—	12.00	18.00

As last, but J within 5-pointed star. (L&P S-45)

The letters J, M and C stood for Jose Maria Castro. The M probably indicated one real, the C 1/4 real, and the J either 2 or 4 reales. They may also have indicated a work unit rather than a money unit.

San Pedro Chimay is in Merida County, Yucatan.

EL PRINCIPAL

Rulau	Date	Metal	Size	VG	F	VF	Unc
Yuc 74	ND	Aluminum	32mm	—	—	—	—

EL PRINCIPAL / 50 / MERIDA. Rv: Same as obverse. (L&P AD-4)

J. R.
Rancho Buena Vista

Rulau	Date	Metal	Size	VG	F	VF	Unc
Yuc 76	1868	Brass	24mm	—	—	30.00	—

RANCHO BUENA VISTA / 2 REALES. / .*. Rv: J. R. / 1868. Plain edge. (L&P B-7)

This token also was issued in red copper; same scarcity.

Rulau	Date	Metal	Size	VG	F	VF	Unc
Yuc 77	1868	Brass	18mm	—	—	25.00	—

As last, but 1. / REAL. (L&P B-6; Eklund 1478)

"EL REGALO" CAFE

Rulau	Date	Metal	Size	VG	F	VF	Unc
Yuc 79	1901	Aluminum	38mm	—	—	15.00	25.00

"EL REGALO" / SIGLO XX / * 1901 * / MERIDA. Rv: OBSEQUIO A SUS FAVORECEDORES / CAFE (bar) / CANTINA (saloon) Y / RESTAURANT / LICORES FINOS / FIAMBRES (cold cuts) / * ARTURO LIZARRAGA. PATRON * / (tiny) L. H. MOISE, S.F. Plain edge. (L&P AD-5)

This token salutes the 20th Century (SIGLO XX) and probably was given out to patrons well before the New Year celebrations January 1, 1901 — when the century "turned." It is well made, by the L.H. Moise Co. in San Francisco, Calif.

LA SOCIED.

Municipios ?

Rulau	Date	Metal	Size	VG	F	VF	EF
Yuc 81	1856	Lead	27mm	—	—	—	—

Similar to next, but + 1856 +. Plain edge. (Guttag 3912; Smithsonian coll.)

Rulau	Date	Metal	Size	VG	F	VF	EF
Yuc 83	1859	Lead	27mm	17.50	—	—	—

MERIDA DE YUCATAN / PART. / DE (monogram) LASO / CIED. / . 1859 . Rv: 1/2 / GRANO / DE PESO / PUERTE / -o-. Plain edge. (Scott; L&P AD-10; K-M L60)

Rulau	Date	Metal	Size	VG	F	VF	EF
Yuc 85	1874		—mm	—	—	—	—

As last, but 1874. (Ulex 1918; Eklund 370)

Rulau	Date	Metal	Size	VG	F	VF	EF
Yuc 87	1876	Lead	27mm	—	—	—	—

Similar to last, but 1876. (Guttag 3912; Eklund 372; L&P AD-11; Smithsonian coll.)

Part. de la Sociedad = Particular (private issue) of the Society. 1/2 Grano de peso fuerte = 1/2 Grain of Hard Peso.

Molas
YAXNIC

Rulau	Date	Metal		Size	VG	F	VF	Unc
Yuc 89	ND	Brass	Rect 32x36mm		—	—	—	—

(All incused): (Tiny) AM. RY. S. CO. NEW YORK / YAXNIC / 2000 / PENCAS. Rv: Blank. Issued with hole near top. (L&P Y-8)

Yuc 90	ND	Brass	Rect 25x36mm		—	—	—	—

Same as last, but smaller. (L&P Y-9)

Yuc 91	ND	Brass	36mm		—	—	—	—

(All incused): (Tiny) AM. RY. S. CO. / (tiny) NEW YORK / YAXNIC / 250 / PENCAS. Rv: Blank. Issued holed. (L&P Y-7)

Yuc 92	ND	Brass	Rect 30x35mm		—	—	—	—

(All incused): YAXNIC (curved) / 2. Rv: Blank. Slotted flan. (L&P Y-12)

Yuc 93	ND	Brass	Rect 27x39mm		—	—	—	—

(All incused): (Tiny) AM. RY. S. CO. / (tiny) NEW YORK / YAXNIC / 300 / HIJOS. Rv: Blank. Issued holed. (L&P Y-10)

Yuc 94	ND	Brass	Rect 30x35mm		—	—	—	—

YAXNIC. Rv: Blank. (L&P Y-11)

PENCAS = Leaves. HIJOS = Suckers.

YAXNIC = Henequen plantation in the town of Molas, Merida County, Yucatan State. The tokens were made for Yaxnic by American Railway Supply Co., New York City, which is why they resemble railway baggage checks more than hacienda tokens.

A hard-working peon could cut and scrape from 1500 to 2500 pencas (leaves) in a day (sunrise to sunset). But 2000 pencas was only 50 centavos for a full day's wages!

Hijos (sons) was the name given to the chupones (suckers) which sprout at the base of the henequen plant (agave rigida sisalana.) These were removed by peons to be transplanted to form new henequen fields.

When shipments of henequen were made to Merida, one of the non-denominational checks, the last one cataloged above, was fastened to each bundle of 50.

The life of a peon on a henequen plantation was, simply put, slavery — the last instance of mass slavery tolerated in North America in the 20th century. Many of the workers were Yaqui Indians captured in the north and sent as forced labor; Mayan Indians who indebted themselves to the plantations; convicts released from prison to work the fields; and illiterate Mexicans who were otherwise free.

The slavery conditions were ended in 1915 (the 1917 consitution put the government between master and peon). The hemp plantations were broken up, peons were permitted to acquire land, the use of tokens was prohibited, and the passage of debts from worker to family members was forbidden.

Motul
CIUDAD DE MOTUL

Municipio

Rulau	Date	Metal	Size	VG	F	VF	Unc
Yuc 96	1878	Lead	22mm	—	—	—	—

CIUDAD DE MOTUL around ornament, all circled by beads. Rv: 1/8 / 1878 between floreate devices. (Ulex 1919; Scott; Eklund 418; Smithsonian coll.)

Scott reported an 1859 date, but this has not been verified. Hubbard possesses 1863 and 1886 dates.

GAMBOA RIVERO
Sakola

Rulau	Date	Metal	Size	VG	F	VF	Unc
Yuc 98	1910	Brass	30mm	—	—	35.00	40.00

Crossed mattock, axe, machete and tilling knife. Around: SAKOLA DE GAMBOA RIVERO / +. Rv: 1000 / PENCAS / - / 1910. Plain edge. (L&P S-8)

Yuc 99	1910	Brass	30mm	—	—	—	—

As last, but 500. (L&P S-7)

The tools shown on obverse were the tools of the trade in caring for and cutting henequen plants.

BENITA PALMA DE C.

Rulau	Date	Metal	Size	VG	F	VF	Unc
Yuc 101	ND	Aluminum	24mm	—	—	—	—

(Incuse) T / (incuse) 20 / BENITA PALMA DE C. Rv: ENTREGO / DOS MIL / PENCAS (delivered 2,000 leaves). Issued holed for stringing. (L&P B-1)

Yuc 102	ND	Aluminum	Oval 42x15mm	—	—	—	—

Obverse similar, no counterstamp. Rv: UN / MECATE / CHAPEO (one parcel of land weeded). (L&P B-2)

Yuc 103	ND	Aluminum	Oct 35mm	—	—	—	—

Similar, but TRES / MECATES / CHAPEO (three parcels of land weeded). (L&P B-3)

Benita Palma de Campos owned Chovenchi, Cabcachen, Timul, Hili and Dzununcan haciendas, all in Motul County, Yucatan, where the tokens were eligible for use.

The three tokens refer to henequen cultivation. Two thousand leaves cut and scraped was a full day's labor. The weeding was necessary to protect the agave plant.

Opichen
E. E. B.
(Eusebio Escalante Bates)
Calcehtok

Rulau	Date	Metal	Size	VG	F	VF	Unc
Yuc 105	ND	CN	19mm	—	—	—	—

(Ornament) / CALCEHTOK / (ornament). Rv: (Ornament) / E. E. B. / (ornament). Plain edge. (L&P C-3)

Opichen is in Maxcano County, Yucatan.

Progreso
PROGRESO

Municipios

Rulau	Date	Metal	Size	VG	F	VF	Unc
Yuc 107	1858	Copper	23mm	25.00	35.00	50.00	—

Radiant star above open book, MUNICIPALIDAD DEL PROGRESO around. Rv: 1/8 within double wreath. Above: ANO DE 1858. Plain edge. (ANS 347; KM L66)

Yuc 108	1859	Copper	23mm	—	—	—	—

As last, but 1859. Crudely reeded edge. (Ulex report; Smithsonian coll. - 2 specimens)

Rulau	Date	Metal	Size	VG	F	VF	EF
Yuc 110	1873	Lead	Oval 33x25mm	20.00	35.00	75.00	—

MUNICIPALIDAD / DE PROGRESO. In center: UN CENT. / 1873. Rv: Flank in oval band. (KM L67)

A. DE R.
(Alonso de Regil y Peon)
Hacienda San Ignacio

Rulau	Date	Metal	Size	VG	F	VF	Unc
Yuc 112	ND	Brass	29mm	—	—	—	—

Twin-turreted castle. Around: HACIENDA Sn IGNA-CIO / + A DE R +. Rv: VL monogram (valor legal) within laurel wreath. (L&P S-21)

| Yuc 113 | ND | Brass | 23mm | — | — | — | — |

As last, but smaller. (L&P S-22)

There are no denominations on these tokens. Based on their size, the larger probably represents 2 reales and the smaller 1 real. An 18mm piece is in the Nicanor Vega collection.

The smaller token occurs counterstamped L.M. on reverse, possibly for a change of owner.

The hacienda owner, Alonso de Regil y Peon, had bloodlines from two of Yucatan's "Fifty Families" of wealthy landowners — his father was a Regil and his mother a Peon.

A. M. R.
(Alonso Manuel Regil)

Rulau	Date	Metal	Size	VG	F	VF	EF
Yuc 115	(ca 1906)	CN	22mm	—	—	—	—

A / M R. Rv: 25 within circle of small circles. All struck over Mexico 5-centavo coins of 1905-14 type. (L&P A-11)

| Yuc 116 | (ca 1906) | Copper | 26mm | — | — | — | — |

A / M R within four stems ending in crude, ragged leaves. Rv: 50 within circle of small circles. All struck over Mexico 2-centavo coins of 1905-06 type. (L&P A-12)

A. M. Regil's hacienda has not been located, but it is likely it was the same as, or near, that of his earlier kinsman Alonso de Regil y Peon.

Samahil
A. L. P.
(Augusto L. Peon)
Tedzidz Hacienda

Rulau	Date	Metal	Size	VG	F	VF	Unc
Yuc 118	ND	CN	22mm	—	—	10.00	20.00

A. L. P. within laurel and oak wreath. Rv: No 10 within laurel and oak wreath; tiny mintmark at bottom rim. A. D. / & CIE. (L&P A-6)

| Yuc 119 | ND | CN | 25mm | — | — | 10.00 | 20.00 |

As last, but No 20. (L&P A-7)

A cupronickel 5 centavos, 17mm, was also issued in this series.

These were issued for Peon's Tedzidz Hacienda in Hunucuma County, Yucatan, in the muncipality of Samahil.

Seye
CASARES HNOS.
Hacienda Nohchan

Rulau	Date	Metal	Size	VG	F	VF	Unc
Yuc 121	1889	CN/Br	28mm	—	—	10.00	—

Steer left. Around: HACIENDA NOHCHAN / . 1889 . Rv: DIOS SOBRE TODO / 1889. / . CASARES HNOS . Reeded edge. Issued holed. (L&P N-5)

Rulau	Date	Metal	Size	VG	F	VF	Unc
Yuc 12	1889	CN/Br	25mm	—	—	10.00	—

As last, smaller. (L&P N-4). Possibly also issed in Brass.

| Yuc 123 | 1889 | CN/Br | 21mm | — | — | 10.00 | — |

As last, but smaller. (L&P N-3)

| Yuc 124 | 1889 | CN/Br | 17mm | — | — | 15.00 | — |

As last, smaller. (L&P N-2)

Seye municipio is in Acanceh county, Yucatan. Dios sobre todo = God above all. The Casares Brothers placed no denominations on these tokens, so they must have passed current by size, perhaps 17mm equaling 1/4 real, 21mm 1/2 real, 25mm 1 real and 28mm 2 reales.

Issued in cupronickel-plated brass, with reeded edges, they resembled coin of the realm at the time.

MANUELA CASARES Q.
Hacienda Holactun

Rulau	Date	Metal	Size	VG	F	VF	Unc
Yuc 126	1889	Brass	26mm	—	—	25.00	—

Steer left at center. Around: HACIENDA HOLAC-TUN. / * 1889 *. Rv: Beehive at center. Around: MAN-UELA CASARES Q. / + 1889 +. Plain edge. (L&)P H-5)

Seye is in Acanceh County, Yucatan.

MARCOS DUARTE T.
Hacienda San Antonio Xuku

Rulau	Date	Metal	Size	VG	F	VF	Unc
Yuc 128	1888	CN	23mm	—	—	—	—

HACIENDA SAN ANTONIO XUKU / -.- / MARCOS / DUARTE T. / -.- / +. Rv: FICHA CONVENCIONAL 1888 / (ornament) . UN REAL / (ornament) / +. Plain edge. (L&P S-16)

| Yuc 129 | 1888 | CN | 19mm | — | — | — | — |

As last, but MEDIO / REAL. (L&P S-15; Gary Beals report)

Suma
OT Monogram (Molina)
Saniahtah

Rulau	Date	Metal	Size	VG	F	VF	Unc
Yuc 131	ND	CN	25mm	—	15.00	25.00	—

SANLAHTAH / OT monogram. Rv: Four floral orna-ments and four rosettes around central floreate device. (L&P S-38)

| Yuc 132 | ND | CN | 21mm | — | — | 35.00 | — |

OT = Olegario and Trinidad Molina of the infamous Molina family of landowners of Yucatan.

Teabo
MEZQUITA GAMBOA HNOS.
Hacienda Kandtirix

Rulau	Date	Metal	Size	VG	F	VF	Unc
Yuc 134	ND	Aluminum	26mm	—	—	—	—

HACIENDA KANDTRIX (sic) / DE / MEZQUITA / GAMBOA / HNOS. Rv: 500 / PENCAS. (L&P K-8)

Teabo is in Tekax County, Yucatan. The blood of the Mezquita and Gamboa families was united in these brother-owners.

Tecoh County
JUAN BERZUNZA G.
Hacienda Oxtapacab y Anexas

Rulau	Date	Metal	Size	VG	F	VF	Unc
Yuc 136	ND	Aluminum	31mm	5.00	7.00	15.00	25.00

HACIENDA OXTAPACAB Y ANEXAS / * / TECOH / * / . JUAN BERTUNZA G. . Rv: * / 1000 / PENCAS / *. Plain edge. (L&P O-3)

| Yuc 137 | ND | Aluminum | 25mm | — | — | — | — |

As last, but 500. (L&P O-2)

| Yuc 137A | ND | Aluminum | 35mm | — | — | 25.00 | — |

As last, but 3000 / PENCAS. (Hubbard coll.)

| Yuc 138 | ND | Aluminm | Rect 30 x 21 mm | 5.00 | 7.00 | 12.00 | 20.00 |

Obverse similar to last. Rv: * 1 * / MECATE / CHAPEO. (L&P O-5)

Pencas = Henequen leaves. Mecate Chapeo = 400 square meters cleared of weeds and cleaned. The drawing for the first token is in error; the T in the surname should be Z.

| Yuc 139 | ND | Aluminum | Oval 39 x 29 mm | — | — | 15.00 | 25.00 |

Obverse similar to last. Rv: * 5 * / MECATES /CHAPEO. Plain edge. (L&P N/L; Henkle N/L; Rulau coll.)

| Yuc 141 | ND | Aluminum | Oct 25mm | — | — | — | 20.00 |

HACIENDA OXTAPACAB Y ANEXAS / * / TECOH / * / * JUAN BERZUNZA G. *. Rv: * / ACARREO / 1000 / *. (L&P N/L; Henkle N/L; Rulau coll.)

Acarreo = Cartage. Probably for a load of 1000 pencas. This design, unknown to all previous catalogers, may be a pattern piece and thus rare.

XCANCHAKAN

Rulau	Date	Metal	Size	F	VF	EF	Unc
Yuc 142	1889	CN	23mm	—	25.00	35.00	

XCANCHAKAN / (compass rose) / 1889. Rv: CONVENCIONAL / C / (laural sprays). Plain edge. (Eklund 1401; L&P X-3; ANS coll.)

This series also exists with 1/2 or 1/4 replacing the C on the cupronickel tokens. All scarce.

C. CAMARA
Ydzincab Hacienda

Rulau	Date	Metal	Size	VG	F	VF	Unc
Yuc 144	1888	CN	21mm	—	8.00	18.00	27.50

Within laurel wreath: YCINCAB (first C is retrograde) / 1/2 / 1888. Rv: FICHA CONVENCIONAL / PARA LAS / FINCAS / DE / C. CAMARA / (rosette). Plain edge. (L&P Y-15)

| Yuc 145 | 1888 | CN | 18mm | — | 8.00 | 18.00 | 27.50 |

As last, but 1/4. (L&P Y-14)

The backward C in the die appears on both denominations. It is the Mayan letter DZ, used frequently on Yucatan tokens.

Camilo Camara also owned Texas Hacienda, which see.

Tekax
DUARTE Y HERMANO

Rulau	Date	Metal	Size	VG	F	VF	Unc
Yuc 147	(1889)		23mm	—	—	—	—

Eagle displayed. DUARTE Y HERMANO / TEKAX around. Rv: No descr. available. (L&P AD-3)

DUARTE HERMANOS
Kakalna Hacienda

Rulau	Date	Metal	Size	VG	F	VF	Unc
Yuc 149	1889	CN	24mm	—	—	—	—

Within laurel wreath: KAKALNA / 1 / 1889. Rv: FICHA CONVENCIONAL / PARA LA / FINCA / DE / DUARTE / HERMANOS / (rosette). Plain edge. (U. 3388; L&P K-3)

This plantation was primarily devoted to sugar cane. 1/2 real tokens, 21mm, and 1/4 real tokens, 17mm, were also issued.

Ulex mistakenly attributed this token to Peru.

MIGUEL PEON
Hacienda San Bernardo

Rulau	Date	Metal	Size	VG	F	VF	Unc
Yuc 151	ND	Aluminum	19mm	—	—	—	—

Circular legend around empty beaded circle: HACIENDA SAN BERNARDO MIGUEL PEON / *. Rv: 1/2 / MECATE. (L&P S-17)

RITTER Y BOCK SUCS.
Hacienda Santa Maria

Rulau	Date	Metal	Size	VG	F	VF	Unc
Yuc 153	ND	Aluminum	25mm	—	—	—	—

HACIENDA STA. MARIA / * / TEKAX / * / RITTER Y BOCK SUCS. S. EN C. Rv: 500 / PENCAS. (L&P S-51)

S. en C. = Sociedad en comandita (silent partnership).

Temax
VILLE DE TEMAX

Municipios

Rulau	Date	Metal	Size	VG	F	VF	Unc
Yuc 155	1872	Copper	—mm	—	—	—	—

VILLA / DE / TEMAX. Rv: 1/8 / 1872 flanked by clusters of dots. (Eklund 631; Ulex 1921)

| Yuc 157 | 1878 | Lead | 23mm | — | — | — | — |

Similar, but 1878. (Eklund 630; L&P AD-15)

In the Julius Guttag collection, a copper piece dated 1848 was reported as number 3898. It is believed the crossbar-type 7 was misread as a 4, but this would indicate the 1878 token may also have been made in copper. The 1878 specimen in lead in the Smithsonian collection has the digits 78 of the date very unclear; they could read 1848.

E. N. P.
(E.N. Perez)

Rulau	Date	Metal	Size	VG	F	VF	Unc
Yuc 159	1881	Lead	30mm	—	—	—	—

E N P / 1/4 / 1881 between branches. Rv: Blank. Very crude. (Eklund 213 and 632; Ulex 1921)

Tepakan
RAMON MEZQUITA
Hacienda Poccheyna

Rulau	Date	Metal	Size	VG	F	VF	Unc
Yuc 161	ND	Aluminum	26mm	—	—	—	—

Empty beaded circle at center. Around: HACIENDA POCCHEYNA RAMON MEZQUITA / *. Rv: 50 / TERCIOS LEÑA. Plain edge. (L&P P-3)

Tercios Leña = Donkey packs of firewood. for a train's "wood up" station?

Ticul
FLORENCIO TAMAYO
Hacienda Yaxkopil

Rulau	Date	Metal	Size	F	VF	EF	Unc
Yuc 163	ND	Aluminum	25mm	—	—	—	—

HACIENDA YAXKOPIL / * / (incused) M C / FLORENCIO / TAMAYO. Rv: 1500 / PENCAS . (L&P Y-6)

PENCAS = Leaves. This token represented a full day's labor in cutting and scraping henequen leaves, as a lard worker could process 1500 to 2500 in a day. These tokens seem always to ben encountered with the M C counterstamp.

Tixkokob
AKE
(Ruinas de Ake)

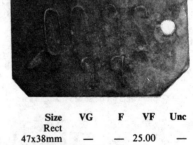

Rulau	Date	Metal	Size	VG	F	VF	Unc
Yuc 164	(1910?)	xx	Rect				
			47x38mm	—	—	25.00	—

xx Galvanized iron; clipped corners.
(All incused): AKE / 2000 / P P. Rv: Intaglio of obverse. Issued holed. (Grove 'Tokens' 1124; Rulau coll.)

| Yuc 164A | ND | xx | Rect | | | | |
| | | | 47x38mm | — | 15.00 | 25.00 | — |

Similar to last, but AKE / 3000 / P P P. (Grove 1126)

There are also shipping tags for sisal of 1000 and 500 pencas. The Ake ruins near Tixkokob are Mayan artifacts.

Tixkokob
A. M. BURGOS
Hacienda Jesus

Rulau	Date	Metal	Size	VG	F	VF	Unc
Yuc 165	1915	Copper	**	—	—	—	**

** Bell-shaped flan, 38x65mm.
(All incuse): HACIENDA / JESUS / PROPIEDAD / DEL SR. / A. M. BURGOS. Rv: VALE / POR UN PASE / A KANCABCHEN / AGOSTO 1o. de 1915 / No. 5. Plain edge. Issued holed. Stamped letter-by-letter. Numeral at end varies. (L&P J-1)

Rulau	Date	Metal	Size	VG	F	VF	Unc
Yuc 166	1915	Copper	**	—	—	—	—

As last, but error PORPIEDAD. Not scarce. (L&P J-1)

Un Pase a Kancabchen = One pass to Kancabchen. These tags were issued at about the end of the era of dominance of the landholding families in Yucatan. The owner was Amador M. Burgos.

AMADOR M. BURGOS
Hacienda San Juan

Rulau	Date	Metal	Size	VG	F	VF	Unc
Yuc 168	ND	Brass	**	—	—	—	—

** Bell-shaped planchet, 67x73mm. (All incused) HACIENDA / SAN JUAN / PROPIE-DAD . DEL . SR. / AMADOR . M. BURGOS / VALE / POR UN PASE A / KANCABCHEN . Rv: Blank. Plain edge. (L&P S-34)

Un pase a Kancabchen = A pass to Kancabchen.

MANUEL MEDINA
Hacienda Oncaan

Rulau	Date	Metal	Size	VG	F	VF	Unc
Yuc 170	ND	WM	19mm	—	—	—	—

Ornate 6-pointed rosette at center. Around: MANUEL MEDINA / * ONCAAN *. Rv: Fraction 1/8. Plain edge. (L&P O-1)

1/8 = 1/8 real, or octavo.

SAN JUAN HAU

Rulau	Date	Metal	Size	VG	F	VF	Unc
Yuc 172	ND	Iron	Rect 55x32mm	—	—	—	—

Crude star (incused). Rv: Blank. (L&P S-35)

Good for 500 pencas.

Rulau	Date	Metal	Size	VG	F	VF	Unc
Yuc 173	ND	Iron	Rect 55x32mm	—	—	—	—

As last, but ctsp 200. (Good for 1500 pencas). (L&P S-36)

The planchets on these are made of thin iron sheets.

Tixpehual
JOSE MA. GUERRA C.
Hacienda Cuca

Rulau	Date	Metal	Size	VG	F	VF	Unc
Yuc 175	ND	WM	29mm	—	—	—	—

Radiant star within beaded central circle. Around: HACIENDA CUCA / . JOSE Ma GUERRA, C. . Rv: Large shaded numeral 1. (L&P C-12)

Rulau	Date	Metal	Size	VG	F	VF	Unc
Yuc 176	ND	WM	25mm	—	—	—	—

As last, but 1/2. (L&P C-11)

Tizimin
CUYO DE ANCONA

Rulau	Date	Metal	Size	VG	F	VF	Unc
Yuc 178	1895	CN	38mm	—	—	—	—

(All incused): ESPECIAL / 500 / . CUYO DE ANCONA 1895 . Rv: Same as obverse. Plain edge. (L&P C-18)

Rulau	Date	Metal	Size	VG	F	VF	Unc
Yuc 179	1895	CN	33mm	—	—	—	—

As last, but 100 (centavos). (L&P C-17)

Rulau	Date	Metal	Size	VG	F	VF	Unc
Yuc 180	1895	CN	27mm	—	—	—	—

As last, but 50 (centavos). (L&P C-16)

Rulau	Date	Metal	Size	VG	F	VF	Unc
Yuc 181	1895	CN	24mm	—	—	—	—

As last, but 25. (L&P C-15)

Rulau	Date	Metal	Size	VG	F	VF	Unc
Yuc 182	1895	CN	20mm	—	—	—	—

As last, but 10. (L&P C-14)

Rulau	Date	Metal	Size	VG	F	VF	Unc
Yuc 183	1895	CN	19mm	—	—	—	—

As last, but 5 (centavos). (L&P C-13)

Hacienda El Cuyo was located in the extreme east of Tizimin County near the border with Quintana Roo. Its products were largely agricultural.

It is reported these tokens were also used in the Ancona interests in chicle (gum) and palo de tinte (dye wood) in Quintana Roo Territory.

F. G. MARQUEZ
Misnebalam

Rulau	Date	Metal	Size	VG	F	VF	Unc
Yuc 185	ND	Aluminum	26mm	—	—	—	—

F. G. MARQUEZ / (fleur) / . MISNEBALAM . Rv: Large ornate numeral 10. Plain edge. (L&P M-5)

Fidencio Gertrudis Marquez also issued an aluminum 20-centavo token, 32mm, of the same design.

Ucu
AUGUSTO L. PEON
Yaxche Hacienda

Rulau	Date	Metal	Size	VG	F	VF	Unc
Yuc 187	1888	CN	23mm	—	12.50	15.00	20.00

Within laruel wreath: YAXCHE / 1 / 1888. Rv: FICHA CONVENCIONAL / PARA LAS / FINCAS / DE / A. L. PEON. Plain edge. (L&P Y-3)

This plantation also issued cupronickel 1/2 real, 21mm, and 1/4 real tokens, 18mm.

Peon soon became one of the largest landowners in Yucatan State, and later he issued two series of tokens for use in all of his henequen plantations.

Yaxche was a "model farm" employing about 1,500 men in henequen cultivation, in Hunucma County about 15 miles from Merida. To hide atrocities toward workers on other henequen plantations from investigators or reporters, Merida officials often took them on a tour of Yaxche where workers were well fed and reasonably content. Documents show that Yaxche was a very non-typical hacienda in that day.

Yaxche was a sort of "Theresienstadt."

AUGUSTO L. PEON

(For use in all Peon plantations)

Rulau	Date	Metal	Size	VG	F	VF	Unc
Yuc 189	1914	CN	32mm	5.00	8.00	15.00	25.00

Within laruel wreath: 50 / 1914 / (tiny mintmark). Rv: FICHA CONVENCIONAL / PARA LAS / FINCAS / DE / A. L. PEON. Plain edge. (L&P A-4)

Rulau	Date	Metal	Size	VG	F	VF	Unc
Yuc 190	1914	CN	26mm	5.00	8.00	15.00	20.00

As last, but 20.

Rulau	Date	Metal	Size	VG	F	VF	Unc
Yuc 191	1914	CN	22mm	7.50	10.00	20.00	30.00

As last, but 10.

Rulau	Date	Metal	Size	VG	F	VF	Unc
Yuc 192	1914	CN	18mm	—	15.00	22.50	—

As last, but 5. (L&P A-1)

On the four tokens above, there is a tiny triangular mintmark which reads: A. D. / & CIE. for the Paris, France maker of the pieces.

This 1914-dated issue was nearly the last token issue in Yucatan. The revolutionary military governor of the province, Gen. Toribio V. de los Santos, issued a decree on Feb. 9, 1915, which freed all peons from bonded servitude, prohibited "tiendas de raya" (company stores) and forbade payment in tokens — national currency had to be paid for wages.

Previous federal government edicts (Nov. 30, 1889; March 25, 1905; Dec. 28, 1913) had prohibited the use of tokens, but these edicts were ignored or evaded by the landowners and corrupt officials of Yucatan. The decree of 1915, however, was backed by bayonets.

Rulau	Date	Metal	Size	VG	F	VF	Unc
Yuc 194	ND	Aluminum	26mm	—	10.00	20.00	—

AUGUSTO L. PEON / (fleur-de-lis) / (star). Rv: Large ornate 10. (L&P A-8)

| Yuc 195 | ND | Aluminum | 29mm | — | 10.00 | 20.00 | — |

As last, but 20. (L&P A-9)

| Yuc 196 | ND | Aluminum | 21mm | — | — | — | — |

Small fleur-de-lis. Rv: 1oo. (L&P A-10)

The 1oo = 1 Peso. The three aluminum tokens may have been replaced by the attractive French-struck 1914 tokens.

All the tokens above, dated 1914 or undated, were for use in Augusto L. Peon's haciendas in Yucatan, which were devoted primarily to henequen (hemp or sisal), such as Yaxche in Ucu and Tedzidz in Samahil. See separate listings for Samahil and Ucu.

Uman
C. CAMARA
Texan Hacienda

Rulau	Date	Metal	Size	VG	F	VF	Unc
Yuc 198	1888	CN	18mm	—	12.50	15.00	20.00

Within laurel wreath: TEXAN / 1/4 / 1888. Rv: FICHA CONVENCIONAL / PARA LAS / FINCAS / DE / C. CAMARA / (rosette). Plain edge. (L&P T-8; Rulau coll.)

| Yuc 199 | 1888 | CN | 21mm | — | 12.50 | 15.00 | 20.00 |

As last, but 1/2. (L&P T-9)

Camilo Camara's henequen plantation was in Humucma County, Yucatan. For similar pieces, see those of Peon at Tankuche Hacienda.

IGNACIO GOMEZ
San Isidro Ochil Hacienda

Rulau	Date	Metal	Size	VG	F	VF	Unc
Yuc 201	1889	Nic/Br	26mm	—	15.00	25.00	50.00

Horse courant. Around: SAN ISIDRO OCHIL / + YUCATAN +. Rv: Eagle displayed. Around: IGNACIO GOMEZ / * 1889. *. (L&P S-24)

Gomez also owned Tixcacal Hacienda in Uman, which see.

IGNACIO GOMEZ
Tixcacal Hacienda

Rulau	Date	Metal	Size	VG	F	VF	Unc
Yuc 203	1889	Nic/Br	25mm	—	—	—	—

Eagle displayed. Around: + TIXCACAL + / YUCATAN. Rv: Horse courant. Around: IGNACIO GOMEZ / * 1889. *. Plain edge. (L&P T-14)

| Yuc 204 | 1889 | Nic/Br | 25mm | — | — | — | — |

As last, but ctsp A on obverse and A A on reverse. (L&P T-15)

The A counterstamp may have indicated a change in ownership or family succession, or it may have indicated some special use of the token.

J. M. P.
(Jose Maria Ponce)
Hacienda Cacau

Rulau	Date	Metal	Size	VG	F	VF	Unc
Yuc 206	ND	CN	20mm	—	—	—	—

(All incused) HACIENDA CACAU / 6 / 1889. Rv: JMP monogram. Plain edge. (L&P C-2)

| Yuc 207 | ND | CN | 16mm | — | — | — | — |

As last, but 3 (centavos). (L&P C-1)

Uncertain
R. ANCONA B.

Rulau	Date	Metal	Size	VG	F	VF	Unc
Yuc 209	ND	Brass	Oval 20x34mm	—	—	—	—

(All incused): 108 (or another number) / R. ANCONA B. Rv: Blank. Issued holed. (L&P R-1)

Identification or shipping tags for agricultural products.

J. J. C.

Rulau	Date	Metal	Size	VG	F	VF	Unc
Yuc 215	ND	Lead	Irreg 21mm	—	—	—	—

.*. / J. J. C. Rv: 1/8 amid 12 dots, three in each of the four angles of the fraction. Beaded border on each side. (L&P AD-8)

JOSE CAMARA VALES
Hacienda San Jose

Rulau	Date	Metal	Size	VG	F	VF	Unc
Yuc 217	ND	WM	28mm	—	—	—	—

Radiant star within beaded circle. Around: HACIENDA SAN JOSE / . JOSE CAMARA VALES. Rv: Large 1 (shaded). Plain edge. (L&P S-27)

Rulau	Date	Metal	Size	VG	F	VF	Unc
Yuc 218	ND	WM	25mm	—	—	—	—
		As last, but 1/2 (real). (L&P S-26)					
Yuc 219	ND	WM	23mm	—	—	—	—
		As last, but 1/4 (real). (L&P S-25)					

JOSE MA. CARPIZO SUCS.

Rulau	Date	Metal	Size	VG	F	VF	Unc
Yuc 221	ND	Brass	Rect 83x38.5mm	—	—	—	—
		(All incused): PENCAS HENEQUEN AL TREN DE RASPA / 2000 DOS MIL / JOSE MA. CARPIZO SUCS. / 191 (vertical). Rv: Blank. Plain edge. (L&P J-2)					

Bundle tag for 2,000 henequen leaves delivered to the train going to a mill for processing. Some plantations did not have their own processing plants.

Sucs. (Sucursales) = Branches. Tren de Raspa = (literally) Train of the Rasp. In this case it means something like Train for Processing.

MONICA CONTRERAS DE CAMPOS
Hacienda Santa Cruz

Rulau	Date	Metal	Size	VG	F	VF	Unc
Yuc 223	ND	Aluminum	3mm	—	—	—	—
		MONICA CONTRERAS DE CAMPOS / (large star) / . HACIENDA STA. CRUZ . Rv: ENTREG'O / 500 / PENCAS. (L&P S-47)					

Monica Contreras also owned Mukuiche hacienda in Acanceh County, Yucatan.

FELIX CRUZ
Hacienda San Francisco Dzi

Rulau	Date	Metal	Size	VG	F	VF	Unc
Yuc 225	ND	WM	25mm	—	—	—	—
		HACIENDA SAN FRANCISCO CI (C of CI retrograde) / (sunburst) / FELIX CRUZ / (sunburst) / .*. Rv: 1/2. (L&P S-20)					
Yuc 226	ND	WM	23mm	—	—	—	—
		As last, but 1/4. (L&P S-19)					
Yuc 227	ND	WM	20mm	—	—	—	—
		As last, but 1/8. (L&P S-18)					

The retrograde C in the hacienda's name is the Mayan letter DZ.

A. B. F.

Rulau	Date	Metal	Size	VG	F	VF	EF
Yuc 229	ND	Lead	Irreg 27mm	—	—	—	—
		A. B. F. / 1/8 (crude). Rv: Blank. (L&P AD-1)					

A. M.
(Audomaro Molina)

Rulau	Date	Metal	Size	VG	F	VF	EF
Yuc 231	ND	Copper	30mm				
		A. M. Rv: 4 B. (L&P A-13)					

Audomaro Molina was the brother of Yucatan governor Olegario Molina, who in 1909 owned enormous landholdings of 15,000,000 acres! Much of this was acquired from Indians and peasants by means of forced sales called "terrenos baldios." Don Olegario actually acquired entire pueblos (villages) such as Kankabachen, Sosichen, Tixcanal, Xbohom, Xpambiha and Xpopepe, displacing their Indian populace, and the entire haciendas (plantations) of San Felipe, Xhahabat, Xpakan and Xtu Ozonot in this manner.

Among the viciously greedy landowning aristocracy of semi-feudal Yucatan, the Molinas stood out as rapacious.

S. PADRON
Hacienda Chuntulak

Rulau	Date	Metal	Size	VG	F	VF	Unc
Yuc 233	ND	Aluminum	Wavy 32mm	—	—	—	—
		HDA. CHUNTULAK / 50 (centavos) / S. PADRON (Sergio Padron). Rv: Blank. (L&P C-10)					

"LA POLAR" SOCIEDAD RECREATIVA

Rulau	Date	Metal	Size	VG	F	VF	Unc
Yuc 235	1912	Aluminum	21mm	—	—	—	—
		SOCIEDAD RECREATIVA / -.- / 10 / -.- / "LA POLAR". Rv: * / 10 / 1912. Plain edge. (L&P) AD-9)					

SOCIEDAD EXPLOTADORA DE PALO DE TINTE

Rulau	Date	Metal	Size	F	VF	EF	Unc
Yuc 237	ND	CN	35mm	—	—	22.50	—
		SOCIEDAD / -.- / EXPLOTADORA / -.- / DE PALO DE TINTE. Rv: 50 (large, shaded). Plain edge. (L&P S-61; Rulau coll.)					
Yuc 238	ND	CN	28mm	7.50	11.00	16.00	—
		As last, but 25. (L&P S-60)					
Yuc 239	ND	CN	25mm	—	9.00	15.00	—
		As last, but 12 1/2. (L&P S-59)					
Yuc 240	ND	CN	20mm	9.00	14.00	25.00	—
		As last, but 6 1/4. (Eklund 2151; L&P S-58)					
Yuc 241	ND	CN	29mm	—	13.50	16.00	25.00
		Obverse as last. Rv: 25 (small, solid). (L&P N/L; Rulau coll.; Grove 'Tokens' 1918)					

This was a logging company for dye wood (palo de tinte). These tokens are probably more scarce than prices indicate; only about 25 specimens have been offered publicly in the past 12 years.

There are several major reverse die varieties, indicating that the original issue must have been quite large. There are at least 2 obverse die varieties.

1000

Rulau	Date	Metal	Size	VG	F	VF	EF
Yuc 260	ND	Brass	Rect	—	—	12.50	—
			37x26mm				

Numeral 1000 ctsp on brass flan with clipped corners. Rv: Intaglio of obverse. Issued holed. Found in Yucatan. (Rulau coll.)

ZACATECAS STATE

Ahualulco
FLORENTINO CUERVO
Hacienda del Carmen

Rulau	Date	Metal	Size	VG	F	VF	Unc
Zac 1	1877	Copper	26mm	—	7.00	11.00	—

FLORENTINO CUERVO / AM monogram / 1877 / (oak and laurel wreath). Rv: Ha DEL CARMEN / 1/4 / (laurel wreath). Plain edge. (Schrotter 74; Eklund 183; Ulex 1649)

| Zac 2 | 1877 | Copper | 21mm | — | 7.00 | 11.00 | — |

As last, but 1/8. (Schrotter 75; Eklund 182)

| Zac 3 | 1877 | Copper | —mm | — | 8.50 | 12.50 | — |

As last, but 1/2.

Fresnillo
25 / I C
(Hacienda La Salada)

Rulau	Date	Metal	Size	VG	F	VF	EF
Zac 8	ND	Brass	27.5mm			40.00	—

25 brand mark ctsp on Zacatecas State cuartilla of 1824-64 type, K-M 366.

| Zac 9 | ND | Wood | 29mm | — | — | 80.00 | 125. |

25 brand mark incused in wooden disc. Rv: I C incused into opposite side. (*Boletin de SNdeM* for July 1984, pg. 65)

Guadalupe
J. L. G.
(Jose Leon Garcia)

Rulau	Date	Metal	Size	VG	F	VF	Unc
Zac 11	1901	Wood	39mm	12.00	—	80.00	125.

(All incused): JLG monogram. Rv: (Ram's head facing / 1901. (*Monedas* for Oct. 1965, fig. 83/2)

TAR Monogram
(Trancoso Hacienda)

Rulau	Date	Metal	Size	VG	F	VF	EF
Zac 13	ND	Wood	24mm	—	—	20.00	30.00

TAR monogram branded incuse into thick mesquite wood planchet. Rv: Blank. (Brunk coll.; *Monedas* for Oct. 1965, pg. 82)

| Zac 14 | ND | Wood | 30mm | — | — | 20.00 | 30.00 |

As last, larger planchet of mesquite wood.

The 30mm piece is also known with numeral 3 branded on reverse, for three sheep shorn. Some authorities feel the TAR monogram is for Trasquila - (fleece sheared). There are also reports of a 28mm wood piece with numeral 2, 3, 4, 5, 6, 7 or 8 on reverse. Letters STA or TZ also appear on some reverses.

Jerez
FERNANDO CABRAL
Rancho de La Noria

Rulau	Date	Metal	Size	VG	F	VF	Unc
Zac 20	ND	CN	Oct 32mm	—	9.00	12.00	—

RANCHO DE LA NORIA / FERNANDO CABRAL / JEREZ, ZAC. Rv: No description available.

Sombrerete
LA VILLA DE SOMBRERETE

			Municipio				
Rulau	Date	Metal	Size	VG	F	VF	Unc
Zac 25	ND	Copper	22mm	20.00	30.00	—	—

DE LA / VILLA. Rv: DE / SOMBRE / RETE. (Ulex 1941 & 1942; Scott; Eklund 606; Schrotter 75; Fernandez 211)

Zacatecas
J. CURTI

Rulau	Date	Metal	Size	VG	F	VF	Unc
Zac 28	ND	CN	25mm	10.00	15.00	—	—

LA COSMOPOLITA / -.- / J. CURTI / * ZACATECAS *. Rv: VALE POR EL CONSUMO DE UN REAL EN LA. / COSMOPOLITA / *. Plain edge.

ZACATECAS is cut over ZACAETAS.

GUTS
(Gutierrez)

Illustration Reduced

Rulau	Date	Metal	Size	VG	F	VF	EF
Zac 40	ND	Copper	22mm	—	—	—	—

S (sideways above t) / Gut in circular frame counter-stamped on octavo of Zacatecas State of the 1825-63 type, KM 338. (Muñoz NOM 259)

Rulau	Date	Metal	Size	VG	F	VF	EF
Zac 41	ND	Copper	20mm	—	—	—	—

Same ctsp on octavo of Guanajuato State of the 1829-30 type, KM 326. (Muñoz NOM 259)

Ko.

Rulau	Date	Metal	Size	VG	F	VF	EF
Zac 44	ND	Brass	22mm	—	—	25.00	—

Ko monogram in relief within circular depression ctsp on worn Zacatecas State octavo of 1825-63 type, KM-338. (Smithsonian coll., ex-Bureau of Customs 1973)

SAUCES

Rulau	Date	Metal	Size	VG	F	VF	EF
Zac 50	(?)	Brass	28mm	—	40.00	—	65.00

SAUCES in relief within dentilated rect. depression ctsp twice, at right angles, on Mexico, Zacatecas State cuartilla in brass * (or copper), KM-366, of the 1824-64 type. (Rulau M20; Brunk 60830)

Rulau	Date	Metal	Size	VG	F	VF	EF
Zac 51	(?)	Brass	28mm	—	—	—	85.00

As 50, but only one punch stamped, on 1865 cuartilla.

Rulau	Date	Metal	Size	VG	F	VF	EF
Zac 52	(?)	Silver	39mm	—	—	—	600.

Ctsp as Zac 50 on Mexico Colonial 1812 8-reales coin, KM-191. (Unique! now in a Mexican collection, ex-William Judd)

This is most likely a hacienda counterstamp. Sauces = Willows. There does not seem to be a location by this name today.

The counterstamp, almost always twice at right angles, has not been encountered on any but Zacatecas coins. The Rulau collection contains two brass cuartillas, one dated 1852 and one with date worn off. The Brunk collection also has two similar pieces. There is one in the ANS collection, but none in the Smithsonian. The Hubbard collection has three pieces on 1859 (2) and 1863 cuartillas. One has a single stamp.

TULA

Rulau	Date	Metal	Size	VG	F	VF	EF
Zac 55	ND	Copper	27.5mm	—	15.00	—	25.00

TULA ctsp on Zacatecas State, Mexico cuartilla of the 1824-64 type, K-M 366. (Eklund 651; Brunk 60920)

Rulau	Date	Metal	Size	VG	F	VF	EF
Zac 56	ND	Copper	33mm	—	25.00	—	40.00

TVLA cstp on Mexico copper cuartilla of the large size, worn smooth. (Ulex 1867)

The TULA stamp is also known on a coin which also bears an A ctsp. A hacienda counterstamp.
Also see Tula in Tamaulipas State.

Uncertain
A. G. CUERVO

Rulau	Date	Metal	Size	G	VG	F	EF
Zac 60	ND	Brass	27.5mm	—	—	35.00	—

A. G. CUERVO ctsp on Zacatecas State cuartilla of 1824-64 type, K-M 366. (Ulex 1926; Alpert report)

L. L.

Rulau	Date	Metal	Size	VG	F	VF	Unc
Zac 65	ND	Brass	21mm	—	—	15.00	

L L ctsp on Zacatecas State octavo of 1846, K-M 339.

MORO

Rulau	Date	Metal	Size	VG	F	VF	EF
Zac 67	ND	Brass	22mm	—	—	75.00	—

MORO in relief ctsp on Zacatecas State 1859 octavo, KM-338. (ANS coll.; Grove 'Tokens' 603)

PROVICIONAL

Rulau	Date	Metal	Size	VG	F	VF	Unc
Zac 70	ND	Brass	26mm	—	60.00	—	100.

PROVICIONAL ctsp on worn Zacatecas State cuartilla of 1824-64 type, K-M 366, and on 1862 piece. (Eklund 489; ANS coll.)

HEo Monogram

Caution: Fantasy!

Rulau	Date	Metal	Size	VG	F	VF	EF
Zac 75F	1883	Copper	35mm	—	—	1.75	

.. ZACATECAS . / HEo monogram / (ornament). Rv: UNA / CARGA / DE LENA / . 1883 . / ...

Una carga de leña = One load of firewood. The crude colonial-style Mexican tokens gradually went out of use in the 1840's and 1850's, replaced by machine-made pieces. Such reality would not bother a forger in creating his concoctions, however.

84

TIENDA DE ENRIQUES

Caution: Fantasy!

Rulau	Date	Metal	Size	VG	F	VF	EF
Zac 77F	1844	Copper	Sq 33mm	—	—	1.75	—

ZACATECAS / TIENDA DE (DE in monogram) / ENRIQUES / : (brand mark) : Rv: VALE POR / UNA CARGA / DE MAIZ / : 1844 :

Una carga de maiz = One load of corn! The forger seems to have selected dates at random for his concoctions. The term "vale por una carga" is not known on genuine tokens of the period.

ZS Monogram
(Hacienda La Salada)

Rulau	Date	Metal	Size	VG	F	VF	EF
Zac 80	ND	Brass	29mm	—	—	15.00	—

Z-over-S ctsp on Zacatecas State 1/4-real. On reverse are ctsp Z-over-S and ampersand (&). (Grove 'Tokens' 2031)

30 / (Cup)

Rulau	Date	Metal	Size	G	VG	F	EF
Zac 82	ND	Brass	27.5mm	5.00	—	15.00	—

30 in rectangular frame / (Cup) / ctsp on Zacatecas State cuartilla of 1824-64 type, K-M 366.

(Trefoil)

Rulau	Date	Metal	Size	VG	F	VF	Unc
Zac 84	ND	Brass	27.5mm	5.00	—	15.00	—

Trefoil (or triquetra ?) brand mark ctsp on Zacatecas State cuartilla of 1824-64 type, K-M 366.

UNATTRIBUTED MEXICO

A

Rulau	Date	Metal	Size	VG	F	VF	Unc
Mxo 1	1802	Copper	27mm	—	—	45.00	—

Within double border or roundels: Orante A /1802 in rectangular frame. Rv: Blank. (Muñox Monograms 21)

A number of tlacos and pilones of the late 18th and early 19th century in Mexico are identified only by a single letter or a monogram. Except in a few instances, these have defied attribution.

It is the hope of the author and his contributors that publication in this new reference work may assist in identifying more of them. No doubt many of them are important to the numismatic history of Mexico.

E.T.C.A.(?)

Rulau	Date	Metal	Size	VG	F	VF	EF
Mxo 3	1799	Copper	26mm	—	—	60.00	—

Within laurel wreath border, star at top: Script monogram ETCA(?) / 1799. Rv: Blank. (ANSI,D)

ABARATEGVY
(Abarategui)

Rulau	Date	Metal	Size	VG	F	VF	EF
Mxo 7	ND	Copper	21mm	—	—	30.00	—

ABA / RATE / GVY within thick border. Rv: Blank. Cast. (Eklund 1; ANS 1; Munoz NOM 1; Hubbard coll.)

The ANS collection contains 3 specimens, measuring 20.4 to 21mm in diameter.

Caution: Concoction!

Rulau	Date	Metal	Size	VG	F	VF	EF
Mxo 8F	ND	Copper	32mm	—	—	1.50	—

ABA / RATE/ GVY within circle of thick slanted bars. Raised border. Rv: Blank. Counterfeit! A somewhat similar concoction measures 29mm.

F. M. A.

Rulau	Date	Metal	Size	VG	F	VF	Unc
Mxo 4	ND	Copper	23mm	12.00	25.00	37.50	—

FMA monogram at center of 3 concentric beaded circles. Rv: 1/4 R at center of 2 concentric beaded circles. Thick planchet. (Eklund 721; Pradeau/Tlaco pg. 112; ANS coll.)

Rulau	Date	Metal	Size	VG	F	VF	Unc
Mxo 5	ND	Brass	23mm	—	25.00	—	—

As last, but thin planchet. (Eklund 722)

Rulau	Date	Metal	Size	VG	F	VF	Unc
Mxo 6	ND	Copper	19mm	—	25.00	—	—

Similar to last, but 1/8 R. (Eklund 720)

These were used in Hacienda La Fama, says Arthur Garnett.

ADAME

Rulau	Date	Metal	Size	VG	F	VF	EF
Mxo 11	ND	Copper	23mm	—	—	—	—

ADAME in relief within pearl-lined rect. depression ctsp on blank flan. Monogram AP in relief in circular resello ctsp below ADAME. Rv: Blank. (Muñoz NOM 5; ANS 6)

ADAN

Rulau	Date	Metal	Size	VG	F	VF	EF
Mxo 13	ND	Copper	xx	—	—	—	—

xx Flan with 8 curved sides, 27mm.
. A / DAn . Rv: Blank. (Muñoz NOM 6; ANS 5; Eklund 4)

Sydney Noe read this name as Adad.

AFRICANO

Rulau	Date	Metal	Size	VG	F	VF	EF
Mxo 15	ND	Copper	28mm	—	—	—	—

AFRI / CANO within irregular circular depression. Rv:
Blank. (Muñoz NOM 8)

| Mxo 16 | ND | Copper | 28mm | — | — | — | — |

(Arrow right) / AFRI / (Sword horizontally) / CANO /
(Arrow left). Rv: Blank. (Eklund 5; ANS 7)

LORENZO AGVILArS
(Lorenzo Aguilar)

Rulau	Date	Metal	Size	VG	F	VF	EF
Mxo 20	ND	Copper	32mm	—	—	—	—

Lore / nzo within circle of wide dots. Rv: AGVI / LArS
within circle of wide dots. Dentilated rim on either
side. Cast copper. (Muñoz NOM 13; ANS 10)

ALCANTARILLA

Rulau	Date	Metal	Size	VG	F	VF	EF
Mxo 22	ND	Copper	+ +	—	—	—	—

+ + Flan shaped like a church with a cupola and a large
door, 27x13mm.
ALCANTA (TA monogram) / Arilla. Rv: Blank.
(Eklund 17; Schrotter 19; ANS 38; Muñoz COM 1)

   Muñoz deduced that the Alcantarilla tlaco is a comercio piece - a trade token -
not a hacienda token.

ALEGRE

Rulau	Date	Metal	Size	VG	F	VF	EF
Mxo 24	(17)72	Copper	25mm	—	—	—	—

ALE / GRE / 72. in crude letters. Rv: Blank. (Muñoz
NOM 28; Banco de Mexico collection)

Some Alegre pieces have an ATo counterstamp on reverse.

ALBAR.S
(Alvarez)

Enlarged	No resello

Rulau	Date	Metal	Size	VG	F	VF	EF
Mxo 26	(1)806	Copper	24mm	—	20.00	—	—

ALBA / R.S 806 / (star and coiled lariat) / within concentric circles of ornamental lines. Rv: Blank. The illustrated specimen from the ANS collection has the resel-
lado o-above-M in circular depression ctsp at left rim.
(Muñoz NOM 25; ANS 20)

| Mxo 27 | (1)806 | Copper | 29mm | — | 40.00 | — | — |

Similar to last, but larger. Resello resembles letter 'S'.
(Clyde Hubbard coll.)

ALBARES
(Alvarez)

Rulau	Date	Metal	Size	VG	F	VF	EF
Mxo 28	ND	Copper	23mm	—	—	—	—

ALBA / RES (S retrograde). Rv: Blank. Cast. (Muñoz
NOM 24; Eklund 15)

ALBAXES
(Alvarez)

Rulau	Date	Metal	Size	VG	F	VF	EF
Mxo 29	ND	Copper	22mm	—	—	—	—

Alba / xes within circle of large dots. Rv: Blank. Cast.
(Muñoz NOM 21; ANSW 17; Eklund 16)

| Mxo 30 | ND | Copper | 26mm | — | — | — | — |

Obverse as last. Rv: S. (Muñoz NOM 22.) Also occurs
with smaller flans, down to 21mm.

AMESCVA
(Amescua)

Rulau	Date	Metal	Size	VG	F	VF	EF
Mxo 35	ND	Iron	22mm	—	—	—	—

AMESCVA above a zigzag line, all within a 16x6mm rect. depression. Rv: Blank. (Muñoz NOM 34)

Rulau	Date	Metal	Size	VG	F	VF	EF
Mxo 37	1828	Copper	20mm	17.50	25.00	35.00	—

Eagle at center. Below: AMESQUA - 1828 .... Rv: Blank. (Muñoz NOM 35; ANS 32; KM L15)

Reading of the date 1828 is uncertain, but is probably correct.

We have been unable to locate a municipality named Amescua and conclude, as Muñoz did, that it is either a family or a hacienda name.

C. MIGUEL AMESCUA

Rulau	Date	Metal	Size	VG	F	VF	EF
Mxo 39	1838	Copper	22mm	20.00	—	40.00	—

Eagle on cactus. Around: C. MIGUEL AMESCUA / 1838. Rv: Blank. (Eklund 35; ANS 33; Muñoz NOM 36; KM L16)

Hubbard coll. contains specimens measuring 20 and 21mm.

ARAGON

Rulau	Date	Metal	Size	VG	F	VF	EF
Mxo 41	1812	Copper	22-24mm	—	15.00	—	—

(Ornament) / ARAGON / A. A. DE * / 1812. Ornamental border arond the rim. Rv: Blank. (Muñoz NOM 38; ANS 35)

Placing a retail value on maverick tlacos is erratic at best, but there is a wholsale pattern. Recently, at auction, small to large lots of such pieces sold at about $6 each when bought as lots in competitive bidding.

In a 1987 sale by Henry Christensen Inc. one lot of miscellaneous octavos of 17 pieces fetched $100, or $5.88 each. Another lot of 54 pieces including 1795 MONEDA copper ⅛-real, Ario, S. L. del Potrero, Cotiva etc. realized $330, or $6.11 each.

FRANSISC OArAVJO
(Francisco Araujo)

Rulau	Date	Metal	Size	VG	F	VF	EF
Mxo 43	1801	Copper	29mm	—	20.00	—	—

(Ornament) / FRANSISC (N retrograde) / OArAVJO / 1801 within beaded rim. Each line of text is separated by a horizontal line. Rv: Blank. (Muñoz NOM 40; Eklund 226; ANS 164)

Also in 25mm.

ARGOMANIS

Rulau	Date	Metal	Size	VG	F	VF	EF
Mxo 45	1801	Copper	31mm	—	—	—	—

Q / ARGOMANIS. / 1801, ornamental border around all. Rv: Blank. (Muñoz NOM 44)

E. ARREOLA Y C.

Rulau	Date	Metal	Size	VG	F	VF	EF
Mxo 47	ND	Copper	23mm	—	—	—	—

Circular legend: E. ARREOLA * Y * C *, between two concentric circles. At center: * (Anchor) *. Rv: ⅛ in circle of 6 stars. (Muñoz NOM 47; Eklund 779)

ARRIAGA

Rulau	Date	Metal	Size	VG	F	VF	EF
Mxo 49	(18)23	Copper	--mm	—	—	—	—

ARRI / AGA / 23 (incuse). Rv: Blank. (Muñoz NOM 48; ANS collection; Schrotter 38; Eklund 49)

Rulau	Date	Metal	Size	VG	F	VF	EF
Mxo 50	ND	Copper	**	—	—	—	—

** Pomegranate-shaped flan, 24x28mm. Half moon between rosettes. Below: ARIAG / + A+. Rv: Blank. (Muñoz NOM 49)

There is a city of Arriaga in San Luis Potosi State.

ASUNI

Rulau	Date	Metal	Size	VG	F	VF	EF
Mxo 52	(1)827	Copper	--mm	—	—	—	—

Q / A / SUNI / 827. Rv: Blank. (Muñoz NOM 53: Eklund 50; ANS coll.)

Rulau	Date	Metal	Size	VG	F	VF	EF
Mxo 53	(1)82(7)	Copper	23.4mm	—	—	—	—

a. / sunig / 82J. Rv: Blank. Plain edge. (Smithsonian coll.)

Q = Cuartilla (¼ real). Mexican tokenmakers of the late 18th and early 19th centuries often left off the first one or two digits in the date; e.g. 807 for 1807 or 23 for 1823. These tlacos, pilones and cuartillas used only the simplest shorthand in their legends; they were, after all, to be understood only by their users and issuers.

B.

Rulau	Date	Metal	Size	VG	F	VF	Unc
Mxo 54	ND	Silver	17.5mm	—	—	25.00	—

B ctsp on Mexico 1876-Ho-F 10-centavos. Reeded edge. (Smithsonian coll., ex-Mendel Peterson 1967)

The host coin (mintage only 3140) is quite rare. Possibly for Sonora State.

A. T. L. B. (?)

Rulau	Date	Metal	Size	VG	F	VF	EF
Mxo 55	ND	Copper	30mm	—	—	—	—

Within laureate border: (Circle) / 3. (dot above 3) / ATLB (?) monogram / (scrollwork). Retrograde S is incused within the small circle. Rv: Plain, but evidence of a design visible in one area. Incised line around rim. (Muñoz NOM 64; ANS XII, A)

Both the E. AoB. and A.T.L.B. monogram tokens are probably important colonial hacienda pieces, not yet identified.

B. X. B. (?)

Rulau	Date	Metal	Size	VG	F	VF	EF
Mxo 57	1770	Copper	**	—	—	150.	—

** 8-scalloped flan, 39mm. Within circular frame: III / BXB monogram / MDCCLXX. (ANS I, B)

Noe and Eklund read the Roman numeral date on this token as 1773, connecting the III above the monogram with the MDCCLXX around and below it. But the diecutter's work is neat and he left a good amount of space on each side of the III. Therefore we feel the reading should be 1770 and the III may indicate something else, possibly 3 reales.

The ANS study in 1949 may be correct in reading 1773, we admit.

D. B.

Rulau	Date	Metal	Size	VG	F	VF	EF
Mxo 59	ND	Copper	27mm	—	—	—	—

76 / DB ctsp on Jalisco State 1858 octavo, KM-330. (Smithsonian coll.)

E. AoB. (?)

Rulau	Date	Metal	Size	VG	F	VF	EF
Mxo 61	ND	Copper	34mm	—	—	—	—

Within ornate border of semicircles: O / E AoB monogram / . S / (squarish geometric pattern, possibly a stylized coiled lariat. Rv: Blank. (Muñoz Monogramas 67; ANS XII, B)

BAREDA

Rulau	Date	Metal	Size	VG	F	VF	EF
Mxo 63	1806	Copper	25mm	—	—	—	—

1806 / BARE / DA. Beaded border. Rv: Blank. (Muñoz NOM 67; ANS 51)

Similar pieces measuring 30mm are concoctions!

BARON

Rulau	Date	Metal	Size	VG	F	VF	EF
Mxo 70	ND	Copper	Oval 24x30mm	—	—	—	—

BA / RO / N in toothed irregular depression. Rv: Large incused letter T. (Muñoz NOM 66)

A Baron family in Mexico City has for the past 30 years operated casas de cambio (money exchange houses). There may be no connection.

| Mxo 72 | 1801 | Copper | 37mm | — | — | — | — |

(Ornaments) / BARON / 1801. Rv: BARON (N retrograde) in rectangular indent. (Grove 'Tokens' 122)

BARRERA

Rulau	Date	Metal	Size	VG	F	VF	EF
Mxo 74	1801	Copper	31mm	—	—	100.	—

Q / ////// / BARRERA / (scrollwork) / 1801. Laurel leaf border. Rv: Monogram RAE (?) in square resello stamped on reverse. Plain edge. (Muñoz NOM 71; Eklund 63; ANS 56)

Q = Quartilla (¼ Real). A resello is a small revalidation stamp applied to a coin or token.

BARRON

Rulau	Date	Metal	Size	VG	F	VF	EF
Mxo 76	1801	Copper	35mm	—	—	—	—

BARRON / 1801. Rv: Blank. (Muñoz NOM 73)

| Mxo 77 | ND | Copper | 35mm | — | — | — | — |

BARRON / (ornaments. Rv: Blank. (Muñoz NOM 72)

BELEN
Hacienda Belen

Rulau	Date	Metal	Size	F	VF	Unc	Proof
Mxo 80	ND	CN	22.7mm	—	—	40.00	

BELEN. Rv: UN REAL. Plain edge. (Eklund 68; Pesant 35)

| Mxo 81 | ND | Copper | 22.7mm | — | — | — | 40.00 |

As last. Thick flan (2.3mm). Rare. (Rulau coll.)

| Mxo 82 | ND | WM | 22.7mm | — | — | — | 50.00 |

As last. Thick planchet (2.3mm). Rare. (Rulau coll.)

| Mxo 83 | ND | CN | 19.5mm | — | — | 40.00 | |

BELEN. Rv: ¾ / DE REAL. Plain edge. (Eklund 67)

| Mxo 84 | ND | WM | 19.5mm | — | — | — | 50.00 |

As last. Thick flan (2.3mm) Rare. (Rulau coll.)

| Mxo 85 | ND | CN | 19.5mm | — | — | 25.00 | |

BELEN. Rv: MEDIO / REAL. Plain edge. (Eklund 66)

| Mxo 86 | ND | Copper | 19.5mm | — | — | — | 50.00 |

As last. Piefort flan (2.9mm thick). Rare. (Rulau coll.)

| Mxo 87 | ND | WM | 19.5mm | — | — | — | 40.00 |

As last. (Pesant 36)

BELIN
(Error for Belen)

Rulau	Date	Metal	Size	F	VF	Unc	Proof
Mxo 88	ND	WM	19.5mm	—	—	—	250.

BELIN. Rv: ¾ / DE REAL. Plain edge. Thick flan (2.3mm). Rejected pattern due to misspelling of name. Only 2 known. (Rulau coll.)

All the Belen tokens were struck by Scovill Mfg. Co., Waterbury, Conn. A Scovill employee's estate was found to contain proof specimens of all the copper and white metal pieces listed above; these were purchased from the estate by Ralph Behringer of Carmel, N.Y. in 1981 and by the author in 1989.

It is believed the cupronickel specimens were struck for circulation. The other pieces may have been patterns, trials or mint sports, except the BELIN errors which were rejected patterns.

Pesant claimed Belen for Havana Province, Cuba.

BETANZOZ
(Betanzos)

Rulau	Date	Metal	Size	VG	F	VF	EF
Mxo 90	ND	Copper	22mm	—	—	—	—

Within toothed rectangular depression: BETAN (N retrograde) / ZOZ. Rv: Blank. (Muñoz NOM 84, Eklund 2333)

Rulau	Date	Metal	Size	VG	F	VF	EF
Mxo 91	ND	Copper	21mm	—			

Similar to last, but BETAN / SOZ / (N. is normal). (Muñoz NOM 84)

BURICIAGO Y MELENDEZ
Minas Nuevas

Rulau	Date	Metal	Size	VG	F	VF	Unc
Mxo 92	ND	Brass	24mm	—	—	25.00	35.00

BURICIAGO Y MELENDEZ / COMERCIANTES / Y / COMISIONISTAS / * MINAS NUEVAS *. R. Large pebbled 12. Plain edge. (Zaffern coll.)

12 centavos.

BSTM ATE (Monograms)
(Bustamante)

Rulau	Date	Metal	Size	VG	F	VF	EF
Mxo 93	1797	Copper	25mm	—	—	—	—

BSTM (monogram) ATE (monogram) / 1797. Ornate border. Rv: Blank. (Muñoz NOM 95; Eklund 710)

Mxo 95	ND	Copper	27mm	—	—	—	—

Circular legend: BUSTAMANTE. At center a flower of eight petals. Rv: Blank. (Muñoz NOM 96)

Mxo 96	ND	Copper	**	—	—	—	—

** Flan with stem.
BVSTA / MANT / E. Rv: Blank. (Schrotter 13)

There may be no connection between these three tokens.

F. C.

Rulau	Date	Metal	Size	VG	F	VF	Unc
Mxo 100	ND	Copper	24mm	—	—	—	150.

F. C. Rv: 1. R. Planchet 2.3mm thick. Plain edge. (Rulau coll.)

Mxo 101	ND	WM	24mm	—	—	—	50.00

As last. Thick planchet (2.7mm). Rare. (Rulau coll.; Eklund 220)

Mxo 102	ND	Copper	19mm	—	—	—	50.00

F. C. Rv: ¾. R. (Rulau coll.; Eklund 218)

Mxo 103	ND	WM	19mm	—	—	—	50.00

As last. Thick flan (2.3mm). Rare. (Rulau coll.; Eklund 219)

Rulau	Date	Metal	Size	VG	F	VF	Unc
Mxo 104	ND	Copper	17mm	—	—	—	100.

F. C. Rv: ½. R. Thick flan. Rare. (Rulau coll.; Eklund 217)

Mxo 105	ND	WM	17mm	—	—	—	100.

As last.

All above struck at Scovill Mfg. Co., Waterbury, Conn., in the 1860-80 era. These are of the same type as Hacienda Belen in Mexico, which see.

J. C. C.

Rulau	Date	Metal	Size	VG	F	VF	EF
Mxo 110	ND	Copper	32mm	—	—	—	—

J C C ctsp on worn Jalisco State cuartilla of 1858-62 type, KM-355. Rv: 7 5 E ctsp on opposite side. (Smithsonian coll.)

R. C.

Rulau	Date	Metal	Size	VG	F	VF	EF
Mxo 112	ND	Copper	29mm	—	—	75.00	—

Brand mark in relief within square depression, flanked on either side by large incuse R -- C, ctsp on San Luis Potosi State 1862-LIBR cuartillo, KM 360. (Brunk coll.)

CAMAÑO COSIO

Rulau	Date	Metal	Size	VG	F	VF	EF
Mxo 114	(18)14	Copper	21mm	—	—	—	—

CAMAÑO / COSIO 24. Rv: Blank. (Muñoz NOM 145; ANS 118; Eklund 84)

CARA

Rulau	Date	Metal	Size	VG	F	VF	EF
Mxo 116	ND	Copper	20mm	—	—	—	—

CARA. Rv: Blank. (Muñoz NOM 105)

Mxo 117	1805	Copper	20mm	—	—	—	—

1805 / CARA. Rv: Blank. (ANS 76; Romero pg. 20)

CARRERA

Rulau	Date	Metal	Size	VG	F	VF	EF
Mxo 119	(1)800	Copper	25mm	—	—	100.	—

CA / RRERA / &oo (The latter probably representing 800). All in 17mm circular depression on plain flan. Rv: Blank. (Muñoz NOM 113; Eklund 2335; ANS coll.)

Rulau	Date	Metal	Size	VG	F	VF	EF
Mxo 120	1800	Copper	--mm	—	—	100.	—
		Similar to last. (ANS)					
Mxo 122	1830	Copper	--mm	—	—	40.00	—
		Similar to last. (ANS)					

CASTILLO Y LLATA

Rulau	Date	Metal	Size	VG	F	VF	Unc
Mxo 124	1806	Copper	32mm	—	—	—	—

CASTILL / O.   Y / LLATA. Rv: 1806 in radiant circle. Thick planchet. (Crozet pg. 225)

CATALANES

Rulau	Date	Metal	Size	VG	F	VF	EF
Mxo 126	1791	Copper	26mm	—	—	200.	—

Barrel within beaded circle. Around: CATALANES / (rosette) 1791 (rosette). Rv: Blank. (Muñoz NOM 124)

CATEL

Rulau	Date	Metal	Size	VG	F	VF	EF
Mxo 128	(1)802	Copper	24mm	—	—	—	—

CA / TEL - / 802 in relief within octagonal depression ctsp on blank flan. Rv: Indescribable monogram in relief in circular depression ctsp on opposite side of token. Plain edge. (Muñoz NOM 125)

CERVANTES
Paramo ?

Rulau	Date	Metal	Size	VG	F	VF	EF
Mxo 130	1806	Copper	32mm	20.00	—	—	—

CERVAN / TES / 1806. Rv: SP / PARAMO. (Muñoz NOM 130)

Mxo 131	ND	Copper	19mm	—	—	—	—

SER / VAN / TES within circle of rays. Rv: Blank. (Muñoz NOM 129; Eklund 555)

The two tokens may not be connected. Cervantes was a very common name. Paramo = Barren land.

CITAC

Municipio?

Rulau	Date	Metal	Size	VG	F	VF	Unc
Mxo 135	1841	Copper	26mm	—	—	—	—

⅛ / CITAC. / 1841 within floral wreath, ctsp on Mexico 1834 ¼-real coin (type not known, possibly KM-358). (Eklund 142; Brunk 50940)

COBO
(Covo)

Rulau	Date	Metal	Size	VG	F	VF	Unc
Mxo 137	1776	Copper	23mm	—	—	—	—

COBO / 1776 with dentilated rectangle. Rv: Blank. (Muñoz NOM 131)

Mxo 139	ND	Copper	23mm	—	—	—	—

As last, but spelled COVO. (Muñoz NOM 132)

COBO CONCHA

Rulau	Date	Metal	Size	VG	F	VF	Unc
Mxo 141	ND	Copper	26mm	—	—	—	—

COBO / CONCHA / (ornamentation) within a rect. frame. Rv: Blank, but chain border. (Muñoz NOM 133; Duffield 1685; Eklund 144; Brunk 50995)

Concha = Seashell.

CONCHOSO Y VCIONDO
(Conchoso and Uciondo)

Rulau	Date	Metal	Size	VG	F	VF	EF
Mxo 143	1801	Copper	30mm	10.00	—	—	—

1801 below globe, CONCHOSO Y VCIONDO around. Border of rays. Rv: Blank. (Muñoz NOM 134)

COUTINO

Rulau	Date	Metal	Size	VG	F	VF	EF
Mxo 144	ND	Copper	30mm	—	—	—	—

Full moonface in beaded circle at center, COUTINO above, three rosettes below — all in a circular depression ctsp on ornamented flan. Rv: Blank. (Muñoz NOM 146)

COXED

Rulau	Date	Metal	Size	VG	F	VF	EF
Mxo 145	1814	Copper	23mm	—	—	—	—

ANO / COXED 1814. Rv: Blank. (Muñoz NOM 147; ANS coll.; Eklund 178)

Frequently the letter X was used to represent R, RR or rr on tlacos of the early 19th century. This is, possibly, the case here.

CUEVAS

Rulau	Date	Metal	Size	VG	F	VF	EF
Mxo 147	ND	Copper	++	—	—	—	—

++ Heart-shaped flan, 23x30mm.
CUE / VAS / -- within squarish indent. Rv: Blank. (Muñoz NOM 149; ANS 127)

Caution: Forgery!

Rulau	Date	Metal	Size	VG	F	VF	EF
Mxo 148F	ND	Silver	xx	—	—	2.00	—

xx Heart-shaped flan, 23.6 by 22.8mm. Base silver. Within square depression: CUE / VAS. Rv: Blank. (Art Garnett coll.)

A similar forgery struck in red copper (not artificially aged) has also been examined. The forger's technique in these pieces is better than in most of his concoctions, and the Cuevas fakes could well cause problems to the hobby.

Crowned M D

ANS specimen
Illustration reduced

Rulau	Date	Metal	Size	VG	F	VF	EF
Mxo 150	ND	Copper	30.5mm	—	—	40.00	—

Wide crown above large M D on plain field. Rv: 4 / RS monogram. Plain edge. (ANS IV, K)

Caution: Fantasy!

Rulau	Date	Metal	Size	VG	F	VF	EF
Mxo 151F	ND	Copper	26mm	—	—	1.50	—

Obverse similar to last, but "crown" is just a series of upright triangles on a band. Rv: Seated monkey left holding ball (very similar to Muñoz Anepigrafas 15). Plain edge. Counterfeit!

Caution: Counterfeit!

Rulau	Date	Metal	Size	VG	F	VF	EF
Mxo 152F	ND	Copper	28mm	—	—	1.50	—

Obverse as last. Rv: Imitation of the first token (4 / RS monogram) in reduced size. Counterfeit! (Brunk coll.)

Caution: Counterfeit!

Rulau	Date	Metal	Size	VG	F	VF	EF
Mxo 153F	ND	Copper	32mm	—	—	1.50	—

Similar to last in larger size, smooth raised border on each side. Counterfeit! (Brunk coll.)

Only the first token above is genuine; the ANS photgraph was prepared in 1949. The clumsy concoctions were made In Guadalajara, Mexico in the 1970's. The concoctions are made of red copper, 'aged' in heat; sometimes they are found dark-toned with chemicals.

Genuine pieces represented 4 reales of value about 1800.

F. Da

Rulau	Date	Metal	Size	VG	F	VF	Unc
Mxo 154	ND	Copper	34mm				

FDa monogram within rope circle. Rv: Blank. (Munoz Monograms 3)

This must have been an important tlaco. At 34mm, it is larger than most such pieces, and seems well made.

JOSE ANTONIO DE LA VEGA

Rulau	Date	Metal	Size	VG	F	VF	EF
Mxo 156	1803	Copper	34mm	—	90.00	—	—

JOSE / ANTONI / O within palm leaf circle. Rv: DE LA / VEGA / DE / 1803. Cast copper. (Muñoz NOM 600)

It was not often that an issuer's full name was spelled out on a tlaco.

DOZAL

Rulau	Date	Metal	Size	VG	F	VF	EF
Mxo 160	ND	Copper	38mm	—	45.00	70.00	—

8-pointed star at center, DOZAL: around. Rectangular 11x2mm resello stamped near edge: DOZAL. All within laurel wreath. Rv: Blank. (Fonrobert 7169; Muñoz NOM 170)

Fonrobert's catalogers guessed that this piece might be connected with the revolutionary movements of 1811-15. One variety of this piece has two additional resellos, both round: Each bearing the capital letter D, one normal and one with a diagonal slash through the D.

D. X. N. E. (?)

Rulau	Date	Metal	Size	VG	F	VF	EF
Mxo 170	1767	Copper	24mm	—	40.00	—	—

. D X (D retrograde) / N . / . E . Rv: (Engraved) Sol / N 1767. Cast. (ANS I, A)

Sydney P. Noe of the ANS staff surmised in 1949 that the 'Sol' might stand for a surname such as Solis. He also thought the four pellets on obverse might indicate 4 reales.

Caution: Counterfeit!

| Mxo 171F | ND | Copper | 28mm | — | — | 1.50 | — |

D / N . X / . E . within border of pellets. Rv: Blank. Plain edge. Counterfeit! (Brunk coll.)

Caution: Fantasy!

Rulau	Date	Metal	Size	VG	F	VF	EF
Mxo 172F	1860	Copper	26mm	—	—	1.50	—

Obverse as last. Rv: 1860 / 1/8 within wreath border. Plain edge. (Brunk coll.)

Caution: Fantasy!

| Mxo 173F | 1860 | Copper | 26mm | — | — | 1.50 | — |

Obverse as reverse of last (1860 / 1/8). Rv: Blank. Plain edge. (Brunk coll.)

EL BAZAR

Rulau	Date	Metal	Size	VG	F	VF	Unc
Mxo 175	(18)38	Brass	22mm	—	—	—	—

EL BAZAR / 38. Rv: VALE / 1 / REAL between crossed branches. Plain edge. (Eklund 210)

El Progreso
C. B.

Rulau	Date	Metal	Size	VG	F	VF	Unc
Mxo 177	(1893-97)	Brass	24mm	—	—	—	—

"ROSA" / + / C. B. / + / * EL PROGRESO *. Rv: Large 2 within wreath. Tiny L. H. MOISE . S.F. at bottom. Plain edge. (Zaffern coll.)

2 Reales.

Anda
ENRIQUEZ

Rulau	Date	Metal	Size	VG	F	VF	EF
Mxo 180	1802	Copper	21mm	—	—	—	—

Monogram VTRO (?) / ENRI / QVEZ. Ornamental border. Rv: ANDA / 1802 (2 retrograde). Ornamental border. Plain edge. (Muñoz NOM 178; ANS 144)

Del Ensall
ERRERA

Rulau	Date	Metal	Size	VG	F	VF	EF
Mxo 182	1770	Copper	23mm	—	—	—	—

(Ornament) / ERRERA / 1770 H / DEL (monogram) ENSALL + (inverted). Rv: Blank. (Muñoz NOM 158)

FO Monogram
Hacienda Ferdinando Cuervo

Rulau	Date	Metal	Size	VG	F	VF	EF
Mxo 184	ND	Copper	19mm	—	—	—	—

Fo monogram within circle. Rv: Blank. (Eklund 725)

Used in Hacienda Ferdinando Cuervo, Faquilla; not located.

FERNANDEZ

Rulau	Date	Metal	Size	VG	F	VF	EF
Mxo 186	ND	Copper	18mm	—	—	—	—

FERNA / NDEZ in oblong depression on plain field. Rv: Blank. Cast. (Muñoz NOM 194)

Mxo 188	1773	Copper	25mm	—	—	—	—

1773 at center, FERNANDEZ + around. Rv: Blank. (Muñoz NOM 195)

FERZ HERRA
(Fernandez Herrera)

Rulau	Date	Metal	Size	VG	F	VF	EF
Mxo 190	ND	Copper	37mm	—	22.50	—	—

FER-Z / HERR / A, all within circle of ornaments. Rv: Blank. (Muñoz NOM 196)

The planchet is one of the largest in the entire series of early Mexican tlacos.

ANTO FERRUSQUIA
(Antonio Ferrusquia)

Rulau	Date	Metal	Size	VG	F	VF	EF
Mxo 192	1806	Copper	30mm	—	—	—	—

1806 above a shield outline. Within the shield: ANTO / FERRUS / QUIA. Rv: Blank. (Muñoz NOM 198)

FICHA

Rulau	Date	Metal	Size	VG	F	VF	Unc
Mxo 195	ND	Brass	30mm	—	11.00	20.00	

Mexican eagle above wreath. Rv: FICHA within oak wreath, small F. V. G. below. Plain edge. (Eklund 223; Schrotter 72)

Ficha = Token. A well made piece. These occur ctsp asterisk (*) on either side.

FLORES

Rulau	Date	Metal	Size	VG	F	VF	EF
Mxo 197	ND	Copper	29mm	—	—	—	—

FLORES in relief within 14x5mm toothed rect. depression ctsp on Mexico 1841-61 cuartilla. (Grove 'Tokens' 353)

FLORES DE ROBLES

Rulau	Date	Metal	Size	VG	F	VF	EF
Mxo 199	1809	Copper	22mm	—	—	—	—

* / FLORES / DE ROBLES / DE 1809. Rv: Blank. (Muñoz NOM 202)

G.

Rulau	Date	Metal	Size	VG	F	VF	EF
Mxo 201	ND	Silver	++	—	—	—	85.00

++ 20x16.5mm pie-shaped 1/5 cut of Carolus IV silver dollar. Distinctive G cstp on 1/5 cut of silver 8-reales of 1789-90, KM-107, Craig-73. (Rulau coll., ex-Byrne)

Mxo 202	ND	Silver	xx	—	—	—	110.

xx 14x18mm irregular-shaped scalloped-edge center cut of Carolus IV silver dollar. Similar ctsp on center cut of silver 8-reales of 1789-90, KM-107, Craig-73. (Rulau coll., ex-Byrne)

Jess Peters withheld these two items from the 1975 Byrne sale because they could not be identified at that time. Probably Mexican hacienda pieces, rather than coins of the West Indies.

GALL

Rulau	Date	Metal	Size	VG	F	VF	EF
Mxo 204	(1)822	Copper	—mm	—	—	—	—

GALL / 822. Rv: Blank. (Eklund 227)

GALVAN

Rulau	Date	Metal	Size	VG	F	VF	EF
Mxo 210	1801	Copper	29mm	—	—	—	—

GAL / VAN / 1801 within double-lined beaded border. Rv: Blank. (Muñoz NOM 213)

Mxo 211	ND	Copper	22mm	—	—	—	—

GAL / VAN in laurel wreath. Rv: Blank. (Muñoz NOM 211)

Mxo 212	ND	Copper	21mm	—	—	—	—

GAL / VAN / (4 small circles) within concentric circles. Rv: Blank. (Muñoz NOM 212)

These tokens may not be connected with each other.

G. G.

Rulau	Date	Metal	Size	VG	F	VF	EF
Mxo 203	ND	Silver	21mm	—		25.00	

G . G in relief within toothed rectangular depression ctsp on Mexico Bust-type 1-real. (ANS coll.)

GARENA

Rulau	Date	Metal	Size	VG	F	VF	EF
Mxo 214	ND	Copper	**				

** 4-scalloped flan, 27mm. GA / RENA. Rv: Blank. (Muñoz NOM 227)

| Mxo215 | (1)800 | Copper | —mm | | | | |

GA / RENA / 800. Rv: Blank. (ANS 176; Eklund 232)

GAYR

Rulau	Date	Metal	Size	VG	F	VF	EF
Mxo 217	(1)822	Copper	20mm	—	—	—	—

Gayr / 822 o in crude letters. Rv: Blank. Cast. (Muñoz NOM 231; ANS 181; Eklund 233)

GERMA

Rulau	Date	Metal	Size	VG	F	VF	EF
Mxo 220	1800	Copper	Irreg —mm	—	—	—	—

Ger / (circle) / ma (circle) / 1800 (inverted). Rv: Blank. (Grove 'Tokens' 385)

GIRON

Rulau	Date	Metal	Size	VG	F	VF	EF
Mxo 222	1779	Copper	22mm	—	—	—	—

GIRON / 1779. Rv: Blank. (Muñoz NOM 233; ANS 183)

J. H.

Rulau	Date	Metal	Size	VG	F	VF	EF
Mxo 230	1851	Copper	18mm	—	—	—	—

J H monogram within beaded circle at center. Rv: 1851 (last 1 inverted) / * 1/8 *, (Muñoz TPM 104)

| Mxo 232 | 1854 | Copper | 18mm | — | — | — | — |

Large J H monogram. Rv: 1854 / ***. (Muñoz TPM 105)

INACIO DIEZ

Rulau	Date	Metal	Size	VG	F	VF	EF
Mxo 238	1828	Copper	29mm	—	—	—	—

.INACIO. (retrograde) / I / L . C / V (inverted) / DIEZ (Z retrograde) . 1828 . Rv: Blank. (ANS coll.)

HACIENDA DEL TORO

Caution: Fantasy!

Rulau	Date	Metal	Size	VG	F	VF	EF
Mxo 235F	1851	Copper	35.5mm	—	—	1.75	

Bull charges right, 1/4 above, 1851 below. Rv: HACI-ENDA / DEL / TORO. Plain edge.

Hacienda del toro = Estate of the bull. Perhaps apt!

HERA

Rulau	Date	Metal	Size	VG	F	VF	EF
Mxo 237	1802	Copper	25mm	—	—	—	—

(Crude lettering): ANO DE / 1802 / HERA. Orna-mented border. (Rv: Blank. Cast. (Muñoz NOM 260)

A. J.

AJ

Rulau	Date	Metal	Size	VG	F	VF	EF
Mxo 239	(17)67	Copper	xx	—	—	—	—

xx Oval with fishtail ends, 30x22mm. AJ script monogram / ,.67. Rv: Blank. (Eklund 698)

JAMOE

Rulau	Date	Metal	Size	VG	F	VF	EF
Mxo 245	1850	Copper	19mm	—	—	—	—

JAMOE (?) monogram in wreath. Rv: LIBERTAD / 1/8 / ANO DE 1850. Crude. Plain edge. (Smithsonian coll.)

Smithsonian Institution has 2 pieces of this otherwise unpublished token.

JOAQIN
(Joaquin)

Rulau	Date	Metal	Size	VG	F	VF	EF
Mxo 250	ND	Copper	25mm	—	—	—	—

JOAQIN counterclockwise around a small rect. depression at center. All within concentric circles of triangles (outer) and rays (inner). Rv: Blank. (Muñoz NOM 270)

| Mxo 251 | (1)800 | Copper | —mm | | | | |

Obverse as last. Rv: 1111 ANa / 800. (Eklund 308) (Quarto of 1800)

JURADO

Rulau	Date	Metal	Size	VG	F	VF	EF
Mxo 253	(1)810	Copper	25mm	10.00	—	—	—

JURADO / 810 within irregular cartouche. Rv: Blank.
(Muñoz NOM 271; Eklund 2343)

LA CORONA

Rulau	Date	Metal	Size	VG	F	VF	EF
Mxo 268	ND	Copper	26mm	—	—	15.00	—

LA / CORONA ctsp on Mexico 1863-Mo 1-centavo
coin, KM 390. L ctsp on reverse.

Similar ctsps have been reported on illegible copper coins of 26mm diameter.

KERN

Rulau	Date	Metal	Size	VG	F	VF	EF
Mxo 262	ND	Silver	27mm	—	—	35.00	—

KE / RN in relief within square depression ctsp on
Mexico 1850-Go-PF 2-reales, KM-374.8. 8-pointed
rosette ctsp on opposite side of coin. (ANS coll.)

LANOME

Rulau	Date	Metal	Size	VG	F	VF	EF
Mxo 270	1812	Copper	Sq 29mm	—	—	—	—

(All incused): LANO: / . ME . / 1812. Rv: 2 R. (Eklund
2344)

LEDO

Rulau	Date	Metal	Size	VG	F	VF	EF
Mxo 275	ND	Copper	25mm	—	—	—	—

LEDO above double underlines, ornaments above and
below. Rv: Blank. (Muñoz NOM 282; ANS 226)

Rulau	Date	Metal	Size	VG	F	VF	EF
Mxo 276F	ND	Copper	26mm	—	—	1.75	—

Similar, from another die. Counterfeit! (Utberg report;
Brunk coll.)

Also see HACIENDA DE LEDO under Cocula (Jalisco State).

LEDO OCHOA

Rulau	Date	Metal	Size	VG	F	VF	EF
Mxo 278	ND	Copper	26mm	—	—	—	—

LEDO below leaf at top. OCHOA in relief within rect.
depression, counterstamped in field below LEDO.
(Muñoz NOM 283)

LOPEZ
Real del Chico ?

Rulau	Date	Metal	Size	VG	F	VF	EF
Mxo 280	1808	Copper	27mm	—	—	—	—

LOPEZ amid flourishes within central circle. Around:
R. DEL CHICO / ANO . DE (monogram). 1808. Rv:
Blank. (Muñoz NOM 292)

TARo DE LOPES
(Tenorio de Lopez)

Rulau	Date	Metal	Size	VG	F	VF	EF
Mxo 282	1819	Copper	23mm	—	—	—	—

DE / LOPES / TA (ligate) Ro (monogram for Tenro.)
Rv: PL (united) / 1819. (Muñoz NOM 293; ANS 233;
Smithsonian coll.; Eklund 336)

Mxo 283	1819	Copper	20mm	—	—	—	—

Obverse as last. Rv: 1819. (Muñoz NOM 294; Eklund
335)

Possibly P. de Lopez. The Smithsonian specimen spells the surname LOPEZ.
Eklund says Michoacan State.

LORTIA

Rulau	Date	Metal	Size	VG	F	VF	EF
Mxo 285	(1815-21)	Copper	Rect 20x24mm	—	—	—	—

LORTIA amid flourishes and dots. A small ctsp has 16 in relief within circular depression below LORTIA. Rv: Blank. (Muñoz NOM 299)

The counterstamp is a republican resello revaluing the piece at 1/16 real from its former 1/8 real status. The ctsp dates the piece to the 1815-21 period. The Lortia tlaco may exist without the resello.

LOS REYES

Rulau	Date	Metal	Size	VG	F	VF	EF
Mxo 287	1828	Copper	18mm	—	—	—	—

Eagle on cactus, serpent in its beak. Around: LOSRE YES 1828. Rv: Blank.

LOXERO

Rulau	Date	Metal	Size	VG	F	VF	EF
Mxo 289	1806	Copper	30mm	—	—	—	—

Comet (?) to left / LOXERO / 1806. Rv: Monogram EAS within square resello stamped on reverse. Plain edge. (Muñoz NOM 300)

10 L MAIZ

Rulau	Date	Metal	Size	VG	F	VF	EF
Mxo 299	ND	Copper	26mm	—	—	—	—

. 10 (incuse) L / MAIZ (Z retrograde) / - 10 - (incuse) / OCSAPAIAI (retrograde). Dentilated border. Rv: Blank. (ANS coll.)

A corn measure? Unpublished.

M

Rulau	Date	Metal	Size	VG	F	VF	EF
Mxo 295	1791	Copper	24mm	—	—	—	—

Small u / * M / 1791 *. Rv: Blank. (ANS I, C)

MAIZA DE L PIEDA
(Maiceria de la Piedad)

Rulau	Date	Metal	Size	VG	F	VF	EF
Mxo 300	ND	Copper	XX	—	—	—	—

XX Pomegranate-shaped flan, 22x24mm. MAIZA / DE L / PIEDA. Rv: Blank. (Muñoz COM 21)

Maiceria = Corn meal store. Corn meal for charity?

MARCIA

Rulau	Date	Metal	Size	VG	F	VF	EF
Mxo 305	1826	Copper	26mm	—	—	—	—

Radiant cap dominates field, MARCIA below. Dentilated border. Rv: 1826. Plain edge. (Muñoz NOM 311)

MANUEL MARTINEZ

Rulau	Date	Metal	Size	VG	F	VF	EF
Mxo 310	1801	Copper	30mm	—	—	—	—

Q / MANVEL / MARTINES (NE united) / (ornament). Dentilated border. Rv: Rectangular resello stamped, reading: 1801. (Muñoz NOM 318; Eklund 356)

MED 820

Caution: Counterfeit!

Rulau	Date	Metal	Size	VG	F	VF	Unc
Mxo 315	(1)820	Copper	20mm	—	—	—	—

820 / MED. Rv: Blank. (Muñoz NOM 323; ANS 254; Eklund 366)

This piece could indicate a surname, such as Medina, or be an abbreviation for Media = Cuartilla. It might also designate a place-name.

Rulau	Date	Metal	Size	VG	F	VF	EF
Mxo 327F	ND	Copper	26mm	—	—	1.50	—

The forgery above is well made and could be a problem. It looks *too good!*, however.

MENDOZA

Rulau	Date	Metal	Size	VG	F	VF	EF
Mxo 317	1801	Copper	27mm	—	—	—	—

MEN / DOZA / 1801. Dentilated border. Rv: Blank. (Muñoz NOM 326)

| Mxo 319 | 1804 | Copper | 22mm | — | — | — | — |

MEN / DOSA / 1804. Dotted border. Rv: Blank. (Muñoz NOM 327; Eklund 368)

| Mxo 320 | 1804 | Copper | 23mm | — | — | — | — |

1804 / MENDOSA (script) in cross form. Rv: Blank. (Muñoz NOM 328; Eklund 369)

MINAS DE ARRAYAN

Rulau	Date	Metal	Size	VG	F	VF	Unc
Mxo 330	1885	++	24mm	—	—	—	—

++ Black vulcanite.
MINAS DE / DE / . ARRAYAN . / 1885 / . / MANGANESO. Rv: VALE EN MERCADERIAS / .+. / 20 C / .+. / -*-. (Sobrino pg. 278)

Manganeso = Manganese.

MOLINA

Rulau	Date	Metal	Size	VG	F	VF	EF
Mxo 333	1801	Copper	32mm	—	—	—	—

Q / MOLINA / CAV monogram / 1801. Floral devices surround. Rv: Blank. (Muñoz NOM 341)

Q = Quartilla, or 1/4 Real.

PEDRO MEXIA

Rulau	Date	Metal	Size	VG	F	VF	EF
Mxo 322	1806	Copper	26mm	15.00	—	—	—

PEDRO / MEXIA / 1805 in beaded circle. Rv: Blank. (Muñoz NOM 424; ANS 314; Eklund 464)

Pedro Mejia?

MONCAYO

Rulau	Date	Metal	Size	VG	F	VF	EF
Mxo 335	1801	Copper	28mm	20.00	—	—	—

(Ornaments) / MONCA / YO 1801. Rv: Blank. (Muñoz NOM 344)

JOSE FCO. MEZA

Rulau	Date	Metal	Size	VG	F	VF	EF
Mxo 324	1801	Copper	25mm	—	—	—	—

JOSE / FCO. / MEZA. Plant at left. Rv: Resello stamped, reading: M 1801. Rv: Blank. (Muñoz NOM 333)

Jose Francisco Meza.

MONEDA (Coin) (Private Issue)

Illustration Enlarged

PABLO MILLA

Rulau	Date	Metal	Size	VG	F	VF	EF
Mxo 326	ND	Copper	26mm	6.50	11.00	25.00	40.00

PABLO MILLA around a large fleur de lis. Rv: Blank. (Muñoz NOM 406; ANS 299; Christensen Apr. 1976 sale, lot 1507; Brunk coll.)

Rulau	Date	Metal	Size	VG	F	VF	EF
Mxo 340	1795	Copper	18mm	—	12.00	20.00	—

Within beaded border: MONEDA / 8 / .1795. Rv: Blank. (Muñoz TPM 301)

Actual Size

Rulau	Date	Metal	Size	VG	F	VF	EF
Mxo 341	1795	Copper	32mm	—	30.00	42.50	—

Die similar to last, but laurel spray is at either side of 8. The 18mm die is struck on copper flan of 32mm. Rv: Blank. (Muñoz TPM 303)

Actual Size

Mxo 343	1806	Copper	18mm	—	15.00	—	—

Similar to first issue, but 1806. (Muñoz TPM 302; Schimmel June 1989 sale, lot 187; Eklund 404)

Numeral 8 = 1/8 Real, or Tlaco. Intermediate dates between 1795 and 1806 are possible.

MOXICA
(Mojica)

Rulau	Date	Metal	Size	VG	F	VF	EF
Mxo 346	1803	Copper	24mm	—	—	—	—

(Ornament) / MOXI / CA / 1803. Rv: Blank. (ANS 270; Muñoz NOM 340)

MUÑOZ SURNAMES
(see footnote below)

Uribe y Muñoz

Rulau	Date	Metal	Size	VG	F	VF	Unc
Mxo 350	1801	Copper	32mm	—	—	—	—

Q / VRIBE / Y / MUÑOS / 1801. Rv: Traces of a monogram, no longer legible. (Muñoz NOM 581)

Q = Quartilla (1/4 Real).

Muñoz

Mxo 352	ND	Copper	34mm	—	—	—	—

MUÑOS amid ornamentation; fancy border around. Rv: Blank. (Muñoz NOM 367)

Muñoz

Mxo 354	1801	Copper	31mm	—	—	—	—

MUÑOS in a beaded oval across center, superimposed on the breast of a double eagle. Q above, 1801 below. Rv: Small resello stamp reading: OR / tis. (Muñoz NOM 368; Eklund 421)

Muñoz

Mxo 356	ND	Copper	24mm	—	—	—	—

MV / ÑOS, diagonal slashes above and below. Rv: Blank. (Muñoz NOM 369)

This token is illustrated on the cover of Miguel L. Muñoz' book "Tlacos y Pilones" (Mexico City, 1976). It may have had familial significance to him.

Mariano Muñoz

Rulau	Date	Metal	Size	VG	F	VF	Unc
Mxo 358	ND	Copper	24mm				

** / MARIANO / MUNOS. Palm leaf border. Rv: Blank. (Muñoz NOM 370)

NOTE: All tokens bearing the name Muñoz have been lumped together under this heading. The surname is uncommon in Mexico, and was proudly borne by our good friend Miguel L. Muñoz, former president of Sociedad Numismatica de Mexico and one of the country's top numismatic writers until his death.

NAR -

Rulau	Date	Metal	Size	VG	F	VF	EF
Mxo 370	1777	Copper	24mm	—	—	—	—

* / nar / 1777. Rv: Blank. (Muñoz NOM 372; Eklund 422)

Miguel L. Muñoz adds: "We cannot explain why this piece has been cataloged as NARVAGAN."

NAVARRO

Rulau	Date	Metal	Size	VG	F	VF	EF
Mxo 372	ND	Copper	22mm	—	—	—	—

NAVARRO in relief within 20x4mm rectangular depression, ctsp on blank copper planchet. (Muñoz NOM 376; Eklund 424)

Mxo 373	ND		—mm	—	—	—	—

Similar ctsp on various Mexican coins. (Brunk 60580; Duffield 1692)

OCAMPO

Rulau	Date	Metal	Size	VG	F	VF	Unc
Mxo 380	1770	Brass	30mm	—	—	—	—

(All incused) Star of four lobes occupies most of the field. Above: OCA — NPO. Within star: ANO / 1770. Rv: Blank. (Muñoz NOM 378)

Frank Grove calls the device a butterfly.

D. OCEGUERA

Rulau	Date	Metal	Size	VG	F	VF	EF
Mxo 382	1840	Copper	20mm	—	—	—	—

D. OCEGUERA / (Horse left) / 1/80 1840. Rv: Blank. (Muñoz NOM 383)

1/80 = 1/8 real, or octavo.

OCULLACA ARAUJO

Rulau	Date	Metal	Size	VG	F	VF	EF
Mxo 384	1798	Copper	25mm	—	—	—	—

* 1798 * (Dagger) OCULLACA / ARAU / * JO * / (rosette). Rv: Blank. (Grove 'Tokens' 638; Eklund 39)

D. OGEGEMA

Rulau	Date	Metal	Size	VG	F	VF	EF
Mxo 386	1840	Copper	19mm	—	—	—	—

D. OGEGEMA / 1 80 1840. Rv: Blank. (Muñoz NOM 386; Eklund 433)

1 80 = 1/8 real, or octavo.

OLBERA
(Olvera)

Rulau	Date	Metal	Size	VG	F	VF	EF
Mxo 388	1801	Copper	33mm	—	—	—	—

(Garland of fruit and flowers) / OLBERA / 1801 / (crossed pennon and cannon). Dentilated border. Rv: Blank. (Muñoz NOM 389)

Rulau	Date	Metal	Size	VG	F	VF	EF
Mxo 390	1806	Copper	33mm	—	—	—	—

Similar to last, but 1806. (Muñoz NOM 388; ANS 286)

There seems little doubt that the Serbin Olbera and Olbera tokens were cut by the same diesinker, most likely for use on either the same hacienda or on neighboring family estates.

SERBIN OLBERA
(Serbin Olvera)

Rulau	Date	Metal	Size	VG	F	VF	EF
Mxo 392	1801	Copper	29mm	—	—	—	—

Fruit branches above SERBIN / OLBERA / 1801. Rv: Blank. (Muñoz NOM 542; Eklund 553; ANS 422)

MARIANO OÑATE

Rulau	Date	Metal	Size	VG	F	VF	EF
Mxo 394	(1)796	Copper	27mm	—	—	—	—

MARIA / NO OÑA / TE / 96 / (scrawl). All within a circle of small triangles. Rv: Blank. (Muñoz NOM 391)

MANUEL ORTIZ

Rulau	Date	Metal	Size	VG	F	VF	EF
Mxo 396	1805	Copper	28mm	—	—	—	—

DEL . MANUEL / ORTIZ ENERO / ANO / (large rosette) / 1805. Rv: Blank. (Grove 'Tokens' 649)

ORTUÑO

Rulau	Date	Metal	Size	VG	F	VF	EF
Mxo 398	17..	Copper	27mm	10.00	—	—	—

ORTVÑO.AÑO 17-in a circular legend, a coiled lariat in circle at center. Rv: Blank. (Muñoz NOM 399; ANS 296; Schimmel June 1989 sale, lot 189; Eklund 443)

Rulau	Date	Metal	Size	VG	F	VF	EF
Mxo 400	ND	Copper	28mm	—	—	—	—

ORTV / ÑO in crude letters within an ornamental circle. (Muñoz NOM 400; ANS 295)

OVIEDO

Rulau	Date	Metal	Size	VG	F	VF	EF
Mxo 402	1804	Copper	32mm	12.00	16.00	40.00	70.00

OVI / EDO / (ornament). Wide dentilated border. Rv: A. D. / 1804 (4 misshapen or inverted). Circle of pellets forms border inside the wide dentilated rim. Plain edge. (Muñoz NOM 401; ANS 297; Schimmel June 1989 sale, lot 190; Eklund 444)

Smaller (25mm), less ornate tokens of this type are concoctions!

A. N. P.

Rulau	Date	Metal	Size	VG	F	VF	EF
Mxo 410	(1)750	Copper	33mm	90.00	—	Rare	—

ANP monogram / 750. Rv: 8 R. Wide plain border on each side. (ANS III, A)

Mxo 411	ND	Copper	26mm	75.00	—	Rare	—

ANP monogram / 4. Rv: Blank. (ANS III, B)

Mxo 412	ND	Copper	21mm	—	—	Rare	—

As last, but 2. (ANS III, C)

This is one of the earliest dated hacienda token issues of Mexico. The issue is denominated in reales, respectively 8 reales, 4 reales and 2 reales in copper.

PANADERIA LAS TRES B'S

Rulau	Date	Metal	Size	VG	F	VF	Unc
Mxo 421	ND	CN	20mm	—	—	8.00	

(All incuse): PANADERIA / LAS TRES Bs. Rv: VALE 3 BOLLO DE PAN. (Zaika coll.)

Vale 3 bollo de pan = Worth 3 loaves of bread. Panaderia Las Tres Bs = 'The Three B's Bakery'. (In Mexico, the three B's are Bueno, Bonita, Barrato = Good, Pretty, Cheap)

PAJOSA

Rulau	Date	Metal	Size	VG	F	VF	EF
Mxo 420	1804	Copper	xx	—	—		

xx Crescent moon-shaped flan, 23x14mm.
1804 / PAJOSA within border of dots. Rv: Blank.
(Muñoz NOM 407; ANS 300)

PANDARON

Rulau	Date	Metal	Size	VG	F	VF	EF
Mxo 422	18..	Copper	25mm				

Eagle atop a fouled anchor, all in beaded oval. Rv:
Within dotted circle: ..... 18.. * / PANDARON. (Grove
'Tokens' 665)

PARA DELA
(De La Parra)

Rulau	Date	Metal	Size	VG	F	VF	EF
Mxo 424	1806	Copper	26mm	—	—	—	—

PARA / DELA / 1806 in ornamented circle. Rv: Blank.
(Muñoz NOM 414; ANS 303)

Noe catalogued this piece as Paradela.

PELAEZ

Rulau	Date	Metal	Size	VG	F	VF	EF
Mxo 426	1804	Copper	24mm	—	—	—	—

(Radiant sun) / PELAEZ. Rv: Blank. (Muñoz NOM
426; ANS 315)

PENYCHET

Rulau	Date	Metal	Size	VG	F	VF	EF
Mxo 430	1806	Copper	27mm	—	—	40.00	70.00

PENY / CHET. Rv: AÑO / DE / 1806. Small resello
with Q stamped near top. Border of large dots on each
side. (Muñoz NOM 427; ANS 317; Eklund 466)

Grove reports this date as 1808.

PEREA

Rulau	Date	Metal	Size	VG	F	VF	EF
Mxo 432	1806	Copper	20mm	—	—	—	—

PEREA / 1806 / (rosette). In rayed circle. Rv: Blank.
(Muñoz NOM 429)

PERES

Rulau	Date	Metal	Size	VG	F	VF	EF
Mxo 434	1802	Copper	23mm	—	—	85.00	

Wreath of palm leaves around: 4 / PErEs / 1802. Rv:
Blank. (Muñoz NOM 436; ANS coll.; Eklund 741; Hubbard coll.)

ANS has this token cataloged as REYES. 4 = 1/4 real, or cuartilla. There are
varieties, including one where letters PE touch.

MIGVEL PERES

Rulau	Date	Metal	Size	VG	F	VF	EF
Mxo 436	(1)1804	Copper	29mm	—	25.00	40.00	—

MI = / GVEL within circle. Rv: PE / RES / 804 within
beaded circle. Crude. (Muñoz NOM 443; Hubbard
coll.)

JUAN PEREZ

Rulau	Date	Metal	Size	VG	F	VF	EF
Mxo 438	ND	Copper	25mm	—	—	27.50	—

JUAN PEREZ (curved) / (crossed palms) ctsp incuse on
Mexico Republic 1869-97 type centavo, KM-391.
(Muñoz NOM 442; ANS coll.)

Varieties exist.

PILON
(1/16 Real)

Rulau	Date	Metal	Size	VG	F	VF	EF
Mxo 440	ND	Copper	**	—	—	30.00	—

** Arrowhead-shaped flan, 23x15mm.
PILon within circular indent. Rv: Blank. (Muñoz
TPM 203; Eklund 476)

Mxo 440A	ND	Copper	**	—	—	30.00	—

PI / LON / D. Rv: Blank. (Hubbard coll.)

1/16
(1/16 Real)

Rulau	Date	Metal	Size	VG	F	VF	EF
Mxo 441	ND	Copper	Rect 18x23mm				

1/16 (both 1's retrograde) within rect. depression. Rv:
Blank. (Muñoz TPM 205)

PITONISA POPOK

Rulau	Date	Metal	Size	F	VF	EF	Unc
Mxo 442	ND	Brass	25mm	—	7.50	9.50	

Radiant sunface at center. Crescent, star and 2 hearts at left. Indian face (?) at right. Above: Scroll, on which is: JALIS ... Below: DE LA PITONISA POPOK. Rv: Symbols surround Indian face in cartouche, ASIRAL below. Crudely reeded edge. Traces of silvering. (Rulau coll.)

PLAGO OTOSA

Rulau	Date	Metal	Size	VG	F	VF	EF
Mxo 443	1786	Copper	26mm	—	—	—	—

Obverse punched with individual letter and numeral dies, which may read: OTOSA 1786 ENROE. around (Brand mark) / PL (joined) AGO. Rv: Blank. (Grove 'Tokens' 717)

PLASORIA

Rulau	Date	Metal	Size	VG	F	VF	EF
Mxo 445	1808	Copper	21mm	—	—	—	—

Lion seated left. Around: PLASORIA . OLADOR / . 1808 . Rv: Blank. (Grove 'Tokens' 720)

PROVIDENCIA

Rulau	Date	Metal	Size	VG	F	VF	EF
Mxo 447	ND	Copper	26mm	—	—	—	—

PROVIDENCIA. curved above 2-story building right, with smoking chimney. Rv: Blank. (ANS coll.)

TFR Monogram

Rulau	Date	Metal	Size	VG	F	VF	EF
Mxo 458	ND	Copper	25mm	—	—	30.00	—

TFR (?) monogram amid ornamentation. Wide, high rim. Rv: Blank. Cast. (Kirtley May 4-9, 1992 sale, lot 1369)

Supposedly from Hacienda Juan Castillon. Not verified. The monogram, which may be TJFR, is probably the brand mark of the hacienda represented. Many of the *tlacos* of the Colonial and Early Republican period used brand marks as their motif, as these were instantly recognizable to the inhabitants of an estate.

RADA

Rulau	Date	Metal	Size	VG	F	VF	EF
Mxo 460	1804	Copper	30mm	—	—	—	—

ANO / RADA / DE 1804 (DE in monogram). All within a circle of beads. Rv: EL / GENIO / (two palm trees) - all within beaded circle. Plain edge. Cast. (Muñoz NOM 466)

El Genio = The Genius. This could refer to a locale.

Rulau	Date	Metal	Size	VG	F	VF	EF
Mxo 462	1804	Copper	32mm	—	—	—	—

EVL monogram between branches / GENIO / (crossed branches). Rv: ANO / (two rosettes) / RADA / DE monogram 1804. Border of large dots on each side. (Grove 'Tokens' 384)

RAMIREZ

Rulau	Date	Metal	Size	VG	F	VF	EF
Mxo 463	ND	Brass	35.3mm	—	—	—	—

(All incused): RAMIREZ / 125 / CENTAVOS. Rv: Intaglio of obverse. Plain edge. Thin flan. (ANS coll.)

Mxo 463A	ND	Brass	35.3mm	—	—	—	—

As last, but 75 / CENTAVOS. (ANS)

Mxo 463B	ND	Brass	35.3mm	—	—	—	—

As last, but 62 / CENTVS. (ANS)

Mxo 463C	ND	Brass	35.3mm	—	—	—	—

As last, but 6 / CENTVS. (ANS)

These tokens are apparently unpublished.

REAL
(Calfskin)

Rulau	Date	Metal	Size	VG	F	VF	EF
Mxo 464	ND	Calfskin	36mm	—	—	—	—

REAL impressed across center. Rv: Blank. (Muñoz report)

This is the only Real de Vaqueta (calfskin leather token) reported for Mexico.

REAL DE LA CONCEPCION

Rulau	Date	Metal	Size	VG	F	VF	EF
Mxo 470	1846	Copper	23mm	—	—	—	—

Three miners and mountain. Around: REAL DE LA CONCEPCION / 1 / 4 / . 1846 . Rv: ABONADAS . POR -. / LA NEn. / CORREA / (knot) / (crossed branches). (Grove 'Tokens' 790; Hubbard coll.)

REINOZO
(Reinoso)

Rulau	Date	Metal	Size	VG	F	VF	EF
Mxo 472	(17)87	Copper	27mm	—	—	—	—

Ornamented circle around: REINO / ZO / 87 A / (ornament). Rv: Blank. (Muñoz NOM 479; ANS coll.)

A = Año (year).

REY

Rulau	Date	Metal	Size	VG	F	VF	EF
Mxo 474	1817	Copper	20mm	—	—	—	—

Within border of alternating laurel leaves and small circles: (Ornament) / REY / 1o 8 / 1817 / (knot). Rv: REY in rect. depression. (Grove 'Tokens' 796)

Rulau	Date	Metal	Size	VG	F	VF	EF
Mxo 475	ND	Copper	28mm				

77 / P. F. / REY ctsp on Jalisco State 1862 octavo, KM-330. Rv: REI ctsp on opposite side of coin.

REYPOPIPIN HISPAN IN

Rulau	Date	Metal	Size	VG	F	VF	EF
Mxo 477	1778	Brass	36mm	—	15.00	25.00	35.00

Head right. Around: PERLIN VII FIGRATIA / 1778. Rv: Crowned shield of arms supported by upright trumpets. REYPOPIPIN HISPAN IN around. Plain edge. (Rulau coll.)

Rulau	Date	Metal	Size	VG	F	VF	EF
Mxo 478	1778	Brass	31mm	—	10.00	15.00	25.00

As last. Plain edge. (Rulau coll.; Henkle 570)

These are deliberately clumsy imitations of the gold coins of Ferdinand VII, last Spanish king of Mexico. Their purpose and approximate date of issue are unknown; they probably were made in the first half of the 19th century. Probably scarce.

The legend could begin FLYPOPIPIN.

On these pieces, the 'king' resembles an Indian wearing a patriot's headband.

JOEL RIJOSO

Rulau	Date	Metal	Size	VG	F	VF	EF
Mxo 480	1801	Copper	27mm	—	—	—	—

Within ornate frame: JOEL / RIJOSO / 1801. Rv: Blank. (Grove 'Tokens' 809)

DE RIVERA

Rulau	Date	Metal	Size	VG	F	VF	EF
Mxo 482	(17)84	Copper	27mm	—	150.	200.	—

DE / RIVERA / AÑO / 84 / +. Rv: PARA / * LA * / PLAZA / (ornament). Double circle border is on each side. (Muñoz NOM 495; ANS 381)

This is an extremely well-made token. Para la plaza = For (use in) the square. Its locale has not been determined.

S. P. M. & M. CA.
Mina Cordovena

Rulau	Date	Metal	Size	VG	F	VF	Unc
Mxo 485	ND	Brass	31mm	—	30.00	—	—

* S. P. M. & M. CA. * / + + + / MINA CORDOVEÑA. Rv: 4 R / EN MERCANCIAS. Plain edge. (Eklund 2314)

Rulau	Date	Metal	Size	VG	F	VF	Unc
Mxo 486	ND	Brass	Oct 26.5mm	17.50	—	—	—

As last, but 2 R. (Bosco May 1980 sale)

PMS Monogram

Caution: Fantasy!

Rulau	Date	Metal	Size	VG	F	VF	EF
Mxo 488F	1830	CN	+ +	—	—	2.00	—

+ + Heart-shaped flan, 23.5 by 24mm. Within sunken cartouche: PMS monogram / 1830. Rv: Blank.

This is a dangerous fantasy piece, well-made!

J. M. SANCHES
(J. M. Sanchez)

Rulau	Date	Metal	Size	VG	F	VF	EF
Mxo 490	(1)806	Copper	32mm	—	—	—	—

J M / SANCHES / Q / 806. Rv: Resello ctsp TORES on plain field. (Muñoz NOM 530; ANS 405; Grove 'Tokens' 870; Eklund 517)

Q = Quartilla. Probably a hacienda token.

SANCHES V.

Rulau	Date	Metal	Size	VG	F	VF	EF
Mxo 492	1837	Copper	22mm	—	—	—	—

SANCHES / V. / 1837. Rv: Blank. (Grove 'Tokens' 874)

SAN JUAN

Rulau	Date	Metal	Size	VG	F	VF	EF
Mxo 494	ND	Copper	Oval				
			28x17mm	25.00	60.00	100.	—

Swan left, on waves. Rv: SAN JUaN / (crossed branches). Dentilated rim on each side. (Muñoz NOM 536; ANS 413; Grove 878; Eklund 529)

SAVCEDA
(Sauceda)

Rulau	Date	Metal	Size	VG	F	VF	EF
Mxo 496	1815	Copper	23mm	—	—	—	—

Within dentilated border; SAVCEDA / MIRANDA (resello) / 1815. Rv: Blank. (Grove 894)

SERA
(Serra)

Rulau	Date	Metal	Size	VG	F	VF	EF
Mxo 498	ND	Copper	24mm	—	—	—	—

SE / RA. Rv: Blank. (Muñoz NOM 545)

SERBIN OLVERA

See this entry under OLVERA.

SERNA

Rulau	Date	Metal	Size	VG	F	VF	EF
Mxo 500	ND	Copper	32m00				

SERNA around rosette, all within octagonal depression. Rv: Blank. (Muñoz NOM 543; Eklund 554)

Freiherr von Schrotter in 1932 reported this same piece counterstamped J in the Karl Uhde collection acquired by the Berlin Museum.

Occasionally this token is found with ctsp letter on reverse: J or S. Grove (1989) illustrates one with S in circular indent.

The token occurs in sizes 28 to 32 millimeters.

YGNACIO SILVA

Rulau	Date	Metal	Size	VG	F	VF	EF
Mxo 503	1830	Copper	18mm	—	—	—	—

YGNACIO / SILVA / ANO D 1830 / (star). Rv: Blank. (Muñoz NOM 548)

An 1828 date is reported.

SOLANO

Rulau	Date	Metal	Size	VG	F	VF	EF
Mxo 505	(17)90	Copper	27mm				

SOLA / NO ANO (AN ligate) / 90. Rv: Blank. (Grove 918)

A. T. SOUNDY
La Fincona

Rulau	Date	Metal	Size	VG	F	VF	Unc
Mxo 510	ND	Bronze	25.5mm	—	—	9.50	16.00

A. T. SOUNDY / - LA FINCONA -. Rv: 25. Plain edge. Centrally holed flan. Scarce. (Rulau coll.; TAMS Maverick 13035)

The Soundy token is not listed by Schimmel, Grove, Rojas-Solano or other writers.

The Rulau collection contains two specimens of this token, part of a small group of 8 which surfaced in late 1989.

Clyde Hubbard has some doubt about attribution to Mexico.

TA. NA. DL. ESTANCO YGLESIS
(Tienda Nexa del Estanco Yglesias)

Rulau	Date	Metal	Size	VG	F	VF	Unc
Mxo 527	ND	Copper	24mm	—	—	—	—

Ta. Na. Dl. / ESTANCO / YGLESIs within beaded double circle. Rv: Blank. (Muñoz COM 53; Eklund 619)

= Bonded store of church monopoly?

TLACO
(⅛ Real)

Rulau	Date	Metal	Size	VG	F	VF	Unc
Mxo 530	ND	Copper	20mm				

TLACO in arc above plain field. Rv: Blank. (Muñoz TPM 101)

⅛
(⅛ Real)

Rulau	Date	Metal	Size	VG	F	VF	Unc
Mxo 531	ND	Copper	21mm	—	—	—	—

Large ⅛ at center. Wide dentilated rim. Rv: Blank. (Muñoz TPM 103)

RITA VRTADO
(Rita Urtado)

Rulau	Date	Metal	Size	VG	F	VF	Unc
Mxo 534	1806	Copper	27mm	—	—	—	—

RITA / VRTA / DO. Rv: AÑO / DE / 1806 (extra large tilde over N of AÑO. (Muñoz NOM 584)

VALE POR 50 AL MOSTRADOR

Rulau	Date	Metal	Size	VG	F	VF	Unc
Mxo 542	ND	Brass	21mm	—	—	2.00	2.50

Ornate Gothic J. Rv: VALE POR / 50 / AL MOSTRA-DOR. Plain edge. (Zaffern coll.)

This issue occurs with Gothic B and Gothic R, all brass, 21mm. Vale por 50 al mostrador = Good for 50 (centavos) to the shower (the bearer). Mostrador (one who shows) is an unusual expression for this form of check or counter, Portador (bearer) being the norm.

V

Rulau	Date	Metal	Size	VG	F	VF	EF
Mxo 540	ND	Copper	27mm	—	—	—	—

Wide toothed border around: 4 / R S. Letter V is ctsp at center. Rv: Blank. (ANS III, E)

Mxo 541	ND	Copper	21mm				

2 / R S. Rv: Blank. (ANS III, D)

VALVERDE

Rulau	Date	Metal	Size	VG	F	VF	EF
Mxo 545	1807	Copper	30mm	15.00	—	—	—

Y / VALVER / DE / 1807. Beaded rim around all. Rv: A / CAMACHO. This copper tlaco is cast in a mold. (Muñoz NOM 586)

VAQUEDANO

Rulau	Date	Metal	Size	VG	F	VF	EF
Mxo 550	1796	Copper	32mm	—	85.00	—	—

Two concentric circles at center. Around: VA 9 VEDANO ANO DE 1796. rv: Blank. (Muñoz NOM 587; Hubbard coll.)

These have been reported ctsp BUTRON incuse.

VILLASENOR

Rulau	Date	Metal	Size	VG	F	VF	EF
Mxo 555	1801	Copper	31mm	—	—	—	—

Q / VILLA / SENOR / 1801 within wreath. Beaded rim around all. Rv: An illegible monogram. (Muñoz NOM 615)

The Q = Quartilla, a quarter real or double tlaco.
The illustration above shows only part of the inscription. These usually occur with much legend missing because of faulty striking or design.

XALPA LOZANO

Rulau	Date	Metal	Size	VG	F	VF	EF
Mxo 558	ND	Copper	30mm	—	—	25.00	—

Circular legend: + XALPA - LOZANO. Rv: Blank. (Muñoz NOM 302)

XARAMILLO
(Jaramillo)

Rulau	Date	Metal	Size	VG	F	VF	EF
Mxo 559	ND	Copper	22mm	—	—	20.00	—

XARA / MILLO in crude letters. Rv: Blank. Cast. (Muñoz NOM 267)

XIMENEZ
(Jimenez)

Rulau	Date	Metal	Size	VG	F	VF	EF
Mxo 560	ND	Copper	29mm	—	—	25.00	—

1/8 / XIME / NEZ (N inverted). All within beaded circle. Rv: Blank. (Muñoz NOM 269)

XIRON

Rulau	Date	Metal	Size	VG	F	VF	EF
Mxo 561	ND	Copper	26mm	—	—	35.00	—

(Incused) XIRON. Rv: Blank. (Muñoz NOM 619)

Muñoz speculates that the surname JIRON may have been intended.

VILLA SUSANA

Rulau	Date	Metal	Size	VG	F	VF	EF
Mxo 557	1783	Copper	28mm	50.00	100.	—	—

Cross above fountain at center. Around: VILLA SUSANA / 1783. Rv: Blank. (Muñoz NOM 616; Fernandez 276)

Villa = City. The more modern term Ciudad is preferred today. There is no Susana today as a geographic location. The term villa might also pertain to a large private estate.

Y N G V . . .

Rulau	Date	Metal	Size	VG	F	VF	EF
Mxo 563	(17)70	Copper	23mm	—	150.	200.	—

* / YNGV- / (line of laurel leaves) / AN 70 / *. Double concentric border. Rv: Blank. (Grove 'Tokens' 1085)

Y NO SOY QUE COBRE

Rulau	Date	Metal	Size	VG	F	VF	Unc
Mxo 565	1861	Brass	32mm	—	30.00	35.00	—

Mexican eagle above laurel branches. Above: Y NO SOY QUE COBRE. Rv: Arm holds Liberty cap on pole above open book. Around: OJALA ME TOMARA POR MEDIA ONZA / * 1861 *. Plain edge. (Rulau coll.)

This satirical piece strongly resembles Mexican republic 4-escudo gold coinage, KM 381.6.

Y no soy que cobre = And I am not as copper. Ojala me tomara por media onza = Would that I could be used for a half ounce (of gold)! The latter phrase is a colloquialism, rendered approximately.

T. Z.

Rulau	Date	Metal	Size	VG	F	VF	EF
Mxo 570	ND	Silver	40mm	—	—	50.00	—

T -- Z above and divided by floreate cross device, all within circle, ctsp on Spanish-American 1818-Mo 8-reales, KM-111. (Krueger April 1991 sale, lot 1720)

ZABALA
(Zavala)

Rulau	Date	Metal	Size	VG	F	VF	EF
Mxo 575	1801	Copper	Oct 19mm	—	—	—	—

ZABALA / 1801 within 13x7mm cartouche. Ornaments above and below. (Rv: Blank. (Muñoz NOM 622)

Rulau	Date	Metal	Size	VG	F	VF	EF
Mxo 576	1802	Copper	22mm	—	—	—	—

ZAB A / * LA * / (knot) *. Rv: * / 1802 / (wavy line). (Grove 'Tokens' 1086)

¼ Z / MO
(Hacienda de Zavaleta)

Rulau	Date	Metal	Size	VG	F	VF	EF
Mxo 578	ND	Copper	Oct 22mm	—	—	—	—

¼ Z amid adornments / MO. Rv: Blank. (Muñoz NOM 623; ANS collection)

Hacienda de Zavaleta was part of the personal holdings of the Count of San Bartolome de Xala, according to Miguel L. Muñoz.

YGO. ZEPEDA
(Ignacio Zepeda)

Rulau	Date	Metal	Size	VG	F	VF	Unc
Mxo 580	1806	Copper	35mm	—	—	—	—

18.6 amid dots forming a zigzag / YGO Q ZEPEDA. Around all is a circle of tiny leaves. Rv: Blank. (Muñoz NOM 625; Eklund 693)

Q = Quartilla.

ZIPIAJO

Rulau	Date	Metal	Size	VG	F	VF	EF
Mxo 582	1833	Copper	20mm	—	—	—	—

ZIPIAJO / (beaded circle) / 1833. Rv: Blank. (*TAMS Journal* for Aug. 1978, pg. 147)

Caution! Probably a fantasy issue!

HACIENDA DE ZOQIAPAM

Rulau	Date	Metal	Size	VG	F	VF	Unc
Mxo 585	ND	CN	24mm	—	12.50	22.50	—

River steamer left, trailing smoke. EL CHALCO below. Rv: HACIENDA DE ZOQIAPAM / VALE / UN / TANTO / . MEXICO . Plain edge. (Eklund 694; Scott; Fischer 369)

Vale un tanto = Worth only so much.

Uncertain Monogram
(S N de P ?)

Rulau	Date	Metal	Size	VG	F	VF	EF
Mxo 600	1882	Wood	35mm	—	—	80.00	100.

Uncertain ornate monogram, possibly S N de P for S. N. de Pedroza. Rv: 1882.

"BOLOS"
(Marriage Medalets)

Rulau	Date	Metal	Size	F	VF	EF	Unc
Mxo 610	ND	Gilt/B	18mm	—	—	4.75	6.00

Couple in wedding finery stand facing, before an adobe church. Rv: Clasped hands superimposed across a heart, wreath around. Plain edge. (Brunk coll.)

Rulau	Date	Metal	Size	F	VF	EF	Unc
Mxo 611	ND	Gilt/B	18.5mm	—	—	6.25	7.50

Mexican eagle as on coinage. RECUERDO MATRIMONIAL (marriage memento) above. Rv: Large church edifice on a square, clouds and birds above. (Appears to be the cathedral in Mexico City). Reeded edge. (Brunk coll.)

The second token greatly resembles a Mexican republic 5-peso gold coin of the type introduced in 1905 (K-M 464). The gold 5-pesos was a favorite wedding gift of the better-off classes; the peon populace usually used these imitation pieces made of base metal.

9. G.

Rulau	Date	Metal	Size	VG	F	VF	EF
Mxo 620	ND	Silver	32mm	—	23.00	—	—

9. G. ctsp on Mexico 4-reales, KM-375. Specimens examined: 1842-Zs-OM, 1853-Go-PF. (Jess Peters July 1986 sale; Kurt Krueger April 1991 sale, lot 1675)

This counterstamp has been claimed, erroneously, for Grenada.

Eagle with Folded Wings

Rulau	Date	Metal	Size	VG	F	VF	EF
Mxo 622	ND	Silver	40mm	—	—	—	—

Eagle with folded wings, head turned right, in relief within oval depression, ctsp on Spanish-American 1818-Mo-JJ 8-reales, KM-111. (Krueger April 1991 sale, lot 1721)

Knot

Rulau	Date	Metal	Size	VG	F	VF	EF
Mxo 625	(1)806	Copper	20mm	—	10.00	—	—

806 / (knot in rope). Rv: Blank. (Muñoz Anepigraphs 13; Schimmel June 1989 sale, lot 196)

Muñoz read this as 800 (1800).

Lion

Rulau	Date	Metal	Size	VG	F	VF	EF
Mxo 630	ND	Copper	24mm	—	—	30.00	—

Lion (?) right, its tail swirled upward. Border of thick denticles. Rv: Blank. (Muñoz Anepigraphs 14)

Issued by the Leon family, according to Arthur Garnett. In the Garnett collection are two examples with the lion facing left.

Some later examples, in brass, bear the numeral 1 on reverse.

Horse

Rulau	Date	Metal	Size	VG	F	VF	Unc
Mxo 631	ND	Copper	34mm	—	—	50.00	—

Horse prancing left, thick plain border around. Rv: Blank. (ANS coll.)

Aztec Lord

Rulau	Date	Metal	Size	VG	F	VF	EF
Mxo 635	ND	Copper	Oval 24x29mm	—	—	35.00	—

Standing Aztec warrior in ceremonial cap left, holding a spear (?) before him. Ornamentation around. Rv: LAR (?) monogram. (Muñoz Anepigraphs 19; ANS coll.)

Fleur de Lis

Rulau	Date	Metal	Size	VG	F	VF	Unc
Mxo 640	ND	Copper	**	—	—	25.00	—

** Oval, tooth-edged flan, 29x31mm. (Fleur de lis) / 2. A small leaf (?) in ctsp at right. Rv: Blank. (ANS III, F)

PART II

WEST INDIES

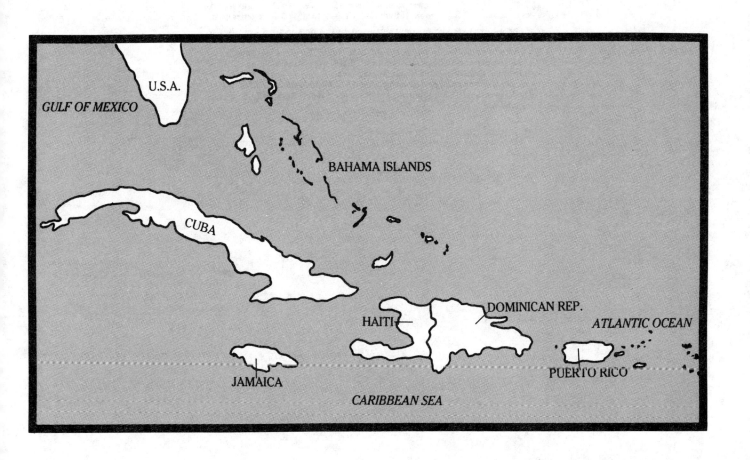

ANTIGUA

St. Johns
H. C.
(Hornel & Coltart)

Rulau	Date	Metal	Size	F	VF	Unc	Proof
Ant 1	1836	Copper	21.5mm	30.00	85.00	175.	300.

Palm tree divides: 18 — 36 / H — C. ANTIGUA below. Rv: ONE / FARTHING / stg within oak and laurel wreath. Plain edge. Weight 4.24 grams. (Pridmore 1; Byrne 1-7; Craig 1; Lyall 1). Die varieties exist.

These tokens are known counterstamped 1, 2, 3 or 4 incused - possibly to increase their trade value. Counterstamped pieces are worth about $80 each.

Hornel and Coltart were merchants in St. John. The firm was founded in 1836 and the tokens issued about 1850. They were acceptable as currency throughout the change-short island for many years.

A proof specimen appeared in the Dec. 1954 Hearn sale in London, lot 77. The Byrne sale of 1975 contained several pieces of the Antigua farthing in varying grades.

BAHAMAS

Almost all the known tokens of the Bahamas are modern gaming pieces made of solid metal or of substances such as fiber, "clay" etc., along with wooden nickels and transportation tokens. All are outside the scope of this catalog. Tokens emitted before 1968 are included.

ABACO ISLAND

Wilson City
THE BAHAMAS TIMBER COMPANY

Rulau	Date	Metal	Size	VG	F	VF	Unc
Bms 1	(1906-16)	Aluminum	23mm	—	—	750.	—

THE / BAHAMAS / -- / TIMBER / COMPANY. Rv: GOOD FOR / 6 C / IN MERCHANDISE. (Lyall 8)

| Bms 2 | (1906-16) | Aluminum | 20mm | — | — | 750. | — |

As last, but 2 C. (Lyall 9)

BIMINI ISLANDS

Cat Cay
ONE KEY (Cat)

Rulau	Date	Metal	Size	VF	EF	Unc	Proof
Bms 5	(1946)	Alum/Brz	38mm	—	—	50.00	

Cat right perched atop a large key. Rv: Old water tower above: ONE KEY. Plain edge. Weight: 21.25 grams. (Pridmore 4; Byrne 15; Lyall 11)

| Bms 6 | (1967) | Gilt/Brz | 38mm | — | — | 60.00 | 90.00 |

As last. Plain edge. Weight: 22 grams. (Byrne 16)

| Bms 7 | (1967) | Silver | 38mm | — | — | — | 180. |

As last. Struck in .925 fine silver, in Proof only. (Byrne 21; Lyall 13)

| Bms 8 | (1946) | WM | 38mm | — | — | 100. | — |

As last, but struck in white metal in double thickness (piefort). Plain edge. Weight: 30 grams. (Byrne 14)

Rulau	Date	Metal	Size	VF	EF	Unc	Proof
Bms 9	(1946)	Alum/Brz	30mm	—	—	40.00	—

Similar to last, but HALF A KEY. Plain edge. Weight: 9 grams. (Pridmore 5; Byrne 18)

| Bms 10 | (1967) | Gilt/Brz | 30mm | — | — | 40.00 | 80.00 |

As last. (Byrne 19; Lyall 16)

| Bms 11 | (1946) | Bronze | 30mm | — | — | 40.00 | — |

As last. (Byrne 17)

| Bms 12 | (1967) | Silver | 30mm | — | — | — | 100. |

As last. Struck in .925 fine silver in Proof only. (Byrne 21)

| Bms 13 | (1946) | Bronze | 24mm | — | — | 300. | — |

Similar to last, but QUARTER KEY. Plain edge. Weight: 5 grams. Extremely rare; only a few specimens are known. (Pridmore 6; Byrne 20)

| Bms 14 | (1967) | Silver | 24mm | — | — | — | 250. |

As last. Struck in .925 fine silver, in Proof only. (Byrne 21)

| Bms 15 | (1967) | Gilt/Brz | 24mm | — | — | — | 100. |

As last. From the gilt bronze Proof sets. (Byrne 22)

These private tokens were issued for Cat Cay (or Cat Key) Islands by their owner, Louis Rice Wasey, for use as gambling pieces and — to a limited extent — as currency in the small group of islets. The denomination "key" was equivalent to one United States dollar.

Designed by Jane Wasey, daughter of the owner, they were struck in 1946 by L. G. Balfour & Co. of Attleboro, Mass.

Sterling silver and gilt bronze proof sets were issued in cases in 1967 for collectors, and these are quite rare. They appeared in the Ray Byrne sale of 1975 as lots 21 and 22.

The quarter key denomination is extremely rare in circulation finish, i.e. bronze finish.

GRAND BAHAMA ISLAND

Grand Bahama Club

Rulau	Date	Metal	Size	VG	F	VF	Unc
Bms 20	(1950)	Silv/Bs	30.5mm	—	7.50	10.00	20.00

Stylized sailfish right, GRAND BAHAMA / CLUB. on ring around. Rv: Sailfish *Istiophorus platypterus* left above 3 / 6. Around: GRAND BAHAMA VALUE / THREE SHILLINGS & SIXPENCE. Plain edge. (Rulau-Fuld Bhm-1; Byrne 27)

| Bms 21 | (1950) | Silv/Bs | 24mm | — | 7.50 | 10.00 | 17.00 |

Obverse as last. Rv: Swordfish *Xiphias gladius* left above 1 / 9. Around: GRAND BAHAMA VALUE / ONE SHILLING & NINE PENCE. Plain edge. (Rulau-Fuld Bhm-2; Byrne 27)

Rulau	Date	Metal	Size	VG	F	VF	Unc
Bms 22	(1950)	Silv/Bs	18mm	—	3.00	5.00	7.50

Obverse as last. Rv: Stylized tuna right, above 9 d.
Around: GRAND BAHAMA VALUE / NINEPENCE.
Plain edge. (Rulau-Fuld Bhm-3; Byrne 27)

Rulau	Date	Metal	Size	VG	F	VF	Unc
Bms 23	(1950)	Silv/Bs	21mm	—	4.00	8.50	12.50

Obverse as last. Rv: Dolphin *Coryphaena hippurus* left,
above 4½ d. Around: GRAND BAHAMA VALUE /
FOURPENCE HALFPENNY. Plain edge.
(Rulau-Fuld Bhm-4; Byrne 27)

In the 1970's a small hoard of these gaming machine tokens entered the
numismatic marketplace and their prices have remained reasonable since. In the
1950 exchange rate, these tokens approximated in U.S. currency: 3 / 6 = 50
cents; 1 / 9 = 25 cents; 9 d = 10 cents; 4½ d = 5 cents. The pound fluctuated near
$2.80.

Fish species were identified by Shedd Aquarium, Chicago personnel.

Used in Grand Bahama Hotel and Country Club.

SOUVENIR OF LUCAYA

Rulau	Date	Metal	Size	F	VF	EF	Unc
Bms 25	(1968)	WM	Irreg 30 mm	—	—	2.75	

Replica of 8-reales cob of pre-1730 Mexico, marked
SOUVENIR / OF / LUCAYA. Rv: Replica of cob
reverse. Cast; the modern inscription is also cast, not
stamped. (Genualdi report)

These pieces exist in thick and thin planchet varieties. This was a promotional
giveaway of Lucayan Land Development about 1968.

LONG ISLAND

EDWIN RAHMING

Rulau	Date	Metal	Size	VG	F	VF	Unc
Bms 28	(1845)	Brass	23mm	—	—	800.	

EDWIN RAHMING / *. Rv: LONG / ISLAND. Plain
edge. (Miller NY 38A; John J. Ford coll.)

Rulau	Date	Metal	Size	VG	F	VF	Unc
Bms 29	(1845)	Brass	14mm	200.	300.	450.	—

As last, but smaller flan. Very rare. (Miller NY 38)

These tokens for 70 years were considered issues of Long Island, New York,
but are now correctly sited.

Long Island is in the southern Bahamas; its principal communities are
Clarence Town and Deadmans Cay.

Edwin Rahming of Clarence Town used these tallies to pay employees raking
salt, according to Bob Lyall. A few pieces were found in the ruins of the Rahming
house in 1960's, but they have been known to collectors since at least 1884.

NEW PROVIDENCE ISLAND

Nassau
THE BRITISH COLONIAL HOTEL

Rulau	Date	Metal	Size	F	VF	EF	Unc
Bms 32	(1934)	Brass	32mm	—	—	60.00	90.00

Palm tree separates B -- C in central circle. Around:
THE BRITISH COLONIAL HOTEL . NASSAU .
BAHAMAS . Rv: Crown above blank panel. Plain edge.
Weight: 11.4 grams. (Byrne 24; Lyall 10)

Gambling piece. These pieces also exist with a number stamped on reverse
panel; EF $50, Unc $80.

DIRTY DICK'S

Rulau	Date	Metal	Size	F	VF	EF	Unc
Bms 34	(1920's)	Brass	Oct 36mm	—	—	250.	

Radiant sun in beaded circle. Around: PRESS SUN
WHEN OVER—WROUGHT / NASSAU. Rv: DIRTY
DICK'S / LUCKY / PIECE / VIRGO (on scroll) / my
monogram / (two cornucopiae). Plain edge. Weight:
14.5 grams. (Byrne 25)

Burned down before 1985. This was a hotel bar.

PILOT HOUSE CLUB

Rulau	Date	Metal	Size	F	VF	EF	Unc
Bms 36	1950	Aluminum	34mm	—	—	—	40.00

PILOT HOUSE CLUB / (sailboat right) / * NASSAU
1950 A.D. *. Rv: GOOD FOR / A DRINK / ON THE
HOUSE. (Lyall 53)

BARBADOS

Bridgetown
T. BOWEN

Rulau	Date	Metal	Size	VG	F	VF	EF
Bbs 3	(1830's)	Copper	36mm	—	—	1400.	—

BOOKSELLER & STATIONER / T. BOWEN / . BARBADOES . in relief, within large double-bordered oval depression, ctsp on England 1797 Cartwheel penny. (Pridmore 30; Byrne 62)

The Bowen family established themselves in Barbados about 1638, only 13 years after British seizure of the island.

Israel Bowen (1802-1880) founded Bowen's Booksellers and Stationers in Church Street, Bridgetown, in 1834. About 1863 he relocated in Broad Street. The firm became Bowen & Sons in 1866 and survived to 1950.

This rare counterstamp appeared in the Dr. H. Peck sale of 1920 as lot 156. It was a feature of the 1975 Byrne sale, where it realized $1300.

It is possible the diesinker used a 'T' rather than an 'I' on his die to create the name T. BOWEN.

THOMAS LAWLOR & CO.

Rulau	Date	Metal	Size	VG	F	VF	Unc
Bbs 7	(ca 1850)	Copper	22mm	—	—	80.00	—

THOMAS LAWLOR & CO. / 11 / BROAD St. / BRIDGETOWN / BARBADOES. Rv: GENERAL / MERCHANTS / AND / COMMISSION / AGENTS. Plain edge. Weight 4.44 grams, (Pridmore 29; Byrne 60)

Bbs 8	(ca 1859)	Brass	22mm 1859)	—	—	65.00	—

As last. Weight 4.24 grams. (Byrne 61)

These tokens are of farthing weight, though they may not have been intended to circulate as farthings.

In 1847, Thomas Lawlor & Co. were at 17 Broad St. and moved to 11 Broad St. in or just before 1850. The firm comprised Thomas Rice Lawlor, William Thomas Barrett, Edward Augustine O'Keefe and Thomas Hayes.

In 1866 Barrett became sole proprietor and changed the firm's name. Lawlor & Co. were dealers in staple and fancy goods, both wholesale and retail.

MOSES TOLANTO

Rulau	Date	Metal	Size	VG	F	VF	Unc
Bbs 10	(1830's)	Copper	29mm	—	—	100.	—

Bale, marked small MT at upper left. Around: MOSES TOLANTO / BARBADOES. Rv: Cask on its side, marked small MT on its top (at left). Around: FREEDOM WITHOUT SLAVERY / *. Plain edge. Heavyweight halfpenny variety, 9.32 grams. (Pridmore 27; Byrne 56-57)

Bbs 11	(1830's)	Copper	29mm	—	—	80.00	—

As last, but lightweight halfpenny variety, 7.75 grams. (Pridmore 27)

Bbs 12	(1830's)	Copper	22mm	—	—	145.	—

Similar to last, but smaller. Farthing, weight 4.52 grams. (Pridmore 28; Byrne 58-59)

Slash-canceled specimens bring about $40 for the halfpenny or $65 for the farthing.

The true name of the issuer was Moses Tolano (no second T). He was a merchant of 33 Swan Street, Bridgetown, who died in May, 1852. His record is in the synagogue in Bridgetown, and his will was published in June, 1852.

Tolano was born late in 1813, the son of Joseph Tolano. He was only 38½ at his death.

Dating the tokens is based upon fabric and style, but also on the fact that slavery was abolished throughout the British West Indies in 1834; it had been a burning question there prior to abolition. Young Jewish men tended to be very liberal and we can assume Tolano espoused abolition.

The heavy and light weight halfpennies indicate a repeat order for tokens was made, but the diesinker's spelling error was not corrected. These pieces were slash/cancelled with a punch to remove their currency status.

The farthing is much more scarce than the halfpennies. The Tolanto pieces are among the "classic" tokens of the West Indies; they were publicized by Scott Stamp & Coin Co. and by Wayte Raymond in their publications. The halfpenny is relatively common in occurrence but has always fetched strong prices.

BRITISH VIRGIN ISLANDS

Buck Island
BUCK ISLAND

Rulau	Date	Metal	Size	F	VF	EF	Unc
Buk 1	1961	CN	36mm	—	—	15.00	20.00

Long-horned goat head facing, divides 19—61. Greek letter Xi between goat's horns. Around: EIRENE / ONE BUCK. Rv: Map of the island. Around: BUCK ISLAND / 18° 25' 45" N B. V. I. 64° 33' 30" W. Plain edge. Mintage: 5,000.(Lyall 135)

Rulau	Date	Metal	Size	F	VF	EF	Unc
Buk 2	(1958)	CN	36mm	—	—	—	35.00

As last, but larger goat head and no date. Pattern (test run) issue. Mintage: 350. (Lyall 134)

Rulau	Date	Metal	Size	F	VF	EF	Unc
Buk 3	(1961)	Bronze	28mm	—	—	20.00	25.00

As first token, but HALF-a-BUCK. Plain edge. Mintage: 2,500 (both bronze and brass).

Rulau	Date	Metal	Size	F	VF	EF	Unc
Buk 4	(1961)	Brass	28mm	—	—	20.00	25.00

As last. Mintage incl. above.

Struck by Osborne Coinage Co., Cincinnati, Ohio. One buck was exchanged for $1 U.S. B.V.I. = British Virgin Islands. Eirene = Peace (in Greek).

Buck Island was owned ca. 1950-78 by William Bailey, who issued these tokens to promote tourism.

Tortola
H.
(Arthur Hodge)

Rulau	Date	Metal	Size	VG	F	VF	EF
Trt 3	(1792-1811)	Copper	22mm	—	20.00	35.00	65.00

H in square frame ctsp on Cayenne sou of 1789 or other date back to 1780. (Pridmore 19A; KM-11)

Genuine Cayenne sous dated 1782 or 1789 with a .208 fine silver content, and contemporary Birmingham counterfeits with no silver content, were equally stamped by Hodge. Arthur Hodge was a planter on Tortola.

Hodge also stamped metropolitan France and colonial 2-sou pieces for use in his plantation (Pridmore 19C), with dates on the host coins ranging from 1738 to 1789.

Rulau	Date	Metal	Size	VG	F	VF	EF
Trt 5	(1792-1811)	Copper	22mm	—	—	35.00	65.00

H in diamond-shaped frame ctsp on Cayenne sou, date worn. (Krueger April 1991 sale, lot 1754; KM-12)

The Krueger cataloger referred to Hodge as the "grand proprietor" and placed his date range as 1800-30.

W. H.

Rulau	Date	Metal	Size	VG	F	VF	EF
Trt 8	(1910-20)	Bronze *	Oct. 33x28mm	—	—	30.00	—

* Bronze, with silver wash on reverse only! (All incused) 50 / W H. Rv: Blank. (Byrne 1176)

Rulau	Date	Metal	Size	VG	F	VF	EF
Trt 9	(1910-20)	Bronze *	Oct 30x29mm	—	—	30.00	—

As last, smaller flan. (Byrne 1177)

CUBA

The Ingenio in Cuba

Each ingenio de azucar (sugar mill) became a large industrial and agricultural complex, resembling a city. In its architecture it displayed the social cleavage existing on each plantation.

There were the houses of the owners or shareholders, who either lived there permanently or visited for some weeks' inspection. Then there were the houses of the senior employees - technical and administrative (permanent or cyclical.) Abodes for the small group of permanent workers and functionaries. And — last — the overcrowded barracks where the mass of migrant workers lived communally in the brief months of the sugar harvest.

The "zafra" (sugar harvest and processing time) annually led to mass migrations of workers graphically called the return of the golondrinas (swallows).

The ingenio controlled the entire commerce around itself — general store for provisions and clothing, barber shop, shoe store, cantina (tavern) and even prostitution.

The tienda mixta (general store, or company store) had its roots in the old slave economy of Cuba. The plantation owners were obligated to satisfy all the basic needs of the slaves, so they maintained stores stocked with rice, codfish, etc., and tools such as machetes; plus blankets, boots and the like.

The ingenio took care of all slave needs, from baptism to burial.

Spain abolished slavery in Cuba quite late, in 1883, and the ingenios had to transform themselves from the slave system to one based upon wage-earning workers. The token system helped the owners to bind the workers to the ingenio almost as firmly as the just-abolished slave system, some authors claim.

The Republic of Cuba banned the use of tokens on ingenios and other plantations in 1902. During the 1930's Cuba banned the use of all tokens as substitutes for money.

Cuban Muncipalities and Provinces

Throughout this catalog, we have attempted to place each token geographically, and then alphabetically, viz: Municipality, State (Province, Department), Nation — all arranged alphabetically. Mavericks are arranged alphabetically.

Where the only geographical location we have is the name of a hacienda or other agricultural, mining or industrial enterprise, the tokens are arranged in that manner. Surnames of issuers are used when other tests of alphabetization fail (remembering that in a Spanish name such as Miguel Gomez Ribero, Gomez - the father's name - is the surname).

Under Cuba we also follow geographic practices used elsewhere in this catalog. Names and boundaries of provinces are given here as they are today, since collectors tend to arrange their tokens in that manner.

Several of Cuba's provinces and cities have different names today than in the Spanish colonial period which ended in 1898. Almost all the hacienda tokens in this catalog were issued before these pieces were outlawed by the new Republic in 1902.

CAMAGUEY PROVINCE
(Puerto Principe Province under Spain)

Maron
YNGENIO SAN SEBASTIAN

Rulau	Date	Metal	Size	VG	F	VF	Unc
Cmg 10	ND	Brass	31mm	—	—	—	—
		YNGENIO / $1oo / SAN SEBASTIAN. Rv: Same as obverse. (Ramsden 119; Eklund 1907; Pesant 344)					
Cmg 11	ND	Brass	21mm	—	—	—	—
		As last, but 50 C. (Ramsden 120; Ek. 1906; Pesant 345)					
Cmg 12	ND	Brass	21mm	—	—	—	—
		INGo. / 10 C / SAN SEBASTIAN. Rv: Same as obverse. (Ramsden 121; Ek. 1905; Pesant 346)					
Cmg 13	ND	Brass	21mm	—	—	—	—
		As last, but 5 C. (Ramsden 122; Ek. 1905; Pesant 346)					

There is dispute over this series. In 1904 Ramsden attributed these to Moron in Oriente Province, and said each bore the legend INGo. (rather than YNGENIO). Pesant, who is occasionally in error, disagrees.

We follow Pesant and David Henkle in the listing above, but acknowledge that Ramsden was an excellent cataloger on the spot, nearly a century ago. No recent sales of these tokens are recorded.

Nuevitas
ALVARO SANCHEZ
Central "Senado"

Rulau	Date	Metal	Size	F	VF	EF	Unc
Cmg 20	ND	Aluminum	Scal				
			26mm	—	26.00	—	37.50
		Sugar mill in circle. Around: CENTRAL / -.- "SENADO" -.-. Rv: 5 in circle. Around: ALVARO / -.- SANCHEZ -.-. (See *TAMS Journal* for Feb. 1986, page 12)					

This owner was, possibly, the father of the next issuer.

BERNABE SANCHEZ ADAN
Central "Senado"

Rulau	Date	Metal	Size	VG	F	VF	Unc
Cmg 22	ND	Aluminum	Oct 25mm	—	25.00	—	—
		Sugar mill in octagonal frame. Around: CENTRAL / -.- "SENADO" -.-. Rv: 10 in octagonal frame. Around: BERNABE SANCHEZ ADAN / -.-. Plain edge. (Schimmel report)					
Cmg 23	ND	Aluminum	Oct 21.5mm	—	20.00	—	—
		As last, but 5. (Pesant 385)					

Operated at least 1913-15. In 1914 this mill produced 200,823 bags of sugar — each weighing 320 pounds, or a total of more than 64 million pounds of sugar.

HAVANA PROVINCE

Aguacate
C. A.

Rulau	Date	Metal	Size	VG	F	VF	Unc
Hav 1	ND	Brass	32mm	—	—	—	—
		C. A. monogram / MADRUGA. Rv: VALE / 1 / PESO. (Pesant 16)					
Hav 2	ND	Brass	27mm	—	—	—	—
		As last, but 50 / CENTAVOS. (Pesant 17)					

Alquizar
INGENIO FORTUNA

Rulau	Date	Metal	Size	VG	F	VF	Unc
Hav 4	ND	Brass	22mm	—	—	—	—
		INGENIO / * FORTUNA *. Rv: MEDIO / * JORNAL *. (Ramsden 36; Eklund 1778; Moreno 23; Pesant 112)					

Medio jornal = Half day's labor. Struck by Francisco Buch, Havana.

Batabano
JULIA R. DE CASUSO
Ingenio La Julia

Rulau	Date	Metal	Size	VG	F	VF	Unc
Hav 8	ND	Brass	32mm	—	—	—	—

INGENIO LA JULIA / * DE LOS / HEREDEROS DE * / JULIA R. DE CASUSO. Rv: VALE A LA TIENDA / 50 / CENTAVOS. Plain edge. (Ramsden 38; Moreno 32; Pesant 130)

Rulau	Date	Metal	Size	VG	F	VF	Unc
Hav 9	ND	Brass	32mm	—	—	—	—

As last, but 20. (Eklund 1796)

Rulau	Date	Metal	Size	VG	F	VF	Unc
Hav 10	ND	Brass	26mm	—	—	—	—

As last, but 10. (Ramsden 39; Eklund 1795; Pesant 131)

Rulau	Date	Metal	Size	VG	F	VF	Unc
Hav 11	ND	Brass	19mm	—	—	—	—

As last, but 5. (Ramsden 40: Eklund 1794: Pesant 132)

Struck by Francisco Buch of Havana. Ingenio La Julia de los herederos de Julia R. de Casuso = La Julia sugar estate of the heirs of Julia R. de Casuso.

F. C. R.
Potrero San Felipe

Rulau	Date	Metal	Size	VG	F	VF	Unc
Hav 13	ND	Brass	19mm	—	—	—	—

POTRERO DILIGENCIA / * SAN FELIPE *. Rv: VALE A LA TIENDA / F. C. R. / * POR CINCO CENTAVOS *. (Ramsden 41; Eklund 1881; Pesant 133)

F. C. R. = Francisco Casuso Rodriguez. Potrero Diligencia = Horse grazing ranch. This was part of Ingenio La Julia at Batabano, according to Ramsden, writing in 1904. Tokens made by Francisco Buch, Havana.

Bejucal
SOLAR
Ingenio Santa Lucia

Rulau	Date	Metal	Size	VG	F	VF	Unc
Hav 15	1882	Copper	18mm	—	—	—	—

INGENIO STA LUCIA / 1882 / SOLAR. Rv: Garland of leaves above: ½ / REAL / VALE. Plain edge. (Moreno 108; Pesant 370)

Rulau	Date	Metal	Size	VG	F	VF	Unc
Hav 16	1882	Copper	22mm	—	—	—	—

As last, but 1 / REAL. (Pesant 369)

Rulau	Date	Metal	Size	VG	F	VF	Unc
Hav 17	1882	Copper	18mm	—	—	—	—

INGENIO STA LUCIA / 1882 / SOLAR. Rv: 10 Cs. (Moreno 109; Pesant 368)

Solar was the proprietor in 1882.

Guines
CENTRAL JOSEFITA

Rulau	Date	Metal	Size	VG	F	VF	Unc
Hav 20	ND	Aluminum	30mm ?	—	—	—	—

TIENDA / DEL / CENTRAL JOSEFITA. Rv: PALOS CUBA / 50 C EN EFECTOS. (Pesant 128)

Rulau	Date	Metal	Size	VG	F	VF	Unc
Hav 21	ND	Brass	18mm	—	—	—	—

As last, but 1 C. (Pesant 129)

HACIENDA SAN FELIPE

Rulau	Date	Metal	Size	VG	F	VF	EF
Hav 23	1874	Copper	27.5mm	—	—	65.00	85.00

(All incused) 1874 at center, HACIENDA SAN FELIPE around. Rv: 30 / CENTAVOS / PLATA. Plain edge. (Ramsden 38; Christensen Nov. 1979 sale, lot 273)

Havana (City)
BELLAIRE

Rulau	Date	Metal	Size	VG	F	VF	Unc
Hav 30	ND	Brass	12-sided 24mm	—	—	35.00	—

Inscription on both sides. (Weyl 1899 catalog; Eklund 1787)

CAFE MARTE Y BELONA

Rulau	Date	Metal	Size	VG	F	VF	Unc
Hav 32	ND	Brass	18mm	—	—	—	—

CAFE / MARTE Y BELONA / HABANA. Rv: 10 / CENTAVOS. (*Numismatic Scrapbook Magazine* for July 1965, pg. 1897)

Waiter check.

CANTINA DE LOS CANOS

Rulau	Date	Metal	Size	VG	F	VF	Unc
Hav 33	ND	Brass	22mm	—	—	Rare	—

(All incused): CANTINA / DE / LOS CANOS. Rv: 5. Plain edge. (ANS coll.)

Unpublished waiter's check. Lettering enameled black.

COCINAS ECONOMICAS
DE LA HABANA

Rulau	Date	Metal	Size	VG	F	VF	Unc
Hav 35	1896	Brass	26mm	—	—	27.50	50.00	—

Two shields, crowned, within wreath. Around: COCINAS ECONOMICAS DE LA HABANA / *. Rv: Seated female facing, anchor, cross and babes around her. Around: UN CENTAVO / * 1896 *. Plain edge.

Cocina Economica = Economic kitchen; a colloquial expression.

EDEN PUBILLONES

Rulau	Date	Metal	Size	VG	F	VF	Unc
Hav 40	ND	Copper	25mm	—	—	—	—

EDEN / 20 / CENTAVOS / PUBILLONES. Rv: Blank. (*Numismatic Scrapbook Magazine* for July 1965, pg. 1899)

Rulau	Date	Metal	Size	VG	F	VF	Unc
Hav 41	ND	Copper	21mm	—	—	—	—

As last, but 10.

Waiter checks.

ENTRADA AL TEATRO

Rulau	Date	Metal	Size	VG	F	VF	Unc
Hav 45	ND	Bronze	27mm	—	—	80.00	125.

Theatrical emblems. Rv: ENTRADA AL TEATRO. / (circular wreath) / (scrollwork).(Ulex 2483; Eklund 1786; Schiaffino 319; ANS coll.)

Entrada al teatro = Admission to the theater. The Ulex collection contained seven pieces. Also claimed as Peru.

ESCUELA "ZAPATA"

Rulau	Date	Metal	Size	F	VF	EF	Unc
Hav 47	(ca 1880)	Brass	36mm	—	—	25.00	—

Within wreath: PREMIO / A LA / APLICACION. Rv: ESCUELA "ZAPATA" / A CARGO / DE LA / SEC-CION DE EDUCACION / Y / BENEFICIENCIA / DE LA /] SOCIEDAD [/ ECONOMICA / DE LA / HABANA. Plain edge.

FERNANDEZ RAMIREZ Y CA

Rulau	Date	Metal	Size	VG	F	VF	Unc
Hav 50	(1860)	WM	Oct 31.5mm	—	—	115.	185.

Two-horse closed carriage (one-axled stagecoach) right, man in tall hat riding one of the horses, while three passengers are seen inside. FERNANDEZ RAMIREZ Y CA around. Exergue is empty. Rv: Two-horse closed carriage left, man in cap riding one horse and three passengers inside. Around: EMPRESA CARRETELAS. Exergue is empty. Plain edge. (Fonrobert 7741; Ulex 2479; Smith 480A)

Empresa carretelas = Carriage enterprise. Kenneth Smith lists this as a transportation token and gives the size as 30mm, as do some other writers. Our catalog does not include transport pieces, but as this is the earliest Cuban TT and the only stagecoach ticket of the West Pubilies, and is not illustrated in Smith, it is included here.

A. GONZALEZ

Rulau	Date	Metal	Size	VG	F	VF	Unc
Hav 55	ND	CN	27mm	—	25.00	—	—

Tobacco plant. Around: ESCOJIDA DE TABACO EN RAMA (choice unprocessed coffee). Rv: SOBS. DE A. GONZALEZ / PPE. ALFONSO / 116 Y 118 / HABANA. Plain edge. (Moreno pg. 42)

B. GUTIERREZ y Ho.

Rulau	Date	Metal	Size	VG	F	VF	Unc
Hav 57	ND	Brass	29mm	—	—	60.00	100.

Crowned Pillar-supported Spanish Arms. Around: B. GUTIERREZ y Ho. / * HABANA. *. Rv: EL 2o NAVIO SOMBRERIA / Y / EFECTOS / MILITARES / -*- / TENIENTE REY No. 24 / ***. Plain edge. Weight 5.59 grams. (Byrne 187)

Navio Sombreria = Ship's hat store. Efectos Militares = Military goods.

Gutierrez and Brother was a store specializing in military goods and ship's hats, caps etc., operating under viceregal authority. The token is well made and official-appearing.

HOTEL YSLA DE CUBA

Rulau	Date	Metal	Size	VG	F	VF	Unc
Hav 60	ND	CN	22mm	—	55.00	75.00	—

(All incused): HOTEL / YSLA DE / CUBA. Rv: 10 / CENTAVOS. Dentilated border on each side. (Eklund 1790; *Numismatic Scrapbook* for July 1965, pg. 1898; Tanenbaum coll.)

A waiter's check. A 20-centavos is also reported. All lettering is blackened with enamel.

LONJA DE VIVERES

Rulau	Date	Metal	Size	VG	F	VF	Unc
Hav 65	ND	CN	23mm	—	30.00	40.00	—

Crowned shield, ENTRADA (admission) below. Rv: LONJA DE VIVERES / (ornament) / DE LA / (ornament) / HABANA. (Byrne 189; Eklund 1782; Zaika coll.)

Lonja de Viveres = Provisions (food) exchange. Admittance check to the Havana Provisions Exchange, a commodity exchange.

Die and size varieties of this token exist. It is said this was a businessmen's club.

LOPEZ Y LLEONART

Rulau	Date	Metal	Size	F	VF	EF	Unc
Hav 67	(1877-79)	Bronze	24mm	—	30.00	45.00	75.00

Head of Alfonso XII right, tiny J MCRAIO R (?) under truncation. Around: JOYERIA * PLATERIA * RELO-JERIA / * BARCELONA *. Rv: Cupid flying over a globe labeled (incuse) LA ISLA DE CUBA. Around: * LOPEZ Y LLEONART **** 12 PLAZA REAL 12 *. Below: (tiny) J FEU FARRICO (?). Plain edge. (Rulau coll., ex-Warmus)

There is another 24mm bronze variety bearing Lauer signature under bust, and with differing reverse.

* According to William Judd, this Barcelona Jewelry firm had branches in Havana, Cuba and in Seville, Spain. The name of the firm was 'La Isla de Cuba'.

David Henkle disputes the attribution to Cuba, saying it is purely Spanish. This token is one of the most beautiful in this reference book.

LOUVRE

Rulau	Date	Metal	Size	VG	F	VF	Unc
Hav 69	ND	Copper	25mm	—	40.00	Rare	

(Eagle) / -LOUVRE- / 40. Letters filled with black enamel. Rv: Blank. (*Numismatic Scrapbook Magazine* for July 1965, pg. 1895; ANS coll.)

This series is also known in denominations of 20, 10 and 5 (centavos), all copper, 25mm. Waiter checks.

Rulau	Date	Metal	Size	VG	F	VF	Unc
Hav 70	ND	Bronze	21mm	—	—	60.00	Rare

Striding youth above laurel sprays at top, * LOUVRE * across center, ornate scrollwork below. Beaded border. Plain edge. (ANS coll.)

MAURI Y FERNANDEZ

Rulau	Date	Metal	Size	VG	F	VF	Unc
Hav 71	ND	Copper	28mm	—	—	—	—

MAURI Y FERNANDEZ / 10. Rv: LA MARNIA / 10. (*Numismatic Scrapbook Magazine* for July 1965, pg. 1898)

Waiter check.

MENDEZ Y CIA.

Rulau	Date	Metal	Size	VG	F	VF	Unc
Hav 73	ND	GS/Zinc	26mm	—	—	60.00	—

LA CAMELIA DE MENDEZ Y Cia * / SAN / RAFAEL 15½, / HABANA / TELEFONO / No 1475. Rv: JMPORTADORES DE JOYERIA * / OBJETOS / DE / ARTE / Y / PERFUMERIA. (Eklund 1788, from 1899 Weyl catalog; Smithsonian coll.)

NOGUES Y LAFITTE

Rulau	Date	Metal	Size	VG	F	VF	Unc
Hav 80	ND	Brass	29mm	—	—	40.00	60.00

Sailing ship at right approaches a beach, sun shining brightly above. Rv: ALMACEN / DE / COMESTIBLES / DE / NOGUES Y LAFITTE / O'REILLY . 13 / HABANA. Plain edge. Weight 6.85 grams. (Byrne 188; Eklund 1789)

Almacen de Comestibles = Grocery (and) provisions. Nogues and Lafitte at O'Reilly No. 13 were partners in the enterprise.

F. SANCHEZ
El Anteojo Jugueteria

Rulau	Date	Metal	Size	VG	F	VF	Unc
Hav 88	1891	Brass	22mm	—	25.00	40.00	—

Baby king of Spain bust right. ALFONSO XIII - POR LA G. DE. DIOS / * 1891 *. Rv: JUGUETERIA QUINCALLERIA / Y JOYERIA / EL ANTEOJO / (quatrefoil) / OBISPO 28 / HABANA. (Eklund 1791)

Rulau	Date	Metal	Size	F	VF	EF	Unc
Hav 90	1897	Brass	38mm	20.00	35.00	—	—

Boy's head of the king left (as on Spanish silver coins of 1896-97). Around: ALFONSO XIII POR LA G. DE DIOS / * 1897 *. Rv: EL ANTEOJO / DE / F. SAN-CHEZ / - / ALMACEN DE NOVEDADES / Y JOYERIA / - / Obispo, 28 / HABANA. Plain edge. (Henkle report)

Jugueteria Quincalleria y Joyeria El Anteojo = 'The Spyglass' toy, hardware and jewelry shop. The address was Obispo 28 in Havana.

M. STACHELBERG & CO.

Rulau	Date	Metal	Size	F	VF	EF	Unc
Hav 92	ND	xx	23mm	—	—	—	55.00

xx Gilt brass shell.

MSC monogram within crowned shield. Around: M. STACHELBERG & CO. FINE HAVANA CIGARS / PAT'D. Rv: Lathe-turned 'target' design. Plain edge. (ANS coll.)

Stachelberg was a New York City importer of tobacco products. The firm issued a number of vulcanite tokens for U.S. use.

The above item may have been a cigar box seal.

TAKEN AT THE HAVANA

Rulau	Date	Metal	Size	F	VF	EF	Unc
Hav 93	1792	Silver	39mm	—	—	—	Rare

TAKEN AT THE / HAVANA 13 AUGt. / 1762 ctsp neatly above the crowned arms on a Spanish-American Pillar 8-reales of 1761-Mo-MM which was new when stamped. Initials W at left and S at right of the Pillars are either stamped or engraved. (Byrne 200)

In the 1975 Byrne sale catalog, auctioneer Jess Peters described this as an engraved piece. It may be, but it appears the main stamp is from a single pre-pared punch.

We believe this punch was applied to a number of fresh Spanish dollars taken in the British capture of Havana in 1762, and these pieces were presented to officers of the expedition, or others, and that differing initials may exist.

A British force of 200 ships and more than 14,000 men commanded by Lord Albemarle and Admiral Sir George Pocock assaulted Havana during the Seven Years War. It was stubbornly defended by the Spaniards, and only when the magazine in Morro Castle blew up was that stronghold taken by storm. Its commanders, Ludovico de Velasco and Vincentio Gonzalez, died in the explosion. The city fell Aug. 13, 1762, and it was held by the British until returned to Spain in the Treaty of Paris, Feb. 10, 1763.

JOSE PABLO XIQUES

Rulau	Date	Metal	Size	VG	F	VF	Unc
Hav 100	ND	Copper	32mm	—	—	35.00	—

Within laurel and palm wreath: Two glasses and a bottle. Rv: JOSE PABLO XIQUES / - / ESCAURIZA. (*Numismatic Scrapbook Magazine* for July 1965, pg. 1895)

Rulau	Date	Metal	Size	VG	F	VF	Unc
Hav 101	ND	Copper	27mm	—	—	35.00	—

As last, but smaller flan.

Waiter checks.

Havana Gambling Tokens

EL CASINO DE CECUTA

Rulau	Date	Metal	Size	F	VF	EF	Unc
Hav 200	ND	CN	Scal 38mm	—	—	20.00	—

EL CASINO / DE CECUTA. Rv: (Ornamentation) / Large ornate 5 / (ornamentation). Weight 11.45 grams. (Byrne 185)

UNA PESETA

Rulau	Date	Metal	Size	F	VF	EF	Unc
Hav 202	(1893-98)	Aluminum	23mm	6.25	11.00	20.00	—

Coronet Liberty head left, 5 stars in arc above, Script J ** P below. Rv: ZO monogram at center, UNA PESETA above, nine 6-pointed stars around. Under 10 known. (Fauver pg. 44)

Rulau	Date	Metal	Size	F	VF	EF	Unc
Hav 203	ND	CN	25mm	6.25	11.00	20.00	—

Coronet Liberty head left within dotted circle, UNA PESETA above, ... (scroll ornament) ... below. Rv: Large 1 in square cartouche surrounded by ornate mantling, PESETA / ....*.... below. Only 6-9 known. (Fauver pg. 44)

CINCO PESETAS

Rulau	Date	Metal	Size	F	VF	EF	Unc
Hav 205	ND	CN	34.6mm	8.50	15.00	27.50	—

Coronet Liberty head right, CINCO PESETAS above, * * * * below. Rv: Crowned, mantled Spanish arms above laurel sprays, * CINCO PESETAS * above. (Fauver pg. 44)

Rulau	Date	Metal	Size	F	VF	EF	Unc
Hav 206	ND	Silv/B	36mm	8.50	15.00	27.50	—

Coronet Liberty head left within shaded circle, * CINCO PESETAS * above, wreath below. Rv: Crowned Spanish arms, CINCO PESETAS above. (Fauver pgs. 20 and 44)

L. B. Fauver in 1990 attributed the above four gaming tokens (202-206) to Spanish Cuba. All are rare, less than 10 known in each case.

Spain has many gaming counters similar to these. Separating the Cuban issues is a tenuous business, without road maps. Havana was a major gaming center in the late Spanish period, 1885-1898, and into the early U.S. period, 1899-1902.

Rulau	Date	Metal	Size	VG	F	VF	Unc
Hav 210	ND	CN	37mm	10.00	—	—	—

* 5 * / PESETAS. Rv: CINCO / (Star in rays) / * PESETAS *. Plain edge. Weight 21.15 grams. (Byrne 184)

Nameless, as are many Cuba pieces of this type. Cinco pesetas ($1) was a standard bet in Havana's casinos. The Byrne specimen in VG realized $9.00 in 1975.

5 PESETAS

Rulau	Date	Metal	Size	VG	F	VF	Unc
Hav 212	ND	CN	38mm	—	9.00	19.00	—

Three riders left jumping their horses over a barrier. Rv: Hexagonal frame encloses numeral 5 in a porthole-like circle, and PESETAS below. Around outside of hexagon is an ornate border. Weight 11.45 grams. (Byrne 186; *World Coins* for July 1971, pg. 946)

Riding club?

Hoyo Colorado
M. DEL C.
Ingenio Jesus Maria

Rulau	Date	Metal	Size	VG	F	VF	Unc
Hav 300	ND	Brass	22mm	—	—	—	—

YNGENIO / -.- / JESUS MARIA. Rv: M. DEL C. / 10 / CENTAVOS. (Moreno 27; Eklund 1793; Ramsden 37)

Hav 301	ND	Brass	20mm	—	—	—	—

As last, but 5. (Moreno 26; Eklund 1792)

M. del C. = Miguel del Corral.

MARTINEZ & GROVE
Central Lucia

Rulau	Date	Metal	Size	VG	F	VF	Unc
Hav 303	ND	Brass	30mm	—	—	25.00	—

(Rosette) CENTRAL LUCIA / TIENDA / MARTINEZ & GROVE (rosette). Rv: 50 / CENTAVOS / EN / EFECTOS / ORO (incuse). Plain edge. (Eklund 1810; Ramsden 42; Pesant 141)

Hav 304	ND	Brass	22mm	—	—	25.00	—

As last, but 10. (Moreno 36; Pesant 142)

These tokens were struck by Francisco Buch in Havana in the 1890's. They can occasionally be found counterstamped R in place of ORO for the new owners of the plantation. En efectos = In goods.

Hav 306	ND	Brass	25.5mm	—	—	40.00	—

CENTRAL LUCIA / TIENDA / * MARTINEZ & GROVE *. Rv: 10 / CENTAVOS / EN / EFECTOS / ctsp R at bottom. Plain edge. Rare. (Rulau coll.)

CENTRAL LUCIA

Rulau	Date	Metal	Size	VG	F	VF	Unc
Hav 308	(1901)	Brass	36mm	—	—	—	—

TIENDA / DEL / "CENTRAL LUCIA". Rv: VALE / $1 / * EN EFECTOS *. Plain edge. (Eklund 1815; Ramsden 43)

Hav 309	(1901)	Brass	30mm	—	—	—	—

As last, but 50 C. (Eklund 1814)

Hav 310	(1901)	Brass	26mm	—	—	—	—

As last, but 20 C. (Eklund 1813)

Hav 311	(1901)	Brass	22mm	—	—	—	—

As last, but 10 C. (Eklund 1812; Moreno 35)

Hav 312	(1901)	Brass	19mm	—	—	—	—

As last, but 5 C. (Eklund 1811)

This set of tokens was made by Buch of Havana in 1901 for the new owners of Central Lucia, who succeeded Martinez & Grove. It is believed the new owner's surname began with R.

Quivican
E. R. H.
Mi Rosa

Rulau	Date	Metal	Size	VG	F	VF	Unc
Hav 320	1884	Brass	22mm	—	—	—	—

Rose. MI ROSA / + 1884 +. Rv: Rose. 25 / E. R. H. (Moreno 52; Pesant 211)

Have 321	1884	Brass	20mm	—	—	25.00	—

As last, but 10. (Moreno 51; Pesant 212)

Hav 322	1884	Brass	18mm	—	—	25.00	—

As last, but 5. (Moreno 50; Eklund 1846; Pesant 213)

Hav 323	1884	Brass	32mm	—	—	—	—

As last, but 50. (Eklund 1847; Ramsden 71; Pesant 210)

E. R. H. = Elena Rosa Hernandez, owner.

San Antonio de las Vegas
INGENIO ALJOVIN

Rulau	Date	Metal	Size	VG	F	VF	Unc
Hav 328	ND	Brass	22mm	—	—	—	—

INGENIO ALJOVIN / SN / ANTONIO / DE LAS / VEGAS. Rv: VALE AL JORNALERO POR 10 CTS. EN BILLETES / EN EFECTOS / DE / BODEGA / DE DICHO / INGENIO. Plain edge. (Moreno 1; Pesant 6)

San Jose de las Lajas
GURE - KAYOLA
(Portugalete)

Rulau	Date	Metal	Size	VG	F	VF	Unc
Hav 330	ND	Brass	27mm	—	—	—	—

Country house with horse in front. Above: GURE - KAYOLA. Rv: Large 20 (shaded) / CENTAVOS. Plain edge. (Ramsden 84; Eklund 1857; Pesant 251)

Hav 331	ND	Brass	22mm	—	—	—	—

As last, but 5. (Ramsden 85; Eklund 1856; Pesant 252)

Ramsden in 1904 reported that these tokens were issued for Portugalete estate, and struck by Francisco Buch of Havana. The phrase Gure - Kayola means "My House" in the Basque language.

Tapaste
STMA. TRINIDAD

Rulau	Date	Metal	Size	VG	F	VF	Unc
Hav 340	1890	CN	31.5mm	—	—	40.00	50.00

STMA. TRINIDAD / (ornaments) / TIENDA / -o- / * 1890 *. Rv: UN PESO / (large open 1, lettered vertically UN PESO) / * EN EFECTOS *. Plain edge. (Eklund 1930; Pesant 381)

Hav 341	1890	CN	26.5mm	—	16.00	25.00	37.50

As last, but CINCUENTA CENTAVOS / *** / 50. (Eklund 1929; Pesant 382)

There are also 20 and 5-centavo CN tokens for Santissima Trinidad plantation dated 1890, all scarce. They are worth 15% less than the 50-centavos.

LAS VILLAS PROVINCE
(Santa Clara Province under Spain)

Cienfuegos
LEON Y CEVALLOS
Ingenio Santa Leocadia

Rulau	Date	Metal	Size	VG	F	VF	Unc
LV 2	1871	Brass	26mm	—	—	—	—
		(All incused): INGENIO STA. LEOCADIA . / ANO / 1871. Rv: LEON Y CEVALLOS / 10 / CENT. Plain edge. (Ramsden 127; Eklund 1915; Moreno 107; Pesant 362)					
LV 3	1871	Brass	19mm	—	—	—	—
		As last, but 5 CENT. (Pesant 363)					

MONTALVO
Ingenio San Lino

Rulau	Date	Metal	Size	VG	F	VF	Unc
LV 5	ND	CN	18.5mm	—	—	—	—
		Sugar cane. Around: AGRICULTURA / * CIENFUEGOS *. Rv: INGE SAN LINO / 10 / * MONTALVO *. Plain edge. (Moreno 98)					

Cruces
INGENIO SAN-FRANCISCO DE SICARD

Rulau	Date	Metal	Size	VG	F	VF	Unc
LV 10	1872	Brass	**	—	—	—	—
		** Star-shaped flan, 31mm. INGENIO / SAN-FRANCISCO / DE / SICARD. Rv: VALE POR / OCHO / REALES FUERTES / 1872. (Ramsden 99; Eklund 1884; Pesant 306)					
LV 11	1872	Brass	28mm	—	—	—	—
		As last, but UN REAL FUERTE. (Fonrobert 10200; Ramsden 100; Eklund 1883; Pesant 307)					

Rulau	Date	Metal	Size	VG	F	VF	Unc
LV 12	1872	Brass	15mm	—	—	—	—
		INGo. / S. FRANCISCO / DE / SICARD. Rv: VALE POR / MEDIO / REAL FUERTE / 1872. (Ramsden 101; Eklund 1882; Pesant 308)					

Ingenio de Azucar is the proper title for a sugar plantation, but the word Ingenio by itself gradually became synonymous with such estates in Latin America, especially in Cuba.

Encrucijada
CENTRAL CONSTANCIA

Rulau	Date	Metal	Size	VG	F	VF	Unc
LV 15	ND	Aluminum	--mm	—	—	—	—
		CENTRAL CONSTANCIA / ENCRUCIJADA. Rv: VIVERES / 50. (Moreno 12)					

Manacas
CENTRAL SAN JOSE

Rulau	Date	Metal	Size	VG	F	VF	Unc
LV 20	ND	Aluminum	25mm	—	—	40.00	65.00
		Sugar mill. CENTRAL SAN JOSE / MANACAS around. Rv: FICHA DEL JORNALLEROS DEL CENTRAL SAN JOSE . / 1 PESETA. Plain edge. (Eklund 1890; Ramsden 107; Pesant 315; Moreno 90; ANS coll.)					

Aluminum 1-peso, 2-peseta and 10 and 5-centavo tokens are known in this series. Eklund has attributed these to Matanzas Province.

Rodas
CENTRAL PARQUE ALTO

Rulau	Date	Metal	Size	VG	F	VF	Unc
LV 25	ND	Brass	23mm	—	—	—	—
		CENTRAL PARQUE ALTO / 50 / * CONGOJAS *. Rv: VALE EN EFECTOS / 50 / * CINCUENTA CENTS *. Plain edge. (Eklund 1855; Moreno 60; Ramsden 77)					
LV 26	ND	Brass	23mm	—	—	—	—
		As last, but 20. (Eklund 1854; Moreno 59)					
LV 27	ND	Brass	23mm	—	—	—	—
		As last, but 10. (Eklund 1853; Moreno 58)					
LV 28	ND	Brass	23mm	—	—	—	—
		As last, but 5. (Eklund 1852; Moreno 57)					

Probably made in U.S.A.

Sagua
THE UNIDAD SUGAR CO.

Rulau	Date	Metal	Size	VG	F	VF	Unc
LV 30	ND	Brass	38mm	—	—	—	—

UN PESO / 100 / . THE UNIDAD SUGAR CO. . Rv: VALEDERA PARA / EMPLEADOS / DE / UNIDAD / * SOLAMENTE *. Plain edge. (Pesant 102)

Rulau	Date	Metal	Size	VG	F	VF	Unc
LV 31	ND	Brass	33mm	—	—	35.00	55.00

As last, but CINCUENTA CENTAVOS / 50. (Pesant 402)

Rulau	Date	Metal	Size	VG	F	VF	Unc
LV 33	ND	Brass	29mm	—	12.50	—	—

As last, but DIEZ CENTAVOS / 10. (Moreno 117; Pesant 404)

Rulau	Date	Metal	Size	VG	F	VF	Unc
LV 35	ND	Brass	19mm	—	—	—	—

As last, but UN CENTAVO / 1. (Eklund 1931; Moreno 115; Pesant 406)

There are also 25 and 5-centavo brass tokens in this series.

Santa Clara
CENTRAL CARACAS

Rulau	Date	Metal	Size	VG	F	VF	Unc
LV 39	ND	Alum	28mm	—	—	—	—

CENTRAL CARACAS / (star) / TIENDA. Rv: VEINTE CENTAVOS / 20 / EN EFECTOS. (Pesant 47)

Rulau	Date	Metal	Size	VG	F	VF	Unc
LV 40	1893	CN	22mm	—	—	—	—

CENTRAL CARACAS / TIENDA / 1893. Rv: DIEZ CENTAVOS / 10 / EN EFECTOS. (Moreno 7; Pesant 48)

Rulau	Date	Metal	Size	VG	F	VF	Unc
LV 41	1893	CN	19mm	—	—	—	—

As last, but 5. (Moreno 6; Pesant 49)

Yaguajay
NARCISA SUGAR CO.

Rulau	Date	Metal	Size	VG	F	VF	Unc
LV 50	ND	Alum	33mm	—	—	—	—

50 / CENTRAL NARCISA / YAGUAJAY. Rv: 50 / NARCISA SUGAR CO. / NEW YORK — HABANA. (Moreno 55)

Rulau	Date	Metal	Size	VG	F	VF	Unc
LV 51	ND	Alum	29mm	—	—	—	—

As last, but 25. (Moreno 54)

Rulau	Date	Metal	Size	VG	F	VF	Unc
LV 52	ND	Alum	24mm	—	—	—	—

As last, but 10. (Moreno 53)

MATANZAS PROVINCE

Alacranes
PEREZ Y ESCARDO
Ingenio Conchita

Rulau	Date	Metal	Size	VG	F	VF	Unc
Mat 3	ND	CN	26mm	—	—	—	—

TIENDA INGENIO CONCHITA / PEREZ / Y / ESCARDO / *. Rv: VALE A LA TIENDA / 25 Cs. / EN / EFECTOS. Plain edge. (Moreno 11; Eklund 1754; Ramsden 20)

Rulau	Date	Metal	Size	VG	F	VF	Unc
Mat 4	ND	Brass	23mm	—	—	—	—

As last, but 10 Cs. (Moreno 10; Eklund 1753)

Rulau	Date	Metal	Size	VG	F	VF	Unc
Mat 5	ND	Brass	19mm	—	—	—	—

As last, but 5 Cs. (Moreno 8-9; Eklund 1752)

These tokens occur with and without countermarked letters E and P, usually found together on the same token.

The tokens were struck by Buch of Havana.

Banaguises
SANTA GERTRUDIS

Rulau	Date	Metal	Size	VG	F	VF	Unc
Mat 8	1861	Copper	20mm	—	—	—	—

Mountain range, SANTA GERTRUDIS. Rv: Garland of leaves, UN REAL / 1861. Plain edge. (Moreno 105; Eklund 2174)

Rulau	Date	Metal	Size	VG	F	VF	Unc
Mat 10	ND	Brass	22mm	—	—	—	—

TIENDA / STA. / GERTRUDIS / BENAGUISES. Rv: 10 Cts. (Eklund N/L; Pesant 358)

Rulau	Date	Metal	Size	VG	F	VF	Unc
Mat 11	ND	Brass	22mm	—	—	—	—

As last, but 5 Cts. (Eklund 1913; Pesant 359; Ramsden 125)

Bermeja
MARAGLIANO
Ingenio La Benita

Rulau	Date	Metal	Size	VG	F	VF	Unc
Mat 15	(1882)	CN	21mm	—	—	45.00	60.00

Shield of arms. Rv: INGENIO LA BENITA / 10 / * MARAGLIANO *. There is a tiny G-L under the coat of arms for the designer, G. Loos. Plain edge. (Ulex 2487; Pesant 37; Moreno 30; Eklund 1799; Ramsden 8)

Rulau	Date	Metal	Size	VG	F	VF	Unc
Mat 16	(1882)	Bronze	21mm	—	—	40.00	50.00

As last, but 5. (Moreno 29; Eklund 1798)

Rulau	Date	Metal	Size	VG	F	VF	Unc
Mat 17	(1882)	Copper	21mm	—	—	40.00	50.00

As last, but 2½. (Ulex 2487; Eklund 1797; Moreno 28)

Benito Maragliano, the owner, caused this issue to be struck at the Imperial German Mint, Berlin. For similar pieces struck for neighboring Matanzas plantations at Berlin, see E. Deschapelles (Eden Park) and Lobeck (Maria Luisa).

Calimete
INGENIO CENTRAL MARIA

Rulau	Date	Metal	Size	VG	F	VF	Unc
Mat 20	ND	Brass	17mm	—	—	—	—

INGENIO CENTRAL MARIA / BODEGA / EL / CARMEN / * CALIMETE *. Rv: VALE A LA BODEGA / 2½ / CENTS. / EN - EFECTOS -. (Ramsden 52; Eklund 1820; Pesant 160; Moreno 38)

Pesant reports 5 and 10-centavo tokens of this type. All made by Buch of Havana, said Ramsden in 1904.

Cardenas
CENTRAL DOS ROSAS

Rulau	Date	Metal	Size	VG	F	VF	Unc
Mat 22	ND	Brass	29mm	—	—	—	—
		(All incused): CENTRAL DOS ROSAS (L inverted) / 40. Rv: Blank. Plain edge. (Eklund 1766; Ramsden 27)					
Mat 23	ND	Brass	29mm	—	—	—	—
		As last, but 20. (Eklund 1765)					
Mat 24	ND	Brass	29mm	—	—	—	—
		As last, but 10. (Eklund 1764)					
Mat 25	ND	Brass	29mm	—	—	—	—
		As last, but 0.5. (Moreno 13; Eklund 1763)					

CAMARIOCA
Central Precioso

Rulau	Date	Metal	Size	VG	F	VF	Unc
Mat 27	ND	CN	26mm	—	—	—	—
		Steer left in central circle. Around: CENTRAL PRECIOSA / . CAMARIOCA . Rv: 40 / CENTAVOS. Plain edge. (Moreno 63; Eklund 1863; Ramsden 86)					
Mat 28	ND	CN	22mm	—	—	—	—
		Plow right at center. Around: CENTRAL PRECIOSO / CAMARIOCA. Rv: 20 / CENTAVOS. (Moreno 62; Eklund 1862)					
Mat 29	ND	Brass	22mm	—	—	—	—
		Sugar mill at center, CENTRAL PRECIOSO / CAMARIOCA around. Rv: 5 / CENTAVOS. (Moreno 61; Eklund 1861)					

All struck by Francisco Buch of Havana.

Cidra
MARQUES DE MONTELO
Hacienda San Cayetano

Rulau	Date	Metal	Size	VG	F	VF	Unc
Mat 33	ND	Brass	37mm	—	—	—	—
		MARQUES DE MONTELO / 1 / (ornament). Rv: Crowned ornamental M (the Montelo monogram). Plain edge. (Eklund 1880; Moreno 80; Ramsden 97)					

1 = One peso.

Rulau	Date	Metal	Size	VG	F	VF	Unc
Mat 34	ND	Brass	30mm	—	—	—	—
		As last, but 50 (centavos). (Eklund 1879; Moreno 79)					
Mat 35	ND	Bras	26mm	—	—	—	—
		As last, but 20. (Moreno 78; Eklund 2407)					
Mat 36	ND	Brass	17mm	—	—	—	—
		As last, but 10. (Eklund 1878; Moreno 77; Pesant 300)					
Mat 37	ND	Brass	15mm	—	—	—	—
		As last, but 5 (centavos). (Eklund 1877; Moreno 76)					

Jose Luis Alfonso, Marques de Montelo, was the owner of San Cayetano hacienda in Cidra municipality.

Colon
S. C.
Angostura

Rulau	Date	Metal	Size	VG	F	VF	Unc
Mat 40	ND	Brass	24mm	—	—	—	—
		(All incused): C. ANGOSTURA / S. C. / 5. Rv: Blank. (Ramsden 2; Eklund 1735; Pesant 15)					

S. C. = Saavedra y Camara. C. Angostura = Central Angostura ?

INGENIO ESPAÑA

Rulau	Date	Metal	Size	VG	F	VF	Unc
Mat 42	ND	Brass	33mm	—	—	—	—
		:Lion rampant, INGENIO / ESPAÑA around. Rv: VALE / 1 PESO. (Moreno 21; Eklund 1772; Ramsden 35)					

Made by Buch, Havana.

LA PERLA

Rulau	Date	Metal	Size	VG	F	VF	Unc
Mat 45	ND	Gilt/Bs	13mm	—	—	45.00	70.00
		LA / PERLA within wreath. Rv: VIVE / RES within wreath. Plain edge. (Pesant 239; Rulau coll.)					
Mat 46	ND	Gilt/Bs	19mm	—	—	65.00	—
		As last, larger. (Pesant 238)					
Mat 47	ND	Gilt/Bs	26mm	—	—	65.00	—
		As last, larger. (Pesant 237)					

The Rulau collection contains three Unc. specimens of the 13mm token which were found among the effects of a Scovill Mfg. Co. employee well after his death. The employee had been a numismatist. Viveres = Provisions.

Other Scovill products in the employee's possession had been dated in the 1855-1880 period, including the Pilar and Belen pieces which Pesant believes were Cuban tokens.

Cuevitas
J. POLLEDO
Yngenio Asturias

Rulau	Date	Metal	Size	VG	F	VF	Unc
Mat 50	1876	CN	23mm	—	—	—	—
		Plow left, 1876 below. Rv: YNGo. ASTURIAS / UN / PESO / * DE J. POLLEDO *. Plain edge. (Ramsden 3; Eklund 1740; Moreno 5; Pesant 22)					
Mat 51	1876	CN	21mm	—	—	—	—
		Upright barrel, 1876 below. Rv: As last, but 50 / CENTAVOS. (Ramsden 4; Eklund 1739; Moreno 4; Pesant 23)					
Mat 52	1876	Copper	23mm	—	—	35.00	45.00
		Cow standing left, 1876 below. Rv: As last, but 20. (Ramsden 5; Eklund 1738; Pesant 24)					
Mat 53	1876	Copper	21mm	—	—	35.00	45.00
		Horse galloping right, 1876 below. Rv: As last, but 10. (Eklund 1737; Moreno 3; Pesant 25)					
Mat 54	1876	Copper	19mm	—	—	—	—
		Indian head left, 1876 below. Rv: As last, but 5. (Ramsden 6; Eklund 1736; Moreno 2; Pesant 26)					
Mat 55	1876	CN	19mm	—	—	—	—
		As last. Possibly trial strike. (Pesant 26)					

Joaquin Polledo, the owner, ordered his tokens struck in the United States.

Pesant assigned these tokens to Cienfuegos in Las Villas Province, but Ramsden in 1904 noted that Yngenio Asturias was at Cuevitas in Matanzas Province.

Guamutas
NICOLAS MARTINEZ DE VALDIVIELSO
Aurora

Rulau	Date	Metal	Size	VG	F	VF	Unc
Mat 58	ND	Copper	30mm	—	—	—	—

(All incused): NICOLAS MARTINEZ DE VALDI-VIELSO / * / AURORA / J. N. M. / DE . Rv: Blank. (Ramsden 7; Eklund 1741; Pesant 27)

Guira de Macurijes
INGENIO SAN MIGUEL

Rulau	Date	Metal	Size	VG	F	VF	Unc
Mat 60	ND	Brass	15.5mm	—	30.00	—	—

INGENIO / SAN / (MIGUEL *. Rv: Large open 5. Beaded border on each side. Plain edge. (Eklund 2408; Gary Pipher Oct. 1987 sale, lot 2273)

This piece fetched $29.50 in a Pipher 1987 auction in Fine, and had realized $15 in VF in a Nov. 1973 sale by Craig.

Mat 62	ND	Brass	20mm	—	—	—	—

INGo. / SAN / * MIGUEL *. Rv: Large 10. Plain edge. (Eklund 1902; Pesant 342; Ramsden 118 in 1904)

Mat 63	ND	Brass	20mm	—	—	—	—

As last, but Cross ctsp on obverse. (Eklund note 1902)

There is another Ingenio San Miguel, in Guantanamo, Oriente, which issued tokens. Please see this.
Ramsden reports that Buch of Havana struck these pieces.

Hato Nuevo
LA MERCED

Rulau	Date	Metal	Size	VG	F	VF	Unc
Mat 65	ND	Brass	26mm	—	—	—	—

INGO. / LA / MERCED . Rv: 50 Cts. / EN EFECTOS / TIENDA. (Eklund 1801; Moreno 34)

Mat 66	ND	Brass	--mm	—	—	—	—

As last, but 10 Cts. (Moreno 33)

Made by Francisco Buch, Havana.

Itabo
SAN JOSE ITABO

Rulau	Date	Metal	Size	VG	F	VF	Unc
Mat 70	1891	Brass	32mm	—	—	—	60.00

SAN JOSE / 1891 / * ITABO *. Rv: EFECTOS / $ 1 / * TIENDA *. Plain edge. (Ramsden 110; Eklund 1898; Moreno 96; Zaffern coll.)

Rulau	Date	Metal	Size	VG	F	VF	Unc
Mat 71	1891	Brass	26mm	—	—	—	—

As last, but 50 Cs. (Moreno 95)

Mat 72	1891	Brass	19mm	—	—	—	—

As last, but 10 Cs. (Moreno 92)

Mat 74	1892	CN	32mm	—	—	—	60.00

As the $1 token above, but dated 1892. (Ramsden 111; Eklund 1898; Pesant 320; Moreno 96). Pesant also reports this token in Brass; not verified.

Mat 75	1892	CN	26mm	—	—	—	—

As last, but 50 Cs. (Ramsden 112; Eklund 1897; Pesant 321)

Mat 76	1892	CN	22mm	—	—	—	—

As last, but 20 Cs. (Ramsden 113; Eklund 1896; Pesant 322; Moreno 94)

Mat 77	1892	CN	19mm	—	—	—	—

As last, but 5 Cs. (Ramsden 114; Eklund 1895; Pesant 323, Moreno 93)

Mat 78	1892	CN	17mm	—	—	—	—

As last, but 5 Cs. (Ramsden 115; Eklund 1894; Pesant 324)

Ramsden reported that the 1892 series was struck by Francisco Buch of Havana from recut 1891 dies. He noted that the 1892 peso clearly showed a '2' cut over the second '1' of the date.
We follow Pesant in attributing these tokens to Itabo in Matanzas. Ramsden had indicated Guamuta in Matanzas was the site.
The 1892 series may exist in Brass, but we have not examined any.

Jovellanos
M. Y J. F. DE LA VEGA
Yngenio Ecuador

Rulau	Date	Metal	Size	VG	F	VF	Unc
Mat 80	1864	Copper	19mm	—	—	67.50	—

Royal palm tree. Around: YNGENIO ECUADOR. Rv: M. y J. F. DE LA VEGA / VALE / POR / UN / REAL / .*. Plain edge. Thick flan. (Fonrobert 8326; Eklund 1166; Moreno 14; Pesant 83)

Mat 81	1864	Brass	19mm	—	—	—	—

As last, but in Brass. Thin flan. (Eklund 1167; ANS collection)

The obverse die has been muled with the "Contrahendo et Solvendo / o 2 o / S. P." die known to have been used about 1863 and sometimes listed as a U.S. Civil War token or token of Brazil or Mexico. (See Russell Rulau's *U.S. Trade Tokens 1866-1889* for full explanation.)
The Yngenio Ecuador tokens were attributed in 1878 by Fonrobert's cataloger to the South American nation of Ecuador, in error, but they were long thought to be from there.
There is a small place named Ecuador in Camaguey Province, Cuba, west of Guaimaro. There may be no connection.

LOBECK
Ingenio Maria Luisa

Rulau	Date	Metal	Size	VG	F	VF	Unc
Mat 85	(1882)	CN	21mm	—	—	45.00	60.00

Ornate crested shield of arms. Rv: INGENIO MARIA LUISA / 10 / * LOBECK *. Plain edge. (*Berliner Munz-Blatter* for July 1882; Ulex 2487; Ramsden 53; Eklund 1823; Pesant 162; Moreno 40)

Rulau	Date	Metal	Size	VG	F	VF	Unc
Mat 86	(1882)	Brass	21mm	—	—	40.00	50.00

As last, but 5. (Ek. 1822; Pesant 163)

Rulau	Date	Metal	Size	VG	F	VF	Unc
Mat 87	(1882)	Copper	21mm	—	—	40.00	50.00

As last, but 2½. (Ulex 2487; Ek. 1821; Pesant 164)

We follow Ramsden in attributing this site to Jovellanos in Matanzas. Pesant advanced Agramonte as the site.

Adolf Weyl in the 1882 *Berliner Munz-Blatter* revealed that the tokens of Ingenio Maria Luisa (and also those of Ingenio Eden Park and Ingenio La Benita) were struck at the Imperial German Mint, Berlin. Blanks for the cupronickel 10-pfennig coin of Germany, KM-4, were used for the 10-centavo tokens, and blanks for the copper 2-pfennig coin, KM-2, were used for the 2½-centavo tokens. Specially prepared 21mm brass planchets were used for the 5-centavo tokens.

The tokens of La Benita and Eden Park carry the tiny initials G -- L flanking the arms on their obverses, and apparently Pesant was led by this to attribute their striking to "G. F. Lovett in New York." George Hampden Lovett of New York normally used the signature G.H.L. and his workmanship was always indifferent, whereas the Maria Luisa, La Benita and Eden Park tokens are of superb execution. They have the look and feel of German craftsmanship.

The owners of the three estates, Lobeck, Maragliano and Deschapelles, were most likely European immigrants accustomed to Old Country workmanship and placed their orders together.

The signature G.L. was well known in Berlin. It had been one of the signatures of Gottfried B. Loos, founder of the private Berlin Medallic Mint 1812-43, and then of his kinsman G. Loos 1881-1907. The Loos firm did much work for the Imperial German Mint in Berlin; its founder, Gottfried B. Loos, had been Berlin Mint director 1806-12 when it was the Prussian State Mint.

It is possible the tokens were struck at Loos' Berlin Medallic Mint, but we see no reason to doubt Weyl's 1882 report. Berlin Mint official records may even reveal the number of pieces made, but we have been unable to find the entries. (See Leonard Forrer's *Biographical Dictionary of Medalists*, vol. VII, pages 561-562.)

TIENDA DEL CENTRAL MERCEDES

Rulau	Date	Metal	Size	VG	F	VF	Unc
Mat 89	ND	Brass	Oct 23mm				

-*- / TIENDA DEL / CENTRAL / MERCEDES / CUBA. / -+-. Rv: -.- / DESPACHE / 5 C / MERCANCIAS / -.-. Plain edge. (Moreno 44; Pesant 179)

Rulau	Date	Metal	Size	VG	F	VF	Unc
Mat 90	ND	Brass	Sq 18.5mm	—	—	—	—

As last, but 1 C. (Moreno 41; Pesant 181)

These are part of a series of tokens, in brass and aluminum, from 50-centavos to 1-centavo.

Macurijes
R. G.
Ingenio Maravilla

Rulau	Date	Metal	Size	VG	F	VF	Unc
Mat 92	ND	Brass	26mm	—	—	—	—

INGENIO MARAVILLA * / R. G. Rv: VALE / 2 / REALES. (Eklund 1819; Ramsden 49)

Rulau	Date	Metal	Size	VG	F	VF	Unc
Mat 93	ND	Brass	22mm	—	—	—	—

As last, but VALE / 1 / REAL. (Eklund 1818)

Rulau	Date	Metal	Size	VG	F	VF	Unc
Mat 94	ND	Brass	16mm	—	—	—	—

As last, but VALE / ½. (Moreno 37; Ek. 1817)

YNGENIO SOCORRO

Rulau	Date	Metal	Size	VG	F	VF	Unc
Mat 96	1882	CN	26mm	—	—	—	—

(All incused): YNGENIO SOCORRO 1882. Rv: 20. (Pesant 387)

Rulau	Date	Metal	Size	VG	F	VF	Unc
Mat 98	1887	Brass	28mm	—	—	—	—

(All incused): SOLO PARA OPERARIOS / 1887. Rv: 20. (Ramsden 133; Eklund 1922; Pesant 388)

Rulau	Date	Metal	Size	VG	F	VF	Unc
Mat 99	1887	Brass	23mm	—	—	—	—

As last, but 10. (Ramsden 134; Ek. 1921; Pesant 389)

Both 1887 tokens may also exist in CN.

Roberto Pesant says that these pieces were used at the plantation Socorro de Armas near Macurijes. Ramsden reported the same fact concerning the 1887 pieces in his 1904 opus.

Matanzas
ARANZABE LABAYEN & CO.

Rulau	Date	Metal	Size	VG	F	VF	Unc
Mat 103	ND	Copper	--mm	20.00	40.00	60.00	—

ARANZABE LABAYEN & CO. / FERRE TERIA. (Ulex 2497; Eklund 1825)

Ferreteria = Hardware store.

LABAYEN Y HERMANO

Rulau	Date	Metal	Size	VG	F	VF	Unc
Mat 104	(1858)	WM	32.5mm	20.00	40.00	70.00	125.

Padlock. Around: LABAYEN Y HERMANO MATANZAS *. Rv: Sidewheeler "Great Eastern" with six masts. Above: VAPOR / LEVIATHAN. In exergue: 293 VARES LARGO / 22300 TONELs. Plain edge. (Fonrobert 7744; Christensen 1; Eklund 1824)

VAPOR = Steamboat.

This was struck for the *Great Eastern* of England when she was still called Leviathan. Once launched, she was known as Great Eastern, and visited New York City in a memorable voyage in 1860. Later (1866) she laid the Atlantic Cable.

RAFAEL VILLAR

Rulau	Date	Metal	Size		F	VF	EF	Unc
Mat 109	ND	Copper	30mm		—	—	—	35.00

Globe, book, wreath and pen. Rv: PREMIO A LA APLICACION / RAFAEL VILLAR / STUDIOS AE (monogram) / JUVENTUTI / MATANZAS. Plain edge. (Rulau coll.)

Struck by Scovill Mfg. Co., Waterbury, Conn.

Mecurijes
A. Y. CA.
Ingenio Andrea

Rulau	Date	Metal	Size	VG	F	VF	Unc
Mat 120	ND	Brass	26mm	—	—	—	—

INGENIO / ANDREA. Rv: A. y Ca. / TERCERA.
(Ramsden 1; Eklund 1733; Pesant 11)

Tercera = Third (of what ?). Probably made by Buch, Havana.

Navajas
E. DESCHAPELLES
Ingenio Eden Park

Rulau	Date	Metal	Size	VG	F	VF	Unc
Mat 125	(1882)	CN	21mm	—	—	45.00	60.00

Coat of arms. Tiny G – L below. Rv: INGENIO EDEN
PARK / 10 / E. DESCHAPELLES. Plain edge. (Ulex
2457; Ramsden 32; Eklund 1770; Pesant 84; Moreno
17)

Rulau	Date	Metal	Size	VG	F	VF	Unc
Mat 126	(1882)	Brass	21mm	—	—	40.00	50.00

As last, but 5. (Ek. 1769; Pesant 85; Moreno 16)

Rulau	Date	Metal	Size	VG	F	VF	Unc
Mat 127	(1882)	Copper	21mm	—	—	40.00	50.00

As last, but 2½. (Ulex 2457; Ek. 1768; Pesant 86;
Moreno 15)

These tokens were struck at the Imperial German Mint, Berlin, designed by G.
Loos. the 1882 *Berliner Munz-Blatter*, pg. 292, recorded the striking. These
pieces greatly resemble the German fractional coins of the late 19th century.
(For full explanation, see the footnotes after Lobeck in Jovellanos, Matanzas
Province in this reference.)

TIENDA DEL
CENTRAL MERCEDES
Sabanilla de Guareiras

Rulau	Date	Metal	Size	VG	F	VF	Unc
Mat 130	ND	Brass	21mm	—	—	—	—

-*- / TIENDA DEL CENTRAL / MERCEDES / -+-.
Rv: -.- / SABANILLA / DE GUAREIRAS / 10 C /
CUBA / -.-. Plain edge. (Moreno 45; Pesant 185)

Rulau	Date	Metal	Size	VG	F	VF	Unc
Mat 131	ND	Brass	19mm	—	—	—	31.00

As last, but 2 C. (Moreno 43; Pesant 187)

Rulau	Date	Metal	Size	VG	F	VF	Unc
Mat 132	ND	Brass	19mm	—	—	—	31.00

As last, but 1 C. (Moreno 42; Pesant 188)

These are part of a series, in brass and aluminum, from 50-centavos down.

ORIENTE PROVINCE
(Santiago de Cuba
Province under Spain)

Bahia de Moa
FREEPORT NICKEL
COMPANY

Rulau	Date	Metal	Size	F	VF	EF	Unc
Ori 3	ND	CN *	39mm	—	—	—	40.00

* Antiqued cupronickel flan.
Map of Caribbean area, showing Port Nickel, Louisiana
and Moa Bay, Cuba. FREEPORT NICKEL COM-
PANY / FIRST PRODUCTION. Rv: Building. COM-
PANIA MINERA / BAHIA DE MOA. Plain edge.
(Grinolds Aug. 1989 sale, lot 313)

Nickel mining company medal issued before Castro's revolution in 1959. Moa
Bay is on the north coast of Oriente Prov.
This medalet fetched $38 in the August 1989 Grinolds sale.

Banes
BANES

Rulau	Date	Metal	Size	VG	F	VF	Unc
Ori 6	1888	Brass	25.5mm	—	27.50	—	—

Stalk of bananas, BANES above. Rv: VALE POR / ½ /
JORNAL / 1888. Plain edge. (Pesant 701)

Banana plantation token. ½ JORNAL = Half day's work.

Rulau	Date	Metal	Size	VG	F	VF	Unc
Ori 8	1888	Brass	20mm	—	—	25.00	—

As last, but UNA / RACION in place of ½ / JORNAL.
(Eklund 2065; Pesant 703)

Rulau	Date	Metal	Size	VG	F	VF	Unc
Ori 9	1888	Brass	20mm	—	—	—	—

As last, but ½ / RACION. (Eklund 2065A; Rich Ecke-
brecht report)

BAYAMO

Municipio

Rulau	Date	Metal	Size	VG	F	VF	Unc
Ori 11	ND	Copper	Oct 30mm	—	—	—	—

(All incused): 1 R within circle. Around: MUNICIPIO
* / DE BAYAMO / S at left divides the inscription. Rv:
Same, but in relief (intaglio). Thin flan. Plain edge.
(Ulex 2454; Eklund 1742)

Chaparra
THE CHAPARRA SUGAR CO.

Rulau	Date	Metal	Size	VG	F	VF	Unc
Ori 15	(1890's)	Aluminum Scal	30mm				

THE CHAPARRA / -*- / SUGAR CO. / -*- / CUBA. Rv: VALE / * 10 * / CENTAVOS. (Moreno 114; Eklund 1751)

Rulau	Date	Metal	Size	VG	F	VF	Unc
Ori 16	(1890's)	Aluminum Scal	26mm	—	—	—	—

As last, but 5. (Moreno 113)

Eklund says was located in Puerto Padre.

Cuavitas
U. DE C.

Rulau	Date	Metal	Size	VG	F	VF	Unc
Ori 19	ND	Brass	22mm	—	—	—	—

U. de C. Rv: 50 / CENTAVOS. (Pesant 407)

U. de C. = Union de Cuavitas, possibly a sugar enterprise.

Gibara
S. R.
El Carmen

Rulau	Date	Metal	Size	VG	F	VF	Unc
Ori 22	ND	Brass	22mm	—	—	—	—

EL CARMEN / S. R. / 10 CTS. Rv: Blank. (Pesant 50)

Rulau	Date	Metal	Size	VG	F	VF	Unc
Ori 23	ND	Brass	22mm	—	—	—	—

As last, but 5 CTS. (Ramsden 12; Eklund 1747; Pesant 51)

RAFAEL L. SANCHEZ
SUCESION
Central Santa Lucia

Rulau	Date	Metal	Size	VG	F	VF	Unc
Ori 25	1882	Copper	20mm	—	20.00	30.00	40.00

SUCESION RAFAEL L. SANCHEZ / DE. Rv: UNA RACION. 1882. (Pesant 364; Ramsden 129)

Rulau	Date	Metal	Size	VG	F	VF	Unc
Ori 27	1884	CN	20mm	—	12.50	20.00	—

Royal palm tree in circle. Around: CENTRAL SANTA LUCIA / GIBARA. Rv: VALE POR / UNA RACION / RLS monogram / 1884. Plain edge. (Ulex 2458; Pesant 365; Moreno 111; Rulau coll.; Zaffern coll.; Ramsden 131). There are 3 die varieties.

Rulau	Date	Metal	Size	VG	F	VF	Unc
Ori 30	1884	CN	35mm	—	15.00	20.00	—

Plow in center. Around: CENTRAL SANTA LUCIA / GIBARA. Rv: VALE POR / UN JORNAL / RLS monogram / 1884. (Moreno 112; Ramsden 130)

Rulau	Date	Metal	Size	VG	F	VF	Unc
Ori 32	1886	CN	16mm	—	10.00	15.00	—

CENTRAL SANTA LUCIA / (palm tree) / GIBARA. Rv: VALE POR MEDIA RACION / $ / 1886. (Gary Pipher Oct. 1987 sale, lot 2274; Ramsden 132)

Sucesion = Succession, or Offspring. Racion = Ration. Jornal = Day's work.

The William Christensen Nov. 1979 sale offered two pieces of the 1882 and four pieces of the 1884 tokens, as lots 275 and 276.

The large sugar central of Santa Lucia in the Gibara area came to dominate the economy of all the surrounding villages. This central, one of the largest such complexes in the world at the end of the 19th century, had: 5 large general stores, 7 purveyors of provisions, 1 shoe store, 1 distillery, 3 barber shops, 1 pharmacy, 9 cantinas (taverns), 1 school, 1 confectionery, 2 inns (the largest in the region), 3 blacksmith shops, 3 bakeries, 3 clothing stores, 2 tailor shops and 1 saddlery.

In all of these shops the exclusive coin used was the nickel token issue of the central, bearing the commercial name "Central Santa Lucia" on them. Notes of low denomination of the Banco Espanol de la Habana were exchanged for tokens at a discount of more than 10 per cent!

In the nearby town of Gibara these tokens circulated freely as money, and reportedly were preferred to Spanish notes.

INGENIO VICTORIA

Rulau	Date	Metal	Size	VG	F	VF	Unc
Ori 36	1890	CN	25mm	—	—	30.00	40.00

Pair of scales. Around: INGENIO VICTORIA / * GIBARA *. Rv: VALE POR UN JORNAL / S. C. / * 1890 *. Plain edge. (Eklund 1934; Pesant 410)

Rulau	Date	Metal	Size	VG	F	VF	Unc
Ori 37	1890	CN	21mm				

As last, but smaller. (Moreno 120; Pesant 411)

Rulau	Date	Metal	Size	VG	F	VF	Unc
Ori 38	1890	CN	21mm	—	—	30.00	40.00

Obverse as last. Rv: VALE POR UNA RACION / S. C. / * 1890 *. (Eklund 1933; Pesant 412; Moreno 119)

Rulau	Date	Metal	Size	VG	F	VF	Unc
Ori 39	1890	CN	18.5mm	—	—	30.00	40.00

As last, but MEDIA RACION. (Ulex 2458; Pesant 413; Eklund 1932; Moreno 118; Christensen Nov. 1979 sale, lot 279)

A 19th century sketch shows the inside of the boiler house of Ingenio Victoria, which the caption said belonged to Simon Perez de Teran. This was reproduced in the Moreno reference published in Cuba about 1979.

Guantanamo
CANTINA DE LA SOLIDAD

Rulau	Date	Metal	Size	VG	F	VF	EF
Ori 41	ND	CN	29mm	—	—	—	—

(All incuse) CANTINA / DE / LA SOLIDAD. Rv: 20. (Ramsden 135; Eklund 1806; Pesant 391)

| Ori 42 | ND | CN | 24mm | — | — | 22.00 | — |

As last, but 10. (Ramsden 136; Eklund 1805; Pesant 392)

Ramsden referred to this place as Central La Solidad. Solidad is a diecutter's spelling error for Soledad. There is also a 20mm CN 5-centavo token.

M. L. B.
La Florida

Rulau	Date	Metal	Size	VG	F	VF	Unc
Ori 44	ND	GS	27mm	—	25.00	40.00	—

Indian head left. Around: LA FLORIDA / . * . Rv: * / M. L. B. / * between laurel sprays. Plain edge. (Eklund 877; Pesant 110; Kirtley Dec. 1989 sale, lot 2726)

This token may also occur in Brass. M. L. B. = Manuel L. Barillas. This piece has been claimed for Guatemala.

INGENIO SAN MIGUEL

Rulau	Date	Metal	Size	VG	F	VF	Unc
Ori 46	ND	Brass	24mm	—	—	32.50	—

INGENIO / SAN / MIGUEL / -.- / * VEINTICINCO *. Rv: 25 / * SAN MIGUEL. Plain edge. (Eklund 1903; Moreno 99; Pesant 341; Limarc May 1983 sale)

| Ori 47 | ND | Brass | 24mm | — | — | — | — |

As last, but ctsp S. (Moreno 100)

The first token above has been reported (by Limarc in 1983) with spelling error VEINTICINCIO. These pieces have also been reported nickel-plated, without verification.

There is another Ingenio San Miguel which issued tokens, in Guira de Macurijes (Matanzas Province ?), which see.

The tokens above were struck by Buch in Havana. Ramsden in 1904 reported a brass 10, 20mm, as number 118. These tokens occur ctsp a Cross.

INGENIO STA. CECILIA

Rulau	Date	Metal	Size	VG	F	VF	Unc
Ori 49	ND	CN	32.5mm	—	25.00	80.00	—

View of sugar mill, three stacks smoking; tiny J. F. SORZANO below. Around: INGENIO STA. CECILIA / GUANTANAMO. Rv: Large 50 within wreath. Plain edge. (Pesant 354; Lepczyk March 1984 sale, lot 2312; Bosco Dec. 1980 sale)

| Ori 50 | ND | CN | 29mm | — | 22.00 | 35.00 | — |

As last, but 20. (Pesant 355; Moreno 104)

| Ori 51 | ND | CN | 23mm | — | 18.00 | 31.00 | — |

As last, but 10. (Eklund 2385; Moreno 103; Pesant 356)

| Ori 52 | ND | CN | 16mm | — | 15.00 | 22.00 | — |

As last, but 5. (Christensen Nov. 1979 sale, lot 274; Moreno 102; Eklund 1911; Pesant 357)

The Guantanamo Bay area was captured by 600 U.S. Marines on June 11, 1898, during the Spanish-American War. The whole area was leased to the United States in 1903 for 99 years, and it has since become a major U.S. naval base, nicknamed "Gitmo" by its armed forces personnel. The bay itself is 4 miles wide and 12 miles long, and it has two port cities, Caimanera and Boqueron.

The city of Guantanamo is in Cuba itself, 21 miles to the north. It is believed Santa Cecilia sugar estate was near the Cuban city.

The designer of Ingenio Santa Cecilia tokens was Julio F. Sorzano, who also designed those for Central San Antonio in Guantanamo, another token issuer.

MANAL Y COMPAÑIA
San Carlos

Rulau	Date	Metal	Size	VG	F	VF	Unc
Ori 54	ND	CN	31mm	—	35.00	—	—

Sugar Mill. Around: MANAL / Y COMPAÑIA. Rv: CANTINA / 50 / .*. SAN CARLOS .*. Plainedge. (Eklund 1020; Pesant 293)

There are 20, 10 and 5-centavo tokens of this type. These have been claimed for Rio San Juan Dept. Nicaragua, and for Panama.

LUIS REDOR
Central San Antonio

Rulau	Date	Metal	Size	VG	F	VF	Unc
Ori 56	1899	CN	32mm	—	—	—	—

Locomotive and factory. Around: CENTRAL SAN ANTONIO / 1899 / (tiny) JULIO F. SORZANO. Rv: LUIS REDOR / 50 / GUANTANAMO. Plain edge. (Moreno 75; Pesant 282)

| Ori 57 | 1899 | CN | 27mm | — | — | 60.00 | — |

As last, but 20. (Moreno 74; Pesant 283)

| Ori 58 | 1899 | CN | 24mm | — | — | 35.00 | — |

As last, but 10. (Moreno 73; Pesant 284)

| Ori 59 | 1899 | CN | 18mm | — | 12.50 | — | — |

As last, but 5. (Moreno 72; Pesant 285)

The owner's name on a 20-centavo token has been reported as LUIZ REDOZ in a 1980 auction.

Holguin
RESP. LOC. "HOLGUIN"

Rulau	Date	Metal	Size	F	VF	EF	Unc
Ori 65	1915	GS	31.8mm	—	—	—	16.50

Compass, square and radiant G within laurel wreath. Around: RESP:. LOC:. "HOLGUIN" / * HOLGUIN - CUBA *. Rv: date 1915 in large, irregular digits; 25- within-triangle superimposed over the 91. Around: CONSTRUCCION TEMPLO / SOUVENIR. Plain edge. (Bill Randel coll.)

Commemorates the erection of a new Masonic temple in Holguin in 1915.

Manzanillo
INGENIO CENTRAL DE CAMPACHUELA

Rulau	Date	Metal	Size	VG	F	VF	Unc
Ori 70	1882	CN	32mm	—	—	—	—

(Wheel design) / INGENIO CENTRAL DE CAMPA-CHUELA / 1882 / LOS DOS AMIGOS / MANZAN-ILLO. Rv: VALE UN / PESO. (Pesant 71)

Rulau	Date	Metal	Size	VG	F	VF	Unc
Ori 71	1882	CN	27mm	—	—	—	—

As last, but VALE ½ / PESO. (Pesant 72)

INGENIO SALVADOR

Rulau	Date	Metal	Size	VG	F	VF	Unc
Ori 73	ND	Brass	25mm	—	—	—	—

TIENDA DEL INGENIO SALVADOR / CENTRAL. Rv: CALICITO MANZANILLO / 25 CENTAVOS / . EFECTOS . (Pesant 272)

Rulau	Date	Metal	Size	VG	F	VF	Unc
Ori 74	ND	Brass	25mm	—	—	—	—

As last, but 10 CENTAVOS. (Moreno 69; Pesant 273)

V. R. & CO.
Esperanza

Rulau	Date	Metal	Size	VG	F	VF	Unc
Ori 76	ND	CN	31mm	—	—	—	—

ESPERANZA / -*- / V. R. & CO. / -*- / (crossed laurel branches). Rv: Within ornate frame: 20 / ... / CEN-TAVOS. Plain edge. (Eklund 1777; Pesant 95)

Rulau	Date	Metal	Size	VG	F	VF	Unc
Ori 77	ND	Copper	26mm	—	—	—	—

As last, but 10. (Ek. 1776; Pesant 96)

Rulau	Date	Metal	Size	VG	F	VF	Unc
Ori 78	ND	Copper	23mm	—	—	—	—

As last, but 5. (Ek. 1775; Pesant 97)

Rulau	Date	Metal	Size	VG	F	VF	Unc
Ori 79	ND	Copper	19mm	—	—	—	—

As last, but 2½. (Ek. 1774; Pesant 98)

V. R. & Co. = Venezia & Co., the estate owners, according to Roberto Pesant.

Palma Soriano
INGENIO HATILLO

Rulau	Date	Metal	Size	VG	F	VF	Unc
Ori 85	ND	Brass	29mm	—	30.00	—	—

Sugar cane. Around: INGENIO (star) HATILLO / CUBA. Rv: Shaded 25 at center. Around: TIENDA (star) MIXTA. Plain edge. (Moreno 24; Pesant 117)

Rulau	Date	Metal	Size	VG	F	VF	Unc
Ori 84	ND	Brass	--mm	—	—	—	—

As last, but 50. (Moreno 25)

Rulau	Date	Metal	Size	VG	F	VF	Unc
Ori 86	ND	Brass	26mm	—	—	—	—

As last, but 10. (Pesant 118)

Tienda Mixta = General store. Pesant says that "Cuba" here means Oriente Province. There is also a brass 5-centavos, 22mm.

San Luis
LINO SALAZAR
Ingenio Sabanilla

Rulau	Date	Metal	Size	VG	F	VF	Unc
Ori 88	1895	CN	25.5mm	—	17.50	35.00	—

INGENIO SABANILLA / 1 / LINO SALAZAR. Rv: SANTIAGO DE CUBA / Large SL / 1895. Plain edge. (Eklund 1870; Pesant 267; Moreno 68)

Rulau	Date	Metal	Size	VG	F	VF	Unc
Ori 89	1895	CN	22.5mm	—	25.00	—	—

As last, but 50. (Eklund 1869; Moreno 67; Pesant 268)

Rulau	Date	Metal	Size	VG	F	VF	Unc
Ori 90	1895	CN	22.5mm	—	18.00	35.00	—

As last (50), but LS in center in place of SL. (Bosco report)

Rulau	Date	Metal	Size	VG	F	VF	Unc
Ori 91	1895	CN	22mm	—	—	—	—

As last, but 20 (SL). (Pesant 269)

Rulau	Date	Metal	Size	VG	F	VF	Unc
Ori 92	1895	CN	19mm	—	—	—	—

As last, but 10 (SL). (Eklund 1868; Pesant 270)

Rulau	Date	Metal	Size	VG	F	VF	Unc
Ori 93	1895	CN	19mm	8.50	15.00	20.00	—

Similar to last, but LS in reverse circle. (Ramsden 93; Moreno 66)

Rulau	Date	Metal	Size	VG	F	VF	Unc
Ori 94	1895	CN	19mm	—	—	—	—

As last (LS), but 5. (Moreno 65)

Rulau	Date	Metal	Size	VG	F	VF	Unc
Ori 95	1895	CN	19mm	—	—	—	—

As last (5), but SL in reverse circle. (Pesant 271)

In the Nov. 1979 sale by Henry Christensen, there were three pieces of the 1-peso token in Fine, as lots 270-271. Ingenio Sabanilla means literally "little bedsheet sugar plantation."

Ramsden said LS stood for Lino Salazar. Eklund said SL stood for San Luis.

Santiago de Cuba
COCINA ECONOMICA DE SANTIAGO DE CUBA

Rulau	Date	Metal	Size	VG	F	VF	Unc
Ori 100	1897	Brass	25mm	—	20.00	37.50	—

Cross divides 18 — 97. Around. COCINA ECONO-MICA DE SANTIAGO DE CUBA. Rv: * UN * / CEN-TAVO / (ornament). Plain edge. (Moreno pg. 35)

Rulau	Date	Metal	Size	VG	F	VF	Unc
Ori 101	1897	Brass	25mm	—	—	32.50	—

Obverse as last, but no date. Rv: Large CE monogram at center. Around: INAUGURADA Y BENDECIDA EN 25 ABRIL / 1897 / . Plain edge. (Pesant 1106a)

The second item above is a medalet for CE = Christian Endeavor.

CENTRO DE RETos Y LICOs DEL
EJERCITO Y ARMADA

Rulau	Date	Metal	Size	VG	F	VF	Unc
Ori 98	(1900's)	++	31mm	—	—	Rare	—

++ Purple on cream plastic.
CENTRO DE RETos Y LICOs DEL EJERCITO Y
ARMADA / ST JAGO / 25 / DE CUBA. Rv: Blank.
(Pesant 1000 var.; ANS coll.)

The Center for Discharged & Disabled Personnel of the Army & Navy, a
Spanish armed forces entity, was the issuer of a brass series, in and after 1899.
Denominations known are 5, 10 and 25 centavos. Token above is a later 25-centavos in plastic with reverse white lettering.
Pesant reports the word 'MARINO' on the brass tokens instead of
'ARMADA.'

LA EMPRESA DE GAS

Rulau	Date	Metal	Size	VG	F	VF	Unc
Ori 103	1857	Sv/Cop	39mm	—	—	—	—

LA EMPRESA DE GAS DE SANTo DE CUBA / A LA
REINA: / AL ESCMO SOR CAPn GENL / Dn JOSE
DE LA CONCHA, / MARQUES DE LA HABANA, /
VIZCONDE DE CUBA / (circular rosette). Rv:
YNAUGURACION DE LAS OBRAS DEL GAS, 6 DE
SETIEMBRE DE 1857. / AL / ESCMO SOR GOBER-
NADOR / COMANDANTE GENERAL / Dn
CARLOS DE VARGAS / MACHUCA: / AL. M. Y.
AYUNTAMIENTO / DE LA CIUDAD DE / CUBA. /
(circular rosette). Plain edge. Weight: 21.15 grams.
(Fonrobert 7746; Byrne 197)

Ori 104	1857	Silver	39mm	—	—	—	—

As last. Weight: 22.9 grams. (Byrne 192)

Commercial medallion struck to honor the opening of the gas works on
Sept. 6, 1857. The gas company pays honor on the piece to the queen through
her representative, Captain-General de la Concha, and to the governor of Cuba,
Carlos de Vargas.

Yareyal
R. F.
Ingenio El Laberinto

Rulau	Date	Metal	Size	VG	F	VF	Unc
Ori 108	ND	CN	22mm	—	40.00	50.00	60.00

Sugar cane crusher in central circle, VALE POR
MEDIO JORNAL / .*. around. Rv: R. F. in central circle, EL LABERINTO / YAREYAL around. Plain edge.
(Ulex 2814; Pesant 134; Christensen Nov. 1979 sale, lot
269)

Ori 109	ND	CN	22mm	—	25.00	35.00	45.00

As last, but spelling YAREGAL instead of YAREYAL.
(Eklund 1935; Limarc Aug. 1986 sale; Randel coll.)

El Laberinto = The Labyrinth, R. F. = Rafael Fernandez, the estate owner.
Ulex placed these tokens under Colombia in error.
David Henkle placed these tokens under Roque, Matanzas Province, in the
belief they are connected with the Colonia Labarinto tokens of that place. Such
assignment would not explain the place-name Yareyal on the tokens, however.

PIÑAR DEL RIO PROVINCE

Artemisa
INGENIO EL PILAR

Rulau	Date	Metal	Size	VG	F	VF	Unc
PDR 1	ND	CN	23mm	—	—	—	—

INGENIO EL PILAR * / 20. Rv: Same as obverse.
(Ramsden 81; Eklund 1860; Pesant 247; Moreno 20)

PDR 2	ND	CN	22mm	—	—	—	—

INGo. EL PILAR * / 10. Rv: Same as obverse. (Ramsden 82; Eklund 1859; Pesant 248; Moreno 19)

PDR 3	ND	CN	18mm	—	—	—	—

As last, but 5. (Ramsden 83; Eklund 1858; Pesant 249;
Moreno 18)

El Pilar = The Pillar.

Cabañas
E. A. L.
Ingenio Mercedita

Rulau	Date	Metal	Size	VG	F	VF	Unc
PDR 6	(1880)	Brass	27mm	—	—	—	—

(All incused): E. A. L. / 2½ / –. Rv: Blank. (Ramsden
70; Eklund 1839; Pesant 198)

Struck in Cuba for Ernesto A. Longo, this was the first token for Ingenio Mercedita. The next series, also bearing the E. A. L. initials, was made in the United States.

YNGENIO MERCEDITA

Rulau	Date	Metal	Size	VG	F	VF	Unc
PDR 8	ND	CN	35mm	—	—	—	—

TIENDA DEL INGo. MERCEDITA / E. A. L. / CABAÑAS / *. VALE POR UN PESO EN EFECTOS/ UN PESO vertically on large 1 *. Plain edge. (Ramsden 67; Eklund 1841; Pesant 196)

Rulau	Date	Metal	Size	VG	F	VF	Unc
PDR 9	ND	CN	27mm	—	—	—	—

As last, but 50 CENTAVOS / EN EFECTOS / 50. (Pesant 195)

Rulau	Date	Metal	Size	VG	F	VF	Unc
PDR 11	ND	Brass	21mm	—	—	—	—

As last, but 5 CENTAVOS EN EFECTOS / 5. (Ramsden 69; Eklund 1840; Pesant 197)

The next series, of 1901 and 1907, do not refer to Longo.

Rulau	Date	Metal	Size	VG	F	VF	Unc
PDR 13	1901	CN	35mm	—	—	40.00	—

YNGENIO MERCEDITA / -.- / CABANAS / TIENDA / -.- / * 1901. Rv: Large 1 (within the 1 vertically: UN PESO. Around: VALE POR UN PESO EN EFECTOS. Flourishes flank the large 1. (Eklund 1845; Moreno 49)

Rulau	Date	Metal	Size	VG	F	VF	Unc
PDR 14	1901	CN	26mm	—	—	—	—

As last, but 50 in circle, 50 CENTAVOS in legend. (Ramsden 68; Eklund 1844; Pesant 199)

Rulau	Date	Metal	Size	VG	F	VF	Unc
PDR 15	1901	CN	24mm	—	—	—	—

As last, but 10 and 10 CENTAVOS. (Eklund 1843; Pesant 200; Moreno 48)

Rulau	Date	Metal	Size	VG	F	VF	Unc
PDR 16	1901	Brass	24mm	—	—	—	—

As last, but 2 and 2 CENTAVOS. (Eklund 1842)

Rulau	Date	Metal	Size	VG	F	VF	Unc
PDR 18	1907	CN	24mm	—	—	—	—

As last, but 10 and 10 CENTAVOS. (Pesant 201)

Rulau	Date	Metal	Size	VG	F	VF	Unc
PDR 19	1907	CN	22mm	—	—	—	—

As last, but 5 and 5 CENTAVOS. (Pesant 202)

Rulau	Date	Metal	Size	VG	F	VF	Unc
PDR 20	1907	CN	20mm	—	—	—	—

As last, but 1 and 1 CENTAVO. (Pesant 203)

UNATTRIBUTED CUBA

ACUEDUCTO

Rulau	Date	Metal	Size	VG	F	VF	Unc
Cub 1	ND	Brass	25.3mm	—	—	—	—

Fountain. Rv: ACUEDUCTO. (Bernal 294; Pesant 422)

La Elvira
MANUEL S. SIERRA

Rulau	Date	Metal	Size	VG	F	VF	Unc
Cub 11	ND	CN	--mm	—	—	—	—

(All incuse): LA ELVIRA / -.- / MANUEL S. SIERRA. Rv: VALE MEDIO REAL / ½ REAL. (Moreno 31; Stohr FL-15; Garriga pg. 93)

This issue occurs counterstamped H. The size is in the 17-20mm range.

Supposedly the non-counterstamped piece was used in Venezuela, along with other denominations in this series. Sierra emigrated to Cuba, according to Garriga.

It is uncertain whether Venezuela or Cuba is the correct locale for these pieces.

TOKENS LABELED BELEN, F. C. AND PILAR

Roberto Pesant, the Cuban author, assigns Scovill Mfg. Co. - made tokens bearing the words Belen, F. C. and Pilar to Cuba.

He says Hacienda Belen was located at Quemado de Guines, Havana Province. He gives no site for the F. C. piece. He says Ingenio El Pilar was located at Cabezas, Matanzas Province.

These same pieces are claimed for locales in Mexico, where this catalog assigns them tentatively, and Guatemala. All such pieces are in the possession of the author, but no conclusive evidence regarding them has ever been obtained. They were made, most likely, before 1885, perhaps as early as 1860.

STAR PLANTATION

Rulau	Date	Metal	Size	F	VF	EF	Unc
Cub 13	ND	Copper	25mm	—	—	10.00	—

Radiant star. Around: STAR PLANTATION / *. Rv: 2½ C. (Byrne 190)

VARONA & CO.
Central Lugareno

Rulau	Date	Metal	Size	VG	F	VF	Unc
Cub 17	ND	Aluminum	20mm	—	—	140.	—

VARONA & CO. / (ornament) / CENTRAL LUGARENO / CUBA. Rv: VALE POR / 0.05 CTS. / EFECTOS. Plain edge. (Paul Cunningham report)

FLORIDA SUGAR MAN'F'G. CO.

Rulau	Date	Metal	Size	VG	F	VF	Unc
Cub 8	ND	--	--mm	—	—	—	—

FLORIDA SUGAR MAN'F'G. CO. / GOOD FOR 25 C ON REGULAR PAY DAYS. Rv: ONLY TRANSFERABLE TO ST. CLOUD STORE. (Moreno 22)

There is doubt that this token in the Numismatic Museum of Cuba collection is in fact Cuban. Its legend seems aimed solely at American workers. However, until evidence is gained, we leave it here on Señor Moreno Fraginalls' assertion.

St. Cloud is in Osceola County in central Florida, south of Orlando and near Kissimmee. It is entirely possible that this firm had Cuban operations.

DOMINICA

DOMINICA

Rulau	Date	Metal	Size	F	VF	EF	Unc
Dmn 1	ND	Brass	17.5mm	—	—	50.00	—

DOMINICA / 10 / (rosette). Rv: Similar to obverse but from different dies with larger DOMINICA. Plain edge. Weight 2.15 grams. (Byrne 449)

Nothing is known of this token. It has been claimed for Guatemala.

One other token, that of J. B. V. (Maison J. B. Vital), was attributed to Dominica by Kurt Fischer of Haiti, but it proved to be a Dominican Republic issue of circa 1880.

DOMINICAN REPUBLIC

NOTE: The use of tokens as money was forbidden by law in 1934.

BARAHONA PROVINCE

Barahona
LUIS E. DELMONTE Y CIA.

Rulau	Date	Metal	Size	VG	F	VF	Unc
Dom 3	1904	Brass	30mm	5.50	8.00	12.00	—

EL PROPIO ESSUERZO DE LUIS E. DELMONTE Y CIA / 50 cs. / *. Rv: BARAHONA / 1904. Plain edge. (Schimmel report)

Rulau	Date	Metal	Size	VG	F	VF	Unc
Dom 4	1904	Brass	27.5mm	5.00	7.00	10.00	—

As last, but 40 cs.

Barahona Province, on the southwest coast of the Dominican Republic, is noted for sugar and coffee production. The Delmonte firm probably operated a sugar mill.

El propio essuerzo (misspelling for ESFUERZO) de Luis E. Delmonte y Cia. = The personal enterprise of Luis E. Delmonte and Company.

See *TAMS Journal* for Feb. 1986, pages 12-13. There are also 25 and 20 CS. tokens of this issuer, the latter scarce.

J. MOTA RANCHE
Hacienda Mercedes

Rulau	Date	Metal	Size	VG	F	VF	Unc
Dom 6	1928	—	31mm	—	—	—	—

J. MOTA RANCHE / 50 / . BARAHONA, R. D. . Rv: HACIENDA MERCEDES / 50 / 1928 / . BARAHONA, R. D. .

DISTRITO NACIONAL

Santo Domingo
A. H.
Yngenio San Ysidro

Rulau	Date	Metal	Size	VG	F	VF	Unc
Dom 10	ND	Brass	29mm	—	—	—	—

* A. H. * / (star) / YNGo SAN YSIDRO. Rv: (Scrollwork) / 50 (large, shaded) / (scrollwork).

Rulau	Date	Metal	Size	VG	F	VF	Unc
Dom 11	ND	Brass	21mm	—	5.00	—	—

As last, but 10.

Rulau	Date	Metal	Size	VG	F	VF	Unc
Dom 12	ND	Brass	19mm	—	9.00	—	—

As last, but 5.

Rulau	Date	Metal	Size	VG	F	VF	Unc
Dom 13	ND	Brass	25mm	—	5.00	15.00	—

INGENIO SAN ISIDRO / 25 / SAN DOMINGO. Rv: Same as obverse. (Moreno 7)

Rulau	Date	Metal	Size	VG	F	VF	Unc
Dom 14	ND	Brass	20mm	10.00	15.00	20.00	—

As last, but 10.

The last two tokens have been claimed as Cuba.

DUARTE PROVINCE

San Francisco de Macoris
C. M. MEJIA

Rulau	Date	Metal	Size	VG	F	VF	Unc
Dom 18	ND	—	25mm	—	—	—	—

C. M. MEJIA / (ornaments) / MERCANCIAS / (ornaments) / S. F. MACORIS. Rv: * VALE * / UNA / CARRETADA.

LA ALTAGRACIA PROVINCE

La Romana
CARL QUENTIN & CO.

Rulau	Date	Metal	Size	VG	F	VF	Unc
Dom 25	1913	Brass	24mm	—	—	35.00	45.00

CARL QUENTIN & CO. / 1913 / LA ROMANA. Rv: 10. Plain edge. (Rulau coll.)

Rulau	Date	Metal	Size	VG	F	VF	Unc
Dom 26	1913	Brass	19mm	—	—	12.50	25.00

As last, but 5. (Zaika coll.)

Struck by Scovill Mfg. Co., Waterbury, Conn.

MONTE CRISTI PROVINCE

Monte Cristi
R. H.

Rulau	Date	Metal	Size	VG	F	VF	Unc
Dom 30	ND	Aluminum	25mm	—	—	—	—

-.- / RH monogram / MONTE CRISTY, R. D. Rv: (Ornaments) / 25 / (ornaments). Token is ctsp 8 / M on obverse.

Rulau	Date	Metal	Size	VG	F	VF	Unc
Dom 31	ND	Aluminum	19mm	9.50	14.00	—	—

As last, but 5. No ctsp.

PERAVIA PROVINCE

San Jose del Ocoa
CENTRAL OCOA

Rulau	Date	Metal	Size	VG	F	VF	Unc
Dom 35	ND	Brass	25mm	—	—	11.00	—

CENTRAL / OCOA. Rv: 5 / CENTAVOS. (Eklund 2150; Pesant 424)

Rulau	Date	Metal	Size	VG	F	VF	Unc
Dom 36	ND	Brass	25mm	—	—	9.50	—

As last, but ctsp 55 / V. (Limarc report)

PUERTO PLATA PROVINCE

Hoja Honcha
UNA LIBRA CARNE
(Hacienda Toncito)

Rulau	Date	Metal	Size	VG	F	VF	Unc
Dom 40	ND	Aluminum	Sq 32mm	—	7.00	9.50	—

UNA / LIBRA / CARNE. Rv: Incused control no. (Numbers examined: 1237, 8161). Plain edge. (Rulau coll.)

Rulau	Date	Metal	Size	VG	F	VF	Unc
Dom 41	ND	Aluminum	Oct 27mm	—	8.50	12.50	—

MEDIA / LIBRA / CARNE. Rv: Incused control no. (Numbers examined: 371, 1414, 7450, 9267, 9946). (Christensen Oct. 1975 sale, lot 208; Rulau coll.; Zaika coll.)

Una libra carne = One pound meat. Media libra carne = Half pound meat. Tonocita ?

SAN PEDRO DE MACORIS PROVINCE

San Pedro de Macoris
YNGENIO PORVENIR

Rulau	Date	Metal	Size	VG	F	VF	Unc
Dom 45	ND	Brass	19mm	—	6.50	—	12.50

Within laurel wreath: * / YNGENIO PORVENIR / 5 (large, shaded) / SAN PEDRO DE MACORIS. Rv: * VALE * / 5 (shaded, in beaded circle) / CENTAVOS. Plain edge. (Rulau coll.; Christensen Oct. 1975 sale, lot 206)

Rulau	Date	Metal	Size	VG	F	VF	Unc
Dom 46	ND	Brass	24mm	—	6.50	—	—

As last, but 10 C.

Rulau	Date	Metal	Size	VG	F	VF	Unc
Dom 47	ND	Brass	29mm	—	7.00	—	—

As last, but 25 C.

The sugar estate was located on the south coast of the Dominican Republic, 50 miles east of San Cristobal and 40 miles east of Santo Domingo.

UNCERTAIN

B. A.
(Batey Angelina)

Rulau	Date	Metal	Size	VG	F	VF	Unc
Dom 50	(1900)	Brass	Sq 23mm	—	6.50	8.50	—

Horizontal C divides B. -- A. / * 5. * (in circle). Rv: + (in circle) 5 + (in circle) / L. All stamped incuse on both sides. (Christensen Oct. 1975 sale, lot 205; Al Almanzar Sept. 1970 sale, pg. 16/A5)

Rulau	Date	Metal	Size	VG	F	VF	Unc
Dom 51	ND	Brass	Sq 23mm	—	7.50	—	—

Obverse as last. Rv: Blank.

Rulau	Date	Metal	Size	VG	F	VF	Unc
Dom 52	(1888)	Brass	23mm	—	—	15.00	—

(All incused) C (horizontal) / 10 (in circle) / B A. Rv: Blank. (Rulau coll.)

According to Alcedo Almanzar, a Dominican Republic expert, Batey Angelina was a sugar mill operating at least 1888-1900. There are more varieties of the 10-centavo token, some with L ctsp on reverse. (See Bodega Angelina).

BODEGA ANGELINA

Rulau	Date	Metal	Size	VG	F	VF	Unc
Dom 55	ND	Brass	28mm	3.00	5.00	8.00	—

BODEGA / 20 / * ANGELINA *. Rv: VALIDO SOLA-MENTE / PARA / TOMAR / EFECTOS / EN LA / BODEGA. Plain edge. (Eklund note before 2061)

Rulau	Date	Metal	Size	VG	F	VF	Unc
Dom 56	ND	CN	28mm	—	8.50	—	—

As last. (Christensen Oct. 1975 sale, lot 210)

Rulau	Date	Metal	Size	VG	F	VF	Unc
Dom 57	ND	Brass	24mm	5.00	9.00	11.00	—

As last, but 10. This token also occurs ctsp V on reverse.

This series also includes brass and cupronickel 5, 2½, 2 and 1-centavo tokens. Alcedo Almanzar says they were used circa 1888 and up until 1912.

Colonia Esperanza
J. T. ESCARRAMAN

Rulau	Date	Metal	Size	VG	F	VF	Unc
Dom 60	ND	Brass	Oct 21mm	3.50	4.50	6.00	—

COLONIA ESPERANZA / 25 / IGo. PORVENIR / J. T. ESCARRAMAN. Rv: 25. (Zaika coll.)

Cut-square 20-centavo tokens, 21mm, are also known, $7. VF.

Colonia Penoncito
V. FELIU

Rulau	Date	Metal	Size	VG	F	VF	EF
Dom 63	ND	Brass	Rect, 25x22mm	—	—	20.00	—

COLONIA / PENONCITO / IGo. PORVENIR / (man's face) / V. FELIU. Rv: 40. (Zaika coll.)

Rulau	Date	Metal	Size	VG	F	VF	EF
Dom 64	ND	Brass	25mm	—	—	8.50	—

As last, but 50.

HACIENDA ITALIA

Rulau	Date	Metal	Size	VG	F	VF	Unc
Dom 67	ND	Brass	--mm	—	15.00	—	—

HACIENDA ITALIA. 5 CENTAVOS. (Christensen Oct. 1975 sale, lot 211)

87
(Ingenio Puerto Rico)

Rulau	Date	Metal	Size	VG	F	VF	Unc
Dom 70	1880	CN	24mm	—	—	50.00	—

2-reales token of Hacienda Mercedita, Ponce, Puerto Rico, ctsp 87. (Archilla-Diez 560a)

Rulau	Date	Metal	Size	VG	F	VF	Unc
Dom 71	1880	CN	20mm	—	—	50.00	—

1-real token of Hacienda Mercedita, Ponce, Puerto Rico, ctsp 87. (A-D 559a)

The sugar estate Puerto Rico in the Dominican Republic counterstamped tokens of Juan Serralles' Mercedita coffee plantation tokens for use there. These were struck originally in Birmingham, England by Heaton's Mint.

Original mintages had been 2,000 2-reales and 4,000 1-real pieces. The counterstamping would have made the original Puerto Rican pieces less common; it is not known how many pieces were overstruck.

San Miguel
Dr. E. R. ROSALES
Finca La Concepcion

Rulau	Date	Metal	Size	VG	F	VF	Unc
Dom 74	ND	Brass	27mm	—	—	—	—

PROPIEDAD DEL / DR. E. R. ROSALES / DE / SAN MIGUEL. Rv: FINCA LA CONCEPCION / 2 / REALES. Plain edge. (Zaika coll.)

INGENIO SAN LUIS

Rulau	Date	Metal	Size	VG	F	VF	Unc
Dom 77	ND	Brass	Sq 27mm	—	—	15.00	—

INGENIO SAN LUIS. Counterstamped 100.

Rulau	Date	Metal	Size	VG	F	VF	Unc
Dom 78	ND	Brass	Sq 20mm	—	—	10.00	—

As last, ctsp (no description of ctsp marking). (Christensen Oct. 1975 sale, lot 207)

S.D. / Anchor

Rulau	Date	Metal	Size	VG	F	VF	Unc
Dom 85	ND	Lead	22mm	—	—	—	—

Anchor. Rv: S D. Crude. Weight 5.95 grams. (Byrne 1155)

This token was unpublished before 1975.

TURCU PELLERIUS

Rulau	Date	Metal	Size	VG	F	VF	EF
Dom 90	(1809-14)	Copper	27mm	16.00	19.00	27.50	35.00

Bearded male bust left, I . K under truncation. Around: TVRCV PELLERIVS. Rv: Seated helmeted female left, a shield at her side, a helmet (?) in her right hand and the left holding a spear. A rising sun is at left. Around: HISPANNIOLA (sic!). Weight 7.5 grams. (Fonrobert 7621; Byrne 1156-57)

Satirical cuartilla of the British occupation period, or else just another evasion halfpenny of Britain with more imagination than most. Diesinker I. K. has not been identified.

The Byrne collection sale featured two specimens, VF and VG.

GRENADA

TOKEN

Rulau	Date	Metal	Size	F	VF	EF	Unc
Grd 1	(1980's)	CN	34.8mm	—	—	4.00	10.00

Large numeral 1 / TOKEN. Rv: Same as obverse. Plain edge. Weight 13.07 grams.

Modern issue. Attribution by Joseph Zaffern.

GUADELOUPE

Basse-Terre
BANQUE DE LA GUADELOUPE

Rulau	Date	Metal	Size	F	VF	EF	Unc
Gpe 1	1826	Silver	Oct 36mm	—	—	—	—

Nude bust left, BARRE Ft under truncation. Around: CHARLES X ROI DE FRANCE. Rv: Within wreath: Montage of industry, agricultural products and flowers of the island group. Around: BANQUE DE LA GUA-DELOUPE / ORDONNce DU ROI DU 10 DECbre 1826. Plain edge. (Byrne 562)

This Jeton marks the founding of the Bank of Guadeloupe by royal ordinance Dec. 10, 1826. The head of King Charles X was designed by Barre at the Paris Mint.

Pointe-a-Pitre
C. D. C.
(Cercle du Commerce)

Rulau	Date	Metal	Size	F	VF	EF	Unc
Gpe 5	(1825)	Copper	37mm	—	500.	—	—

Bale, Mercury staff and barrel lie at foot of palm tree. Rv: Ornate monogram CDC (Cercle du Commerce) at center. Around: oo POINTE-A-PITRE oo / (three orna-ments.) Plain edge. (F. 7721; U. 2435; Byrne 572; Gadoury 2.5)

Rulau	Date	Metal	Size	F	VF	EF	Unc
Gpe 6	(1825)	WM	37mm	—	500.	—	—

As last. (F. 7722; Byrne 563; Gadoury 2.6)

Rulau	Date	Metal	Size	F	VF	EF	Unc
Gpe 7	(1825)	Copper	27mm	—	400.	—	—

Mercury staff, Gallic cock, anchor, bale, barrel at foot of palm tree; sun above and three-masted ship in back-ground. Rv: Similar to last, but only one ornament below monogram. (Ulex. 2435; Gadoury 2.1)

Rulau	Date	Metal	Size	F	VF	EF	Unc
Gpe 8	(1825)	WM	27mm	—	400.	—	—

As last. (F. 7723; Gadoury-Elie 2.2)

Rulau	Date	Metal	Size	F	VF	EF	Unc
Gpe 10	(1825)	Copper	Oct 30mm	—	450.	—	—

Barrel, anchor and bale on grassy mound. Rv: As last (single ornament). Plain edge. (F. 7724; U. 2435; Byrne 559; Gadoury 2.3)

Rulau	Date	Metal	Size	F	VF	EF	Unc
Gpe 11	(1825)	Iron	Oct 30mm	—	450.	—	—

As last. (F. 7724; Byrne 573; Gadoury 2.4)

The Cercle du Commerce (chamber of commerce) in Pointe-a-Pitre, the lar-gest city on Grande-Terre Island, distributed these medallic jetons as a business promotion. Silver specimens are reported to have been given to officials.

Gaudeloupe, a French possession since 1635, is now an overseas department of France (since 1946). Its 687 square miles consists of the two large sister islands, Basse-Terre and Grande-Terre separated by the Salt River; marie Galante I.; Les Saintes island group; Desirade I.; St. Barthelemy I.; and more than half of St. Martin I. which is shared with the Netherlands. The capital is Basse-Terre on Basse-Terre Island.

Rulau	Date	Metal	Size	F	VF	EF	Unc
Gpe 13	(1825)	Bronze	32mm	—	160.00	400.00	—

Anchor before bush and bale. Rv: Ornate C. No inscription on the jeton. Plain edge. (Byrne 558; Gadoury-Elie 1.1)

CERCLE DU COMMERCE

Rulau	Date	Metal	Size	F	VF	EF	Unc
Gpe 15	1825	Silver	40mm	—	600.00	1000.	—

CERCLE DU COMMERCE / DE LA / POINTE A PITRE / 1825. Rv: 16 / GOURDES / (signature in oval) / (crossed branches). Plain edge. (Gadoury 3.4)

Rulau	Date	Metal	Size	F	VF	EF	Unc
Gpe 16	1825	Silver	30mm	—	800.00	1100.	—

As last, but 8 / GOURDES. (G. 3.3)

Also issued were silver 4 and 2-gourde tokens, worth $600 VF to $1000 EF.

Rulau	Date	Metal	Size	F	VF	EF	Unc
Gpe 20	(1825)	Silver	40mm	—	Ex.	Rare	—

Similar to last, but 1 / DOUBLON. (Gadoury 4.4)

Rulau	Date	Metal	Size	F	VF	EF	Unc
Gpe 21	(1825)	Silver	35mm	—	Ex.	Rare	—

As last, but ½ / DOUBLON. (Gadoury 4.3)

Also struck as patterns were ¼ and ⅛-doublon tokens in silver. All were struck at Paris Mint in 1825.

A. B.

Rulau	Date	Metal	Size	VG	F	VF	Unc
Gpe 27	ND	WM	Oct 35mm	—	—	—	—

Crown above crossed flags, monogram AVB (?) below. Rv: 2 / F. Crude. (Byrne 561)

G. P.

Rulau	Date	Metal	Size	F	VF	EF	Unc
Gpe 30	(1825)	Copper	24.5mm	—	—	—	—

Crowned oval shield between sprays, three fleur-de-lis in the shield. Rv: (Crown) / G P / (Lis) / (Crossed torches. Plain edge. (Byrne 560)

P (Lis) P

Rulau	Date	Metal	Size	VG	FF	VF	EF
Gpe 25	(ca 1825)	Copper	31mm	—	—	—	—

P (Lis) P incuse, ctsp on England penny of the 1806-07 type. (Byrne 564)

There is no evidence that this Ray Byrne-listed piece is connected with Pointe-a-Pitre or Guadeloupe.

GUADELOUPE ET DEPENDANCES

Rulau	Date	Metal	Size	F	VF	EF	Unc
Gpe 40	(ca 1905)	Shell *	19.2mm	—	20.00	—	—

* Dark brown fibrous material. Two shells joined at edge.

Imitation of obverse of 1903 Guadeloupe 50-centime coin, KM 45 (Male bust in feather headdress left; around: REPUBLIQUE FRANCAISE / . GUADELOUPE ET DEPENDANCES .). Rv: Laureate head left, NAPOLEON III EMPEREUR / 1861 around. Plain edge. (Rulau coll., ex-Jim Keller)

It is difficult to assess the purpose of this piece.

HAITI

Cap Haitien
GLACIERE DU CAP HAITIEN

Rulau	Date	Metal	Size	VG	F	VF	Unc
Hai 3	ND	Copper	24mm	—	—	125.	—

GLACIERE DU CAP HAITIEN. Rv: 2.
(Henkle report)

Jacmel
GLACIERE DE JACMEL

Rulau	Date	Metal	Size	VG	F	VF	Unc
Hai 5	ND	Brass	23.5mm	—	50.00	75.00	—

GLACIERE DE JACMEL. Rv: UNE / GOURDE.
Plain edge. Weight 3.65 grams. (Byrne 777)

Jeremie
CERCLE DE L'UNION

Rulau	Date	Metal	Size	VG	F	VF	Unc
Hai 7	ND	CN	23.5mm	—	—	65.00	—

CERCLE DE L'UNION / 10 cents / JEREMIE. Rv: 10
CENTS. Letter V is ctsp on each side of the token.
Plain edge. (Byrne 784)

Petit Goave
CERCLE DE L'UNION

Rulau	Date	Metal	Size	VG	F	VF	Unc
Hai 10	ND	CN	25mm	—	—	40.00	—

CERCLE DE L'UNION / 20 CENTS / PETIT
GOAVE. Rv: 20. Plain edge. (Byrne 783)

Port au Prince
GRAND HOTEL BELLEVUE

Rulau	Date	Metal	Size	VG	F	VF	Unc
Hai 13	ND	Brass	24mm	35.00	—	—	—

GRAND HOTEL BELLEVUE PORT AU PRINCE.
Rv: BON POUR / 10 / DIX CENTIMES. Plain edge.
(Byrne 776)

ROYAL HAITIAN CASINO

Rulau	Date	Metal	Size	VF	EF	Unc	Proof
Hai 15	(1980)	CN	37mm	5.00	7.00	8.00	—

Negro male kneeling right, drinking from a gourde?
Around: ROYAL HAITIAN CASINO / PORT-AU-
PRINCE. Rv: Crowned shield of arms. Around: ONE
DOLLAR GAMING TOKEN / (ornament). Reeded
edge.

Rulau	Date	Metal	Size	VF	EF	Unc	Proof
Hai 16	(1983)	CN	24mm	1.00	2.00	—	—

Kneeling negro male left. Around: ROYAL HAITIAN
CASINO. Rv: Crowned shield of arms. Around:
TWENTY-FIVE CENT GAMING TOKEN /
(branches). Reeded edge.

The obverse designs are reminiscent of the British and American kneeling
slave tokens of 1797-1838.

A. T. & B. R.

Rulau	Date	Metal	Size	VG	F	VF	Unc
Hai 18	ND	WM	27mm	—	—	75.00	—

-*- / GLACIERE / *** / PORT AU PRINCE / -*- / (tiny
2-word name of token maker, not legible). Rv: A. T. /
& / B. B. within wreath. Plain edge. (Byrne 770; Eklund
1936)

Uncertain
AMERIQUE

Rulau	Date	Metal	Size	VG	F	VF	Unc
Hai 30	1824	Copper	39mm	—	Rare	—	—

(All incused): AMERIQUE / L'AN / 1824 / (small
wreath). Rv: 15 / CENTIMES. (Henkle report)

J. B.

Rulau	Date	Metal	Size	VG	F	VF	EF
Hai 32	(1905-10)	Silver	39.5mm	—	—	225.	—

Palm tree separates J -- B in relief within large upright oval depression, ctsp on Mexico 1901-Mo-AM silver peso. (Byrne 779)

The Byrne sale specimen in VF fetched $130.

CAILLE

Rulau	Date	Metal	Size	VG	F	VF	Unc
Hai 34	ND	Brass	21.5mm	—	—	10.00	—

CAILLE. Rv: VALE / 10 CMI / IN MERCE. Plain edge. (Byrne 775)

Hai 35	ND	CN	21.5mm	—	—	10.00	—

*/ CAILLE / *. Rv: CENT. / 20 / -.-. Plain edge. (Byrne 781)

Hai 36	ND	CN	21.5mm	—	—	10.00	—

TCCo monogram. Rv: LA COMPANIE CAILLE / *. (Byrne 780)

The Caille Co. is a Detroit & Toledo firm, but all the pieces above were acquired in Haiti.

THE CAILLE ROULETTE

Rulau	Date	Metal	Size	VG	F	VF	Unc
Hai 38	ND	CN	21mm	—	—	10.00	—

THE CAILLE ROULETTE. Rv: GOOD FOR / 5 cents / IN TRADE. Plain edge. (Byrne 773)

The Caille Co., Detroit, Mich., was a maker of gambling equipment and supplied tokens to its customers.

CASINO INTERNATIONAL HAITI

Rulau	Date	Metal	Size	F	VF	EF	Unc
Hai 40	ND	++	23mm	—	10.00	20.00	—

++ Enameled blue on aluminum. See below.
CASINO INTERNATIONAL / HAITI / $1.00. Rv: Blank. Plain edge. Issued with hole at center. (Byrne 786; Christensen Oct. 1975 sale, lot 313; ANS coll.)

In this series of tokens, there are five pieces denominated from 10 cents to $1, each with a different color enamel applied. All are centrally holed, and each measures 23mm. Worth $10 each in VF.

Rulau	Date	Metal	Size	F	VF	EF	Unc
Hai 41	ND	CN	24mm	—	—	10.00	20.00

CASINO INTERNATIONAL d'HAITI. / 25. Rv: Same as obverse. (ANS coll.)

CERCLE MILITAIRE GARDE D'HAITI

Rulau	Date	Metal	Size	VG	F	VF	Unc
Hai 42	(1880)	Brass	23mm	—	—	17.50	—

CERCLE MILITAIRE / (crossed swords) / GARDE D'HAITI. Rv: G / 2 / DOLLARS. Plain edge. (Byrne 787)

In this series, there are 23mm brass tokens of $1, and 50, 25 and 10 cents. The weights vary, from 4.3 to 5.15 grams.

FR. DELUGAN

Rulau	Date	Metal	Size	F	VF	EF	Unc
Hai 44	ND	Brass	24mm	—	—	10.00	20.00

FR. / DELUGAN / (Rosette). Rv: 50 / CENT. / -.- Plain edge. (Rulau coll.)

This piece has die links and surface tone similar to 19th century Guatemala tokens. It is not cataloged anywhere, to our knowledge.

GRENADIERS DE LA GARDE

Rulau	Date	Metal	Size	VG	F	VF	Unc
Hai 46	ND	Brass	24mm	—	—	30.00	—

Haitian mantled arms, REPUBLIQUE D'HAITI above, . GRENADIERS DE LA GARDE . below. Rv: Blank. (Fauver pg. 45)

Button.

LAITERIE DU BOIS DE LA CAMBRE

Rulau	Date	Metal	Size	VG	F	VF	Unc
Hai 48	ND	CN	37mm	—	—	25.00	—

LAITERIE DU BOIS / 5 / DE LA CAMBRE. Rv: Same as obverse. Plain edge. Weight 13.3 grams. (Byrne 778)

F. X. MASSONI

Rulau	Date	Metal	Size	VG	F	VF	Unc
Hai 50	1902	CN	33mm	—	—	75.00	—

BRIQUETERIE SAINT-JOSEPH ARCAHAIE F. X. MASSONI. Rv: BON POUR / UNE / PIASTRE / PAYABLE A' / L'USINE / 1902. Plain edge. Weight 9.15 grams. (Byrne 782)

Rulau	Date	Metal	Size	VG	F	VF	Unc
Hai 51	1899	Brass	29mm	—	—	160.	—

Similar, but 20 CENTIMES and 1899.

Rulau	Date	Metal	Size	VG	F	VF	Unc
Hai 52	1899	Brass	24mm	—	—	160.	—

As last, but 10 CENTIMES.

PORTLAND HOUSE

Rulau	Date	Metal	Size	VG	F	VF	Unc
Hai 54	(ca 1850)	Gilt Silver	31mm	—	60.00	—	—

PORTLAND HOUSE ctsp on Haiti An-27 (1830) 100-centimes coin of President J. P. Boyer, KM-23. (Byrne 785)

REPUBLIQUE D'HAYTI

Rulau	Date	Metal	Size	VG	F	VF	Unc
Hai 56	ND	Gilt/Cop	21mm	6.00	11.00	20.00	—

REPUBLIQUE D'HAYTI / 29 / *. Rv: .EDSAM / & SON around button-shank. (Fauver pgs. 45-46)

Rulau	Date	Metal	Size	VG	F	VF	Unc
Hai 57	ND	Brass	22mm	6.00	11.00	20.00	—

Obverse as last, but 31. Rv: * FINE * / ** COLOUR ** around button-shank. (Fauver pgs. 45-46)

Rulau	Date	Metal	Size	VG	F	VF	Unc
Hai 58	ND	Brass	16.5mm	6.00	11.00	20.00	—

Obverse as last, but 17. Rv: Similar to last. (Fauver pg 46)

These are all buttons, or struck from button dies.

W. QUINTIN WILLIAMS

Rulau	Date	Metal	Size	F	VF	EF	Unc
Hai 60	ND	Aluminum	18mm	—	—	75.00	—

W. QUINTIN WILLIAMS / HAITI. Rv: Large numeral 1. Plain edge. (Byrne 774)

HAITI KAFFEE

Rulau	Date	Metal	Size	F	VF	EF	Unc
Hai 80	ND	Brass	24mm	—	1.00	—	2.50

HAITI (in oval frame) / KAFFEE. Rv: Blank.

NOT from Haiti. An Austrian coffee machine token!

JAMAICA

Jamaica's basic unit of reckoning in the early 19th century was the GILL, equal to three British farthings. Two gills equaled a QUATTLE (1½ pence, or ½ Spanish real).

Tokens in the gill denomination (¾ penny) were issued because there was no comparable regal coin, and the tokens were called locally 'gill-tickets.'

Britain's silver 1½-penny coin, struck specifically for colonial use 1834-1862, seems not to have been seen in Jamaica — even though most standard coin catalogs say they were circulated there and in Ceylon.

Slavery was abolished in Jamaica in 1834, and this occasion gave rise to certain token innovations which are discussed under various issuers.

Bowden
U. F. C. / B.
(United Fruit Co., Bowden)

Rulau	Date	Metal	Size	VG	F	VF	Unc
Jam 1	ND	Brass	Sq 19.8mm	—	37.50	—	—

U. F. C./ B. Rv: Blank. (Christensen Aug. 1979 sale, lot 1096)

This Bowden token can be found counterstamped K for Kingston. Value $37.50 in VF.

Rulau	Date	Metal	Size	VG	F	VF	Unc
Jam 3	ND	Aluminum	Sq 20mm	—	30.00	40.00	—

U. F. Co./B.L. (Bowden Loading). Rv: Blank. (Christensen Aug. 1979 sale, lot 1105; Lyall 430)

Buff Bay
S. S. / W. / B. B.
(S. S. Steadman, 'Woodstock,' Buff Bay)

Rulau	Date	Metal	Size	VG	F	VF	Unc
Jam 5	ND	Brass	23mm	—	—	75.00	—

S S / W / B B. Rv: Blank. Plain edge. Issued holed. Rare. (Christensen Aug. 1979 sale, lot 1090; Lyall 446)

Fox says for Wentworth estate.

Golden Grove
ROBERT KIRKLAND

Rulau	Date	Metal	Size	VG	F	VF	Unc
Jam 8	ND	CN	20mm	100.	—	175.	—

ROBERT KIRKLAND / 1½ in circle / *. Rv: DRY GOODS / HARDWARE / PROVISIONS / & DRUGS. Defacing cross on reverse. Plain edge. (Pridmore 142; Byrne 860; Lyall 155)

Rulau	Date	Metal	Size	VG	F	VF	Unc
Jam 8A	ND	CN	20mm	200.	250.	400.	—

As last, but not defaced. (Lyall 154)

Kingston
GEORGE BRANDON

Rulau	Date	Metal	Size	VG	F	VF	Unc
Jam 10	ND	CN	23.5mm	400.	600.	—	—

GEORGE BRANDON / 54 / HARBOUR / ST. / . KINGSTON . Rv: OBSERVE / BRANDON'S / SIGN. Plain edge. (Pridmore 134; Ulex 2569; Eklund 1970; Byrne 853; Lyall 164; ANS coll.)

George Brandon (1823-72) was proprietor of a general store. These tokens are very rare; a VG-plus specimen in the 1975 Byrne sale fetched $350! The Ford specimen brought $738!

GALL'S BAZAAR

Rulau	Date	Metal	Size	VG	F	VF	Unc
Jam 12	(1870-90)	Brass	23mm	—	—	400.	—

(All incused): GALL'S BAZAAR / GOOD FOR / ONE / GILL / MYRTLE BANK. Rv: Blank. (Pridmore 136; Lyall 151)

James Gall operated the Sanatorium Hotel, Bazaar and Circulating Library at Myrtle Bank, Harbour Street, Kingston, 1870-90, according to Fred Pridmore.

M. HOWARD

Rulau	Date	Metal	Size	VG	F	VF	EF
Jam 14	(1790's)	Copper	29mm	18.50	35.00	85.00	150.

Coachman drives a two-horse coach right, M. HOWARD above, FERRY GRASS below. Rv: Groom holds a saddled horse left. Around: KINGSTON / JAMAICA. Diagonally reeded edge. (Pridmore 131; Byrne 850; Fonrobert 7822; Ulex 2566; Lyall 153)

Mark Howard was a Kingston tavernkeeper in 1779 and later may have operated a coach service or a stable service. The token seems connected with fodder; the term ferry grass may refer to grass grown in the Ferry area for use as fodder.

Mark Howard owned the well-known South Sea House in Kingston until 1779. The halfpenny tokens were struck in England.

Uncirculated pieces exist and fetch $250.

JAMAICA BANANA PRODUCERS ASSOCIATION

Rulau	Date	Metal	Size	VG	F	VF	Unc
Jam 16	1937	Aluminum	27.5mm	—	15.00	35.00	—

JAMAICA / BANANA / PRODUCERS / ASSOCIA-
TION / LIMITED. Rv: J. B. P. A. / 1937 / JAMAICA.
Plain edge. (Christensen Aug. 1979 sale, lot 1089;
Lyall 328)

Rulau	Date	Metal	Size	VG	F	VF	Unc
Jam 17	1932	Aluminum	27.5mm	—	15.00	35.00	—

Similar to last, but 1932. (Lyall 327)

JAMAICA FRUIT & SHIPPING CO. LTD.

Rulau	Date	Metal	Size	VG	F	VF	Unc
Jam 20	1919	Aluminum	21mm	—	40.00	—	—

JAMAICA FRUIT & SHIPPING CO. LTD. / 1919 /
.JAMAICA. Rv: Blank. Rare. (Byrne 855; Rulau coll.)

Rulau	Date	Metal	Size	VG	F	VF	Unc
Jam 21	1921	Aluminum	21mm	20.00	40.00	55.00	—

As last, but 1921. Rare. (Pridmore 138; Byrne 856;
ANS collection; Lyall 332)

Rulau	Date	Metal	Size	VG	F	VF	Unc
Jam 22	1923	Aluminum	21mm	—	35.00	—	—

As last, but 1923. Rare. (Byrne 857)

Rulau	Date	Metal	Size	VG	F	VF	Unc
Jam 23	ND	Aluminum	21mm	—	20.00	—	—

Similar to last, but date is obscured by a counterstamped 6-spoke wheel. This may have been applied by
the company about 1928. (Lyall 331)

Rulau	Date	Metal	Size	VG	F	VF	Unc
Jam 25	1928	Aluminum	27mm	—	17.50	37.50	—

JAMAICA FRUIT & SHIPPING CO. LTD. / KING-
STON / *. Rv: 1928. Plain edge. (Pridmore 139; ANS
collection; Lyall 335)

KINGSTON AND LIGUANEA WATERWORKS COMPY.

Rulau	Date	Metal	Size	VG	F	VF	Unc
Jam 27	1848	Brass	34mm	—	—	650.	—

KINGSTON AND LIGUANEA / FOUNDED / 1848 /
. WATERWORKS COMPY . Rv: RETAIL / SALES /
8 PAILS 1½ D / E. LEVY / COLLECTOR. Plain edge
(Pridmore 143; Byrne 861; Lyall 194)

This firm was incorporated in 1842 but did not deliver any water until 1849.
These checks were used by persons purchasing water by the pail at the then-
familiar 'quattie' (1½ pence) rate.
The Jamaica government took over the waterworks on Jan. 1 1871.

K. W. L. (Kingston Wharves Ltd.)

Rulau	Date	Metal	Size	VG	F	VF	Unc
Jam 29	ND	Aluminum	25.8mm	—	—	65.00	—

(All incuse): K. W. L. Rv: Blank. (Pridmore N/L; Byrne
N/L; Christensen Aug. 1979 sale, lot 1116; Lyall 344)

Rulau	Date	Metal	Size	VG	F	VF	Unc
Jam 30	ND	Aluminum	21.5mm	—	—	27.50	—

(All incuse): (three arcs) / K. W. L. / (three arcs). Rv:
Blank. (Lyall 337)

There are other tokens of this issuer.

THOMAS LUNDIE & CO.

Rulau	Date	Metal	Size	VG	F	VF	Unc
Jam 32	1844	Brass	23mm	—	50.00	75.00	—

Three-masted paddle steamer left, EARL OF ELGIN
above, JAMAICA below. Rv: THOMAS LUNDAY &
CO. / IRONMONGERS / WATER STREET 1844.
Diagonally reeded edge. (Pridmore 144; Byrne 862)

Rulau	Date	Metal	Size	VG	F	VF	Unc
Jam 33	1844	Brass	23mm	20.00	60.00	85.00	—

Two-masted paddle steamer left, EARL OF ELGIN
above, JAMAICA below. Rv: THOMAS LUNDIE &
CO. / 1844. / . KINGSTON . Diagonally reeded edge.
(Pridmore 145; Byrne 863-864). Also known with plain
edge, possibly a pattern.

Lundie is the correct spelling. The spelling error on the first token forced the
second issue, and the ship was also altered in the treatment. The Lunday and
Lundie tokens are about equally scarce.
The steamer *Earl of Elgin* arrived at Kingston Aug. 27, 1844 for Lundie's
coastwise and interisland trade. The vessel was sold to the Haitian government
in 1847.

MYRTLE BANK

Rulau	Date	Metal	Size	VG	F	VF	Unc
Jam 35	(1870)	Brass	23.5mm	—	—	80.00	—

MYRTLE BANK / GOOD FOR / ONE / DOLLAR.
Rv: Blank. Plain edge. Weight: 3.88 grams. (Byrne 868)

Myrtle Bank Hotel was erected 1870 by James Gall, who also issued the Gall's
Bazaar tokens, which see.

WILLIAM SMITH

Rulau	Date	Metal	Size	VG	F	VF	Unc
Jam 37	(1829)	Copper	29.5mm	15.00	35.00	50.00	—

PAYABLE IN KINGSTON / d / 1 / JAMAICA / CUR-
RENCY / BY / * WILLIAM SMITH *. Rv: Indian-sup-
ported Jamaica arms. Plain edge. (Pridmore 132; Byrne
851; Rulau coll.)

Rulau	Date	Metal	Size	VG	F	VF	EF
Jam 38	(1829)	Copper	22mm	20.00	40.00	60.00	—

PAYABLE / IN / KINGSTON / BY / . WILLIAM SMITH . Rv: ONE HALF PENNY / JAMAICA / . CURRENCY . Plain edge. (Pridmore 133; Byrne 852; Lyall 163)

Issuer William Smith was a wealthy Kingston merchant. The tokens were made to his order by Matthew Boulton of Birmingham in 1829; paperwork on the order still exists in Boulton's records.

They were struck in the style of Boulton's cartwheel penny coinage for Great Britain in 1797, and for many years it was thought they had been made in 1798.

U. F. CO.
(United Fruit Co.)

Rulau	Date	Metal	Size	VG	F	VF	Unc
Jam 40	ND	Brass	19mm	—	—	37.50	—

(Three curved lines) / U. F. CO. / (three curved lines). Rv: Incused K. Plain edge. Issued holed. Weight 1.75 grams. (Pridmore 150; Byrne 876)

Jam 41	ND	Brass	18.5mm	—	—	50.00	—

Obverse as last. Rv: Blank. Issued holed. (Pridmore 151; Byrne 151; Rulau coll.)

Jam 42	ND	Brass	18.5mm	—	—	40.00	—

As last, but larger letters. Rv: Blank. Issued holed. (Pridmore 152)

Jam 43	ND	Brass	18.5mm	—	—	11.00	—

U. F. CO. (no lines). Rv: Blank. Issued holed. (Pridmore 153; Byrne 877)

Jam 45	ND	WM	21mm	—	—	25.00	—

(Three curved lines) / U. F. CO. / (three curved lines). Rv: Blank. Plain edge. Weight 1.5 grams. Scarce. (Byrne 880)

Jam 46	ND	Brass	Oval 24x16mm	—	—	75.00	—

U. F. CO. / -.- / -K-. Rv: Blank. Plain edge. Weight 2.02 grams. Issued holed. Rare. (Byrne 885)

Rulau	Date	Metal	Size	VG	F	VF	Unc
Jam 47	ND	Brass	Oval 26x16mm	—	—	65.00	—

Similar to last, but thinner letters. Rv: Blank. Plain edge. Weight 2.2 grams. Issued holed. (Byrne 886)

Jam 48	ND	Brass	25mm	—	—	15.00	—

UNITED FRUIT COMPANY around blank center. Rv: Blank. Plain edge. Weight 2.3 grams. Scarce. (Byrne 882)

Jam 49	ND	Brass	24.5mm	—	—	30.00	—

Four-petaled rosette at center, UNITED FRUIT COMPANY around. Rv: Blank. Plain edge. Thickness 2.2mm. Weight 6.55 grams. Issued holed. (Byrne 883)

Jam 50	ND	Brass	24.5mm	—	—	30.00	—

As last, but thinner flan (thickness 1.5mm). Weight 4.85 grams. (Byrne 883)

Jam 52	1912	Brass	19.2mm	—	—	80.00	—

U. F. CO. / 1912. Plain edge. Issued holed. (Christensen Aug. 1979 sale, lot 1093)

Jam 53	ND	Brass	22.3mm	—	—	80.00	—

U. F. C. Rv: Blank. Star-shaped cutout. (Christensen Aug. 1979 sale, lot 1095)

Jam 54	ND	Brass	Tri 20mm	—	—	37.50	—

U. F. CO. Rv: Blank. (Christensen sale Aug.1979, lot 1102). Triangular flan.

All United Fruit Co. tallies were issued to workers carrying bananas. Most were issued pierced for stringing. The 'K' appearing on some of these tokens stands for Kingston, Jamaica.

Montego Bay
A. F. CO.
(Atlantic Fruit Co.)

Rulau	Date	Metal	Size	VG	F	VF	Unc
Jam 58	ND	Brass	21mm	—	40.00	—	—

A. F. CO. within incised beaded border. Thin letters variety. Rv: Blank. Weight 2.5 grams. (Byrne 887; Christensen Aug. 1979 sale, lot 1107)

Jam 59	ND	Brass	24mm	—	40.00	—	—

Same as last, but larger. (Christensen Aug. 1979 sale, lot 1107)

Jam 60	ND	Brass	21mm	—	40.00	—	—

Obverse as last. Rv: Incused 8 / M. (Byrne 887)

Jam 61	ND	Brass	21mm	—	40.00	—	—

Obverse as last. Rv: Incused M / B. (Byrne 887)

Jam 62	ND	Brass	21mm	—	40.00	—	—

Similar to first token above, but thick letters variety. Rv: Blank. (Byrne 888)

Jam 63	ND	Brass	21mm	—	40.00	—	—

Obverse as last. Rv: Incused 8 / M. (Byrne 888)

Jam 64	ND	Brass	21mm	—	40.00	—	—

Obverse as last. Rv: Incused D / C. (Byrne 888)

Jam 65	ND	Brass	19.5mm	—	18.50	25.00	—

(Three arcs) / A. F. CO. / (three arcs). Rv: Blank. Weight 2.5 grams. (Byrne 889; Christensen Aug. 1979 sale, lot 1108; Lyall 224)

Jam 66	ND	Brass	19.5mm	—	30.00	—	—

Obverse as last. Rv: Incused M / B. (Byrne 889)

Jam 67	ND	Brass	19.5mm	—	25.00	32.50	—

Obverse as last. Rv: Incused M / 8. (Byrne 889)

Jam 68	ND	Brass	19.5mm	—	25.00	32.50	—

Obverse as last. Rv: Incused D / C. (Byrne 889)

Jam 69	ND	Brass	19mm	—	30.00	—	—

A. F. CO. on plain field. Rv: Incused 8 / M. (Byrne 890)

Jam 70	ND	Brass	19mm	—	25.00	32.50	—

As last, but Rv: Incused M / B. (Byrne 890; Rulau coll.)

Jam 71	ND	Brass	19mm	—	30.00	—	—

As last, but Rv: Incused D / C. (Byrne 890)

Jam 72	ND	Brass	20mm	—	60.00	—	—

A.F. Co. in sans serif letters on plain field. Rv: Blank. (Byrne 891; Christensen Aug. 1979 sale, lot 1109)

Rulau	Date	Metal	Size	VG	F	VF	Unc
Jam 73	ND	Brass	20mm	—	60.00	—	—

Obverse as last. Rv: Incused M / B. (Byrne 891)

Jam 74	ND	Brass	20mm	—	60.00	—	—

Obverse as last. Rv: Incused M / 8. (Byrne 891)

Jam 75	ND	Brass	19.2mm	—	30.00	—	—

A. F. CO. / LTD. Rv: Incused M / B. (Byrne (829)

Jam 76	ND	Brass	19.2mm	—	30.00	—	—

Obverse as last. Rv: Blank. (Christensen Aug. 1979 sale, lot 1111)

Jam 77	ND	Brass	19.2mm	—	30.00	—	—

Obverse as last. Rv: Incused M / B. (Byrne 892; Rulau coll.)

Jam 78	ND	Brass	19.2mm	—	30.00	—	—

Obverse as last. Rv: Incused D / C. (Byrne 892; Rulau coll.)

Jam 79	ND	Brass	25mm	—	50.00	—	—

A. F. CO. / LTD. within two concentric beaded circles. Rv: Blank. Plain edge. (Christensen Aug. 1979 sale, lot 1110)

The M and B on the reverse of several of these checks may stand for Montego Bay.

None of the A. F. CO. tokens were listed in Fred Pridmore's reference. Ray Byrne possessed many of them, which were sold in his 1975 auction by Jess Peters. Byrne incorrectly labeled the issuer "American Fruit Company" but William Christensen in 1979 corrected this to "Atlantic Fruit Company."

From the style, it appears that United Fruit Co. and Atlantic Fruit Co. checks were made in a number of instances by the same firm.

WILLIAM BREAKSPEAR

Rulau	Date	Metal	Size	VG	F	VF	Unc
Jam 82	ND	CN	40.5mm	—	—	750.	—

WILLIAM BREAKSPEAR / IMPORTER / & / GENERAL / MERCHANT / MONTEGO / BAY / JAMAICA. Rv: IRONMONGERY. PLANTATION & OTHER TOOLS / CUTLERY, / LEATHER SADDLERY . / FOWLING PIECES. / EARTHEN & GLASSWARE. / OILS. PAINTS. & COLOURS. / STATIONERY / PROVISIONS / WINES & SPIRITS. / DRAPERY. CLOTHING / BOOTS & SHOES / HOSIERY / PERFUMERY &C. Plain edge. (Pridmore 135; Lyall 165)

FLETCHER & CO. LTD.

Rulau	Date	Metal	Size	VG	F	VF	Unc
Jam 84	1928	WM	27mm	—	—	30.00	—

FLETCHER & CO. LTD. / 1 / * MONTEGO BAY *. Rv: ONE / 1928 / STEM. Plain edge. (Byrne 871)

Jam 85	1928	Brass	27mm	—	—	30.00	—

As last. (Byrne 871; Christensen Aug. 1979 sale, lot 1091)

Jam 86	1928	Aluminum	27mm	—	—	40.00	—

As last. (Byrne 871; Christensen Aug. 1979 sale, lot 1092; Lyall 307)

Jam 88	1932	Brass	27mm	—	—	40.00	—

As last, but 1932. (Byrne 871)

Jam 89	1932	Aluminum	27mm	—	—	60.00	—

As last. (Byrne 871; Lyall 309)

Fruit company checks. These have been reported in 27.3mm size.

U. F. CO. / M. B. L.
(United Fruit Co., Montego Bay Loading)

Rulau	Date	Metal	Size	VG	F	VF	Unc
Jam 91	ND	WM	Oct 20mm	—	—	35.00	—

U. F. CO. / M. B. L. Rv: Blank. Plain edge. (Byrne 881)

Jam 92	ND	WM	Rect 24x17mm	—	—	35.00	—

Similar to last, but rectangular. (Byrne 884)

Morant Bay
I. J. M. & CO.
(I. J. Mordecai & Co.)

Rulau	Date	Metal	Size	VG	F	VF	EF
Jam 95	(1880)	CN	19.5mm	—	85.00	125.	175.

I J M & Co / 1½ / + MORANT BAY. Rv: DRY GOODS / HARDWARE / CROCKERY etc. (Pridmore 146; Byrne 865)

Ivanhoe J. Mordecai had these struck at the Heaton Mint in Birmingham.

U. F. C. / M. B.
(United Fruit Co., Morant Bay)

Rulau	Date	Metal	Size	VG	F	VF	Unc
Jam 97	ND	Brass	Tri 20mm	—	—	100.	—

U. F. C. / M. B. Rv: Blank. (Christensen Aug. 1979 sale, lot 1103)

New Ramble
LEO GEORGE SILVERA

Rulau	Date	Metal	Size	VG	F	VF	Unc
Jam 100	(1901)	Copper	24mm	—	—	300.	—

3D.. in central circle. Around: LEO GEORGE SILVERA / . NEW RAMBLE . Rv: Intaglio of obverse. Plain edge. Weight: 2.25 grams. (Byrne 870; Lyall 158)

19th century estate token of Silvera, a justice and estate owner. There are also 6d, 1 / and 2 / 6d tokens in this series.

Portland
U. F. CO. / P. L.
(United Fruit Co., Portland Loading)

Rulau	Date	Metal	Size	VG	F	VF	Unc
Jam 103	ND	Aluminum	Rec				
			25x17mm	—	—	40.00	—

U.F.CO/P.L. Rv: Blank. (Christensen Aug. 1979 sale, lot 1106; Lyall 434)

The August, 1979 auction by William Christensen in New York placed before the numismatic marketplace the best collection of Jamaica fruit handler checks yet seen at one time. Many pieces could not be found in the Pridmore or Byrne references or in the American Numismatic Society collection.

MARQUIS OF SLIGO
St. Catherine Parish

Rulau	Date	Metal	Size	VG	F	VF	EF
Jam 106	(1834)	Lead	36mm	—	—	—	1500.

* MARQUIS OF SLIGO * / TOKEN FOR / (circle) / ONE SHILLING / STERLING / *. Rv: PAYABLE AT KELLY'S ESTATE / EACH FRIDAY EVENG. 6 O'CLOCK. / *. Plain edge (Pridmore 147)

Rulau	Date	Metal	Size	VG	F	VF	EF
Jam 107	(1834)	Lead	30.5mm	—	—	—	1500.

As last, but centrally holed flan and SIX / PENCE. (Pridmore 148)

Rulau	Date	Metal	Size	VG	F	VF	EF
Jam 108	(1834)	Lead	27.5mm	—	—	—	1500.

As last, but THREEPENCE. (Pridmore 149)

Kelly's was the "great house" where the sugar furnaces and factory buildings stood on the marquis' sugar estates. Howe Peter Browne, second Marquis of Sligo, born 1788, was appointed governor of Jamaica in 1834 to carry out the emancipation of slaves. Slavery was abolished there August 1, 1834.

The tokens were for use on his estates after workers started being paid. Sligo left Jamaica late in 1834, and died in 1845 at age 57. In 1816-17 the estate had been for cattle, but converted to sugar in 1817.

Three tokens, ex-CoKayne collection, Pridmore, Glendining, Sept. 1981, sold for: £800, £820 and £850, respectively (1, 6d, 3d). They were called "tin" there.

Uncertain Location
B. F. CO.
(Boston Fruit Co.)

Rulau	Date	Metal	Size	VG	F	VF	Unc
Jam 120	(1890-99)	Brass	Sq 19mm	—	60.00	85.00	—

(Three curved lines) / B. F. CO. / (three curved lines). Rv: Blank. Plain edge. Issued holed. (Christensen Aug. 1979 sale, lot 1087)

Rulau	Date	Metal	Size	VG	F	VF	Unc
Jam 121	ND	Brass	18.5mm	30.00	50.00	70.00	—

As last. Weight 1.75 grams. Issued holed. (Byrne 875; Rulau coll.)

Rulau	Date	Metal	Size	VG	F	VF	Unc
Jam 122	ND	Brass	Oct.				
			18.5mm	—	—	100.	175.

As last. (Lyall 292)

These tokens were made by the same firm which prepared the United Fruit Co. tokens for Kingston. Boston Fruit Co. was founded by Captain Baker and others in 1885.

Boston Fruit and other firms formed United Fruit Co. in 1899.

R. B. B.
(R. B. Braham)

Rulau	Date	Metal	Size	VG	F	VF	Unc
Jam 123	(1891)	—	--mm	—	—	—	—

V.F.D. / 1 / / R. B. B.

Braham owned a provision store in 1891. There is also a 1½-pence token of this type.

BRITISH COLONIES

Rulau	Date	Metal	Size	VG	F	VF	Unc
Jam 125	1825	Copper	28.3mm	25.00	35.00	50.00	—

Male bust in civil attire left, BRITISH COLONIES around. Rv: Seated Commerce on a bale, a flower extended in her right hand. Around: TO FACILITATE TRADE / 1825. Plain edge. Weight 10 grams. (Pridmore 130; Byrne 849; Lyall 147)

Also used in Canada.

HALCOT FARM

Rulau	Date	Metal	Size	VG	F	VF	Unc
Jam 127	(1900-10)	Brass	19.5mm	—	—	500.	—

HALCOT FARM / 1 D. Very rare.

The farm is now included in Kingston.

I. D. W. I.
(Imperial Direct West India)

Rulau	Date	Metal	Size	VG	F	VF	EF
Jam 129	(1901-03)	Brass	Sq 23mm	—	50.00	70.00	100.

I D W I in large letters across center of flan. Rv: Intaglio of obverse. Plain edge. Flan holed at top, as issued. Rare. (Pridmore N/L; Byrne N/L; Lyall 326; Rulau coll.)

A Fine specimen fetched $80 in the Aug. 1979 Christensen auction, lot 1115. Neither the extensive Byrne nor ANS collections possessed this token. The Rulau specimen is in VF condition.

Carol Plante reports selling 5 or more pieces over the years.

I. D. W. I. was a mail service company. Imperial Direct West India Mail Service Co., organized 1901 and bought out by United Fruit Co. 1903.

Jamaica 1803

Rulau	Date	Metal	Size	VG	F	VF	Unc
Jam 131	1803	Copper	--mm	—	—	—	—

Alligator left, JAMAICA above, 1803 below. Rv: Blank. (Pridmore 137; Glendining Parsons sale of May 1954, lot 1049)

Not a token, this is a belt buckle for the Jamaican militia.

STANDARD
(Standard Fruit and Steamship Co.)

Rulau	Date	Metal	Size	VG	F	VF	Unc
Jam 133	ND	Brass	20mm	—	—	30.00	—

STANDARD incused. Rv: Blank. Plain edge.
(Christensen Aug. 1979 sale, lot 1112; Lyall 368)

TROPICAL FRUIT CORP.

Rulau	Date	Metal	Size	VG	F	VF	Unc
Jam 135	1923	WM	21mm	—	25.00	45.00	—

TROPICAL FRUIT CORP. / 1923 / . JAMAICA .Rv: f
T c. Plain edge. Weight 1.7 grams. (Byrne 874-74;
Rulau coll.; Lyall 377)

There are thick (1.9 grams) and thin (1.24 grams weight) varieties reported. All are scarce.

U. F. CO. / G. S. P. W.

Rulau	Date	Metal	Size	VG	F	VF	Unc
Jam 140	ND	Brass	19.5mm	—	50.00	65.00	—

(Tiny) Am. RY. S. Co. / NEW YORK / U. F. CO. / G.
S. P. W. Rv: Blank.Plain edge. Weight 1.75 grams.
Issued holed. (Byrne 878)

Rulau	Date	Metal	Size	VG	F	VF	Unc
Jam 141	ND	Brass	18.5mm	—	60.00	75.00	—

G.S. W. P. / U. F. CO. Rv: Blank. Issued holed. (Lyall
405)

AM. RY. S. CO. NEW YORK = American Railway Supply Co., New York
City. This firm also supplied tallies to henequen plantation owners in Yucatan.
G. S. P. W. = General Service Power Works.

△△ Incorrect Attributions △△

The following group of tokens, attributed to Jamaica by Fred Pridmore or Ray
Byrne, has been shown to be non-Jamaican in origin. They are cataloged here as
a reader service.

JAMAICA TAVERN CLUB

Rulau	Date	Metal	Size	VG	F	VF	Unc
Jam 200	ND	Brass	Oct 26mm	—	—	25.00	—

JAMAICA / D / 3 / TAV -- ERN / CLUB / (tiny) H.
NEAL 13 PERCIVAL STREET LONDON. Rv: ..+.. /
JAMAICA / TAVERN / ..+.. Plain edge. Weight 6.4
grams. (Byrne 869)

Not from Jamaica! From Rotherhithe, Surrey, England. This piece fetched
$95 at the 1975 Byrne sale.
Struck by H. Neal of 13 Percival St., London. 3 D = Three pence.

M. & S.

Rulau	Date	Metal	Size	VG	F	VF	Unc
Jam 201	ND	Brass	Oct 26mm	—	—	—	—

M & S. Rv: Blank. Plain edge. Weight: 3.85 grams.
(Byrne 872; Lyall 189)

Not from Jamaica! Fantasy attribution by Ray Byrne, who called it Mordecai
& Sligo of Morant Bay. Henkle says from Peru.

W. SMITH

Rulau	Date	Metal	Size	VG	F	VF	Unc
Jam 202	ND	Brass	22mm	—	—	3.00	5.00

W. SMITH / ... Rv: GOOD FOR 1D. IN TRADE. Plain
edge. Centrally holed flan. (Byrne 867)

This is a British token from Birmingham not connected with Jamaica. There
is no relationship between this issuer and William Smith of Kingston.

Ut & Ly

Rulau	Date	Metal	Size	VG	F	VF	Unc
Jam 203	1786	Lead	23mm	—	—	75.00	—

Ut & L y. Rv: 1786. Crude. Plain edge. Weight: 7.6
grams. (Pridmore 154; Byrne 866)

Not from Jamaica, though specimens have been found in Jamaica. One specimen is in the Institute of Jamaica collection; another in about VF fetched $75 in
the 1975 Byrne sale.
This is a communion token from Rothshire, U.K. Ut & Ly = Urquhart &
Logy. It is rare in its own right; a VF specimen was offered in 1992 at $97.50.

MARTINIQUE

H. DUPUIS & CIE.

Rulau	Date	Metal	Size	F	VF	EF	Unc
Mqe 2	(1900-13)	**	38mm	—	100.	—	—

** Silvered brass shell card. Female bust facing ¾ left. Around: MODES. TISSUS. CHAUSSURES. CHAPELLERIE. PARAPLUIES / -*-. Rv: AU SANS PAREIL. H. DUPUIS & CIE. / SEULE MAISON / VENDANT REELEMENT / LE MEILLEUR MARCHE / DE TOUTE LA / MARTINIQUE / (ornament). (Byrne 929)

Rulau	Date	Metal	Size	F	VF	EF	Unc
Mqe 3	ND	Brass shell	38mm	—	100.	—	—

As last, but yellow brass shell card. (Byrne 930)

H. Dupuis et Cie was a general store operation headquartered in Fort de France and with branches in Le Francois, Le Marin, Riviere Pilote, Riviere Salee and Le Saint Esprit. According to directory evidence, it began after 1891 and disappeared before 1922, since directories for those years do not list it. It is listed in the 1913 *Commercial Almanac* at a period when it was at its height of influence.

Specialist Roland Elie commented: "This kind of shell card is typical of advertising tokens at the turn of the century. Similar tokens in France are dated 1900-1925."

MARTINIQUE

Rulau	Date	Metal	Size	F	VF	EF	Unc
Mqe 7	ND	—	23.5mm	—	65.00	—	—

MARTINIQUE / 5 (punched out). Rv: Blank. Weight 2.92 grams. (Byrne 931)

CIE. GLE. D'ALIMENTATION

Rulau	Date	Metal	Size	VG	F	VF	Unc
Mqe 10	ND	Brass	22.5mm	—	500.	700.	—

Bee surrounded by JETONS A REMBOURSABLE within beaded circle. Around: Cie Gle D'ALIMENTATION / * MARTINIQUE *. Rv: Blank. (Gadoury-Elie 1.1)

BOUTIQUE

Rulau	Date	Metal	Size	VG	F	VF	Unc
Mqe 14	1892	**	30mm	—	300.	500.	—

BOUTIQUE / 1892 / BASSE-POINTE. Rv: 10 / CENT. (Gadoury-Elie 2.1)

Rulau	Date	Metal	Size	VG	F	VF	Unc
Mqe 16	1910	**	25mm	—	400.	600.	—

** Nickel-plated zinc. BOUTIQUE / 1910 / VIVE. Rv: 50 / CENT. (G-E 3.2)

Rulau	Date	Metal	Size	VG	F	VF	Unc
Mqe 17	1910	**	18.5mm	—	300.	500.	—

As last, but 5 / CENT. (G-E 3.1)

The Boutique tokens were used, respectively, in Basse-Pointe and in Vive, the latter in the commune of Le Lorrain.

NETHERLANDS ANTILLES

ARUBA

V.B.C.

Rulau	Date	Metal	Size	VG	F	VF	Unc
Aru 3	ND	CN	20mm	—	—	15.00	—

V B C / ARUBA. Rv: GOOD FOR / (empty circle) / ONE / DRINK. Plain edge. (Byrne 239)

CURACAO

R. D. I. Co.

Rulau	Date	Metal	Size	VG	F	VF	Unc
Cur 1	(ca 1800)	Silv/C	26mm	—	—	350.	—

Indian canoe on beach. Rv: R D I / Co. Reeded edge. (Eklund 2050A; Guttag 4887; Scholten 1411; Byrne 226)

| Cur 2 | (ca 1800) | Silv/C | 21mm | — | — | 350. | — |

As last, smaller. (Ulex 2535; Ek. 2050; Sch. 1411)

No satisfactory explanation for these rare tokens has ever been advanced. They have been attributed to Ontario, Michigan and St. Eustatius, but seem properly to belong to Curacao.

Willemstad
J. x CO.
(Jesurun & Company)

Rulau	Date	Metal	Size	VG	F	VF	Unc
Cur 5	(1880)	GS	15.5mm	—	10.00	25.00	60.00

J x Co— / (long bar). Rv: 1 / STUIVER / (long bar). Plain edge (Ulex 2537; Eklund 2051; Scholten 1408)

| Cur 6 | (1880) | Lead | 17mm | 200. | — | — | — |

J x C. Rv: ½. (Byrne 233)

| Cur 7 | ND | Lead | 18.5mm | — | 75.00 | — | — |

J x Co- / (long bar). Rv: 1 / STUIVER / (long bar). (Byrne/Dutch T-5)

| Cur 8 | ND | Brass | 22.5mm | — | 75.00 | — | — |

As last. (Byrne/Dutch T-5)

| Cur 9 | ND | Silver | 27mm | — | — | 200. | — |

J x C (relief, within toothed rectangular depressions), ctsp on Spanish-American 1802 2-reales. (Byrne,/Dutch T-24)

The tokens listed above were issued by Jesurun & Company, a Jewish Willemstad enterprise. The family had kinship links to the Jesuruns of Venezuela, issuers of the Concesion Jesurun tokens.

L. x C.
(Leyba & Co.)

Rulau	Date	Metal	Size	VG	F	VF	Unc
Cur 11	(1880)	GS	15.5mm	—	30.00	50.00	90.00

L x C / (long bar). Rv: 1 / STUIVER / (long bar). Plain edge. (Ulex 2537; Eklund 2053; Scholten 1410; Scott)

The Leyba & Co. 1880 tokens of Curacao have always been more difficult to find than the Jesurun and Naar pieces of the same era. Original mintages on the three issues are not known.

J. J. N.
(J. J. Naar)

Rulau	Date	Metal	Size	VG	F	VF	Unc
Cur 13	(1880)	GS	15.5mm	—	15.00	30.00	50.00

J. J. N. / (long bar). Rv: 1 / STUIVER / (long bar). Plain edge. (Ulex 2537; Eklund 2052; Scholten 1409; Scott)

Issued by J. J. Naar. The tokens were struck by the same maker as those of Jesurun & Co. and Leyba & Co., who used an identical reverse die for each firm.

C.
(S.E.L. Maduro & Sons)

Rulau	Date	Metal	Size	VG	F	VF	EF
Cur 16	ND	GS	15.5mm	—	100.	—	—

Large serif C ctsp on J x Co 1880 token. (Scholten 1408b)

| Cur 17 | ND | GS | 15.5mm | — | 150. | — | — |

Similar ctsp on J. J. N. 1880 token. (Scholten 1409b)

| Cur 18 | ND | GS | 15.5mm | — | 150. | — | — |

Similar ctsp on L x C 1880 token. (Scholten 1410b; Byrne 232; *The Numismatist* for Nov. 1931, pg 786)

| Cur 19 | ND | Brass | 25.5mm | — | 150. | — | — |

Similar ctsp on L x C brass stuiver. (Byrne/Dutch T-11)

C = Coal. S. E. L. Maduro & Sons Coal Co. counterstamped the older struck tokens of other Curacao enterprises for use as payment talleys for loading coal on ships. This practice had ceased well before Thomas W. Voetter wrote a 1931 article on the subject for the American Numismatic Association magazine.

C. T. C.
(Curacao Trading Co.)

Rulau	Date	Metal	Size	VG	F	VF	Unc
Cur 21	ND	Zinc	19mm	—	85.00	—	—

C. T. C. Rv: Blank. (Scholten 1412; Byrne 231)

Rulau	Date	Metal	Size	VG	F	VF	Unc
Cur 23	ND	Silver	19mm	—	100.	—	—

C.T.C. "etched" on smoothed Netherlands 1/4 guilder. Reeded edge. (Scaife 227)

Curacao Trading Co. used these talleys to pay workers for loading coal on ships.

WARNING: A quite common cupronickel 20.5mm token bearing a complex TCCo monogram on obverse is occasionally passed off as a C.T.C. token. These are machine tokens of the Caille Co., Detroit.

J x C / W. B.

Rulau	Date	Metal	Size	VG	F	VF	Unc
Cur 25	(ca 1880)	Lead	19mm	—	300.00	—	Ex.Rare

J x C / W. B. Rv: K C F / 2 d. Plain edge. Weight 3.5 grams. (Byrne 234)

THE GOLDEN TANKARD

Rulau	Date	Metal	Size	VG	F	VF	Unc
Cur 30	(1950's)	S/Brass	26mm	—	—	75.00	—

Crowned shield of arms, CURACAO below. Rv: Tankard, its handle at right. Around: THE GOLDEN TANKARD / * DE . GOUDEN . BEKER *. Plain edge. Issued with loop. Weight 4.45 grams. (Byrne 235)

V. N. C. X.
(Vereeniging Numismatica Curacao)

Rulau	Date	Metal	Size	F	VF	EF	Unc
Cur 40	(1980's)	Silver	Triang 26x18mm	—	—	15.00	—

V / N / C / X within circle ctsp on quarter cut segment of Curacao 1944-D 2½-guilder crown. Issued by the Curacao Numismatic Association.

SINT EUSTATIUS

HERMAN GOSSLING

Rulau	Date	Metal	Size	VG	F	VF	EF
STE 1	1771	Brass	22.5mm	—	—	300.	400.

Goose left, eating grass. Around: GOD BLESS ST. EUSTATIUS & GUVn. Rv: 1 Bt at center, HERMAN GOSSLING / 1771. around. Wide dentilated rim on either side. Plain edge. Weight 1.9-2.2 grams. (Scholten 1432; Byrne 1006-07; Scott; Lyall 452)

STE 2	1771	Brass	20mm	—	—	375.	500.

Similar to last, but ½ Bt. Weight 1.05-1.15 grams. (Scholten 1433; Byrne 1009; Eklund 1977)

The bit, or real, equaled 12½ cents.

Fred Pridmore says these were struck during British occupation 1781-1814.

The date 1771 refers to the founding of Gossling's spice and sugar business in Lower Town.

PUERTO RICO

Some Puerto Rican Token Terms

Ril (plural Riles) (pronounced ree' lace)	= Real (token form)
Vale (pl. Vales)	= Paper or cardboard scrip
Chapa (pl. Chapas)	= Metal Identity tag for workers (mostly used 1900-1950)
Almud	= Basketful of coffee berries, about 8.3 pounds. One almud yielded 5 lbs. of dried hulled coffee beans.
Fanega	= 12 Almudes of coffee berries, or about 100 lbs. of berries (99.6 lbs. Yielded about 60 lbs of coffee beans.

About Puerto Rican Tokens

The tokens of no Latin American nation are as avidly collected and as well cataloged over a long period of time as those of Puerto Rico. American and European collectors find this area fascinating and have devoted years of study to it.

Specialists should consult the references given in the Bibliography under Puerto Rico for complete treatment of the subject, impossible in this Catalog and Guide Book.

ADJUNTAS MUNICIPIO

Guilarte
TOMAS PIETRI & HERMANO
Hacienda Esperanza

Rulau	Date	Metal	Size	VG	F	VF	Unc
Adj 3	ND	Copper	28mm	—	45.00	70.00	—

TOMAS PIETRI & HERMANO / 3 / *. Rv: HACIENDA ESPERANZA / 5 / * GUILARTE *. Plain edge. (Gould-Higgie 248; Vaia 183; Archilla-Diez 435)

Also issued were 2, 1 and ½-almud tokens, all about equally scarce.

Jahueca
ANTONIO BENAUZAR

Rulau	Date	Metal	Size	VG	F	VF	Unc
Adj 9	ND	Copper	24mm	30.00	45.00	65.00	—

Eagle displayed. Around: ADJUNTAS / .*. JAHUECA P.R. .*. Rv: HACIENDA DE CAFE / ½ (large) / * ANTONIO BENAUZAR *. (Vaia 266; Archilla-Diez 344)

Rulau	Date	Metal	Size	VG	F	VF	Unc
Adj 10	ND	Copper	21mm	—	30.00	50.00	—

As last, but ¼. (Gonzales 95; Gould-Higgie 201; Roehrs 9; Vaia 265; A-D 343)

A coffee estate, called Hacienda Mayorquina. There is also a very rare 1-almud, brass, 25mm, worth $75 in Fine.

PEDRO CARDONA
Hacienda Florida

Rulau	Date	Metal	Size	VG	F	VF	Unc
Adj 14	ND	Brass	30.3mm	—	—	75.00	—

(All incused): PEDRO / 40 / CARDONA. Rv: HACIENDA / 40 / FLORIDA / V-in-star ctsp. Ex. rare. (Archilla-Diez 449)

40 = 40 almudes.

Portillo
ALFONSO CASTAÑER
Hacienda Portillo

Rulau	Date	Metal	Size	VG	F	VF	Unc
Adj 18	ND	Brass	30mm	18.00	23.00	30.00	—

HACIENDA DE CAFE / PORTILLO (in beaded circle) / * ALFONSO CASTAÑER *. Rv: 3 (in beaded circle). Plain edge. (Gonzales 13; Gould-Higgie 313; Roehrs 12; Vaia 399; Archilla-Diez 393)

Also in the series are brass 2, 1 and ½-almud tokens. Coffee plantation.

Vega Arriba
C. P. / AD Monogram
Hacienda Central Pellejas

Rulau	Date	Metal	Size	VG	F	VF	Unc
Adj 22	ND	Brass	43mm	—	100.	—	—

C P / AD monogram. Rv: 25. (Vaia 369; Archilla-Diez 097)

Rulau	Date	Metal	Size	VG	F	VF	Unc
Adj 23	ND	Brass	25mm	—	35.00	—	—

As last, but 5. (Vaia 368; A-D 095a)

Colonia Pellejas? There are also 10-centavo and no-denomination tokens in this series.

These tokens exist with a variety of counterstamps: AD Vq; UVq Z U; H R; AD AD; U Aq; or ZU. U Aq = Al Reves. 25 = 25 centavos.

AGUADILLA MUNICIPIO

Aguadilla
HACIENDA YRURENA

Rulau	Date	Metal	Size	VG	F	VF	Unc
Agd 3	ND	Copper	28mm	—	—	65.00	—

Sugar mill with two smoking stacks, numeral 5 above. Rv: Three stalks of sugar cane on ground. Above: HACIENDA YRURENA. Very rare. (Eklund 2250; Vaia 549; Roehrs 34; Archilla-Diez 532)

Rulau	Date	Metal	Size	VG	F	VF	Unc
Agd 4	ND	Copper	29mm	—	—	65.00	—

As last, but 10. Very rare. (Vaia 550; Roehrs 34; A-D 533)

Archilla-Diez believes this sugar plantation was at Aguadilla. The tokens were erroneously attributed to Honduras by Ole P. Eklund.

CIALES MUNICIPIO

Toro Negro
JOSE RAMON FIGUEROA
Hacienda Constancia

Rulau	Date	Metal	Size	VG	F	VF	Unc
Cls 10	ND	Brass	28mm	—	—	30.00	—

JOSE RAMON FIGUEROA / HACIENDA / CON-STANCIA / * TORO-NEGRO *. Rv: Blank. (Gould-Higgie 224; Vaia 132; A-D 330)

GUANICA MUNICIPIO

Arena
J. D.
Hacienda Fraternidad

Rulau	Date	Metal	Size	VG	F	VF	Unc
Gnc 3	ND	Brass	20mm	—	35.00	—	—

HACIENDA / FRATERNIDAD / GUANICA. Ctsp J D. Rv: 10. Ctsp HF / HF. (Eklund 1940; Roehrs 32A; Vaia 201; Archilla-Diez 450b)

| Gnc 4 | ND | Brass | 22mm | — | 50.00 | — | — |

HACIENDA / FRATERNIDAD / GUANICA. Ctsp * JD *. Rv: 25. Ctsp HF. (Vaia 201a; A-D 451b)

| Gnc 5 | ND | Brass | 25mm | — | 35.00 | — | — |

HACIENDA / FRATERNIDAD / GUANICA. Rv: 50. Ctsp HF / HF. (Vaia 202; Roehrs 32; A-D 452a)

| Gnc 6 | ND | Brass | 25mm | — | 35.00 | — | — |

HACIENDA / FRATERNIDAD / GUANICA. Ctsp J D. Rv: 50. (Roehrs 32C; A-D 452b)

Sugar cane plantation. There are other tokens known.

JAYUYA MUNICIPIO

Cialito
B. BORRAS Y HERMANOS
Hacienda Santa Catalina

Rulau	Date	Metal	Size	VG	F	VF	AU
Jyy 1	1881	Tin	23mm	—	—	45.00	—

HACIENDA STA. CATALINA / 1881 (in wreath) / P. R. Rv: B. BORRAS Y HERMANOS / 1. D. (in wreath) / -*-. Plain edge. (Eklund 1957; Archilla-Diez 519; Vaia 472; Gould-Higgie 328)

Rulau	Date	Metal	Size	VG	F	VF	AU
Jyy 2	1881	Tin	18mm	—	—	45.00	—

As last, but ½ D. (Dia). (Eklund 1956; G-H 326; Vaia 471; A-D 518; Randel coll.)

| Jyy 3 | 1881 | Tin | 15.5mm | — | — | 45.00 | — |

As last, but ¼ D. (Eklund 1955; Vaia 470; A-D 517; Randel coll.)

D = Dia (one day's work). There is an extremely rare 2 D. token reported by Archilla-Diez as number 520, worth $100. This was a coffee plantation.

Tin is one of the worst metals from which to make coins and tokens because of tinpest oxidation. Few of these pieces have survived in collector condition.

Coabey
JOSE ANTONIO MATTEI
Hacienda Guavey

Rulau	Date	Metal	Size	VG	F	VF	Unc
Jyy 7	ND	Brass	26mm	—	—	70.00	90.00

HACIENDA DE CAFE / 2 / REAL (value in beaded circle) / * GUAVEY *. Rv: JOSE ANTONIO MATTEI / JAYUYA (in beaded circle) / * PUERTO-RICO *. Plain edge. Ex. Rare. (Archilla-Diez 361)

| Jyy 8 | ND | Brass | 21mm | — | — | 70.00 | — |

As last, but 1 / REAL. Ex. Rare. (A-D 360)

The tokens for this coffee plantation were struck in Spain, according to Archilla-Diez.

MATTEO MATTEI

Rulau	Date	Metal	Size	VG	F	VF	Unc
Jyy 12	ND	Copper	30mm	—	30.00	—	—

MATTEO MATTEI / * JAYUYA. Rv: In laurel wreath: 1 (almud). Rare. (Vaia 339; Archilla-Diez 685; G-H 279)

Coffee plantation.

Jayuya Arriba
JAIME OLIVER MAYOL
Hacienda Las Gripinas

Rulau	Date	Metal	Size	VG	F	VF	Unc
Jyy 18	ND	Aluminum	29mm	—	30.00	45.00	—

JAIME OLIVER MAYOL / 25 / PONCE, PORTO RICO. Rv: HACIENDA LAS GRIPINAS / 25 / TIRADA DE / 750 / JAYUYA, PTO. RICO. Plain edge. Mintage 750 pcs. (Gonzalez 66; Goudl-Higgie 256; Roehrs 43B; Vaia 285; Archilla-Diez 469)

| Jyy 20 | ND | Aluminum | 29mm | — | 20.00 | 50.00 | — |

As last, but 10, and TIRADA DE / 2000. Mintage 2000 pcs. (Gonz. 65; G-H 255; Roehrs 43A; Vaia 284; A-D 468)

This issue also includes aluminum 29mm 5-centavos, mintage 1900, and aluminum 25mm 2-centavos, mintage 500.

Tirada de 750 = Issue of 750. This series is unusual in that its mintage is specified on each token! (Also see Wantzelius, Oliver & Co. under Ponce, P.R.).

Probably issued about 1900, as the name 'Porto' Rico came into use in the early stages of American rule.

EUSEBIO PEREZ
Hacienda Santa Barbara

Rulau	Date	Metal	Size	VG	F	VF	Unc
Jyy 24	1882	CN	27mm	—	—	60.00	—

EUSEBIO PEREZ / JAYUYA / * 1882 *. Rv: HACIENDA DE CAFE / 2 / *. (Roehrs 42; Vaia 466; Archilla-Diez 358)

| Jyy 25 | 1882 | CN | 22mm | — | — | 60.00 | — |

As last, but 1. (Vaia 465; A-D 357)

| Jyy 26 | 1882 | CN | 16mm | — | — | 60.00 | — |

As last, but ¼ (almud). (Vaia 464; A-D 356)

There is also an ex. rare 3-almudes, CN 32.1mm, worth $75 in VF.

A. TRIAS & CO.

Rulau	Date	Metal	Size	VG	F	VF	Unc
Jyy 30	ND	CN	26.5mm	—	—	80.00	—

A TRIAS & CO. / (Cruciform ornament) / . JAYUYA . Rv: 2. (G-H 372; A-D 039)

| Jyy 32 | ND | CN | 24mm | — | — | 60.00 | — |

As last, but 1. (G-H 371; Vaia 526; A-D 038)

There is also a ½ almud piece in this issue.

LAJAS MUNICIPIO

Lajas
LA AURORA

Rulau	Date	Metal	Size	VG	F	VF	Unc
Laa 1	ND	Brass	34mm	—	—	65.00	—

(All incused): LA AURORA / 10 / LAJAS. Rv: Blank. (Archilla-Diez 627)

Sugar cane plantation. Tokens, in denominations of 10, 5 and 1 centavos, are very rare, probably less than 5 pieces known in each denomination.

LARES MUNICIPIO

Bartolo
HACIENDA SAN JUAN BTA.

Rulau	Date	Metal	Size	F	VF	EF	Unc
Lrs 7	ND	Gilt/Bs	37.3mm	—	15.00	20.00	30.00

HACIENDA . DE . CAFE / 5 (shaded) /.*. SAN . JUAN-Bta .*. Rv: BARRIOS . DE . INDIERA . ALTA . BARTOLO / 5 (shaded) / * MARICAO . LARES . P.R. *. Plain edge. Common. (Vaia 446; Archilla-Diez 395)

This is the only denomination issued. This token mentions the barrios (wards) of Indiera, Alta and Bartolo in Lares municipio.

Indiera
FRANCISCO LLUCH BARRERA
Hacienda Engracia

Rulau	Date	Metal	Size	VG	F	VF	Unc
Lrs 11	ND	Brass	27mm	12.50	15.00	40.00	70.00

Floreate device in beaded circle. Around: FRANCISCO . LLUCH . BARRERA / *. Rv: HACIENDA . ENGRACIA / 1 / . ALMUD . / * INDIERA *. Plain edge. (A-D 428; Vaia 175; G&H 239; Roehrs 53B)

| Lrs 12 | ND | Brass | 30mm | 17.50 | 20.00 | 40.00 | 70.00 |

As last, but 2. (A-D 429; Gonzales 45; Vaia 176)

There is also a ½ almud, 23mm, worth $30 in VF, for this coffee estate. The beautiful tokens were struck in Germany by the same firm which made the Vega Redonda riles.

La Torre
MIGUEL MARQUEZ Y ENSEÑAT

Rulau	Date	Metal	Size	F	VF	EF	Unc
Lrs 16	1882	Brass	32.5mm	7.50	11.00	13.50	25.00

Radiant sunface in beaded circle. Around: PUERTO-RICO * LARES BARRIO LATORRE / 10 MAYO 1882 *. Rv: Blank space within beaded circle in which numeral is stamped. Around: HACIENDA DE MIGUEL MARQUEZ Y ENSEÑAT / *. (Numeral 1 is: Gonzalez 30; Gould-Higgie 280; Roehrs 56; Vaia 322; Archilla-Diez 409)

All tokens in this series are stamped with the number of almudes represented, from 1 through 10, and each token exists without further counterstamp, and with ctsp 'waves'. Thus there are 20 separate tokens in the set. The commonest are 2, 3, 4, 5 and 6 almudes. The 7 and 8 almudes are quite scarce, worth $55 in VF.

The series is plentiful, but BU pieces are scarce. Most tokens are in F, VF or EF condition. While one piece of the series is easy to obtain, completing a set of all known varieties is extremely difficult.

Your author bought one of these pieces in 1941 for 75 cents, then a fair amount; it was the first Puerto Rican token we owned. It was of the 2-almudes denomination, minus waves ctsp. These pieces have been rising slowly in price, and have passed the $10 per piece mark in VF since about 1980.

Pesuela
GIOVANETTI HOS.
Hacienda C'Orcega

Rulau	Date	Metal	Size	VG	F	VF	Unc
Lrs 20	ND	Nic/Br	29mm	—	35.00	75.00	—

(All incused): Hda C'ORCEGA / 3 / PESUELA. Rv: GIOVANETTI Hos / Pte RICO. (Gould-Higgie 226; Vaia 142; Archilla-Diez 572)

Lrs 22	ND	Nic/Br	30mm	—	—	75.00	—

As last, but 1 (alumud). (Vaia 140; A-D 571)

Lrs 23	ND	Nic/Br	25mm	—	—	75.00	—

As last, but ½. (Eklund 1849; G-H 225; Vaia 139; A-D 570)

A coffee estate.

Rulau	Date	Metal	Size	VG	F	VF	Unc
Lrs 32	ND	GS	27mm	—	—	20.00	30.00

As last, but 10, and 6-pointed star below. Plain edge. (Vaia 309; Brunk coll.; A-D 381)

Also in German silver are known: No value, 23mm; 4 (almudes), 27mm. These tokens also were struck in tin, which are scarcer.

HACIENDA LEALTAD

Rulau	Date	Metal	Size	VG	F	VF	Unc
Lrs 27	(ca 1900)	Zinc	24mm	—	40.00	75.00	—

HACIENDA LEALTAD / FRONTERA / LARES. Rv: 25. (Vaia 557; Archilla-Diez 470)

Issued for Baltasar Marquez.

Rio Prieto
MARGARITA DE MAGRANER

Rulau	Date	Metal	Size	F	VF	EF	Unc
Lrs 30	ND	GS	27.2mm	—	—	8.00	15.00

Large shaded 5 at center. Around: HACIENDA . DE . CAFE . MARGARITA . DE . MAGRANER / (six-pointed star). Rv: LARES RIO PRIETO / (floral ornament) / * PUERTO RICO *. Plain edge. Common. (Vaia 308; Rulau coll.; A-D 379)

Rulau	Date	Metal	Size	F	VF	EF	Unc
Lrs 31	ND	GS	32mm	—	—	8.00	15.00

As last, but 2, and rosette below. (Vaia 311; Brunk Coll.; A-D 375)

P. J. P.
Hacienda Salvacion

Rulau	Date	Metal	Size	VG	F	VF	Unc
Lrs 36	ND	Brass	Scal 28mm	—	—	65.00	—

HACIENDA / SALVACION / P. J. P. / RIO / PRIETO. Rv: VALE / EN LA / HACIENDA / POR / 1 FANEGA / (ornament). Ex. rare. (Archilla-Diez 494; Vaia 500)

Rulau	Date	Metal	Size	VG	F	VF	Unc
Lrs 37	ND	Brass	Scall 28mm	—	—	30.00	—

As last, but ctsp large ½ on each side. Scarce. (A-D 494a; Vaia N/L; Tanenbaum coll.)

Salvacion was a coffee estate. There is also a series of its tokens in almud values: 1, 4, 6 almudes and 1 fanega, all scarce to rare. The 4-almudes is extremely rare.

JOSE PIETRI
Hacienda Santa Teresa

Rulau	Date	Metal	Size	VG	F	VF	Unc
Lrs 40	ND	Brass	26mm	—	—	55.00	—

HACIENDA STa TERESA / * P.R. * / 3 ALMU. Rv: RIO PRIETO / * JOSE PIETRI * / (small) CARTAUX-PARIS. (Vaia 487; Archilla-Diez 526; Gould-Higgie 353)

Lrs 41	ND	Brass	26mm	—	—	55.00	—

As last, but 2 ALMU. (Vaia 486; A-D 525; Gould-Higgie 352)

Lrs 42	ND	Brass	26mm	—	—	55.00	—

As last, but ½ ALMU. (Vaia 484; A-D 524; G-H 351)

Lrs 44	ND	Brass	26mm	—	—	70.00	—

As last (½ almud), but ctsp J P (for Jose Prieti ?). (Archilla-Diez 524a). Extremely rare; less than 5 pieces known.

Lrs 46	ND	Aluminum	23.5mm	—	—	55.00	—

HACIENDA STa TERESA / * P.R. * / 6 ALMU. Rv: RIO PRIETO / * JOSE PIETRI * / (small) CARTAUX-PARIS. Plain edge. (Vaia 490; A-D 527; G-H 354)

All these tokens were struck by Cartaux in Paris, France.

LAS MARIAS MUNICIPIO

Anones
SAN JOSE

Rulau	Date	Metal	Size	VG	F	VF	Unc
Lsm 1	(1900)	Brass	32mm	—	15.00	30.00	—

SAN JOSE / 1 / * LAS MARIAS *. Rv: Same as obverse. Plain edge. (A-D 789; G&H 340; Roehrs 65A; Vaia 431)

1 = 1 almud. This coffee plantation also issued brass 5, 10 and 25-almud riles, all measuring 32mm; each is worth about $30 in VF.

The owner was Guillermo Martinez.

Bucarabones
MANUEL MONSEGUR

Rulau	Date	Metal	Size	VG	F	VF	Unc
Lsm 8	ND	Brass	27mm	—	50.00	—	—

MANUEL MONSEGUR / (coffee plant) / * BUCARA-BONES *. Large 5 (in beaded circle). Plain edge. (Paul Bosco 1980 report)

Similar 27mm brass tokens occur with numerals 25, 20, and 10. They usually are found counterstamped large F (Hacienda, Fernanda), I (Hacienda Isabel) or J (Hacienda Josefa). The numerals probably represent almudes.

HACIENDA VEGA REDONDA

Rulau	Date	Metal	Size	F	VF	EF	Unc
Lsm 15	ND	Brass	32mm	—	8.00	10.00	12.50

HACIENDA / Large 2 (pebbled) / ALMUD / .*. VEGA . REDONDA .*. Rv: Same as obverse. Plain edge. (Vaia 535; Archilla-Diez 531)

Rulau	Date	Metal	Size	F	VF	EF	Unc
Lsm 16	ND	Brass	27mm	—	6.50	8.50	11.00

As last, but 1 / ALMUD (the 1, shaded, resembles a script capital J). Plain edge. (Vaia 534)

Rulau	Date	Metal	Size	F	VF	EF	Unc
Lsm 17	ND	Brass	23mm	—	5.00	7.00	9.00

As last, but ½ / ALMUD. (Gould-Higgie 375; Vaia 533; Gonzalez 21; Roehrs 66)

Rulau	Date	Metal	Size	F	VF	EF	Unc
Lsm 18	ND	Brass	18mm	—	5.00	7.00	9.00

As last, but ¼ / ALMUD. (G-H 374; Vaia 532)

Vega Redonda was a coffee hacienda in the municipio of Las Marias, owned by Francisco Baco. The tokens were struck in Germany.

All Vega Redonda tokens are quite common in EF or Unc., as a large hoard was placed on the numismatic market some 20 years ago. The tokens are seldom encountered with much wear.

Some 1-almud pieces are reported with a counterstamped ampersand (&). Some authorities place these in Lares municipio.

Palma Escrita
Y. L.
(Ysabel Laracuente)

Rulau	Date	Metal	Size	VG	F	VF	EF
Lsm 35	ND	Copper	30.2mm	—	40.00	—	—

Large Y L ctsp on Spain 1870 10-centimos, Yeoman-54.2. Rv: Two small joined circles, resembling an 8 on its side, ctsp on opposite side of the coin. (Roehrs 59; Archilla-Diez 856)

Lsm 26	ND	Copper	26.3mm	—	40.00	—	—

Similar ctsp on Spain 1870 5-centimos, Y-53. (Roehrs 59B; Vaia 299; A-D 855)

Lsm 27	ND	Copper	26.5mm	—	40.00	—	—

Similar ctsp on Spain Isabella II 25-centimos of 1854-64 type, Y-26.2. (Roehrs 59C; Vaia 299; A-D 854)

Lsm 28	ND	Brass	30mm	—	35.00	—	—

Similar stamp(s) on blank brass disc. (Roehrs 58; A-D 851)

The final type above is encountered with ½, 1 or 2 (almudes) ctsp on reverse along with the double-O mark, some in smaller size flans. Each is worth $45-55 in F-VF condition.

MARICAO MUNICIPIO

Indiera Alta
DOCTOR PIÑA
Cafetal Isabelita

Rulau	Date	Metal	Size	VG	F	VF	Unc
Mrc 4	ND	Brass	32mm	—	—	45.00	—

CAFETAL * ISABELITA / 25 / .*. MARICAO * PTO. RICO .*. Rv: PROPIETARIO / 25 / .*. DOCTOR . PIÑA .*. (Vaia 247; A-D 113)

This coffee estate also used 1 and 5-almud brass tokens of this type.

MAYAGUEZ MUNICIPIO

Mayaguez
KRAEMER & CA.

Rectangular brass tokens of this design, though unlisted by Kenneth Smith, are transportation tokens, not catalogued in this reference. (See Vaia, page 67, or Archilla-Diez, 622-624).

PONCE MUNICIPIO

Bermesos
JUAN PONS COLOM
Hacienda Discordia

Rulau	Date	Metal	Size	F	VF	EF	Unc
Pnc 3	1898	Brass	28.5mm	—	30.00	—	—

JUAN PONS COLOM / 20 / CENTAVOS / * PONCE. P.R. *. Rv: HACIENDA DISCORDIA BARRIO BER-MESOS / 20 / CENTAVOS / .1898. Plain edge. (Zaffern coll.; A-D 425; Vaia 171)

Rulau	Date	Metal	Size	F	VF	EF	Unc
Pnc 4	1898	CN	28.5mm	—	30.00	—	—

As last. (Eklund 1952; A-D 424)

| Pnc 5 | 1898 | CN | 22mm | — | 30.00 | — | — |

As last, but 5 / CENTAVOS. (Eklund 1951; A-D 423)

| Pnc 6 | 1898 | CN | 19mm | — | 30.00 | — | — |

As last, but 2 / CENTAVOS. (Eklund 1950; A-D 422)

| Pnc 7 | 1898 | CN | 16mm | — | 50.00 | — | — |

As last, but 1 / CENTAVO. (A-D 421)

Coffee plantation. There is a 40-centavos, 33mm, $55 in VF.

Maraguez
COLLAZO, PEREZ GUERRA & CO.
Carmelita Hacienda

Rulau	Date	Metal	Size	VG	F	VF	Unc
Pnc 11	ND	Copper	20mm	—	—	25.00	—

CARMELITA in central circle. Around: HACIENDA DE CAFE / . PONCE . Rv: 2 in central circle. Around: COLLAZO, PEREZ GUERRA & CO. / . Plain edge. (Vaia 120; A-D-348)

These are known in 1, 3, 4 and 5 denominations.

Ponce
MANUEL CORTADA

Rulau	Date	Metal	Size	VG	F	VF	Unc
Pnc 15	ND	CN	18mm	35.00	40.00	45.00	—

Floreate cross in beaded central circle. Around: MAN-UEL . CORTADA / * PONCE . P.R. *. Rv: MERCAN-CIAS / 5 (shaded) / * DE . TODAS . CLASES *. Plain edge. (Archilla-Diez 677; Gould-Higgie 411; Roehrs 93A)

| Pnc 16 | ND | CN | 23mm | 40.00 | 45.00 | 50.00 | — |

As last, but 10. (A-D 678; Roehrs 93B)

Cortada was a general store proprietor. Mercancias de todas clases = Goods of all types. These tokens are scarce.

JOYERIA RAMIREZ

Rulau	Date	Metal	Size	VG	F	VF	Unc
Pnc 20	ND	Brass	32mm	—	—	60.00	—

JOYERIA RAMIREZ / USELA EN / EL PRONTO PAGO / POR DINERO NO LO HAGA. Rv: GOOD FOR / $3.00 / IN TRADE. Plain edge. V. Rare. (Zaika coll.; Archilla-Diez 616)

There are also 50 c, $1 and $5 tokens in this series, all on 32mm brass flans.

MANHATTAN DAIRY INC.

Rulau	Date	Metal	Size	VG	F	VF	Unc
Pnc 22	ND	xx	Rect 59x27mm	—	—	7.50	20.00

xx Pink cardboard obverse, reverse white. MANHATTAN DAIRY, INC. / LECHE GRADO / Telefono 842-4060-Ponce, P.R. Rv: UN CUARTILLO / (trademark). Hand signature. (Archilla-Diez 676; Christensen Oct. 1975 sale, lot 402)

MORALES

Rulau	Date	Metal	Size	VG	F	VF	Unc
Pnc 24	ND	Brass	24mm	—	—	65.00	—

(All incused): MORALES / PONCE / PUERTO RICO. Rv: VALE / 1 / REAL. Plain edge. (Eklund 1953; Jacques Schulman 1911 sale: Archilla-Diez 692)

SAURI-SUBIRA & COMPA.

Rulau	Date	Metal	Size	VG	F	VF	Unc
Pnc 28	1881	Brass	26mm	—	35.00	60.00	—

SAURI-SUBIRA & COMPa. / 1881 / . PONCE P. RICO . Rv: *** VALE *** / 10 / CENTAVOS. Plain edge. (Eklund 1954; Gould-Higgie 440; Roehrs 94; Vaia 552; Archilla-Diez 795)

Rulau	Date	Metal	Size	VG	F	VF	Unc
Pnc 29	1881	Brass	21mm	—	25.00	55.00	—

As last, but 5. (Vaia 551; Roehrs 94A; A-D 794)

Struck for Hacienda Estrella.

WANTZELIUS, OLIVER & CO.

Rulau	Date	Metal	Size	VG	F	VF	Unc
Pnc 33	ND	Aluminum	28mm	—	—	75.00	—

WANTZELIUS, OLIVER & CO. / 25 / PLAYA PONCE. Rv: EXPORTADORES DE CAFE / . 25 . / TIRADA DE 500. (Archilla-Diez 847)

Mintage: 500 pcs. Exportadores de cafe = Exporters of coffee. See also Jaime Oliver Mayol under Jayuya Municipio.

Sabaneta
J. S.
(Juan Serralles)
Hacienda Mercedita

Rulau	Date	Metal	Size	VG	F	VF	Unc
Pnc 37	1880	CN	28mm	—	—	50.00	—

Hda MERCEDITA / J. S. / 1880. Rv: 4. Plain edge. (Vaia 349; A-D 561). Mintage: 1,000.

Rulau	Date	Metal	Size	VG	F	VF	Unc
Pnc 38	1880	CN	24mm	—	—	50.00	—

As last, but 2. Mintage: 2,000. (Vaia 347; A-D 560)

| Pnc 39 | 1880 | CN | 20mm | — | — | 40.00 | — |

As last, but 1. Mintage: 4,000. (Vaia 346; A-D 559; Gould Higgie 290)

| Pnc 40 | 1880 | CN | 15mm | — | — | 40.00 | — |

As last, but ½. Mintage: 8,000. (Vaia 345; A-D 557)

| Pnc 41 | 1880 | CN | 15mm | — | — | 40.00 | — |

Obverse as last. Rv: Star design. Plain edge. Mintage: 8,000. (Vaia 343; A-D 556; G-H 288)

This series of tokens was struck by R. H. Heaton & Sons in Birmingham, England. Mintage statistics are from their archives.

The 4-reales token of this series was cut into four equal pie-shaped parts (measuring 20x13.5mm) and used on the plantation as 1-real pieces. In VF condition, these are worth $40 each.

Juan Serralles had his attractive sugar workers' tokens made in England. Only the Antongiorgi Brothers among Puerto Rican plantation owners also used Heaton's Mint in the 19th century to prepare riles for plantation use.

The 1 and 2-reales tokens of this issuer can be found counterstamped with the numeral 87. These are not Puerto Rican tokens; they were for use of Ingenio Puerto Rico in the Dominican Republic (which see).

Yayas
M. A.
(M. Antongiorgi)

Rulau	Date	Metal	Size	VG	F	VF	Unc
Pnc 45	1880	CN	24mm	—	—	75.00	—

Hda RESTAURADA / M. A. / 1880. Rv: 2. Plain edge. Mintage: 250. Ex. rare. (Archilla-Diez 565)

| Pnc 46 | 1880 | CN | 20mm | — | — | 75.00 | — |

As last, but 1. Mintage: 500. Ex. rare. (A-D 564)

| Pnc 47 | 1880 | CN | | 15.00 | — | 75.00 | — |

As last, but ½. Mintage: 5,000. Ex. rare. (A-D 563)

| Pnc 48 | 1880 | CN | 15mm | — | — | 75.00 | — |

Obverse as last. Rv: Star design. Mintage: 1,000. (A-D 562)

Sugar estate. The Antongiorgi Brothers also controlled Maria and Florida haciendas at Yauco, which see.

All struck by Heaton, Birmingham, England. Mintage statistics are from Heaton archives; it is now called The Mint, Birmingham, Ltd.

SABANA GRANDE MUNICIPIO

Tabanuco
D. H. H. T.
(Damiani Hermanos, Hacienda Tabanuco)

Rulau	Date	Metal	Size	VG	F	VF	Unc
SGM 11	ND	Copper	43mm	—	—	35.00	—

D H / 40 / H T. Rv: Blank (intaglio of obverse). Plain edge. (40 = 40 almudes). (Vaia 522; Archilla-Diez 167; Gould & Higgie 368)

SGM 12	ND	Copper	Oct 40x35mm	—	—	20.00	—

As last, but 20 (almudes). (Vaia 521; A-D 166)

SGM 13	ND	Copper	Oct 36x29mm	—	—	20.00	—

As last, but 10. (Vaia 520; A-D 165)

SGM 14	ND	Copper	26mm	—	—	20.00	—

As last, but 5. (Vaia 519; A-D 164)

SGM 15	ND	Copper	Oct 30x22mm	—	—	20.00	—

As last, but 2. (Vaia 516; A-D 163; G-H 364; Krueger 1734)

Coffee plantation. Crude handmade tokens.

CALIXTO CARRERA

Rulau	Date	Metal	Size	VG	F	VF	Unc
SGM 20	ND	Brass	27mm	—	—	55.00	—

CALIXTO CARRERA / *. PRECIOS .* / (Rosette) / . EQUITATIVOS . / * SABANA . GRANDE . P.R. *. Rv: *. PROVISIONES .* / *. DE. TODAS .* / (Rosette) / . PROCEDENCIAS . / . QUINCALLA . Y . MER-CANCIAS . Plain edge. (Archilla-Diez 117; photo courtesy Dale Seppa; very rare)

Probably struck in Europe.

SAN JUAN MUNICIPIO

San Juan (City)
BURGER KING

Rulau	Date	Metal	Size	F	VF	EF	Unc
Sjn 3	1979	Brass	32mm	—	—	—	4.00

Foot-and-ball logo. Around: FUTBOL / VIII JUEGOS PANAMERICANOS . SAN JUAN 1979. Rv: (Semisphere) / BURGER / KING / (semisphere inverted) R-in-circle. Reeded edge. (Rulau coll.)

The reverse device is the registered trademark of the Burger King chain of fast food restaurants. It represents a thick hamburger. Issued to honor the 8th Pan-American Soccer Games held in San Juan.

CASINO ESPAÑOL

Rulau	Date	Metal	Size	F	VF	EF	Unc
Sjn 9	1909	WM	35mm	—	—	120.	—

Veiled woman bows before altar, radiant cross above. Around: CASINO ESPAÑOL / * DE LA SAN JUAN DE PUERTO RICO *. Rv: Landing scene, sunrise in background. Around: JUAN PONCE DE LEON / * 1508 * 12 AGOSTO * 1909 *. Plain edge (Byrne 975; Rulau Discovery S23)

This issue of the Casino Español (Spanish Casino) in San Juan commemorates the 400th anniversary of the arrival in Puerto Rico of Ponce de Leon on Aug. 12, 1508. The celebrated seeker after the Fountain of Youth was the island's first Spanish governor.

The workmanship is beautiful. This medalet also occurs in aluminum, silver and gold.

EL SOL DE ORO

Rulau	Date	Metal	Size	VG	F	VF	Unc
Sjn 12	ND	Brass	36.7mm	—	—	75.00	—

EL SOL DE ORO / DE SEVERO BASTON / (radiant sunface) / * 45, SAN FRANCISCO, 45 * / SAN JUAN PUERTO-RICO. Rv: 8-line legend beginning: COMERCIO DE TEJIDOS NACIONALES Y ESTRANGEROS. Plain edge. (Archilla-Diez 195.5; Gould-Higgie 441; Roehrs 125B)

Rulau	Date	Metal	Size	VG	F	VF	Unc
Sjn 13	ND	Brass	27.6mm	—	—	80.00	—

Obverse similar to last; differing legend on reverse. Plain edge. (A-D 195; Roehrs 125A)

SUIZA DAIRY

Aluminum tokens, 25mm, with letters of the alphabet A thru Z, were issued. In average Fine, each is worth $3.50. (Roehrs 115; Archilla-Diez 806a thru 806z).

A brass token, 25.3mm, 1 quart, is worth $7 in VF-EF. (A-D 805).

PUERTO RICO DAIRY TOKENS

In VF, each = $3.50

Bordens Milk 1 qt.
Borinquen Dairy 1 qt.
Buenavista Dairy 1 qt.
Caparra Dairy 1 qt.
Cia. Pasteurizadora 1 qt.
Dairy Farmers Coop
Espasas Dairy 1 qt.
Gilbert Medina 25 c
Tres Monjitas 1 qt.

SANTA ISABEL MUNICIPIO

ALOMAR HERMANOS
Hacienda Santa Ysabel

Rulau	Date	Metal	Size	VG	F	VF	Unc
Sib 1	1883	CN	28mm	—	—	75.00	—

Plow right in beaded circle. Around: ALOMAR HERMANOS / * 1883 *. Rv: HDA. STA. YSABEL / 10 (in beaded circle) / * STA. YSABEL *. (Archilla-Diez 569)

Rulau	Date	Metal	Size	VG	F	VF	Unc
Sib 2	1883	CN	22mm	—	—	75.00	—

As last, but 5 (reales). (Eklund 1046)

Santa Isabel is on Puerto Rico's south coast, about in the center east to west. These are sugar plantation riles (tokens), says Efrain Archilla-Diez. All extremely rare.

Tokens in CN for 1 and ½-real are known. The Alomar Brothers pieces have been attributed erroneously to Costa Rica and Mexico.

UTUADO MUNICIPIO

Caonillas
L. RIGUAL & COMPA.
Hacienda Catalana

Rulau	Date	Metal	Size	VG	F	VF	Unc
Utu 3	1894	CN	24mm	—	20.00	30.00	—

(All incuse) HACIENDA CATALANA / 10 * 1894 *. Rv: L. RIGUAL Y COMPA / 10 / UTADO P R. Plain edge. (Gonzalez 88; Gould-Higgie 218; Vaia 129)

Rulau	Date	Metal	Size	VG	F	VF	Unc
Utu 4	1894	CN	22mm	—	20.00	30.00	—

As last, but 5. (Gould-Higgie 217; Vaia 128)

Juaco
HACIENDA PURGATORIO

Rulau	Date	Metal	Size	VG	F	VF	Unc
Utu 8	ND	**	24mm	—	25.00	—	—

** Galvanized iron.
HACIENDA PURGATORIO / 5 ALUMUD (in beaded circle) / JUACO UTADO. Rv: Same as obverse. (Roehrs 133; Vaia 417)

Rulau	Date	Metal	Size	VG	F	VF	Unc
Utu 10	ND	**	24mm	—	25.00	—	—

As last, but 3 ALMUD. (Vaia 415)

Rulau	Date	Metal	Size	VG	F	VF	Unc
Utu 12	ND	**	25mm v	—	25.00	—	—

As last, but 1 ALMUD.

One can only wonder at working conditions at Purgatory Hacienda!

YAUCO MUNICIPIO

Barina
ANTONGIORGI HERMANOS
Hacienda Florida

Rulau	Date	Metal	Size	VG	F	VF	Unc
Yau 1	1882	CN	29mm	—	—	75.00	—

Hda FLORIDA / YAUCO / 1882. Rv: ANTONGIORGI HERMANOS 4 *. Plain edge. Mintage: 300. (Vaia 199; A-D 541). 4 = 4 reales.

Rulau	Date	Metal	Size	VG	F	VF	Unc
Yau 2	1882	CN	23mm	—	—	60.00	—

As last, but 2. Mintage: 400. (Vaia 197; A-D 540)

Rulau	Date	Metal	Size	VG	F	VF	Unc
Yau 3	1882	CN	19mm	—	—	75.00	—

As last, but 1. Mintage: 300. (Vaia 196; A-D 539)

Rulau	Date	Metal	Size	VG	F	VF	Unc
Yau 4	1885	CN	15mm	—	—	75.00	—

As last, but ½. Mintage: 200. (Vaia 196a; A-D 538)

All struck at Heaton's Mint, Birmingham, England. The Antongiorgi Brothers also owned Restaurada and Maria haciendas in Ponce and Yauco, respectively. Florida was a sugar estate.

ANTONGIORGI HERMANOS
Hacienda Maria

Rulau	Date	Metal	Size	VG	F	VF	Unc
Yau 8	1882	CN	28mm	—	—	75.00	—

Hda MARIA / BARINA / 1882. Rv: ANTONGIORGI HERMANOS / 4. Plain edge. Mintage: 300. (Archilla-Diez 555)

Rulau	Date	Metal	Size	VG	F	VF	Unc
Yau 9	1882	CN	23mm	—	—	60.00	—

As last, but 2 (reales). Mintage: 400. (Vaia 333; A-D 554; Gould & Higgie 278)

Rulau	Date	Metal	Size	VG	F	VF	Unc
Yau 10	1882	CN	19mm	—	—	75.00	—

As last, but 1 (real). Mintage: 300. (Vaia 332; A-D 553)

Rulau	Date	Metal	Size	VG	F	VF	Unc
Yau 11	1882	CN	15mm	—	—	75.00	—

As last, but ½. Mintage: 200. (A-D 552)

All struck at Heaton's Mint, Birmingham, England. (Also see Antongiorgi haciendas Florida at Yauco and Restaurada at Ponce.) Sugar estate.

Yauco
JUAN VARGAS

Rulau	Date	Metal	Size	VG	F	VF	Unc
Yau 30	ND	Brass	25mm	—	—	70.00	—

LA YAUCANA / COMERCIO / J (script, represents numeral 1) / * YAUCO . P.R. * / * DE . JUAN . VARGAS *. Rv: SOMBRERERIA / ARTICULOS / DE / * NOVEDAD * / * CAMISERIA *. Very rare. (Archilla-Diez 646)

Rulau	Date	Metal	Size	VG	F	VF	Unc
Yau 31	ND	CN	18mm	—	—	70.00	—

As last, but 10. (A-D 647)

Probably struck in Germany. Reverse legend reveals Vargas sold hats, novelties and shirts.

MONA ISLAND
MONA

Rulau	Date	Metal	Size	VG	F	VF	EF
Mna 1	(1881-90)	Copper	33.5mm	—	—	250.	—

MONA in relief within dentilated rect. depression ctsp on Dominican Republic 1844 ¼-real coin, K-M 1. Only 2 known. (Archilla-Diez 690)

Rulau	Date	Metal	Size	VG	F	VF	EF
Mna 2	(1881-90)	Brass	33.5mm	—	—	250.	—

Similar ctsp on Dominican Rep. 1848 ¼-real coin. K-M 2. Only 2 known. (A-D 691)

Guano mines on Mona, a 4 by 7-mile Puerto Rican island midway between Puerto Rico and the Dominican Republic, commenced operations in 1878 under Sociedad Porrata Doria, Contreras & Cia. of P.R. The Canadian John G. Miller extracted 100 tons of guano a day in 1881. By 1890 Miller had 400 men digging guano in the mines.

Mona passed from Spain to the United States in 1898. Mining continued in lesser fashion until 1927.

The plentiful Dominican ¼-real coins, overvalued and demonetized by 1877, and well-known to the Dominican workmen Miller hired, provided an ideal host coin for this counterstamped token. The 4 known specimens were found together since 1980 in a hoard in Mayaguez, the Puerto Rican port serving Mona.

The ruins of the company store building are still visible on Mona, which today is a wildlife refuge island.

NOTE: See Brz 52 under Brazil!

VIEQUES ISLAND
RODRIGUEZ

Rulau	Date	Metal	Size	VG	F-VF	EF	Unc
Vqs 1	ND	Aluminum	35mm	—	75.00	—	—

RODRIGUEZ / 50 / VIEQUES, P.R. Rv: Same as obverse. Ex. rare. (Archilla-Diez 767)

Rulau	Date	Metal	Size	VG	F-VF	EF	Unc
Vqs 2	1984	Silver	36mm	—	—	—	50.00

Obverse as last (struck). Rv: (All incused): PRUEBA DE CUNO / 1984 / JOM—EAD / (numeral) /10. (A-D 767a)

Aluminum 50, 25, 10, 5 and 1-centavo tokens were struck for the merchant Rodriguez by R. Quint & Sons, Philadelphia. All are extremely rare, fetching $75 each in acceptable (F-VF) condition. These are the only genuine merchant tokens of Vieques, except for ultra-modern plastic and wooden issues.

In 1984, the Puerto Rican numismatists Jorge Ortiz Murias and Efrain Archilla-Diez (JOM and EAD) commissioned the striking, in silver, of restrikes off the original dies, using a blank reverse stamped as described above. Only 10 pieces of each denomination were restruck, and these sell in Unc. at prices from $40 to $60 each when offered.

Each restrike is numbered, as for example 1/10 or 7/10, for number 1 of 10, 7 of 10, etc. Restrikes of the smaller 5 and 1-centavo tokens do not contain the line reading JOM-EAD.

(Information courtesy Ernesto Ruiz and Efrain Archilla-Diez)

Vieques, or Crab Island, is organized as Vieques Municipio.

ST. LUCIA

Castries

Most St. Lucia tokens are those used by coal loading workers in the 19th and 20th centuries. In addition to those cataloged here, others were issued by Chastanet circa 1870-1885; R. M. S. P. Co. (Royal Mail Steam Packet Co., 1883-1919; M. & C. (Minvielle & Chastanet), 1885-1940; G. I. B. W. I. LTD. (Geest Industries British West Indies Ltd.), 1957-1967.

BERNARD, SONS & CO.

Rulau	Date	Metal	Size	VG	F	VF	Unc
SL 5	ND	Brass	29mm	—	—	—	—
		BERNARD, SONS & Co. / DAY / (diamond) / (tiny) NEAL . LONDON. Rv: Blank. (Devaux 18)					
SL 6	ND	Brass	24mm	—	—	20.00	—
		Large open B. Rv: Blank. (Pridmore 5; Devaux 19)					

Commercial depot, 1891-1944.

BARNARD, PETER & CO.

Rulau	Date	Metal	Size	VG	F	VF	Unc
SL 15	ND	Brass	Oval 49x20mm	—	—	200.	—
		BARNARD, PETER & Co. / ONE / SHILLING / (tiny) B & R. LONDON. Rv: Blank. (Pridmore 1; Devaux 6)					
SL 16	ND	Brass	43mm	—	—	150.	—
		BARNARD, PETER & Co. / 4 / + / (tiny) NEAL . LONDON. Rv: Blank. (Pridmore 2; Devaux 5)					
SL 17	ND	Brass	38mm	—	—	200.	—
		As last, but 2. (Devaux 4)					
SL 18	(1879-91)	Brass	29mm	—	—	150.	—
		As last, but NIGHT. (Pridmore 4; Devaux 8)					
SL 19	(1879-91)	Brass	29mm	—	—	125.	—
		As last, but DAY. (Devaux 7)					

Coaling workers' tokens. 4 = Four loads of coal. 2 = Two loads. R. NEAL = Struck by Ralph Neal, London. B & R = Struck by Baddeley & Reynolds, 20 Old Bailey, London.

PETER & CO.

Rulau	Date	Metal	Size	VG	F	VF	Unc
SL 25	ND	Brass	Oval 45x24mm	30.00	45.00	80.00	—
		PETER AND CO / 1 / - / (tiny) R. NEAL * LONDON. Rv: Blank. (Byrne 1029; Devaux 14; *Numismatic Circular* for Feb. 1975, pg. 51)					
SL 26	ND	Bras	39mm	15.00	20.00	35.00	—
		PETER / 4 / AND CO / (tiny) R. NEAL * LONDON. Rv. Blank. (Pridmore 11; *World Coins* for Aug. 1966; Byrne 1036; Devaux 13)					

Rulau	Date	Metal	Size	VG	F	VF	EF
SL 27	ND	Brass	32mm	—	30.00	60.00	—
		PETER / 2 / AND CO / *. Rv: Blank. (Byrne 1046; Devaux 13)					

Rulau	Date	Metal	Size	VG	F	VF	Unc
SL 28	ND	Brass	Sq 27mm	—	35.00	55.00	—
		PETER / AND / CO / *. (All serif letters). Rv: Blank. (Byrne 1042; Devaux 16)					
SL 29	ND	Brass	Sq 26mm	25.00	40.00	60.00	—
		Similar to last, but all block letters. (Byrne 1043; Devaux 16a)					

N (Night) Series

Rulau	Date	Metal	Size	VG	F	VF	Unc
SL 30	ND	Brass	25mm	15.00	20.00	25.00	40.00
		PETER / N / AND CO / * (all block letters). Rv: Blank. (Pridmore 12; Byrne 1039; Devaux 17 & 17a)					
SL 31	ND	Brass	25mm	—	25.00	30.00	—
		Similar to last, but all serif letters. (Byrne 1040; Devaux 17b; Lyall 483)					

THE PETER COALING CO. LD.

D (Day) Series

Rulau	Date	Metal	Size	VG	F	VF	Unc
SL 35	ND	Brass	Sq 27mm	—	40.00	55.00	—
		THE PETER / D / COALNG (sic!) Co. Ld. (all block letters). Rv: Blank. (Byrne 1034; Devaux 25a)					

Rulau	Date	Metal	Size	VG	F	VF	Unc
SL 36	ND	Brass	Sq 27mm	15.00	25.00	35.00	—
		THE PETER / D / COALING Co. Ld. (all block letters). Rv: Blank.					

The Day Series was used 1901-1944.

Rulau	Date	Metal	Size	VG	F	VF	Unc
SL 38	ND	Brass	25mm	15.00	20.00	30.00	—

THE PETER / N / COALING Co. Ld. Rv: Blank.
(Pridmore 9; Byrne 1031; Devaux 26)

Denomination/Load Series

Rulau	Date	Metal	Size	VG	F	VF	Unc
SL 40	ND	Brass	Oval				
			45x24mm	—	25.00	30.00	45.00

THE PETER / 1 /- * / COALING Co. Ld. Rv: Blank.
(Byrne 1028; Pridmore 8; Devaux 24)

SL 41	ND	Brass	39mm	20.00	25.00	50.00	—

THE PETER / 4 / COALING Co. Ld. / *. Rv: Blank.
Two varieties exist. (4 = Four loads of coal). (Byrne
1037; Devaux 23 & 23a)

SL 42	ND	Brass	32mm	—	20.00	25.00	50.00

As last, but 2 (loads of coal). (Byrne 1044; Devaux 22)

JAMES BURNESS & SONS

Rulau	Date	Metal	Size	VG	F	VF	Unc
SL 10	ND	Brass	30mm	—	15.00	25.00	40.00

JAMES / BURNESS / & / SONS / (tiny) NEAL. LON-
DON. Rv: Blank. (Pridmore 6; Devaux 20)

SL 11	ND	Brass	24mm	—	28.00	40.00	—

J. B. / & / SONS / (tiny) NEAL . LONDON. Rv: Blank.
(Pridmore 7; Devaux 21; Byrne 1027; Lyall 465)

Coaling tokens used 1896-1944. The larger token was for day rate and the
smaller for night rate.

D'Ennery
ANSE CANOT

Rulau	Date	Metal	Size	VG	F	VF	Unc
SL 50	ND	Copper	28.5mm	—	300.	500.	Rare

ANSE / CANOT. Rv: Large 20. Plain edge. (Byrne
1052; Remick/James T4)

SL 53	ND	Copper	20mm	—	—	185.	250.

As last, but 1. (Breton 924; Byrne 1055)

There also are copper 40 sous, 32mm, very rare; 10, 25mm, $700 in VF, and 5,
22.5mm, possibly unique. These tokens were long considered from Canada or
Guadeloupe.

They are late 19th century coaling tokens of D'Ennery, St. Lucia. Anse Canot
is the old French name for D'Ennery. Denominations are supposedly in sous.

The attribution to St. Lucia is contested by Bob Lyall.

TRINIDAD

Port of Spain
H. E. RAPSEYS

Rulau	Date	Metal	Size	VF	EF	Unc	Proof
Tri 1	(1860)	Copper	27mm	—	100.	175.	—

REDEEMABLE AT / HALF / STAMPEE / . H. E. RAPSEYS. Rv: Rose, thistle and shamrock in central circle. Around: BAKERY & GROCERY / + 9 FREDRICK ST PORT OF SPAIN +. Reeded edge. Weight 5.4 grams. (Pridmore 5; Byrne 1182-83; Ulex 2588; Eklund 1974; Lyall 508)

Half stampee = One cent, or halfpenny. Less than 10 pieces known.
This token was written up in the 1868 *Numismatic Chronicle* (page 5). Issued by Horatio Edwin Rapsey, who immigrated from England.

San Fernando
W. J.

Rulau	Date	Metal	Size	VG	F	VF	Unc
Tri 6	(1880-90)	CN	23.5mm	—	65.00	—	—

SAN / FERNANDO / W. J. Rv: 1 / REAL. Plain edge. Scarce. (Byrne 1188)

Rulau	Date	Metal	Size	VG	F	VF	Unc
Tri 7	(1880-90)	CN	18.5mm	—	—	50.00	—

W. J. Rv: / ½ / REAL. Plain edge. (Byrne 1189)

It is doubtful these are from Trinidad.

I. T. B.

Rulau	Date	Metal	Size	VG	F	VF	Unc
Tri 10	(1910-20)	WM	31mm	11.00	—	—	—

I T B / 1. Plain edge. Weight 2.5 grams. (Byrne 1197). Reverse numbers known: 1, 6, 36, 72.

In the 1976 Byrne sale catalog, these pieces were described as made of tin.

JAMES BELL & CO.

Rulau	Date	Metal	Size	VG	F	VF	Unc
Tri 12	ND	Brass	33mm	—	—	75.00	—

Large numeral 1 and small capital S within beaded central circle. Around: JAMES BELL & Co. / * * *. Plain edge. Weight 10.05 grams. (Byrne 1196; Lyall 526)

| Tri 13 | ND | Brass | 26mm | — | — | 75.00 | — |

As last, but 6 and small capital D in beaded circle. (Lyall report)

1 S = One shilling.
Ray Byrne estimated that this token was produced about 1840. Its style and denomination, however, indicate a much later period, perhaps 1880. A directory search should establish the dating. Doubtful attribution; could be England.

J. G. D'ADE & CO.

Rulau	Date	Metal	Size	VG	F	VF	Unc
Tri 14	(1870)	Copper	20.5mm	60.00	—	85.00	125.

REDEEMABLE BY / J. G. / D'ADE & CO. / -.- / *TRINIDAD *. Rv: -.- / ONE / FARTHING / TOKEN / -/-. Plain edge. Weight 3.1 grams. Mintage: 10,000. (Pridmore 6; Byrne 1184; Ulex 2588; Eklund 1975; Lyall 498)

F. D.
(Francois Declos)

Rulau	Date	Metal	Size	F	VF	EF	Unc
Tri 16	(1854-74)	Copper	28mm	60.00	—	70.00	—

Deep incuse F D ctsp on Great Britain halfpenny tokens of 1790's. Examined: 1794, 1795, ND. D&H Middlesex (351c, 954, 986; Lancaster 51) (Pridmore 7A; Rulau T1; Lyall 501)

| Tri 17 | (?) | Copper | 29mm | — | 75.00 | — | — |

Similar ctsp on U.S. Large cents of various date. Examined: 1853. (Pridmore 7; Rulau T6; Byrne 1187)

| Tri 18 | (?) | Copper | 28mm | — | 80.00 | — | — |

Similar ctsp on U.S. 1837 or 1841 Hard Times token. (Bushnell 12, 16 and 18; Brunk 51530; Rulau T2)

| Tri 19 | (?) | Bronze | 26mm | 25.00 | — | — | — |

Similar ctsp on Great Britain halfpenny. Examined: 1834, 1861, 1863, 1864, 1869, 1870, 1872. (Pridmore 7D; Rulau T3; Byrne 1186)

Rulau	Date	Metal	Size	F	VF	EF	Unc
Tri 20	(?)	Copper	28mm	—	—	80.00	—

Similar ctsp on Canada 1814 Nova Scotia halfpenny. Breton 880. (Pridmore 7C; Rulau T4)

| Tri 21 | (?) | Copper | 28mm | — | — | 80.00 | — |

Similar ctsp on Canada 1815 Nova Scotia halfpenny, Breton 890. (Pridmore 7B; Rulau T5)

| Tri 22 | (?) | Copper | 28mm | — | — | 150. | — |

Similar ctsp on Canada tokens. Examined: 1814, 1832, 1842, 1846, 1852, 1861, 1864. (Rulau T7)

| Tri 23 | (1854-74) | Copper | 27mm | — | — | 75.00 | — |

Similar ctsp on French Colonies 1828 5-centimes. (Byrne 1185)

| Tri 24 | (?) | Copper | —mm | — | — | 35.00 | — |

Similar ctsp on coppers of halfpenny size from Barbados, Gibraltar, India, Ireland, Jamaica, Austria, Denmark, France, Sardinia, Spain, Russia, Venezuela — 1767 to 1859.

Francois Declos, a barber, created stampee tokens (2 cents local value) by counterstamping halfpenny (cent) sized coins and tokens. In all 18 types of punchmark were used over a long period of time. Pridmore deduces that Declos counterstamped his "stampees" in the 1854-1874 period.

Apparently they were accepted as 2-cent values all over Trinidad in the absence of sufficient small change. It is possible that due to their general acceptance, the *FD* mark was copied and used on various coins/tokens by other persons.

ICE ESTABLISHMENT

Rulau	Date	Metal	Size	F	VF	EF	Unc
Tri 30	(1890's)	Brass	36mm	—	—	85.00	—

ICE ESTABLISHMENT / 2 d. / TRINIDAD. Rv: (tiny) JOHN ROBBINS BOSTON. Plain edge. Weight 9.5 grams. (Byrne 1190; Eklund 1976; Lyall 502)

| Tri 31 | ND | CN | 36mm | — | — | 100. | — |

As last, but 4/9d at center. Weight 9.7 grams. (Byrne 1191; Lyall 504)

Ice establishment at 46-48 King St., Port of Spain, was founded before 1869. John Robbins of Boston struck the tokens.

La Brea
LEE LUM

Rulau	Date	Metal	Size	VG	F	VF	Unc
Tri 33	(1890's)		Sq 25mm	—	—	60.00	—

Lee Lum No. 1 / 7 CENTS / La Brea. Rv: Blank. Centrally holed flan. (Lyall 506)

John Lee Lum in 1885 started his export firm and grocery chain. La Brea is a town where he had a store. Denominations of 3 CENTS to 24 CENTS are known.

P. & CO.

Rulau	Date	Metal	Size	VG	F	VF	Unc
Tri 36	(1910-20)	CN	31mm	—	—	40.00	—

(All incused): 1 (on its side) / ⅓ / P & CO. Rv: ⅓. Plain edge. 4.95 grams. (Byrne 1192; Lyall 528)

⅓ = One shilling threepence.

TRINIDAD MISCERIQUE
PROBAT

Rulau	Date	Metal	Size	F	VF	EF	Unc
Tri 40	(ca 1910)	Gold	14mm	—	—	400.	—

View of port with ships. Around: TRINIDAD / MISCERIQUE PROBAT / POPULOS ET FOEDERA / JUNGI (She is satisfied to unite nations and make treaties). Rv: Sailing ship right. Around: DAMUS PETIMUSQUE VICISSIM / . BRITISH GUIANA . Plain edge. Issued with loop. (Pridmore 70; Byrne 1361)

Jewelry token made at Georgetown, British Guiana about 1910. Obverse device is the Trinidad & Tobago badge, reverse device the badge of British Guiana. The reverse Latin legend translates: "We both give and seek."

TUCKER'S VALLEY ESTATE

Rulau	Date	Metal	Size	VG	F	VF	Unc
Tri 42	(1885-1904)	Brass	34mm	—	—	200.	—

TUCKER'S VALLEY ESTATE / * 1 TASK * around central hole. Rv: Blank. Reeded edge. Weight 7.7 grams. (Byrne 1194; Lyall 513)

Rulau	Date	Metal	Size	VG	F	VF	Unc
Tri 43	(1885-1904)	Brass	24mm	—	200.	300.	—

TUCKER'S VALLEY ESTATE / * 1 ROD * around central hole. Rv: Incused letter T. Reeded edge. Weight 3.85 grams. V. Rare. (Byrne 1195; Christensen Dec. 1982 sale, lot 1178; Lyall 515)

The second token above may have been struck on different sized blanks. The Christensen specimen measured only 22mm. W. Tucker owned this coconut estate and cacao producer until about 1896.

J. VILA Y CO.

Rulau	Date	Metal	Size	VG	F	VF	Unc
Tri 50	ND	CN	19.5mm	—	—	25.00	40.00

J VILA Y CA. / CABEZA / DE / QUESO / - TRINI-DAD -. Rv: UN / CUARTILLO. Plain edge. Weight 3.25 grams. (Byrne 1193; Pesant 434; Eklund 1926)

This token is probably *not* from Trinidad, and not from El Beni Department, Bolivia. It has also been claimed for the Trinidad in Las Villas Province, Cuba.

TURKS & CAICOS ISLANDS

W.C.S. CO.

Rulau	Date	Metal	Size	VG	F	VF	Unc
TCI 3	ND	Copper	33mm	—	—	70.00	—

W.C.S. CO. on plain field. Rv: STORE TOKEN / SIX PENCE. (Lyall 522; Carol Plante 1992 stocklist, lot 566)

W.C.S. Co. = West Caicos Sisal Company. Also known are 2 and 1 shilling and 3, 1 and ½ penny tokens.

U.S. VIRGIN ISLANDS

SPECIAL NOTE: A number of the scarce 19th century tokens of St. Thomas Island, all resembling in general those of Senior, Tissot and Russell Bros. listed here, may be found cataloged in the excellent works of Carlsen, Higgie, Somod and others (see Bibliography).
Such tokens are inscribed:
G. BERETTA (Georgio Beretta, store, founded 1861)
A. BURNET (Auguste Burnet, before 1887)
C. A. DANIEL & CO. (Christopher Alfred Daniel,
  successor to O. Ffrench & Co., before 1887). VF tokens $25
DELVALLE & CO. (Jacob Benjamin Delvalle, before 1892). VF tokens $25
G. FERRARINI (Giuseppe Ferrarini, before 1892)
O. FFRENCH & CO. (Oscar A. Ffrench, before 1887)
D. G. FONSECA (David Gomez Fonseca, before 1887)
FRATELLI COPELLO ET CIA. (before 1890)
G. LEVITI (Gerolanio Leviti, before 1890). VF tokens $25
A. LUGO & CO. (Antonio Lugo, before 1887)
J. MULLER & CO. (John Francois Muller, before 1890)

Rulau	Date	Metal	Size	VG	F	VF	EF
Vrg 6	1856	Copper	36mm	—	165.	—	200.

Similar to last, but 1856. (Byrne 1081)

Similar counterstamped pieces bearing dates 1857, 1858, 1859 and 1860 occur on worn 1797 Cartwheel pennies, $55 in F, $90 in EF.

Rulau	Date	Metal	Size	VG	F	VF	EF
Vrg 8	1855	Copper	36mm	225.	—	—	—

Large 1855 (relief, in circle) / ATA monogram (incuse) ctsp on England 1797 Cartwheel penny. (Carlsen 59; *Numismatic Circular* for March, 1960)

No satisfactory explanation for these tokens has been advanced. They may well be from England rather than the Virgin Islands.

Our collaborator Gregory Brunk rejects them outright as West Indies issues, pointing out quite correctly that the British Cartwheel coinage of 1797 didn't fit into any West Indian currency system and did not circulate there.

He adds: "(These are) almost certainly British 'soup kitchen' or 'charity' tokens. These were common in English junk boxes during the early 1960's. Also, some of these marks have been noted on Victorian bronze coins."

He opined that St. Thomas might indicate something or someone other than the name of the island, e.g. Thomas a Becket. The high price achieved in the 1975 Byrne sale for these pieces was due solely to their attribution there by Ray Byrne and Jess Peters. Their continued listing as Virgin Islands by Carlsen and others has tended to keep prices high.

ST. JOHN ISLAND

LOUIS DELINOIS

Rulau	Date	Metal	Size	VG	F	VF	Unc
Vrg 200	(1880's)	Brass	26mm	—	30.00	70.00	—

LOUIS DELINOIS / 5 C / . MEXICAN TOKEN . Rv: Blank. Plain edge. (Eklund 1988; Carlsen 9; Guttag 1627; Higgie 410; Byrne 401)

Vrg 201	(1880's)	Brass	22mm	—	—	70.00	—

As last, but 3 C. (Eklund 1987; Carlsen 10; Byrne 401)

Delinois ran a coffee and cocoa plantation on St. John Island before 1887.

ST. THOMAS ISLAND

Charlotte Amalie
ATA Monogram

Rulau	Date	Metal	Size	VG	F	VF	EF
Vrg 3	1852	Copper	36mm	—	55.00	—	90.00

ST. THOMAS (incuse) / ATA monogram (relief, in circular depression) / 1852 (relief, in circular depression) — all ctsp on England 1797 Cartwheel penny.

Vrg 4	1853	Copper	36mm	—	55.00	—	90.00

Similar to last, but 1853. (Carlsen 57)

Vrg 5	1854	Copper	36mm	—	55.00	—	90.00

Similar to last, but 1854. (Carlsen 58; Byrne 1080)

W. B. & CO.
(W. Brondsted & Co.)

Rulau	Date	Metal	Size	VG	F	VF	EF
Vrg 11	(1890-1915)	Zinc	Rect				
			58x38mm	—	—	50.00	—

W B & Co monogram / 1 Cent. Rv: Intaglio of obverse. (Carlsen 64; Byrne 1074; Eklund 2041)

Coaling token for the Brondsted steamship company.

RAVEN & CO.

Rulau	Date	Metal	Size	VG	F	VF	Unc
Vrg 50	(1915-30)	Brass	Sq 35mm	—	—	60.00	—

(All incused): RAVEN & CO. / GOOD FOR / 3 lbs. / ICE / * ST. THOMAS *. Rv: Blank. (Byrne 1076)

Rulau	Date	Metal	Size	VG	F	VF	Unc
Vrg 51	(1915-30)	Brass	Oct 35mm	—	60.00	80.00	—

As last, but 2 lbs. (Byrne 1077)

Rulau	Date	Metal	Size	VG	F	VF	Unc
Vrg 52	(1915-30)	Brass	35.5mm	—	75.00	95.00	—

As last, but 1 lb. (Byrne 1078; Carlsen 71; Eklund 2049)

RUSSELL BROS.

Rulau	Date	Metal	Size	VG	F	VF	EF
Vrg 60	1890	CN	Oct 17mm	—	30.00	50.00	70.00

Steamboat with sails left, ST. THOMAS above, 1890 below. Rv: RUSSELL BROs / 2 C / MEX TOKEN. Plain edge. (Eklund 2026; Carlsen 49; Guttag 1658; Higgie 446; Byrne 413)

Rulau	Date	Metal	Size	VG	F	VF	EF
Vrg 61	1888	CN	28mm	—	—	30.00	—

RUSSELL BROs / 1888. Rv: 10 CENT MEX TOKEN / X (large) / ST THOMAS. Plain edge. (Eklund 2025; Higgie 451; Carlsen 44; Guttag 1653; Byrne 413)

Rulau	Date	Metal	Size	VG	F	VF	EF
Vrg 62	1888	CN	21mm	—	—	25.00	45.00

As last, but 5 CENT and large V. (Eklund 2024; Higgie 450)

Rulau	Date	Metal	Size	VG	F	VF	EF
Vrg 63	1890	CN	21mm	—	—	20.00	25.00

As last, but date 1890. (Ulex 2402; Carlsen 45; Byrne 413; Eklund 2023)

Also issued were 3-cent tokens of 1888 and 1890.

RDO. D. SENIOR

Rulau	Date	Metal	Size	F	VF	EF	Unc
Vrg 70	(1880's)	CN	19mm	25.00	40.00	65.00	—

Rdo D. SENIOR / 5 C / MEXIC / * ST. THOMAS *. Rv: Same as obverse. Plain edge. (Eklund 2028; Carlsen 50; Guttag 1659; Byrne 414; Higgie 453)

Rulau	Date	Metal	Size	F	VF	EF	Unc
Vrg 71	(1880's)	Copper	23mm	30.00	40.00	60.00	—

As last, but 1 C. / MEXIC. (Eklund 2027; Carlsen 51; Higgie 452; Guttag 1660)

Issued by Ricardo Doloris Senior before 1890.

R. SENIOR ET CO.

Rulau	Date	Metal	Size	F	VF	EF	Unc
Vrg 73	(1890)	CN	19mm	—	40.00	65.00	—

R. SENIOR et Co. / 5 C. / MEXIC / (rosette) / ST THOMAS. Rv: Same as obverse. Plain edge. (Eklund 2030; Guttag 1661; Carlsen 52; Higgie 455; Byrne 415)

Rulau	Date	Metal	Size	F	VF	EF	Unc
Vrg 74	(1890)	Copper	23mm	25.00	32.50	60.00	—

As last, but 1 C. / MEXIC. (Ulex 2402; Carlsen 53; Eklund 2029; Higgie 454; Byrne 415)

Issued by Robert Senior before 1892.

L. TISSOT & CO.

Rulau	Date	Metal	Size	F	VF	EF	Unc
Vrg 76	ND	CN	24mm	—	50.00	—	—

L. TISSOT & Co. / 10 C. / MEXIC / (rosette) / St THOMAS. Rv: Same as obverse. Plain edge. (Eklund 2034; Carlsen 56; Higgie 459; Byrne 419)

A 5-cent CN token, 20mm, was also issued by Louis Tissot, worth $40 in VF.

THE WEST INDIAN COMPANY

ST Monogram

Rulau	Date	Metal	Size	F	VF	EF	Unc
Vrg 90	1920	Brass	24mm	—	45.00	60.00	—

THE WEST INDIAN COMPANY / COAL / ST.
THOMAS / 1920 / ***. Rv: Blank. (*TAMS Journal* for
Feb. 1980. pg. 25; Byrne 1083)

This occurs with triangular cutout; probably a cancellation mark, which
reduces its value in numismatics by 10-15 percent.

Rulau	Date	Metal	Size	VG	F	VF	Unc
Vrg 150	(1910)	Aluminum	Triang 24x21mm	—	—	6.00	9.00

Script monogram ST. Rv: Same as obverse. (Byrne
1073; Smith 750A)

Not from St. Thomas, but a transportation token from Trondheim, Norway.

PART III
CENTRAL AMERICA

BELIZE

Belize City
HENRY GANSZ

Rulau	Date	Metal	Size	VG	F	VF	Unc
Bze 1	1885	Copper	21mm	—	100.	135.	—

HENRY GANSZ / 1½ d. / *. Rv: BELIZE HONDU-RAS / 1885 / *. Plain edge. (Pridmore 76)

1½ pence equaled ¼ rial. The rial was introduced as 6 pence in 1855 but was abolished in 1864. The rial (British Honduras equivalent of the Spanish real) continued in local use for some years after 1864, however. The J. Jex token, for example, is dated 1871 and denominated ¼ rial (or 1½ pence).

Gansz was a general store proprietor and baker in Belize on Queen Street from about 1853.

J. J.
(John Jex)

Rulau	Date	Metal	Size	VG	F	VF	Unc
Bze 3	1871	Bronze*	19mm	100.	200.	400.	—

Indian head left, BELIZE HONDURAS / 1871 around. Rv: Within laurel wreath: RECEIVABLE FOR /1¼ / RIAL / BY J. J. Plain edge. Weight 2.17 grams. 7 Pieces known. (Pridmore 75; Lyall 130)

Struck in the United States. Worth 1½ pence sterling at time of issue.

*Termed "bronze" here for simplicity. There are 4 known pieces in yellow brass and 3 in red copper. (Ray Byrne — Fred Reed census of 1976).

A holed specimen fetched $100 in a Sept. 22, 1978 auction. VF specimens realized $225, $394 and $365 in the 1973-78 period in the U.S. and England. No true Unc specimens are known.

Jex was a general merchant and wholesaler in Belize from about 1866-1885.

B (Arrow) O

Rulau	Date	Metal	Size	VG	F	VF	EF
Bze 5	ND	Copper	41mm	—	—	50.00	—

(Arrow pointed upward) / B O ctsp incuse on Great Britain 1797 Cartwheel twopence. Only 1 piece reported (Brunk 50285)

| Bze 6 | ND | Copper | 32mm | 35.00 | — | 50.00 | — |

Similar ctsp on Essequibo & Demerara 1813 stiver, KM 10. 5 pieces known. (B&M Nov. 1990 sale, lot 209; Lyall 112).

The broad arrow mark is that of the British War Office. Homeland British coins are known with various initials, such as PO for Portsmouth Dockyard and W for Woolwich Arsenal, ctsp with the short, stock arrow (in relief) of the War Office.

According to Lyall (1989), the BO may indicate a British installation in Belize.

BELIKIN BEER & STOUT

Rulau	Date	Metal	Size	VG	F	VF	Unc
Bze 10	1981	Alum	40.3mm	—	—	—	12.00

BELIKIN / BELIZE / 1981 / x BEER & STOUT x. Rv: INDEPENDENCE / SEPT. 21 / 1981 / *** BELIZE ***. Plain edge. (Rulau coll.)

Enlargement

COCA-COLA (and) FANTA

Rulau	Date	Metal	Size	VG	F	VF	Unc
Bze 12	1981	Alum	40.3mm	—	—	—	10.50

COCA-COLA / BELIZE / 1981 / +. Rv: Same as last reverse. Plain edge. (Rulau coll.)

Research courtesy William Williamson, Belize City. These advertising tokens were given out to persons attending the independence celebrations in 1981 as Belize became an independent member of the Commonwealth.

WATER SUPPLY

Rulau	Date	Metal	Size	VG	F	VF	EF
Bze 15	(ca 1892)	Zinc	26mm	—	—	Unique	—

2 / GALLONS / WATER SUPPLY. Rv: Blank. Reeded edge. Square central hole in flan. (Lyall 132)

Rainwater was sold by the government at 2 gallons per day for 25 cents per month. Tokens in 2- and 4-gallon values were used, but no 4-gallon piece seems to exist today.

Corozal
J & Y
(Jones & Young)

Rulau	Date	Metal	Size	VG	F	VF	Unc
Bze 20	1875	Copper	20.5mm	—	—	500.	—

15TH OCTOBER 1875 / J & Y /. Rv: 1 1/2 d. Plain edge. (Lyall 131)

William J. Jones and David A. Young were shopkeepers in Corozal, and each owned sugar plantations. The 1875 date may have been the firm's foundation. 1½ pence = ¼ real. Only about 3 pieces known.

COSTA RICA

ALAJUELA PROVINCE

Alajuela
D. S. SABORIO

Rulau	Date	Metal	Size	VG	F	VF	Unc
Ala 1	ND	Copper	15mm	—	10.00	—	—

D.S. SABORIO / (5-pointed star) / -o-. Rv: Blank. Plain edge. (Rulau coll.: Schimmel N/L)

Rulau	Date	Metal	Size	VG	F	VF	Unc
Ala 2	ND	Lead	16mm	—	—	—	—

As last (Zaika coll.)

CARTAGO PROVINCE

Cerro Redondo
SATURNINO TINOCO

Rulau	Date	Metal	Size	VG	F	VF	Unc
Cto 3	ND	Brass	19.5mm	—	—	—	—

SATURNINO TINOCO / * / *. Rv: CERRO REDONDO / * / *. Reeded edge. (Fonrobert 10180; Eklund 1623; Rojas-Solano pg. 44)

Cerro redondo = Round hill. Attributed for many years to Uruguay, but Rojas-Solano says Costa Rica.

TINOCO VOLIO

Rulau	Date	Metal	Size	VG	F	VF	Unc
Cto 6	ND	Brass	21.5mm	—	5.00	—	—

TINOCO VOLIO / (wreath). Rv: CERRO REDONDO / (wreath). Plain edge.

Las Pavas
JUAN RAFAEL MORA
Finca Franfort

Rulau	Date	Metal	Size	VG	F	VF	Unc
Cto 10	ND	Brass	13mm	—	11.00	—	—

JUAN RAFAEL MORA / JRM monogram. Rv: FRANFORT / VALE / 1/2 / REAL. Plain edge. (Zaika coll).

Rulau	Date	Metal	Size	VG	F	VF	Unc
Cto 11	ND	Brass	13mm	—	5.00	—	—

As last, but ctsp J.G. in oval. Much more common than the token without cstp.

Orosi
Z. GARCIA

Rulau	Date	Metal	Size	VG	F	VF	Unc
Cto 20	ND	Brass	19mm	—	—	—	—

ESPIRIDION / Z. GARCIA / -.- within double-ring border of 15 small rings. Rv: Double-ring border of 13 rosettes around: OROSI / -.-. (Eklund 2384)

La Union
ALEJO C. JIMENEZ
Hacienda de Colima

Rulau	Date	Metal	Size	VG	F	VF	Unc
Cto 14	ND	Brass	19.5mm	6.50	10.00	15.00	—

ALEJO. C. JIMENEZ / (Coffee tree) / *. Rv: HACIENDA DE COLIMA / (Basket of coffee beans) / *. Plain edge. (Rulau coll.; Rojas-Solano pg. 40)

Alejo = Alejo. = Alejandro. These pieces may have been struck by Scovill Mfg. Co., Waterbury, Conn.

ALEJO JIMENES

Rulau	Date	Metal	Size	VG	F	VF	Unc
Cto 16	ND	Brass	18mm	—	—	—	—

ALEJO JIMENES / (Olive branches). Rv: LA UNION/ (Tree). (Schimmel 102)

Relatively common.

San Francisco
JOSE MARIA OREAMUNO
Hacienda La Peninsula

Rulau	Date	Metal	Size	VG	F	VF	Unc
Cto 26	ND	GS	26mm	—	—	30.00	—

JOSE MARIA OREAMUNO / (crosslike ornament) / * CARTAGO *. Rv: HACIENDA LA PENINSULA / (crosslike ornament) / * SAN FRANCO *. Plain edge. Rare. (Eklund 1038, from the 1899 Weyl listing: Randel coll.)

Eklund reports this was valued at 10 centavos. In 1983 Limarc said this was a sugar estate, but Limarc and others may have been reporting a different piece, one with TUCARRIQUE in the legend.

CELSO ROBLES
Hacienda La Esperanza

Rulau	Date	Metal	Size	VG	F	VF	Unc
Cto 28	ND	GS	26mm	—	—	30.00	—

HACIENDA LA ESPERANZA / (crosslike ornament) / * SAN FRANCO. *. Rv: Within open-top laurel wreath: CELSO ROBLES / CARTAGO. Plain edge. Rare. (Randel coll.: Rojas-Solano pg. 38?)

This token was probably struck by the same firm, at the same time, as the J.M. Oreamuno token listed earlier.

Tres Rios
PIZA

Rulau	Date	Metal	Size	VG	F	VF	Unc
Cto 31	ND	Brass	25.5mm	—	—	4.50	—

CAFE COSTA RICA (relief) / PIZA (incuse). Rv: 1 (relief). (Schimmel 33A; Zaika coll.)

Rulau	Date	Metal	Size	VG	F	VF	Unc
Cto 32	ND	Brass	21mm	—	—	3.50	—

As last, but 1/4. (Schimmel 33)

Rulau	Date	Metal	Size	VG	F	VF	Unc
Cto 34	ND	Brass	30mm	—	—	6.00	—

PIZA. Rv: C 1 (shaded), with ornaments above and below. Stands for One Colon. (Rojas-Solano pgs. 18-19; Zaika coll.)

Rulau	Date	Metal	Size	VG	F	VF	Unc
Cto 35	ND	Brass	Hex 22mm	—	—	5.00	—

As last, but 60 (shaded). (Zaika coll.)

| Cto 36 | ND | Brass | 25.5mm | — | — | 3.00 | — |

As last, but 50. (Zaika coll.)

| Cto 37 | ND | Brass | Sq 18mm | — | — | 3.00 | — |

As last, but 40.

| Cto 38 | ND | Brass | 21mm | — | — | 3.00 | — |

As last, but 30.

| Cto 39 | ND | Brass | 21.5mm | — | — | 3.00 | — |

As last, but 25 in starburst. (This also occurs in 20mm diameter)

| Cto 40 | ND | Brass | Tri 15mm | — | — | 3.50 | — |

As the 30, but 15. (Zaika coll.)

| Cto 41 | ND | Brass | 18.5mm | — | — | 3.50 | — |

As last, but 10. (Zaika coll.)

Turrialba
GUARDIA HOS.

Rulau	Date	Metal	Size	VG	F	VF	Unc
Cto 45	ND	Aluminum	24mm	—	—	—	—

HACIENDAS / DE LA / GUARDIA Hos / -.-. / TURRIALBA / COSTA RICA. Rv: "LA CECILIA" / 1 MEDIDA / -DE- / CAFE. Plain edge. (Zaffern coll.; Zaika coll.)

| Cto 46 | ND | Brass | 24mm | — | — | — | — |

As last. (Zaika coll.)

Verbena
TINOCO Y CA.

Rulau	Date	Metal	Size	VG	F	VF	Unc
Cto 48	(1865-77)	Brass	19mm	—	12.00	16.00	—

TINOCO Y CA / (Rosette) / * * *. Rv: VERBENA. (Fonrobert 7367; Eklund 1049; Rojas-Solano pgs. 23 and 44; Pesant 409)

Sugar estate, founded in 1865. Fonrobert reported this token in 1878. Federico Tinoco was president of Costa Rica 1917-19.

HEREDIA PROVINCE

Heredia
LLINAS

Rulau	Date	Metal	Size	VG	F	VF	Unc
Hrd 5	1903	Brass	24mm	—	—	—	—

(All incused): LLINAS / (radiant 4-pointed star) / 1903. Rv: BOLETO DE CAFE / 5 / COSTA RICA. (Schimmel 146)

| Hrd 6 | 1903 | Brass | —mm | — | — | — | — |

Similar to last, but 10. (Schimmel 148)
Both tokens above may be found with counterstamped numeral 7.

C. SALAZAR CH.

Rulau	Date	Metal	Size	VG	F	VF	Unc
Hrd 9	(1920-35)	Copper	25mm	—	—	—	—

* CAFE * / B / C. SALAZAR. CH. Rv: HEREDIA / B / * SAN JOSE *. Plain edge. (TAMS Journal for Aug. 1985, page 134)

Issued by Carlos Salazar Chaverria for use on his coffee fincas (plantations) in Heredia and San Jose Provinces, Costa Rica. Cafe = Coffee.

Carlos' father, Francisco Salazar Chacon, founder of the Salazar family coffee business, established a coffee bean processing mill (beneficio) in La Uruca, San Jose Province, on the banks of the Pirro River, in 1884.

LIMON PROVINCE

Limon
J.S.G.

Rulau	Date	Metal	Size	VG	F	VF	Unc
Lim 5	ND	Brass	25mm	—	—	—	—

* / J.S.G. / 15 / CENTAVOS. Rv: R / DE / C - R / LIMON. Plain edge. (Eklund 2383)

| Lim 6 | ND | Brass | 25mm | — | — | — | — |

As last, but 10. (Roberts coll.)

| Lim 7 | ND | Brass | 24mm | — | — | — | — |

As last, but 5. Plain edge. (Zaffern coll.)

PUNTARENAS PROVINCE

Puntarenas
RAFAEL PORRAS
Finca Mata Redonda

Rulau	Date	Metal	Size	VG	F	VF	Unc
Pns 3	(?)		22mm	—	—	—	—

RAFAEL PORRAS / 10 C / . MATA REDONDA . Rv: PUNTA ARENAS. (Georg Forster coll.)

SAN JOSE PROVINCE

Alajuelita
U.B.R.
(Uriel Badilla Rojas)

Rulau	Date	Metal	Size	VG	F	VF	Unc
SJS 5	ND	Brass	22mm	—	—	4.00	—

Cafe de Costa Rica (in relief) / U B R (ctsp incuse). Rv: Blank. Beaded rim on each side. Plain edge. (Schimmel 25; Rojas-Solano pg. 25; Rulau coll.)

Curridabat
F.Y N. JIMENEZ
Finca Curridabat

Rulau	Date	Metal	Size	VG	F	VF	Unc
SJS 9	ND	Brass	Scal 26mm	—	—	15.00	—

F.Y.N. JIMENEZ / (5-pointed star) / .*. Rv: FINCA CURRIDABAT / (Bee) / .*. (Schimmel 46; Zaffern coll.)

MANUEL F. JIMENEZ
Hacienda Curridabat

Rulau	Date	Metal	Size	F	VF	EF	Unc
SJS 11	1928	Brass	26mm	—	4.00	—	—

HACIENDA CURRIDABAT / - COSTA RICA - / (tiny) WHITEHEAD-HOAG. Rv: MANUEL F.JIMENEZ / (5-pointed star) / .1928. Plain edge. (Schimmel 103; Zaika coll.)

Rulau	Date	Metal	Size	F	VF	EF	Unc
SJS 13	1937	Brass	28mm	—	—	—	—

HACIENDA CURRIDABAT / MFJ (in circle) / * 1937 *. Rv: VALE CINCO MEDIDAS / (cornucopia, in circle). (Rojas-Solano pg. 38)

M.F.J.
Hacienda La Vijagua

Rulau	Date	Metal	Size	VG	F	VF	Unc
SJS 15	1937	Brass	28mm	—	—	—	—

Cornucopia within circle. Around: VALE CINCO MEDIDAS / - * -. Rv: M F J in circle. Around: HACIENDA LA VIJAGUA / * 1937 *. Plain edge. (Schimmel 178; Zaffern coll.)

M F J = Manuel Francisco Jimenez, who also owned Hacienda Curridabat, which see.

Desamparados
AUSONIA

Rulau	Date	Metal	Size	VG	F	VF	Unc
SJS 20	ND	Brass	29.5mm	—	—	6.50	—

(Ornament) / AUSONIA / (ornament). Rv: 1 (in beaded circle). Plain edge. (Schimmel 19b).

Rulau	Date	Metal	Size	VG	F	VF	Unc
SJS 21	ND	Brass	24mm	—	2.75	4.00	—

As last, but 20. (Schimmel 19a)

Rulau	Date	Metal	Size	VG	F	VF	Unc
SJS 22	ND	Brass	21mm	—	—	5.00	—

As last, but 10. (Schimmel 19; Rulau coll.)

Rulau	Date	Metal	Size	VG	F	VF	Unc
SJS 23	ND	Brass	18.5mm	—	2.75	4.00	—

As last, but 5. (Schimmel 18)

Jerry Schimmel (in *Costa Rica Tokens*, 1984, valued the first three tokens above in F-EF at about $12 each. All tokens in this series were considered scarce except the last one (5 C.), though somewhat more readily available than was thought at first. Then in mid-1989 a hoard of about 30 of the 20-centimo token surfaced, dropping its price also.

Montes de Oca
ELISA

Rulau	Date	Metal	Size	VG	F	VF	Unc
SJS 30	ND	Brass	19mm	—	11.00	—	—

F. BOLANDI / ELISA (incuse) / (Rosette). Rv: 7 (incuse) / CAFE. Plain edge. (Schimmel 21; Zaffern coll.)

Francisco Balandi. This also occurs without ctsp. 7.

FRANCISCO MONTEALEGRE

Rulau	Date	Metal	Size	VG	F	VF	Unc
SJS 90	ND	**	29mm	—	—	—	25.00

** Red vulcanite. FRANCISCO MONTEALEGRE / (6-pointed star). Rv: Large fleur de lis. Scarce. (Schimmel 153)

Rulau	Date	Metal	Size	VG	F	VF	Unc
SJS 91	ND	++	29mm	—	—	—	25.00

++ Blue vulcanite. As last. (Schimmel 152)

These tokens are also known in red vulcanite, 21mm, and pale blue-grey vulcanite, 21.5mm, all very scarce.

Primavera
TEODOSIO CASTRO

Rulau	Date	Metal	Size	VG	F	VF	Unc
SJS 35	ND	Bronze	22mm	—	—	—	—

Mantled shield of arms. Around: TEODOSIO CASTRO / * SAN JOSE *. Rv: PRIMAVERA / 1 / **. Plain edge. (Eklund 1040, from 1899 Weyl listing; Randel coll.)

San Jose
J. T. CHAVES

Rulau	Date	Metal	Size	VG	F	VF	Unc
SJS 40	ND	Brass	30mm	—	—	—	—

PAGARE 10 Cs AL PORTADOR / J.T. CHAVES between ornate bars / EN ARTICULOS DE LA ESPERANZA. Rv: Anchor between cask and bottle. Around: SAN-JOSE-DE-COSTA-RICA (rosette). (Eklund 2386)

Rulau	Date	Metal	Size	VG	F	VF	Unc
SJS 41	ND	Brass	30mm	—	—	—	—

As last, but ctsp M / 5 on obverse and V on reverse. (Roberts report)

ESCOJIDA DE CAFE

Rulau	Date	Metal	Size	VG	F	VF	Unc
SJS 43	ND	Bronze	19mm	—	—	—	45.00

ESCOJIDA / DE CAFE. Rv: SAN JOSE. Plain edge. (Fonrobert 8334; Eklund 1041; Rulau coll.)

Rulau	Date	Metal	Size	VG	F	VF	Unc
SJS 44	ND	WM	19mm	—	—	—	45.00

At last. (Rulau coll.)

Rulau	Date	Metal	Size	VG	F	VF	Unc
SJS 45	ND	Bronze	22.5mm	—	—	—	60.00

Obverse as last. Rv: SAN JOSE / C.R. Plain edge. (Eklund 1042; Rulau coll.)

Rulau	Date	Metal	Size	VG	F	VF	Unc
SJS 46	ND	WM	22.5mm	—	—	—	60.00

As last. (Eklund N/L)

Rulau	Date	Metal	Size	VG	F	VF	Unc
SJS 47	ND	WM	22.5mm	—	—	—	250.

As last, but double thickness (piefort) flan. (Behringer coll.; Eklund N/L)

Rulau	Date	Metal	Size	VG	F	VF	Unc
SJS 48	ND	WM	24mm	—	—	—	250.00

As last, but normal thickness. Struck without collar. Probably a test strike. Unique. (Rulau coll.)

Escojida de Cafe – Choice Coffee, Selected Coffee. C.R. – Costa Rica.

Collector Ralph W. Behringer, Carmel, N.Y., purchased the holdings of a former Scovill Mfg. Co. employee in 1981 from the employee's estate. Included were a number of uncirculated or proof Latin American tokens, including one of each of five of the tokens listed above. Possession of the WM piefort and white metal splasher versions of this issuer seems to confirm that Scovill (in Waterbury, Conn.) made these pieces.

Since the first item (19mm bronze) was listed by Jules Fonrobert's cataloger, it had to be issued prior to 1878. The Fonrobert catalog, however, assigned the token to Ecuador.

GERONIMA FERNANDEZ

Rulau	Date	Metal	Size	VG	F	VF	Unc
SJS 50	ND	Brass	21mm	—	4.00	—	—

GERONIMA FERNANDEZ / *. Rv: 1 / CANASTO. Plain edge.

Rulau	Date	Metal	Size	VG	F	VF	Unc
SJS 51	ND	Brass	21mm	—	7.00	—	—

As last, but ctsp M. (Rojas-Solano pg. 13)

F.N. MILLET

Rulau	Date	Metal	Size	VG	F	VF	Unc
SJS 54	ND	CN/Br	15mm	—	20.00	—	—

ESCOGIDA / 5 Cts. / . F.N. MILLET . Rv: Same as obverse. Reeded edge. (Zaika coll.)

Rulau	Date	Metal	Size	VG	F	VF	Unc
SJS 55	ND	CN/Br	18mm	—	—	—	—

As last, but 10 Cts. Reeded edge. (Zaika coll.)

Francisco Napoleon Millet. A 20 Cts. token is also known.

NANNE & AGUILAR

Rulau	Date	Metal	Size	VG	F	VF	Unc
SJS 57	ND	Bronze	22mm	—	—	—	—

NANNE & AGUILAR / (Tree) / *******. Rv: SAN JOSE DE COSTA RICA / (Tree) / *****. Plain edge. (Fonrobert 7366; Eklund 1045)

PALACE HOTEL

Rulau	Date	Metal	Size	VG	F	VF	Unc
SJS 59	ND	Brass	29mm	—	—	—	—

R.C. CHILDS / PROP. / (ornament) / SAN JOSE C.R. Rv: VALE POR / 25 CTS. / * PALACE HOTEL. Beaded border on each side. Plain edge. (Eklund 2385)

JOSE J. RODRIGUEZ

Rulau	Date	Metal	Size	VG	F	VF	Unc
SJS 61	ND	CN	21mm	—	—	6.00	—

JOSE J. RODRIGUEZ. Rv: REPUBLICA DE COSTA RICA / +.+ / SAN JOSE / *.*. (Zaika coll.)

Jose Joaquin Rodriguez, a former president of Costa Rica. This token is also known ctsp R.

JUAN HERNANDEZ
Hacienda del Patalillo

Rulau	Date	Metal	Size	VG	F	VF	Unc
SJS 65	ND	Brass	22mm	—	—	—	—

Costa Rican arms, AMERICA CENTRAL on a band above. Around: HACIENDA DEL PATALILLO *. Rv: JUAN HERNANDEZ / I / SAN JOSE *. (Eklund 1036)

| SJS 66 | ND | Brass | —mm | | | | |

As last, but II (centavos). (Eklund 1034)

| SJS 67 | ND | Brass | —mm | | | | |

As last, but III (centavos). (Eklund 1035)

According to Weyl (1899), this set also exists in copper.

MINA LA UNION

Rulau	Date	Metal	Size	VG	F	VF	Unc
SJS 70	ND	CN	29mm	—	—	—	—

MINA / LA UNION between ornate bars / COSTA RICA. Rv: VALE VEINTE Y CINCO / 25 (radiant) / CENTAVOS. (Eklund 2382)

| SJS 71 | ND | CN | 24mm | — | — | — | — |

Obverse as last. Rv: VALE DIEZ / 10 (radiant) / CENTAVOS. (Ulex 2153; Eklund 1039)

LA UNION

Rulau	Date	Metal	Size	F	VF	EF	Unc
SJS 76	ND	Copper	18mm	—	—	—	35.00

LA UNION. Rv: Blank. Border of dots on each side. Plain edge. (Rulau collection)

Struck at Scovill Manufacturing Co., Waterbury, Conn. The Rulau collection contains 5 specimens of this piece in proof condition.

La Union is a large suburb of San Jose.

MARIA Y AURELIA MONTEALEGRE
Hacienda del Desengano

Rulau	Date	Metal	Size	VG	F	VF	Unc
SJS 80	ND	Bronze	20mm	—	—	30.00	100.

Basket in central circle. Around: MARIA Y AURELIA MONTEALEGRE / *. Rv: 5-pointed star in central circle. Around: HACIENDA DEL DESENGANO / +++. Plain edge. (Fonrobert 7365; Ulex 2153; Eklund 1031; Rulau coll.)

Struck by Scovill Mfg. Co., Waterbury, Conn.

This Montealegre token, which must have been issued before 1878 since it was cataloged by Fonrobert, is the precursor of the token isues of Montealegre y Compania and of Francisco Montealegre, which see.

| SJS 81 | ND | Bronze | 20mm | — | — | — | 100. |

Obverse as last, but no basket (circle is empty). Rv: As last, but no star. Plain edge. Pattern? (Randel coll.; Smithsonian coll.)

MARIANO MONTEALEGRE

Rulau	Date	Metal	Size	VG	F	VF	Unc
SJS 83	ND	Brass	20mm	—	—	—	—

MARIANO MONTEALEGRE (quatrefoil) around a plain field. Rv: Blank, but small M ctsp. (Eklund 2313)

This token was found at Puntarenas, Costa Rica. Dana Roberts disputes the attribution, pointing out that the Guttag collection had this under Mexico.

Santa Ana
MONTEALEGRE Y COMPANIA

Rulau	Date	Metal	Size	VG	F	VF	Unc
SJS 85	ND	Brass	19mm	—	—	—	—

SANTA ANA. Rv: MONTEALEGRE / & / CO. Reeded edge. (Schimmel 149)

| SJS 86 | ND | Brass | 19mm | 5.00 | — | — | — |

As last, but obverse ctsp M M and reverse ctsp O P. (Schimmel 149a)

UNATTRIBUTED COSTA RICA

J.B.
(Jose Borquero)

Rulau	Date	Metal	Size	VG	F	VF	Unc
CR 2	ND	Brass	20mm	—	4.00	9.00	—

Large H. Ctsp J.B. Rv: Large 3. Ctsp J B. Plain edge. (Rulau coll.)

H / 8
(Cojullo Heredia)

Rulau	Date	Metal	Size	VG	F	VF	Unc
CR 4	ND	Brass	20.5mm	—	4.00	6.50	—

H. Rv: 8. Plain edge. (Schimmel 192; Rojas-Solano pg. 40; Rulau coll.)

H = Cojullo Heredia. Apparently Heredia was succeeded in ownership by Jose Borquero.

There exists an H // 8 token without counterstamp (Schimmel 192; Rojas-Solano page 40) for Heredia, and the H // 3 piece above must also exist without counterstamp.

J. B. Q.
(Juan Bautista Quiros)

Rulau	Date	Metal	Size	VG	F	VF	Unc
CR 9	ND	Brass	20mm	—			

Palm tree. Rv: J B Q incused. (Rojas-Solano pg. 46; Zaika coll.)

Juan Bautista Quiros was a president of Costa Rica. His Finca La Teresita also issued tokens in 1874, 1884, 1889 and 1900. Location not known.

BARRIOS
Hacienda Santa Rosa

Rulau	Date	Metal	Size	VG	F	VF	Unc
CR 11	1904	Bronze	21mm	—	—	8.00	—

HACIENDA SANTA ROSA / * / 1904 / * / COSTA RICA. Rv: VALE / 5 C/ BARRIOS. Plain edge. (Rulau coll.)

R. CASTELLA M.

Rulau	Date	Metal	Size	VG	F	VF	Unc
CR 14	ND	Brass	24mm	—	1.00	2.00	3.50

R. CASTELLA M. / (rosette). Rv: VALE POR 25 CENTIMOS EN MERCANCIA / (rosette) Plain edge. Centrally holed flan. (Schimmel 190; Rulau coll.)

The Rulau collection contains nine pieces of this token. They came from a large hoard of Salvadoran hacienda tokens.

COSTA RICA MINT COMPANY

Rulau	Date	Metal	Size	F	VF	EF	Unc
CR 16	ND	Brass	24mm	—	2.50	4.00	6.00

COSTA RICA MINT COMPANY / . Rv: VALE POR 25 CENTIMOS EN MERCANCIA / . Plain Edge. Centrally holed flan. (Schimmel 220)

The Rulau collection contains 5 pieces, all found in El Salvador in a hoard. The Centimo was introduced in 1902, but became a permanent part of the Costa Rican currency only in 1920.

E. E.
(E. Esquivel)

Rulau	Date	Metal	Size	VG	F	VF	Unc
CR 19	ND	Brass	20mm	—	4.00		

E E in beaded circle. Rv: Large U ctsp on plain field. Plain edge. (Schimmel 193; Zaffern coll.)

ELENA

Rulau	Date	Metal	Size	VG	F	VF	Unc
CR 21	1868		—mm	—	—	—	—

5 CENTS. ELENA. (Ulex 2153)

ESTABLECIMIENTO DE CAFE

Rulau	Date	Metal	Size	VG	F	VF	Unc
CR 23	ND	Brass	27mm	—	8.00	—	—

Tree. ESTABLECIMIENTO/DE CAFE / SAN JOSE. Rv: VALE UN REAL / (tree). (Eklund 1044, from 1899 Weyl listing)

BELIZARIO FERNANDEZ

Rulau	Date	Metal	Size	VG	F	VF	Unc
CR 25	ND	CN/Zinc	26mm	—	4.50		

BELIZARIO / FERNANDEZ. Rv: BOLETA / DE / CAFE. (Zaika coll.)

This is also reported bearing a ctsp C.

LIC. MAXIMO FERNANDEZ

Rulau	Date	Metal	Size	VG	F	VF	Unc
CR 27	ND	GS	25mm	—	—	—	—

LIC. MAXIMO FERNANDEZ. 20 CENTAVOS. (Eklund 1050, from 1908 Ulex listing)

F. GIRALT

Rulau	Date	Metal	Size	VG	F	VF	Unc
CR 29	ND		—mm	—	—	—	—

F. GIRALT. (Eklund 1051)

A. E. JIMENEZ
Hacienda Entre Rios

Rulau	Date	Metal	Size	VG	F	VF	Unc
CR 31	ND	Brass	20mm				

HACIENDA / * / ENTRE RIOS / -* *-. Rv: A. E. JIMENEZ / *** / COSTA RICA / -* *- / *. (Eklund 2381)

ROBERTO JIMENEZ S.

Rulau	Date	Metal	Size	VG	F	VF	Unc
CR 33	1890	Brass	20mm	—	—	—	—

ROBERTO JIMENEZ S / 1890 / * COSTA RICA *.
Rv: CONTRASENA / DE / * CORTE DE CAFE *.
(Eklund 1043)

Corte de Cafe = Cutting of coffee. Contrasena = Check (token).

LA ESPERANZA

Rulau	Date	Metal	Size	F	VF	EF	Unc
CR 36	ND	Brass	18mm	—	—	12.00	18.00

Tree. Rv: LA ESPERANZA / 10. (Behringer coll.)

LUIS MORALES

Rulau	Date	Metal	Size	VG	F	VF	Unc
CR 38	ND	Nic/Br	22mm	—	—	7.00	10.00

LUIS / 2 (in beaded circle) / + MORALES +. Rv: Same as obverse. Plain edge.

Rulau	Date	Metal	Size	VG	F	VF	Unc
CR 39	ND	Nic/Br	22mm	—	—	7.00	10.00

As last, but 1 (real). (Rulau coll.)

Rulau	Date	Metal	Size	VG	F	VF	Unc
CR 40	ND	Nic/Bs	22mm	—	3.00	5.00	—

LUIS / 2 / + MORALES +. Rv: Same as obverse. One side is counterstamped F V incuse. Plain edge.

The counterstamp appears to have been applied to the tokens when they were new. Attributed to Costa Rica (locale not known) by Schimmel 1982 and Almanzar 1983 and Garretson 1983.

There are 8 specimens in the Rulau collection, part of a hoard unearthed in El Salvador.

F. PINTO M.
Brene San Miguel

Rulau	Date	Metal	Size	VG	F	VF	EF
CR 45	ND	CN	19mm	—	—	275.	Rare

HABILITADO / POR / F. / PINTO / M. in relief within 7mm circular depression ctsp on U.S. Indian cent of 1859-64 type. Rv: BRENE SAN MIGUEL ctsp on reverse of the coin. (Byrne 1153; Randel coll.)

The Byrne specimen, sold in 1975, exhibited two round stamps of the HABILITADO type on obverse. Habilitado = Enabled, or Habilitated.
Byrne misattributed this to Dominican Republic.

SOCIEDAD ALVARADO-CHACON

Rulau	Date	Metal	Size	VG	F	VF	Unc
CR 48	ND	Brass	26mm	—	—	7.00	—

Male bust facing ¾ left, Rv: SOCIEDAD ALVARADO-CHACON / 1 (in circle) / *. Plain edge. (Rojas-Solano pg.25; Rulau coll.)

Rulau	Date	Metal	Size	VG	F	VF	Unc
CR 49	ND	Brass	20mm	—	—	5.00	—

As last, but ½ (real).

Rulau	Date	Metal	Size	VG	F	VF	Unc
CR 50	ND	Brass	16mm	—	—	5.00	—

As last, but ¼ (real).

The male bust is that of Santiago Alvarado Ramirez. Sociedad Alvarado-Chacon was a holding company for several coffee fincas, according to Hector Rojas-Salano in his 1972 book, *El Cafe en Costa Rica Origen Desarollo Leyendas*.

These tokens have been attributed to Guatemala in the past.

They may be more common than once thought; the Rulau collection contains 11 pieces of 1-real ad 10 of ½-real. Also other pieces surfaced in 1989 in Schimmel and Grinolds sales.

TABLON

Rulau	Date	Metal	Size	VG	F	VF	Unc
CR 53	ND	Brass	20mm	3.00	7.00	9.00	—

* / TABLON / *. Rv: J A (large). Plain edge. (Zaffern coll.)

This token is not listed in any Costa Rican reference.

U. N. A.

Rulau	Date	Metal	Size	VG	F	VF	Unc
CR 60	ND	Aluminum	19mm	—	—	—	—

. BOLETO DE CAFE . / -.- / U. N. A. / -.- / CAJUELA. Rv: COSTA RICA / 1 / .*. (Eklund 1027)

Cajuela = Measure of coffee, apparently used only in Costa Rica.

(Costa Rica arms)

Rulau	Date	Metal	Size	VG	F	VF	EF
CR 63	ND	Brass	19mm	4.00	6.25	11.00	25.00

Mantled arms of Costa Rica above laurel branches. Rv: within a wreath, a large numeral or letter. Plain edge. (Rojas-Solano pg. 39; Bernal 95; Fauver pg. 42; Zaika coll.; Zaffern coll.; Schimmel 198)

This type token is known with all these numerals struck in relief on reverse 3, 4, 7, 8, 13, 16, 25. It is also known with these capital letters on reverse C, D, L, T, V. There are minor obverse die varieties. Some '8' pieces occur conterstamped with long U.

(Elephant) P

Rulau	Date	Metal	Size	VG	F	VF	Unc
CR 65	ND	Brass	20.5mm	—	4.50	6.00	—

Asian elephant left; three 5-pointed stars above. Rv: Large numeral 1. Tall thin P ctsp at right of 1. Plain edge. (Schimmel 191; Fauver pg. 42; Rulau coll.)

Six pieces of this maverick counter turned up in a 1986 Salvadoran hoard which may have been buried about 1920. These elephant pieces are probably quite a bit older than that.

("Minerva" Shells)
Type 1 - Short Bonnet/Sunrise

Rulau	Date	Metal	Size	VG	F	VF	EF
CR 67	ND	**	23.5mm	2.50	6.00	9.00	20.00

** Brass shell; fibrous stuffing inside. Small female bust left. Forward point of her bonnet is far from border of denticles, and truncation of her bust is near the border. Rv: Pennon flutters right from staff on shore in foreground; sea in background. Ship on left, sunrise at right. Border of denticles. Plain edge. (Schimmel 199)

Type 2 - Long Bonnet / Sunrise

Rulau	Date	Metal	Size	VG	F	VF	EF
CR 68	ND	**	23.5mm	3.00	7.00	10.00	25.00

Large female bust left. Point of her bonnet almost touches border; truncation of bust is more rounded than on Type 1, and equally distant from border. Rv: Similar to last (sunrise). Plain edge. (Schimmel 199a)

Type 3 - Short Bonnet / Rocks

Rulau	Date	Metal	Size	VG	F	VF	EF
CR 69	ND	**	23.5mm	6.50	10.00	20.00	40.00

Small female bust left. Forward point of her bonnet is far from denticle border, but comes to a point, whereas the point is rounded on Type 1. Crown of bonnet is larger than Type 1. Rv: As last, but large rocks replace sunrise under tip of the pennon. Plain edge. Very scarce variety.

All three above are embossed shells joined on reverse after their manufacture. Some have been found in hoards of Central American hacienda tokens unearthed in El Salvador and Costa Rica.

Some veteran collectors have handled these without realizing they were shells rather than solid tokens, according to Bill Judd.

The Rulau collection contains 12 pieces of Type 1, but only 1 of Type 2, and none of Type 3.

L.B. Fauver (in 1990 "American Counters, Part 6", pages 20 and 43) isolated Type 3, Jerry Schimmel and others had cataloged Types 1 and 2.

The lady on the token was called Minerva and her bonnet a helmet until Fauver published blowup photographs after examining sufficient specimens. Still, the name "Minerva Shells" attaches to these pieces. Their purpose is not known, but they seem to fit the mold of counters.

These are the only shell cards of Latin America intended for circulation rather than advertising. Shells and their delicate fabric do not wear well either as gaming counters or as small change.

EL SALVADOR

AHUACHAPAN DEPARTMENT

Ataco
JOSE ANTONIO AGUIRRE

Rulau	Date	Metal	Size	VG	F	VF	Unc
Ahu 1	ND	Brass	27mm	—	—	6.50	10.00

Coffee branch. Rv: JOSE ANTONIO AGUIRRE / UNA TAREA/ * ATACO *. Plain edge. (Ulloa A5.8; Zaika coll.)

Rulau	Date	Metal	Size	VG	F	VF	Unc
Ahu 2	BD	Brass	23mm	—	—	6.50	—

As last, but UN CAJON. (Ulloa A5.7)

Tarea = Task. Cajon = Box.

MERCEDES MORAN

Rulau	Date	Metal	Size	VG	F	VF	Unc
Ahu 3	ND	Brass	27mm	—	—	15.00	25.00

MERCEDES MORAN / (radiant cross) / . ATACO . Rv: EL RECUERDO / (ornament) / .VALE Un CAJON. Plain edge. (Zaffern coll.)

Un Cajon = One box.

Buena Vista
J. A. CACERES

Rulau	Date	Metal	Size	VG	F	VF	Unc
Ahu 6	ND	Aluminum	20mm	—	—	7.00	—

J. A. CACERES / -*- / BUENA VISTA / -*- / AHUA-CHAPAN. Rv: 12 / CENTAVOS. Plain edge. (Clark 56; Ulloa 3.8)

San Pedro Puxtla
JOSE DOMINGO DE LEON

Rulau	Date	Metal	Size	F	VF	EF	Unc
Ahu 9	ND	Brass	25mm	3.50	6.00	9.00	—

JOSE DOMINGO DE LEON * / 1 / REAL / (tiny) L. H. MOISE. S. F. Rv: SAN JOSE / (cruciform ornament) / SAN PEDRO PUSTLA. Plain edge. (Clark 387; Ulloa D9.3)

DIONISIO C. DUARTE

Rulau	Date	Metal	Size	VG	F	VF	Unc
Ahu 20	(1893-97)	Aluminum	29mm	—	—	15.00	25.00

NUEVA ZAPATERIA / DE / DIONISIO C. DUARTE / S / AHUACHAPAN, C.A. Rv: Same as obverse, but line of tiny text added along bottom rim: L. H. MOISE. S. F. Plain edge. (Zaffern coll.)

Zapateria = Shoe store. Ahuachapan is in the west, near the Guatemalan frontier.

ILDEFONSO VELASCO

Rulau	Date	Metal	Size	VG	F	VF	Unc
Ahu 25	ND	Aluminum	24mm	—	—	10.00	20.00

Man plowing behind 2-horse team, building and mountains in background. Rv: ILDEFONSO VELASCO / (ornament) / AHUACHAPAN. REP. / SALVADOR. Plain edge. (Zaffern coll.)

Uncertain
LAS CONCHAS

Rulau	Date	Metal	Size	VG	F	VF	Unc
Ahu 35	1900	Brass	25mm	—	12.00	18.00	25.00

Coffee tree on ground. Below: (tiny) Maker's name. Rv: LAS CONCHAS / 1900 / (tiny) L.H. MOISE. S.F. Plain edge. (Ulloa L11.7; ANS coll.)

LA LIBERTAD DEPARTMENT

Comasagua
KORN

Rulau	Date	Metal	Size	VG	F	VF	Unc
LL 5	ND	Brass	26mm	5.00	7.50	10.00	20.00

KORN / 1 / REAL / COMASAGUA. Rv: Blank. Plain edge. (Clark 95)

LL 6	ND	Brass	31mm	—	—	10.00	—

KORN / 2 / REALS / COMASAGUA. Rv: Blank. Plain edge. (Rulau coll.)

German family surname, Korn. Also at Comasagua was the Germania coffee plantation owned by Fy. E. Ulloa M. (which see).

ANTONIO MARTINEZ

Rulau	Date	Metal	Size	VG	F	VF	Unc
LL 8	(ca 1920)	Brass	24.5mm	—	—	4.50	—

ANTONIO MARTINEZ / 25 C / . COMASAGUA . / (tiny) PATRICK & CO. S. F. Rv: ANTONIO MARTINEZ / 25 C / . COMASAGUA . (Ulloa M6.8)

FY. E. ULLOA M.
Cafetal Germania

Rulau	Date	Metal	Size	VG	F	VF	Unc
LL 12	ND	Brass	25mm	5.00	7.50	10.00	20.00

FY. E. ULLOA M. / 4 / * COMASAGUA *. Rv: Coffee plant, GERMANIA above. Plain edge. (Clark 447; Rulau coll.)

LL 13	ND	Brass	26mm	5.00	7.00	9.00	17.00

As last, but 2. (Clark 446)

LL 14	ND	Brass	20mm	3.50	6.00	8.00	—

As last, but 1. (Clark 445; Zaika coll.)

Previously thought to be from Guatemala.

Jayaque
MATIAS CASTRO DELGADO
El Paraiso

Rulau	Date	Metal	Size	VG	F	VF	Unc
LL 18	(1893-97)	Brass	28mm	—	—	7.00	

Tree. Tiny C.A. KLINKNER & CO. S.F. at bottom. Rv: EL PARAISO / * / JAYAQUE / * 1 * / CAJON / * / MATIAS CASTRO DELGADO. Plain edge. (Ulloa C17.7; Eklund 836)

1 Cajon = One box.

Talnique
CARLOS BRENNER

Rulau	Date	Metal	Size	VG	F	VF	Unc
LL 21	ND	Brass	32mm	—	—	7.00	—

CARLOS BRENNER / 4 / REALES / . TALNIQUE . Rv: 4 / REALES. Plain edge. (Clark 436; Jason 118-A; Ulloa B20.5)

Uncertain
FEDOR DEININGER
(Finca) Mirasol

Rulau	Date	Metal	Size	VG	F	VF	Unc
LL 30	ND	Copper	26.5mm	—	—	8.50	—

Coffee tree. Rv: * FEDOR DEININGER * / 1 / CAJON / MIRASOL. (Ulloa D5.10)

LL 31	ND	Copper	26mm	—	5.00	6.50	—

As last, but issued with center hole. CAJON curved. (Ulloa D5.8)

LL 32	ND	Copper	26mm	—	5.00	6.50	—

As last (center hole), but no stars before and after FEDOR DEININGER. CAJON straight. (Ulloa D5.9)

LL 33	ND	Copper	Sq 24mm	—	—	6.50	—

Similar to last, but ½. Center hole. (Ulloa D5.7)

Cajon = Box.

FINCA SAN LUIS

Rulau	Date	Metal	Size	VG	F	VF	Unc
LL34	ND	Brass	23mm	—	3.00	7.00	—

* / SAN LUIS *. Rv: 1/2 (large). Plain edge. (Ulloa-Llach S27.2)

There is also a hexagonal brass 25mm 1-real token, same price range.

LL34A	ND	vv	30mm	—	3.00	6.50	—

vv Nickel-plated zinc flan. FINCA : SAN LUIS / (Coffee tree). Rv: 4 / REALES. Plain edge. Issued holed. (Ulloa F15.5)

In this second series, plated zinc 2-reales and 1-real tokens were also issued, all common.

Rulau	Date	Metal	Size	VG	F	VF	Unc
LL34D	ND	Aluminum	30mm	2.00	3.00	5.00	—

FINCA SAN LUIS / (Coffee tree). Rv: 4 (large). Plain edge. Issued holed. (Ulloa F15.5A)

| LL34E | ND | Aluminum | 20mm | — | 1.50 | 3.00 | — |

As last, but 1/2. (Ulloa F15.2; Rulau coll.)

A substantial hoard of this third, aluminum series was dispersed about 1983, according to David Henkle, keeping prices on circulated specimens quite low.

Ulloa-Llach was able to locate this coffee finca in La Libertad Dept. but was unable to pinpoint its site.

VICENTE HUEZO

Rulau	Date	Metal	Size	VG	F	VF	Unc
LL 35	(1893-97)	Brass	25mm	—	—	5.00	—

VICENTE HUEZO / (fleurs-de-lis in cross form) / *** / (tiny) L.H. MOISE, S.F. Rv: PAGARA AL PORTADOR / . UN . / -.- / REAL / *. (Ulloa H8.3)

| LL 36 | (1893-97) | Brass | 22mm | — | — | 5.00 | — |

As last, but MEDIO / . / REAL and starburst replaces fleurs motif. (Ulloa H8.2; Zaika coll.)

"LA LABRANZA"

Rulau	Date	Metal	Size	VG	F	VF	Unc
LL 38	ND	CN	24.5mm	5.00	6.50	11.00	—

Coffee branch. Around, below: "LA LABRANZA". Rv: VALE / 1½ / DOS REALES Y MEDIO. Plain edge. (Ulloa 5.7; Clark 199; Jason 38-B; Rulau coll.)

This token has been claimed for Guatemala. It is easily confused with another Salvadoran token, from "La Labranza" in San Miguel Dept., which see.

SAN JOSE

Rulau	Date	Metal	Size	VG	F	VF	Unc
LL 50	ND	CN	Oct 28mm	3.00	5.00	7.00	—

SAN / *o* / JOSE. Rv: 2 / REALES. Plain edge. (Ulloa-Llach S26.4)

| LL 51 | ND | CN | Sq 27mm | 2.50 | 4.00 | 6.00 | 11.00 |

As last, but UN / -1- / REAL. (Ulloa S26.3)

| LL 52 | ND | CN | 24mm | — | 4.50 | — | — |

As last, but 1/2 / * / REAL. (Ulloa S26.2)

This well-made and relatively common series has been claimed as Costa Rica, but Ulloa-Llach says La Libertad department, El Salvador, location uncertain.

MORAZAN DEPARTMENT

BUTTERS DIVISADERO COMPANY

Rulau	Date	Metal	Size	VG	F	VF	Unc
Mzn 3	1916	Bronze	24mm	—	4.50	6.50	—

Swastika, with B D C O in angles. Around: BUTTERS DIVISADERO COMPANY / 1916. Rv: 2 / DOS REALES under laurel branches. Plain edge. (Ulloa B23.4; Zaika coll.)

| Mzn 4 | 1916 | Bronze | 21mm | — | 8.00 | 10.00 | — |

As last, but 1 / UN REAL. (Ulloa B23.3; Zaika coll.)

BUTTERS SALVADOR MINES LTD.

There is an extensive series of swastika-motif tokens in bronze, CN-plated bronze or aluminum, dated 1915, 1916, 1917 and 1918, of this firm. They are worth $3 to $7 in F-VF.

SAN MIGUEL DEPARTMENT

A. G. PRIETO
Hacienda Bellavista

Rulau	Date	Metal	Size	VG	F	VF	Unc
SM 3	ND	CN	29mm	5.00	7.50	10.00	—

BELLAVISTA / * A.G. PRIETO *. Rv: Same as obverse. Plain edge. (Clark 43)

C. ULLOA
Hacienda La Labranza

Rulau	Date	Metal	Size	VG	F	VF	Unc
SM 6	ND	Copper	29mm	—	8.00	15.00	20.00

Star. Around: HACIENDA "LA LABRANZA" / . C. ULLOA. Rv: 1 / REAL. (Ulex 3389; Schrötter 78; Ulloa U1.3; Eklund 1317 & 1318)

Freiherr von Schrötter attributed this to Mexico; others assigned it to Peru. It is, however, Salvadoran.

| SM 8 | ND | CN | 25mm | 4.65 | 6.75 | 11.00 | — |

Coffee tree. Below: "LA LABRANZA". Rv: VALE / 2 (large, shaded) / DOS REALES. Plain edge. (Clark 198; Jason 38-A; Ulloa 4.4; Schiaffino 254)

This attractive token has been claimed for Guatemala and Peru, but is clearly Salvadoran. Do not confuse with the "La Labranza" 2½-real token, which is listed under La Libertad Dept., El Salvador.

SAN SALVADOR DEPARTMENT

San Salvador
CASINO SALVADOREÑO

Rulau	Date	Metal	Size	VG	F	VF	Unc
SS 3	1880	Copper	—mm	—	—	45.00	—

CASINO SALVADOREÑO / 1880. Rv: DOS REALES. (Ulex 2284)

| SS 4 | 1880 | Copper | 32mm | — | — | 45.00 | — |

As last, but VALE / UN REAL. (Ulex 2284; Eklund 997; Ulloa C11.3)

| SS 5 | 1880 | Copper | 26mm | — | 15.00 | 25.00 | — |

As last, but MEDIO REAL. (Eklund 996; Ulloa C11.2)

Berliner Munz-Blatter for July, 1894 described these pieces.

M. E. AGUILAR
Hacienda Germania

Rulau	Date	Metal	Size	VG	F	VF	Unc
SS 8	(1893)	CN	31mm	—	—	35.00	—

HACIENDA GERMANIA / M.E. AGUILAR / . / * / (tiny) W NATHAN SEN. Rv: VALE / 2 / REALES. Mintage 500 pieces. (Ulex 2284)

| SS 9 | (1893) | Copper | 31mm | — | — | 35.00 | — |

As last, but 1½ / REALES. Mintage 500.

| SS 10 | (1893) | Bronze | 31mm | — | — | 35.00 | — |

As last, but 1¼ / REALES. Mintage 500.

Struck in Hamburg, Germany by the diesinking firm of W. Nathansen, who struck 500 pieces of each denomination for export to the plantation owner, Aguilar, in El Salvador.

This series was written up in the July, 1894 issue of *Berliner Munz-Blatter*, on page 1694.

BENJAMIN SOL M.

Rulau	Date	Metal	Size	VG	F	VF	Unc
SS 14	1927	Aluminum	31mm	—	—	10.00	—

BENJAMIN SOL M. / 50 / 1927 / * SAN SALVADOR. C.A. *. Rv: Same as obverse. Plain edge. (Wes Scharlow coll.; Henkle N/L; Ulloa-Llach N/L)

Earlier and later tokens of this issuer have been known for some time.

F. B.
La Laguna S.A.

Rulau	Date	Metal	Size	VG	F	VF	Unc
SS 17	ND	++	38mm	—	—	10.00	—

++ Black celluloid. FB script monogram / LA LAGUNA S.A. Rv: DESAYUNO. (Limarc report)

| SS 18 | ND | vv | 34mm | — | — | 10.00 | — |

vv Brown celluloid. As last, smaller. (Ulloa L6.8)

Rulau	Date	Metal	Size	VG	F	VF	Unc
SS 19	ND	++	38mm	—	—	10.00	—

++ Black celluloid. FB script monogram / LA LAGUNA S.A. Rv: CENA. (Zaika coll.)

| SS 20 | ND | ** | 34mm | — | — | 10.00 | — |

** Grey celluloid. As last, smaller. (Ulloa L6.7)

Desayuno = Morning meal. Cena = Evening meal. S.A. = Sociedad Anonima (Incorporated). Little is known about this interesting series.

COMPANIA AGRICOLA DEL SALVADOR

Rulau	Date	Metal	Size	VG	F	VF	Unc
SS 25	ND	Brass	24.5mm	—	—	6.50	—

COMPANIA AGRICOLA DEL SALVADOR / 2 (in circle). Rv: Blank. Plain edge. (Ulloa C21.4; Zaika coll.)

| SS 26 | ND | Brass | —mm | — | — | 6.00 | — |

As last, but 1.

| SS 27 | ND | Brass | 18mm | — | — | 6.00 | — |

As last, but ½. (Ulloa C21.2)

SANTA ANA DEPARTMENT

Chalchuapa
J. SALVADOR MORAN D.

Rulau	Date	Metal	Size	VG	F	VF	Unc
Sta 4	ND	Brass	24mm	—	—	8.00	—

J. SALVADOR MORAN D. / EL SALVADOR, C.A. Rv: Same as obverse. Plain edge. Six-pointed star center hole.

Modern piece. There are also aluminum tokens of this issuer in real denominations, issued circa 1905-15.

Santa Ana
CASINO SANTANECO

Rulau	Date	Metal	Size	VG	F	VF	Unc
Sta 9	(1893-94)	Aluminum	28mm	—	—	20.00	40.00

CASINO / (fancy scrollwork) / SANTANECO / (tiny) C.A. KLINKNER & CO. S.F. Rv: * / 2 / REALES within wreath. Plain edge. (Zaffern coll.; Ulex 2286; Eklund 1000 & 2173)

| Sta 10 | (1893-94) | Aluminum | 25mm | — | — | 15.00 | 25.00 |

As last, but 1 / REAL. (Eklund 999 & 2172)

| Sta 11 | (1892) | Celluloid | 35mm | — | — | 45.00 | — |

CASINO-SANTANECO * / $5. Rv: Blank. Red celluloid. (Eklund 1003)

| Sta 12 | (1892) | Celluloid | 35mm | — | — | 45.00 | — |

As last, but $2. Blue celluloid. (Ulex 2286; Eklund 1002)

| Sta 13 | (1892) | Celluloid | 35mm | — | — | 45.00 | — |

As last, but $1. White celluloid. (Eklund 1001)

The gaming tokens of this casino were written up in the July, 1894 issue of *Berliner Munz-Blatter*, on page 1694.

EDO. LOPEZ Y LOPEZ

Rulau	Date	Metal	Size	VG	F	VF	Unc
Sta 16	ND	Brass	21mm	—	6.00	10.00	—

EDO. LOPEZ Y LOPEZ / SANTA-ANA / -.- / C.A. Rv: VALE DE TRABAJO / 5 / CENTAVOS / -.-. Plain edge. (Rulau coll.; Eklund 998; Ulloa L13.7)

Also occurs in copper. The only other denomination reported is a 20-centavos brass, 27mm, worth $17.50 in VF.

MARCOS GALLARDO
Finca La Comunidad

Rulau	Date	Metal	Size	VG	F	VF	Unc
Sta 31	(Before 1898)	Brass	Scal 26mm	—	—	16.00	—

MARCOS GALLARDO / (radiant cross) / * SANTA ANA * / (tiny) C.A. KLINKNER & CO. S.F. Rv: FINCA / "LA COMUNIDAD" / -*- 12½ / -*- / o / CENTAVOS. (Zaffern coll.)

Santa Ana is the largest city in northeastern El Salvador.

Uncertain
E. G. BELISMELIS
Cafetal San Gotardo

Rulau	Date	Metal	Size	VG	F	VF	Unc
Sta 25	ND	Aluminum	24mm	—	5.00	7.00	—

CAFETAL / -.- / SAN GOTARDO / -.- / SANTA ANA. Rv: E.G. BELISMELIS / (ornament) ./ ***. Plain edge. (Jason 105-A; Ulloa B10.7)

FINCA SANTA ROSA

Rulau	Date	Metal	Size	F	VF	EF	Unc
Sta 28	ND	Brass	30mm	4.00	6.50	9.00	—

Coffee tree. Border of dentilations. Rv: FINCA SANTA ROSA / 2 / Reales — last two lines in beaded circle. Beaded border all around. Plain edge. Issued holed for stringing. (Ulloa F17.4)

The Rulau collection contains five pieces. Issued ca. 1920? There are ½, 1 and 4-real tokens in this series — all CN-plated zinc.

CLAUDIA DE GUIROLA
Hacienda La Presa

Rulau	Date	Metal	Size	VG	F	VF	Unc
Sta 33	ND	Aluminum	25mm	—	—	9.00	—

CLAUDIA / DE GUIROLA / REP. DEL / SALVADOR. Rv: HCDA. / LA PRESA / VALE UN / CANASTO. Plain edge. (Ulloa G8.7)

Vale un canasto = Worth one large basket.

ANTONIO MARTINEZ RUBIO
Finca Granada

Rulau	Date	Metal	Size	VG	F	VF	Unc
Sta 36	1903	Brass	26mm	—	—	15.00	—

ANTONIO MARTINEZ RUBIO / 2 (in beaded circle) / 1o. DE ABRIL DE 1903. Rv: GRANADA / (coffee branch). Plain edge. (Ulloa M5.4A)

Rulau	Date	Metal	Size	VG	F	VF	Unc
Sta 37	1903	Brass	26mm	—	—	15.00	—

As last, but ctsp star and V R on reverse. (Ulloa M5.4A)

Also see the issues of Martinez Rubio under Finca San Jose in Santa Ana Dept.

ADELA A. DE MARTINEZ RUBIO
Finca Granada

Rulau	Date	Metal	Size	VG	F	VF	Unc
Sta 40	ND	Copper	31mm	—	—	11.00	—

(All incused): (Star) / V M R. Rv: ADELA DE MARTINEZ RUBIO / 1 C. (Ulloa M3.12)

Rulau	Date	Metal	Size	VG	F	VF	Unc
Sta 41	ND	Copper	31mm	—	—	11.00	—

As last, but ½ C. (Ulloa M3.10)

Rulau	Date	Metal	Size	VG	F	VF	Unc
Sta 42	ND	Copper	31mm	—	—	11.00	—

As last, but ¼ C. (Ulloa M3.8)

Rulau	Date	Metal	Size	VG	F	VF	Unc
Sta 43	ND	Copper	31mm	—	—	14.00	—

(All incused): ADELA DE MARTINEZ RUBIO / 1 C. Rv: Blank. (Ulloa M3.11)

Same values for ½ C and ¼ C of this type, both copper, 31mm.

Rulau	Date	Metal	Size	VG	F	VF	Unc
Sta 45	1914	Aluminum	24.5mm	—	—	10.00	—

ADELA A. DE MARTINEZ RUBIO / (Ornaments) / -.-. Rv: GRANADA / No. 2 / 1914. (Ulloa M2.7)

Rulau	Date	Metal	Size	VG	F	VF	Unc
Sta 46	1914	Aluminum	24.5mm	—	—	9.00	—

As last, but ctsp star on obverse and V R on reverse. (Ulloa M2.8)

ANTONIO MARTINEZ RUBIO
Finca San Jose

Rulau	Date	Metal	Size	VG	F	VF	Unc
Sta 48	1895	Brass	25.5mm	—	—	7.50	—

FINCA SAN JOSE / 17 de ABRIL 1895. Rv: ANTONIO MARTINEZ RUBIO / 2 / +. Reeded edge. (Ulloa M4.4)

Rulau	Date	Metal	Size	VG	F	VF	Unc
Sta 49	1895	Brass	25.5mm	—	—	7.50	—

As last, but 1. (Ulloa M4.3)

Apparently Finca San Jose passed from ownership by Martinez Rubio to the 'T.R.' of the next series.

T. R.
Finca San Jose

Rulau	Date	Metal	Size	VG	F	VF	Unc
Sta 51	1903	Aluminum	28mm	1.50	3.00	—	—

TR monogram. Rv: FINCA SAN JOSE / 1903 / . VALE 2 REALES . Plain edge. (Ulloa F14.4)

Rulau	Date	Metal	Size	VG	F	VF	Unc
Sta 52	1903	Aluminum	28mm	—	1.50	6.00	—

As last (2 REALES), but ctsp with crude Rosette. The ctsp reduced the value to 1 R. (Ulloa F14.4A)

Rulau	Date	Metal	Size	VG	F	VF	Unc
Sta 53	1903	Aluminum	24mm	3.50	5.50	—	—

As the first token (2 REALES), but VALE 1 REAL. (Ulloa F14.3; Zaika coll.; Rulau coll.)

MATHEU HS.
Cafetal Crucitas

Rulau	Date	Metal	Size	VG	F	VF	Unc
Sta 60	ND	Brass	26mm	—	14.00	—	—

Coffee tree. Around: MATHEU Hs. / CAFETAL CRUCITAS. Rv: Within laurel wreath: 1 / REAL. Plain edge. (Jason 23-A; Ulloa M10.3)

SAN VICENTE DEPARTMENT

San Vicente
BOTICA DE ANGULO

Rulau	Date	Metal	Size	VG	F	VF	Unc
Svc 2	ND	Copper	25mm	7.00	9.50	14.00	—

BOTICA DE ANGULO / ¼ in circle / . SAN VICENTE. Rv: Same as obverse. (Clark 9; Ulloa B16.1B)

J. E. CANDRAY
Farmacia Colon

Rulau	Date	Metal	Size	VG	F	VF	Unc
Svc 5	ND	Copper	27mm	3.50	6.50	10.00	—

FARMACIA COLON / J. E. CANDRAY / ¼ / REAL / * SAN VICENTE *. Rv: IMPORTACION DIRECTA / ¼ / * SAN VICENTE *. Plain edge. (Clark 92; Ulloa C9.1)

SONSONATE DEPARTMENT

A. ARAUJO
Hacienda "El Sunza"

Rulau	Date	Metal	Size	VG	F	VF	Unc
Sns 1	1928	Brass	34mm	—	—	5.50	8.00

Numeral 8 in 5-pointed star outline at center. Around: HACIENDA "EL SUNZA" / * EL SALVADOR *. Rv: 1928 / A. ARAUJO / DOA monogram. (See *TAMS Journal* for Aug. 1985, page 134; (Ulloa A17.6)

A. Araujo was part of a family that operated coffee fincas in La Libertad, Usulutan and Sonsonate Departments. The 8 = 8 Reales.

Juayua
HARRY A. BOWNIE

Rulau	Date	Metal	Size	VG	F	VF	Unc
Sns 4	ND	Brass	25mm	—	—	15.00	—

HARRY A. BOWNIE / -+- / JUAYUA / -+- / JAYAQUE. Rv: PAGARA AL PORTADOR / 2 / . REALES . / ctsp S. (Ulloa B19.4; Jason 35-A)

For Bownie's haciendas at Juayua in Sonsonate Dept. and Jayaque in La Libertad Dept.

DAVIDSON HERMANOS

Rulau	Date	Metal	Size	VG	F	VF	Unc
Sns 7	ND	Brass	19mm	—	—	7.50	—

DAVIDSON HERMANOS . / JUAYUA. Rv: ½ / REAL. (Ulloa D3.2; Jason 36-A)

MAXIMO JEREZ
Finca Buenos Aires

Rulau	Date	Metal	Size	VG	F	VF	Unc
Sns 10	ND	Aluminum	31mm	—	—	15.00	—

MAXIMO JEREZ / BUENOS AIRES / JUAYUA. Rv: 50 / CENTAVOS. (Zaika coll.)

Sonsonate
GRAN HOTEL

Rulau	Date	Metal	Size	VG	F	VF	Unc
Sns 12	ND	Brass	21mm	7.00	9.00	14.00	—

GRAN HOTEL / (ornament) / * SONSONATE *. Rv: 1 / REAL. Plain edge. (Clark 161; Ulloa G6.3)

GABINO MATA
Finca El Progreso

Rulau	Date	Metal	Size	VG	F	VF	Unc
Sns 20	ND	Brass	25mm	—	12.50	—	—

Six-pointed star on 8-pointed star. Rv: EL PROGRESO / 2 / * GABINO MATA *. Plain edge. (Ulloa M8.4; Rulau coll.)

Sns 21	ND	Brass	20mm	—	5.00	—	—

Obverse as last. Rv: Similar to last, but 1 (real) and no stars flank GABINO MATA. (Ulloa M8.3)

USULUTAN DEPARTMENT

Berlin
M. MEARDI

Rulau	Date	Metal	Size	VG	F	VF	Unc
Usu 4	(1893-97)	Brass	Oct. 30mm	—	—	15.00	25.00

M. MEARDI / (ornament) / * BERLIN * / (tiny) L. H. MOISE, S. F. Rv: 1 (large) / TAREA. (Eklund 2074)

Usu 5	(1893-97)	Brass	Oct 30mm	—	—	15.00	25.00

Obverse as last. Rv: 1 (large) / CAJONADA. (Eklund 2075)

Tarea = Task. Cajonada = Box.

M. MEARDI
Finca San Antonio

Rulau	Date	Metal	Size	VG	F	VF	Unc
Usu 7	ND	Brass	21.5mm	—	—	6.00	-

M. MEARDI / (beaded circle) / * BERLIN *. Rv: FINCA SAN ANTONIO / (beaded circle) / *. (Ulloa M17.7)

This token occurs with ctsp radiant sun; worth same prices.

J. V. DE V.
Finca "La Tegucigalpa"

Rulau	Date	Metal	Size	VG	F	VF	Unc
Usu 10	ND	Brass	23mm	3.00	5.00	7.50	—

FINCA "LA TEGUCIGALPA" / J. V. DE V. / BERLIN / SALVADOR. C. A. Rv: VALE / DOS / REALES. Plain edge. (Ulloa F9.4)

Usu 11	ND	Brass	19mm	2.25	4.00	7.00	—

As last, but UN / REAL. (Ulloa F9.3)

A hoard of these pieces, 14 of the 2-reales and 8 of the 1-real, was acquired by the author in 1989. All contained green patination from lengthy exposure to earth. These were, undoubtedly, excavated from a subsurface place of burial.

VELASQUEZ & DEL'PECH

Rulau	Date	Metal	Size	VG	F	VF	Unc
Usu 15	ND	Brass	24mm	2.00	4.00	6.00	—

VELASQUEZ & DEL'PECH / . BERLIN . around empty center. Rv: VALE / 2 REALES.

Usu 16	ND	Brass	24mm	2.00	4.00	6.00	—

As last. Large 6-point flower ctsp on obverse. Small numeral ctsp on reverse. Examined: 5, 6. (Ulloa V3.4A, B and C)

Usu 17	ND	Brass	19mm	3.00	5.00	6.00	—

As the first token above, but VALE / 1 REAL. (Ulloa V3.3)

Usu 18	ND	Brass	19mm	3.00	5.00	6.50	—

As last, but with ctsp on obverse. The ctsp is either 6-point flower, small 5 or small 6. (Ulloa V3.3A, B & C)

The Rulau collection contains 5 ctsp pieces of the 2-real and 2 ctsp pieces of the 1-real, all culled from a large hoard of Salvadoran hacienda pieces excavated about 1986.

Jucuapa
ENRIQUE GALVEZ
Finca La Providencia

Rulau	Date	Metal	Size	VG	F	VF	Unc
Usu 22	ND	Brass	35mm	1.50	3.00	6.00	—

FINCA LA PROVIDENCIA / DE / ENRIQUE GALVEZ / JUCUAPA / + REPUBLICA DEL SALVADOR +. Rv: Large 5-pointed star. Plain edge. (Rulau coll.; Kirtley March 1989 sale, lot 882)

Usu 23	ND	Svd/Bs	35mm	1.50	3.00	7.00	—

As last. (Rulau coll.)

The large 5-pointed star, partly shaded, resembles the star on the Cuban silver peso of 1915.

In October, 1989, your author examined part of a hoard of 85 of these Jucuapa tokens, about 50 of the silvered brass and 35 of the brass, in the inventory of a Florida coin dealer. All seen were in the F to VF condition range — part of a hoard the dealer had been trying to liquidate for some three years without success. They were offered at $1.60 each if taken as a lot. Our counteroffer of $1 each was rejected and the lot is still (to our knowledge) overhanging the market.

These numbers could make the Jucuapa one of the commonest of all Salvadoran hacienda pieces. They are quite attractive tokens.

San Agustin
M. E. ARAUJO
Finca Galingagua

Rulau	Date	Metal	Size	VG	F	VF	Unc
Usu 27	ND	Aluminum	24mm	2.00	2.50	3.50	5.50

Coffee tree. Around: FINCA GALINGAGUA / SAN AGUSTIN. Rv: SUCESION / 2 / REALES / * M. E. ARAUJO *. Plain edge. (Ulloa A20.4; Clark 144; Kirtley Dec. 1988 sale, lot 1152)

Rulau	Date	Metal	Size	VG	F	VF	Unc
Usu 28	ND	Aluminum	Sq 17mm	—	3.50	6.00	—

As last, but ½ / REAL. Border of dots on each side. Plain edge. (Ulloa A20.3)

Rulau	Date	Metal	Size	VG	F	VF	Unc
Usu 26	ND	Aluminum	26mm	—	8.00	13.00	20.00

As last, but 4 / REALES. (Clark 145; Ulloa A20.5)

The Rulau collection contains 10 pieces of the 2-real and 1 of the ½-real, all emanating from a Salvadoran hoard excavated in 1986.

These pieces had long been consigned, erroneously, to Guatemala.

MARIANO RUIZ
Cafetal San Francisco

Rulau	Date	Metal	Size	VG	F	VF	Unc
Usu30	ND	Bronze	27mm		6.00	8.00	—

MARIANO RUIZ / 2 / REALES / (ornaments) / * SAN AGUSTIN. Rv: CAFETAL / (ornaments) / * SAN FRANCISCO *. (Ulloa R9.4)

Rulau	Date	Metal	Size	VG	F	VF	Unc
Usu 31	ND	Bronze	22mm	—	—	11.00	—

As last, but 1 / REAL.

Specimens are known counterstamped N.

San Ambrosio
CODECONA

Rulau	Date	Metal	Size	VG	F	VF	Unc
Usu 35	1880	Brass	31mm	3.00	8.50	—	

SAN - AMBROSIO / 1880 / ½ REAL. Rv: CODECONA / 12 Agosto 1908 / ½ REAL. Plain edge. Issued holed. (Jason 83-A; Clark 363; Ulloa S15.2)

The acronym CODECONA means Coffee Developing Co. of North America.

Santiago de Maria
DR. JAIME AVILA

Rulau	Date	Metal	Size	VG	F	VF	Unc
Usu 38	ND	GS	15mm	—	—	—	—

SANTIAGO MARIA / DR. JAIME AVILA. Rv: ½ REAL. (Eklund 947; Weyl 1766)

FINCA LA PAZ

Rulau	Date	Metal	Size	VG	F	VF	Unc
Usu 40	1879	Brass	29mm	—	3.50	6.00	—

FINCA LA PAZ / 1879 / . SANTIAGO DE MARIA. Rv: Same as obverse. (Ulloa F8.7; Kirtley Dec. 1988 sale, lot 1152)

Finca = Farm or Ranch. This token has been claimed for Guatemala.

FINCA SAN FRANCISCO

Rulau	Date	Metal	Size	VG	F	VF	Unc
Usu 42	1878	Brass	28mm	5.00	9.00	15.00	—

FINCA SAN FRANCISCO / 1878 / . SANTIAGO DE MARIA . Rv: Same as obverse. Plain edge. (Clark 379; Ulloa F13.7)

JUAN MAYNER

Rulau	Date	Metal	Size	VG	F	VF	Unc
Usu 45	ND	Brass	40mm	—	12.50	17.50	—

JUAN MAYNER / 4 Rls. / *SANTIAGO DE MARIA. Rv: 50 / CINCUENTA CENTAVOS. Plain edge. (Clark 232; Ulloa M13.5)

| Usu 46 | ND | Brass | 30mm | — | 8.50 | 11.00 | — |

As last, but 2 Rls. and 25 / VENTICINCO CENTAVOS. (Clark 231)

| Usu 47 | ND | Brass | 25mm | — | 6.50 | 9.50 | — |

As last, but 1 Rl. and 12½ / CANTAVOS. (Clark 230; Ulloa M13.3)

| Usu 48 | ND | Brass | 22mm | — | 6.50 | 9.50 | — |

As last, but ½ and 6¼ / SEIS Y CUARTO CENTAVOS. (Clark 229)

LUCO. BARRIOS

Rulau	Date	Metal	Size	VG	F	VF	Unc
Usu 60	ND	Copper	22mm	—	—	9.00	—

LUCo. / BARRIOS / ++. Rv: 2 / REALES / (ornament). (Clark 33; Jason 2-A; Ulloa B5.4)

| Usu 61 | ND | Copper | 17mm | — | — | 9.00 | — |

As last, but 1 / REAL. (Clark 32; Ulloa B5.3)

Luciano Barrios. The 1-real token occurs counterstamped F.G.

Uncertain
RAMON BAUTISTA
Alegria

Rulau	Date	Metal	Size	VG	F	VF	Unc
Usu 63	(1893-97)	Brass	Oct 23mm	—	—	25.00	40.00

BOTICA / DE / RAMON BAUTISTA / EN / ALEGRIA. / (tiny) L. H. MOISE. S. F. Rv: A. PAGAR / ½ / * REAL *. Plain edge. (Zaffern coll.)

Usulutan is in eastern Salvador.

HACIENDA ARAUCARIA

Rulau	Date	Metal	Size	VG	F	VF	Unc
Usu 65	ND	Brass	22mm	—	—	10.00	—

HACIENDA / (Coffee bush) / . ARAUCARIA. Rv: Large numeral 1. Ctsp A right of numeral. Plain edge. (Clark 10; Ulloa H1.3A)

SIMONA MONTERROSA
Santa Catarina

Rulau	Date	Metal	Size	VG	F	VF	Unc
Usu 68	(Before 1898)	Brass	24mm	—	—	10.00	18.00

SANTA CATARINA / (sunburst) / SIMONA / -.- / * MONTERROSA.* . Rv: VALE / ½ / * REAL * / (tiny) KLINKNER & CO. S.F. Plain edge. (Zaffern coll.; Ulloa M30.2)

MAURICIO MEARDI

Rulau	Date	Metal	Size	VG	F	VF	Unc
Usu 80	1919	Brass	22.5mm	6.00	7.00	9.00	—

(All incused): MAURICIO MEARDI / 13 DE / NOVIEMBRE / 1919 / SALVADOR. Rv: MAURICIO MEARDI / 31 / DICIEMBRE / 1919 / 2 RLS. Plain edge. (Ulloa M20.4)

This token occurs with ctsp letters B and N.

M. MEARDI & CIA.

Rulau	Date	Metal	Size	VG	F	VF	Unc
Usu 82	ND	Bronze	20mm	—	—	5.00	—

M. Meardi (script). Rv: Same as obverse. (Ulloa M15.7)

| Usu 83 | ND | Brass | 19.5mm | — | — | 5.00 | — |

-.- / M. MEARDI / -.-. Rv: VALE ½ CAJONADA / (ornaments) / PAGADO / -+-. (Ulloa M15.9)

| Usu 84 | ND | Aluminum | 25mm | — | — | 8.00 | — |

M. MEARDI & Cia / ½ / REAL (in beaded circle) / -EL SALVADOR, C.A.-. Rv: VALE POR / * / MEDIO REAL / EN TODAS / NUESTRAS / * / CASAS. Plain edge. (Ulloa M21.2A)

Vale por medio real en todas nuestras casas = worth half real in all our houses. This token suggests Meardi's was a far-flung enterprise.

See related tokens under the names Meardi, Meardi y Del'Pech and Velasquez & Del'Pech, all in Usulutan Department.

MEARDI Y DEL'PECH

Rulau	Date	Metal	Size	VG	F	VF	EF
Usu 87	1915	Brass	22.5mm	—	3.00	4.50	—

* Round, clipped by slicing off lower arc to remove the mark of value. About ⅔ of the disc remains. (All incused): MEARDI Y DEL'PECH / 2 DE / MAYO / 1905 / SALVADOR. Rv: MAURICIOS / 1o DE JULIO / 1915. Plain edge. (Ulloa M22.4A)

This token was never regularly issued without clip! The Rulau collection contains eight pieces.

SIN VALOR A

Rulau	Date	Metal	Size	VG	F	VF	Unc
Usu 90	(1894)	Brass	vv	—	6.00	12.50	—

vv Triangular flan with rounded corners, 30mm. Within dentilated circle: SIN / VALOR / A. Rv: Within beaded circle: A / NO CIRCULA. Plain edge. (Ulloa B1.7)

This token also occurs in rectangular form, 33x19mm.

Rulau	Date	Metal	Size	VG	F	VF	Unc
Usu 91	ND	Brass	Rect				
			33x19mm	2.00	4.00	12.00	—

NO B / CIRCULA. Rv: SIN B / VALOR. (Ulloa B1.7)

Usu 92	1894	Brass	Rect				
			33x19mm	3.00	5.00	15.00	—

As last but ctsp 1894.

Sin valor = Without (exchange) value. No circula = Does not circulate. Undoubtedly these words were used to avoid problems with the government over production of currency tokens.

SOL TAREA

Rulau	Date	Metal	Size	VG	F	VF	Unc
Usu 96	ND	Brass	26mm	2.00	3.00	8.50	—

(All incused): SOL / TAREA. Rv: Blank. Plain edge. Issued holed. (Clark 428; Ulloa S41.7)

Used in Usulutan and Sonsonate Depts.

UNATTRIBUTED EL SALVADOR

MIGUEL ARAUJO
Finca El Porvenir

Rulau	Date	Metal	Size	VG	F	VF	Unc
Slv 2	ND	CN	29mm	—	—	10.00	20.00

* FINCA * / (radiant cross) / EL PORVENIR / (radiant cross) / MIGUEL ARAUJO. Rv: Large ornate shaded 1 within wreath. Incised beaded rim on each side. Plain edge. (Zaffern coll.)

Joseph Zaffern believes the 1 on this piece is for 1 Dia (one day's work). It is a large, impressive token.

FINCA MATILDE

Rulau	Date	Metal	Size	VG	F	VF	Unc
Slv 4	ND	Brass	24mm	—	4.00	6.00	8.50

FINCA MATILDE / (beaded circle) / *. Rv: UN / REAL. Plain edge. (Jason 46A; Ulloa F11.3)

Slv 5	ND	Brass	20mm	—	3.50	5.00	7.00

As last, but MEDIO / REAL. (Ulloa F11.2)

These pieces have been claimed as Guatemala.

FINCAS DEL DR. A. ZELAYA

Rulau	Date	Metal	Size	F	VF	EF	Unc
Slv 8	ND	Brass	26mm	—	—	10.00	16.00

Radiant, smiling sunface. Rv: FINCAS DEL Dr. A. ZELAYA / "UNA / BOLSA / CAFE" *. Reeded edge. (Ulloa Z2.8; Zaika coll.)

Rulau	Date	Metal	Size	F	VF	EF	Unc
Slv 9	ND	Brass	26mm	—	6.50	—	—

FINCAS DEL Dr. A ZELAYA / "UNA / TAREA" / *. Rv: 25 in scrollwork frame. Reeded edge. (Ulloa Z2.7)

These have been attributed to Honduras in past years.

G. GUTIERRES

Rulau	Date	Metal	Size	VG	F	VF	Unc
Slv 12	1885	Brass	Oct 30mm	—	—	25.00	—

G. GUTIERRES / -.- / UN CAJON / 1885. Rv: Same as obverse. Plain edge. (Ulloa G9.7)

Y J monogram

Rulau	Date	Metal	Size	VG	F	VF	Unc
Slv 15	(?)	Bronze	19mm	—	—	50.00	—

Y J monogram ctsp on both sides of El Salvador 1909 ¼ real, KM 120, a coin valued at about 3 centavos in rural areas. (Georg Forster coll.)

KM 120 was an apparent attempt by El Salvador to control and service real-denomination transactions in rural areas where tokens prevailed. Decimalized coins had been introduced in 1889.

LUIS JACOBY
El Horizonte

Rulau	Date	Metal	Size	VG	F	VF	Unc
Slv 18	(1893-97)	Aluminum	Tri 29x32mm	—	—	80.00	—

L. JACOBY / EL / HORIZONTE. Rv: (Ornament) / FAENA / (tiny) L. H. MOISE, S.F. Plain edge. (Eklund 2291)

Rulau	Date	Metal	Size	VG	F	VF	Unc
Slv 19	(1893-97)	Aluminum	Oct 34mm	—	—	80.00	—

* / L. JACOBY / - EL - / HORIZONTE / *. Rv: MAIZ / 1 ARROBA / (tiny) L. H. MOISE, S.F. Plain edge. (Eklund 2100)

Rulau	Date	Metal	Size	VG	F	VF	Unc
Slv 20	ND	Brass	24.5mm	—	—	12.50	—

LUIS JACOBY / - / * EL HORIZONTE *. Rv: 2 / REALES. (Ulloa J1.4)

Rulau	Date	Metal	Size	VG	F	VF	Unc
Slv 21	ND	Brass	22mm	—	—	10.00	—

As last, but 1 / REAL.

Ole P. Eklund pictured the Faena and Arroba pieces in his unpublished work. They are considered very rare.

IGNACIO PANAMA

Rulau	Date	Metal	Size	VG	F	VF	Unc
Slv 25	1894	Aluminum	25mm	—	—	17.50	(tiny)

IGNACIO PANAMA / 29 / ABRIL / DE / 1894 / (tiny) L. H. MOISE. S.F. Rv: "LAS JOYAS" / REPUBLICA / DEL / SALVADOR. Plain edge. (Schimmel report)

Rulau	Date	Metal	Size	VG	F	VF	Unc
Slv 26	1894	Aluminum	25mm	—	—	17.50	—

Obverse as last. Rv: PERSEVERANCIO / REPUBLICA / DEL / SALVADOR. (Limarc report)

GREGORIO TOLEDO

Rulau	Date	Metal	Size	VG	F	VF	Unc
Slv 30	(1893-97)	Brass	27mm	—	—	12.50	20.00

GREGORIO TOLEDO. / Large pebbled 1 / * + *. Rv: REPUBLICA DEL SALVADOR / large pebbled 1 / * C.A. * / (tiny) C.A. KLINKNER & CO. S.F. Plain edge. (Zaffern coll.)

1 Real.

Cerrillos
YNGO. SAN SALVADOR

Rulau	Date	Metal	Size	VG	F	VF	Unc
Slv 32	1864	WM	20mm	—	—	Rare	—

V. N. within wreath, which is open at the bottom. 1864 below. Rv: YNGo. SAN SALVADOR / ½ / . CERRILLOS . (Fonrobert 7471; Eklund 990)

V. Nuñez Ulloa-Llach says attribution to El Salvador is dubious; suggests Cuba.

GUATEMALA

Minting Guatemalan Tokens

The governmental Guatemala Mint struck tokens of brass or copper for agricultural estates and other private issuers in the nation, but did not strike tokens in nickel alloys or in aluminum.

Such official mintage was regulated by law on Nov. 21, 1894. Mint Director A. Henry published articles 5 and 6 of the law which stated:

"Article 5 - The national mint is allowed to engage in the fabrication of tokens of copper."

"Article 6 - The copper token cannot have the same measurements as the national money and those fabricated will be of the following sizes: Of *17 millimeters,* of *22mm,* of *26mm,* and they will have the name of the plantation or finca on one side, and on the other side the numbers, as 1, 2, 3, 4, etc."

Two competing San Francisco, Calif. firms, C. H. Klinkner & Co. (1889-97) and L. H. Moise & Co. (1893-97) made many tokens for Guatemala, in all base metals, usually signing their works: **C. A. KLINKNER & CO. S. F.** or **L. H. MOISE. S. F.** These two firms merged in 1897 as Moise-Klinkner Co., which in turn was purchased by Patrick & Co. in 1930.

Thus it is possible to date many signed Klinkner or Moise tokens to the period 1897 or earlier.

The 1800's-era brass tokens of Herrera & Co. (Finca San Andres Osuna) were struck by A. Popert of Paris, France. They are signed **A. POPERT PARIS.**

Money Tokens Outlawed in 1925

The circulation of tokens in Guatemala as a substitute for legal tender was prohibited by law on May 6, 1925, making Guatemala one of the last Latin American nations to abandon the hacienda token system of payments.

German Influence in Guatemala

German names are very common on Guatemalan hacienda tokens of the 19th and early 20th centuries. Germans in substantial numbers emigrated to Guatemala in the last quarter of the 19th century and many of them became owners of coffee and other agricultural plantations, and of mercantile entities in the major cities.

Many of the German families seem to have come from the north, especially around Hamburg, probably following German merchants who resided in the country and decided to make it their home.

The German influence was pervasive in the coffee-growing regions known in the 19th century as Costa Cuca, Costa Grande and Costa de Cucho in the southwestern departments of San Marcos, Quezaltenango and Retalhuleu. We are engaged in research on this Teutonic influence, but unfortunately it was not ready for this guide book (it will be included in full in our coming specialized catalog on Central American tokens).

Guatemala declared war on Germany on April 23, 1918 and moved quickly to seize enemy assets in the country. This included some plantations owned by German companies such as Compania Hamburguesa de Plantaciones with estates at La Rochela and San Andres Osuna.

German residents who had become Guatemalan citizens before 1918 were not affected directly by the seizures, but their influence in the halls of government waned and tokens with Teutonic names disappeared.

Guatemala's Oligarchic Families

The oligarchic control of the land and the nation has been moderated in Guatemala by the rise in the 20th century of a large middle class, but many of the tokens reflect family empires in the 19th century, now long gone.

Such names as Herrera, Castillo, Sanchez, De Leon and others recur over and over. Guatemala has always been a poor nation, though, and its oligarchs never tread the same lofty paths as the Catorce Grande (Big Fourteen) in El Salvador or the Rabiblancos (White Birds, or 20 Families) in Panama.

ALTA VERAPAZ DEPARTMENT

Coban
C.
(E. Cary)

Rulau	Date	Metal	Size	VG	F	VF	EF
AV1	ND	Bronze	21mm	—	—	—	35.00

C. ctsp on Guatemala copper centavo of 1871 (KM-196). (Duffield 1614; Brunk 60080; Eklund 825)

Ebenezer Cary in the 19th century owned Chama Plantation, 25 miles west of Coban in central Guatemala (Alta Vera Paz) and counterstamped the 1871 centavos, still fresh from the mint, with the letter C for Chama. These were used by the Indians (Mayan) workers at the hacienda store to buy goceries, cloth etc.

The 1871 centavo was a favorite vehicle for hacienda owners for use as a plantation chit. From the number of pieces found with various marks, it would seem that much of the issue was used this way rather than being used as small change without countermarking.

Cary replaced his counterstamped tokens with struck pieces, Frank Duffield wrote in 1919.

COMPAÑIA CHAMA

Rulau	Date	Metal	Size	VG	F	VF	Unc
AV3	ND	CN	19mm	—	6.00	12.00	16.00

Building with spire, tree and grass around. Around: COMPAÑIA CHAMA / ***. Rv: 1/2 / REAL within wreath. Plain edge. (Clark 71; Jason 3-A)

Rulau	Date	Metal	Size	VG	F	VF	Unc
AV4	ND	CN	Oct.25mm	—	6.00	12.00	16.00

As last, but 1 1/2 / REALES. Plain edge. (Clark 72)

Rulau	Date	Metal	Size	VG	F	VF	Unc
AV5	ND	CN	28mm	—	6.50	14.00	20.00

As last, but 2 / REALES. Plain edge. (Clark 73; Eklund 1192)

There is also a 3/4-real, Oct 22mm CN, and 1-real, 22mm CN.

ERNESTO MARROQUIN & CO.

Rulau	Date	Metal	Size	VG	F	VF	Unc
AV8	ND	Brass	23mm	4.50	6.50	10.00	—

ERNESTO MARROQUIN & Co- / * / COBAN / * / **. Rv: PLANTACIONES DE CAFE / ALTA- / VERA-PAZ / ** / *. Plain edge. (Clark 222)

FRANCISCO MATHIES

Rulau	Date	Metal	Size	VG	F	VF	Unc
AV11	ND	Brass	27mm	3.50	5.50	8.00	12.00

FRANCISCO / MATHIES / FINCAS. / COBAN / GUATEMALA. Rv: 1 / DIA. Plain edge. (Clark 228)

Rulau	Date	Metal	Size	VG	F	VF	Unc
AV12	ND	Aluminum	20mm	3.00	5.00	7.50	10.00

Obverse as last. Rv: 25 / CENTAVOS. (Clark 227)

R. SAPPER

Rulau	Date	Metal	Size	VG	F	VF	Unc
AV15	1898	CN	19mm	4.00	6.00	9.00	—

R. SAPPER COBAN / 1/2 within beaded circle / 1898.
Rv: Same as obverse. Plain edge. (Ulex 2091; Clark 421)

Rulau	Date	Metal	Size	VG	F	VF	Unc
AV16	1898	CN	22mm	5.00	8.00	12.00	—

As last, but 1. (Clark 422)

Rulau	Date	Metal	Size	VG	F	VF	Unc
AV17	1898	CN	24mm	5.00	8.00	12.00	—

As last, but 2. (Clark 424; Jason 26-A)

Rulau	Date	Metal	Size	VG	F	VF	Unc
AV19	1906	CN	22mm	4.50	6.50	11.00	—

R. SAPPER. COBAN / 1 / (wreath) / * 1906 * around a central hole. Rv: Wreath around rim. Center blank. Plain edge. (Clark 423)

Rulau	Date	Metal	Size	VG	F	VF	Unc
AV20	1906	CN	24mm	6.00	8.00	11.00	—

As last, but 2, (Clark 425; Jason 26-B)

Coban is an important city in central Guatemala, at the center of a major coffee growing area. It served as headquarters for the extensive coffee plantations of Roberto Sapper, one of the large number of German immigrants near the end of the 19th century.

Karl Sapper, his brother, was a prominent geologist.

CHIMALTENANGO DEPARTMENT

Pochuta
JUAN ANDERSON
Finca Santa Anita

Rulau	Date	Metal	Size	VG	F	VF	Unc
Chm1	ND	Copper	22.7mm	6.00	9.00	15.00	30.00

SANTA ANITA / 1 / POCHUTA. Rv: JUAN ANDERSON / 1 / *. Plain edge. (Clark 396; Jason 106-A; Eklund 1097)

Rulau	Date	Metal	Size	VG	F	VF	Unc
Chm2	ND	Copper	19mm	—	—	15.00	30.00

As last, but 1/2. Plain edge. (Clark N/L)

Santa Anita was 1/2 mile south of Pochuta.

J. FERNANDEZ ROMERO
El Retiro

Rulau	Date	Metal	Size	VG	F	VF	Unc
Chm4	ND	Copper	20mm	—	—	25.00	—

J. FERNANDEZ ROMERO / 2. / *. Rv: EL RETIRO / 2. POCHUTA. Plain edge. (Weyl 1718; Clark 335; Jason 75-A)

Rulau	Date	Metal	Size	VG	F	VF	Unc
Chm5	ND	Copper	20mm	—	—	25.00	—

As last, but 1. (Weyl 1718; Clark 334; Eklund 841)

Rulau	Date	Metal	Size	VG	F	VF	Unc
Chm6	ND	Copper	20mm	—	—	25.00	—

As last, but 1/2. (Weyl 1718; Clark 333)

Rulau	Date	Metal	Size	VG	F	VF	Unc
Chm8	ND	CN	26mm	—	12.00	25.00	—

Tree at center. Around: EL RETIRO / * POCHUTA *. Rv: Large numeral 2. Plain edge. (Clark 332)

El Retiro was located 2½ miles south of Pochuta.

FINCA EL PACAYAL

Rulau	Date	Metal	Size	VG	F	VF	Unc
Chm11	ND	Copper	Rect 32x19mm	—	—	25.00	—

FINCA / EL PACAYAL / POCHUTA. Rv: - COLONOS - / 1/2 CAJA / - CAFE -. Plain edge. *TAMS Journal*, Aug. 1967 issue)

El Pacayal was located in the municipio of Pochuta, 2 miles southeast of the village of Pochuta.

FLORENCIA

Rulau	Date	Metal	Size	VG	F	VF	Unc
Chm16	ND	Brass	22mm	—	—	25.00	—

FLORENCIA / (Star) / POCHUTA. Rv: 1.

CARLOS JARAMILLO E HIJO

Rulau	Date	Metal	Size	VG	F	VF	Unc
Chm13	ND	Copper	22mm	—	—	16.00	—

CARLOS JARAMILLO E HIJO * around circular wreath. Rv: PACAYAL / 1 / (wreath). Plain edge. (Jason 61-A)

Other tokens denominated MEDIA CAJA and UN CAJA are known.

KLEE & RUBIO
Finca San Perdito

Rulau	Date	Metal	Size	VG	F	VF	Unc
Chm18	ND	Bronze	24mm	—	—	30.00	—

FINCA * SAN PERDITO * POCHUTA. Rv: KLEE & RUBIO GUATEMALA / 2 / REALES.

NOTTEBOHM Y CIA.

Rulau	Date	Metal	Size	VG	F	VF	Unc
Chm20	ND	Brass	25mm	—	—	30.00	—

NOTTEBOHM Y Cia. / POCHUTA. Rv: 1 (real).

IGNACIO G. SARAVIA
Finca La Esperanza

Rulau	Date	Metal	Size	VG	F	VF	Unc
Chm22	ND	Brass	Scal				
			24mm	7.50	10.00	20.00	—

IGNACIO G. SARAVIA / 1/2 / * POCHUTA *. Rv: LA / ESPERANZA. (Clark 128; Jason 31-A; Eklund 1111)

Rulau	Date	Metal	Size	VG	F	VF	Unc
Chm24	ND	Brass	30mm	9.00	15.00	30.00	—

PLANTATION DE CAFE / LA / ESPERANZA / *. Rv: IGNACIO G. SARAVIA / 1 / * POCHUTA *. Plain edge. (Eklund 1112; Clark 129)

Finca Las Conchas

Rulau	Date	Metal	Size	VG	F	VF	Unc
Chm26	ND	Brass	23mm	—	—	20.00	—

IGNACIO G. SARAVIA. Rv: LAS CONCHAS / 1. (Eklund 1118 & 2140; Clark N/L)

La Esperanza was located just ½ mile north of Pochuta and Ignacio G. Saravia was still its onwer in 1914. Other tokens of both fincas are known.

VITERI HNOS.
Finca San Antonio

Rulau	Date	Metal	Size	VG	F	VF	Unc
Chm29	ND	Brass	Oct 20mm	—	—	10.00	—

VITERI / 1/2 / POCHUTA. Rv: FINCA / * SAN ANTONIO *. Plain edge. (Clark N/L; Eklund 1144)

| Chm31 | ND | Brass | 21mm | — | 7.50 | 10.00 | — |

VITERI HNOS. / 1 /. REAL. Rv: "SAN ANTONIO" / (ornaments) / POCHUTA. Plain edge. (Clark 364)

San Antonio was 1½ miles east of Pochuta. Other tokens are reported.

WYLD HNOS.
Ceilan Colima

Rulau	Date	Metal	Size	VG	F	VF	Unc
Chm33	ND	Brass	Oct 27mm	—	—	25.00	—

CEILAN / 2 / POCHUTA. Rv: No descr. available.

Rulau	Date	Metal	Size	VG	F	VF	Unc
Chm34	ND	Brass	Hexag				
			25mm	5.00	7.00	10.00	—

WYLD HNOS. / 1 / POCHUTA. Rv: CEILAN / C / COLIMA. (Ulex 1550; Eklund 1107; Clark 468)

| Chm35 | ND | Brass | 30.5mm | — | — | 12.50 | — |

As lat, but on round planchet. (Jason 14-A)

Wyld Hnos. = Wyld Brothers. Guillermo Wyld and his brother(s) owned Finca Liberia, La Florida, Ceilan Colima and San Carlos at Pochuta (Chimaltenango Dept.) and other properties. Tokens were issued for Liberia, Ceilan Colima, San Carlos, La Florida and for Guillermo Wyld alone.

Ceilan was 1½ miles northeast of Pochuta. In 1914 Jorge Wyld was the owner, and another related firm, Wyld y Linares, is listed as a coffee exporter.

WYLD HNOS.
La Florida

Rulau	Date	Metal	Size	VG	F	VF	Unc
Chm38	ND	Copper	30mm	—	—	60.00	—

LA FLORIDA / F (large, shaded). Rv: WYLD Hnos. / 1 / POCHUTA. Rare. (Clark N/L; Eklund 1115)

An issue of the Wyld Brothers, it greatly resembles those of Liberia and San Carlos fincas. The 1-real token was also struck in hexagonal brass, 30mm. There are 1/2-real tokens in both round and hexagonal format.

La Florida was located 5 miles northeast of Pochuta. It was still in business 1914.

WYLD HNOS.
Finca Liberia

Rulau	Date	Metal	Size	VG	F	VF	Unc
Chm40	ND	Brass	20mm	5.00	7.50	10.00	18.00

WYLD Hnos / 1/2 / POCHUTA. Rv: LIBERIA / Large shaded L. Plain edge. (Clark 202; Jason 40-A; Eklund 1120)

| Chm41 | ND | Brass | 30mm | — | — | 18.00 | — |

As last, but 1. (Eklund 1121)

Clark placed this series in El Rodeo, San Marcos Dept. Liberia was located 4 miles northeast of Pochuta.

WYLD HNOS.
Finca San Carlos

Rulau	Date	Metal	Size	VG	F	VF	Unc
Chm43	ND	Brass	Hexag 22mm	—	—	45.00	—

WYLD Hnos / 1/2 / POCHUTA. Rv: SAN CARLOS / Large S. Plain edge. (Clark N/L; Eklund 1092)

| Chm44 | ND | Brass | 30mm | — | — | 35.00 | — |

As last, but 1. (Jason 89-A)

San Carlos was located 2½ miles southeast of Pochuta.

San Rafael Panam
JUAN ANDERSON

Rulau	Date	Metal	Size	VG	F	VF	Unc
Chm55	ND	Brass	22mm	—	—	15.00	—
		SAN RAFAEL / 1 / * PANAM *. Rv: JUAN ANDER-SON / 1 / *.					
Chm56	ND	Brass	18mm	—	—	15.00	—
		As last, but 1/2 (real).					

San Rafael Panam hacienda was located 10 miles west of Pochuta.

HERMANN HOPFNER

Rulau	Date	Metal	Size	VG	F	VF	Unc
Chm58	ND	CN	22mm	—	15.00	—	—
		HERMANN / HÖPFNER / GUATEMALA. Rv: FINCE (sic!) SAN RAFAEL P. / 2. Plain edge. (Jason 101-A)					
Chm59	ND	CN	22mm	—	15.00	—	—
		FINCA SAN RAFAEL P. / (beaded circle) / *. Rv: HERMANN HOEPFNER / 2 (in beaded circle) / * GUATEMALA *.					

Yepocapa
M. W.
Montellano

Rulau	Date	Metal	Size	VG	F	VF	EF
Chm60	ND	Copper	Scal 28mm	3.50	6.00	—	Rare
		MONTELLANO / TRES. Rv: MONTELLANO / M. W. At center: Ctsp V.M. (Zaffern coll.; Clark N/L)					

V.M. = Victor Matheu Z. Specimens of this token without countermark are worth $8 Fine. Tres = 3 Reales?

VICTOR MATHEU Z.
Montellano

Rulau	Date	Metal	Size	VG	F	VF	Unc
Chm62	(1893-97)	Brass	34mm	—	—	7.50	—
		VICTOR MATHEU Z. * around radiant cross, all within wreath with star at top opening. Rv: ******* / 2 / MONTELLANO / (tiny) L. H. MOISE. S. F. Plain edge. (Clark 265; Jason 53-A; Eklund 2148)					

2 = 2 Reales. Matheu apparently acquired Montellano estate from M. W. A ½-real, brass 22.5mm, is known.

Uncertain
ALAMEDA

Rulau	Date	Metal	Size	VG	F	VF	Unc
Chm70	ND	Brass	32mm	—	—	—	—
		ALAMEDA / DEPTO. DE CHIMALTENANGO. Rv: 4 REALES.					

GUILLERMO WYLD

Rulau	Date	Metal	Size	VG	F	VF	Unc
Chm73	ND	Brass	23mm	—	—	11.00	—
		Two mountain peaks. In exergue: DUENAS. Rv: GUILLERMO / w (on diamond) / WYLD. Plain edge. (Clark 467; Jason 28-B)					
Chm74	ND	Brass	19mm	—	—	6.00	9.50	—
		As last, but smaller. (Clark 466; Rulau coll.)					

Dueñas = Owners. These tokens indicate no value, except by size. These pieces occur counterstamped M.

EL QUICHE DEPARTMENT

San Miguel Uspantan
RAFAEL COBIAN
Finca San Jose del Soch

Rulau	Date	Metal	Size	VG	F	VF	Unc
EQ3	ND	Brass	26mm	—	2.50	3.00	10.00
		Large 2 within ornamented circle of small plants. Around: FINCA SAN JOSE DE SOCH /. RAFAEL COBIAN. Rv: 2 on similar ornamented circle. Around: PLANTACION DE CAFE / -+ USPANTAN +-. Plain edge. (Clark 388; Jason 98-A)					

ESCUINTLA DEPARTMENT

Concepcion
PLANTAGEN GESELLSCHAFT "CONCEPCION"

Rulau	Date	Metal	Size	VG	F	VF	Unc
Esc1	ND	Brass	31mm	14.00	—	25.00	—

PLANTAGEN GESELLSCHAFT / 4 / "CONCEP-CION". Rv: Large PGC monogram. Plain edge. (Ulex 2092; Clark 100; Jason 20-C)

Esc2	ND	Brass	26mm	12.00	—	22.50	—

As last, but 2. (Clark 99)

Esc3	ND	Brass	22mm	—	—	20.00	—

As last, but 1 R. (Ulex 2092; Clark 98; Jason 20-B)

Esc4	ND	Brass	18mm	10.00	—	20.00	—

As last, but 1/2. (Clark 97; Jason 20-A)

Esc5	ND	Brass	31mm	14.00	—	25.00	—

As last, but 4 R. This and the 1-real are the only pieces in this series with the 'R' sign for Reales. (Clark 101; Ulex 2092; Eklund 834)

There was a Finca La Concepcion in Costa Cuca which also issued tokens, but it seems to be another place than the German Company above. Plantagen Gesellschaft = Plantation Company.

Escuintla
FARMACIA J. M. OCHAITA

Rulau	Date	Metal	Size	VG	F	VF	Unc
Esc8	ND	Nic/Bs	18mm	—	—	—	—

FARMACIA J. M. OCHAITA / . ESCUINTLA . / GUATEMALA. Rv: CUARTILLO / 1/2 / REAL VALE. (Eklund 845)

Santa Lucia "EL BAUL"

Rulau	Date	Metal	Size	VG	F	VF	Unc
Esc11	1892	Brass	27mm	6.00	9.00	15.00	—

"EL BAUL" / -.- / GUATEMALA / -.- * DEPARTA-MENTO ESCUINTLA *. Rv: 1892 / 1 / (branding tool). Plain edge. (Clark 39; Jason 7-A)

	1892	Brass	Oct26mm	—	—	20.00	—

As last, but 3 (reales).

	1892	Brass	25mm	—	—	—	—

As last, but ½ (real). (Eklund 2231)

Santa Lucia is in Cotzumalguapa District.

Uncertain
LA COLONIA

Rulau	Date	Metal	Size	VG	F	VF	Unc
Esc14	(1893-97)	CN	25mm	6.00	9.00	12.00	20.00

LA COLONIA / (6-pointed ornament) / * ESCUINTLA *. Rv: Large 1 in wreath. Tiny L. H. MOISE S. F. at bottom. Plain edge. (Clark 94; Jason 18-C)

Esc16	(1893-97)	CN	20mm	—	—	10.00	—

LA COLONIA / (Erupting volcano) / ESCUINTLA. Rv: Large fraction 3/4 / (tiny) L. H. MOISE. S. F. Plain edge. (Clark 93; Zaika coll.)

These pieces occur ctsp O.

GUATEMALA DEPARTMENT

Amatitlan
MANUEL GALVEZ

Rulau	Date	Metal	Size	VG	F	VF	Unc
Gtm1	ND	Copper	22mm	—	—	8.00	—

MANUEL GALVEZ / (ornament) / . AMATITLAN . Rv: 1 / REAL / -.-. Plain edge. (Clark 146; Jason 1-A)

Morazan
B. & N.
San Agustin

Rulau	Date	Metal	Size	VG	F	VF	Unc
Gtm4	ND	Brass	25mm	—	—	12.00	—

* B & N * / ctsp Rococco Triangle / SAN AGUSTIN. Rv: COSECHA / 1 RL. Plain edge. (Clark 360)

Rulau	Date	Metal	Size	VG	F	VF	Unc
Gtm5	ND	Brass	17mm	—	—	8.00	—

SAN AGUSTIN / (ornament) / CORTE. Rv: 1/2 within rococco triangle. (Clark 359; Jason 82-A)

Cosecha = Harvest. Finca San Agustin was a few kilometers south of the nation's capital, near Morazan. The rococco (wavy-sided) triangle was apparently the finca's brand mark.

Guatemala City

MUNICIPALIDAD DE GUATEMALA

MUNICIPIOS

Rulau	Date	Metal	Size	VG	F	VF	Unc
Gtm10	1903	Bronze	31mm	—	15.00	30.00	60.00

MUNICIPALIDAD DE GUATEMALA / 1903 / $ (central hole) $ / (panel, on which numerial 12 is ctsp) / -*-. Rv: Blank. Plain edge. Centrally holed flan. (Clark 163; Jason 20-A)

Rulau	Date	Metal	Size	VG	F	VF	Unc
Gtm12	ND	Aluminum	38mm	—	—	25.00	35.00

GUATEMALA / -+- / 25 / -.- / (ornament). Rv: VEINTICINCO / -*- / $25oo / -*- / PESOS. Plain edge. (Clark 162)

The 25-peso token above may not be an issue of the city of Guatemala.

BANCO CENTRAL DE GUATEMALA

Rulau	Date	Metal	Size	F	VF	EF	Unc
Gtm14	1926	CN	20mm	6.00	8.00	11.00	20.00

Guatemalan arms. Rv: BANCO CENTRAL / 15 DE / SEPTIEMBRE / DE 1926 / DE GUATEMALA. Plain edge. (Rulau coll.)

Commemorates the foundation of the central bank. Probably struck at Guatemala Mint. Possibly base (.720 fine) silver?

CAMPAÑA NACIONAL DE 1906

Rulau	Date	Metal	Size	F	VF	EF	Unc
Gtm16	1906	Silver	22mm	3.00	5.00	7.00	10.00

Guatemalan arms. Above: CAMPAÑA NACIONAL DE 1906. Rv: Within wreath: HONOR / AL / MERITO. Plain edge. Issued with loop. (Rulau coll.)

Merit medal of the 1906 National Campaign.

CIOGGA CARISSIMI

Rulau	Date	Metal	Size	VG	F	VF	Unc
Gtm18	ND	Brass	26mm	—	6.00	10.00	20.00

Glass within floreate wreath. Rv: CIOGGA CARISSIMI / 1 R / * JARDIN DE ITALIA. Plain edge. (Ulex ; Clark 190)

Jardin de Italia = Garden of Italy, probably a bar, restaurant or both.

CLUB DE OBREROS

Rulau	Date	Metal	Size	F	VF	EF	Unc
Gtm20	1898	Silver	21.5mm	5.00	10.00	—	20.00

CLUB DE OBREROS / (wreath) / * CABRERISTA *. Rv: RECUERDO AL MERITO / AGOSTO 1 / DE / * 1898 *. Plain edge. Issued with loop. (Rulau coll.)

Merit medal of the Cabrerista Workers Club. Rafael Cabrera was Guatemala's first president, 1839-65.

CLUB GUATEMALA

Rulau	Date	Metal	Size	VG	F	VF	Unc
Gtm22	ND	Brass	26mm	5.00	6.00	8.00	—

* CLUB * / 2 / GUATEMALA. Rv: 2 / REALES . (ornament). (Ulex 2086; Clark 87; Jason 6-A)

Rulau	Date	Metal	Size	VG	F	VF	Unc
Gtm23	ND	Brass	22.5mm	—	—	—	—

As last, but 1 /REAL. (Smithsonian coll.)

DEUTSCHER VEREIN ZU GUATEMALA

Rulau	Date	Metal	Size	F	VF	EF	Unc
Gtm25	(1888)	CN	22mm	—	—	20.00	35.00

Bust of emperor Friedrich III. Around: FRIEDRICH DEUTSCHER KAISER KONIG V. PREUSSEN around. Rv: DEUTSCHER VEREIN ZU GUATEMALA / 2. (Ulex 2086; Clark 110; Jason 8-B)

Rulau	Date	Metal	Size	F	VF	EF	Unc
Gtm26	(1888)	CN	20mm	—	—	20.00	35.00

As last, but 1. (Ulex 2086; Clark 109)

Deutscher Verein zu Guatemala = German Union (Club) at Guatemala. Friedrich III ruled only a brief time in 1888 after succeeding Wilhelm I, and this issue undoubtedly was struck by the German club's board to honor the new kaiser.

AMADEO GARCIA

Rulau	Date	Metal	Size	VG	F	VF	Unc
Gtm28	ND	Aluminum	38mm	—	—	12.00	—

AMADEO GARCIA / $5oo / GUATEMALA, C. A. Rv: No descr. available.

GRAN BAR

Rulau	Date	Metal	Size	VG	F	VF	Unc
Gtm30	ND	Brass	21mm	—	—	10.00	—

GRAN / (ornament) / BAR. Rv: VALE / 20 / CTOS. / EN CONSUMO. Plain edge. (Clark 151)

In the Gran Hotel.

GRAN HOTEL UNION

Rulau	Date	Metal	Size	VG	F	VF	Unc
Gtm32	ND	Copper	21mm	8.00	—	17.00	—

GRAN HOTEL UNION / 2 RS in beaded circle / GUATEMALA. Rv: Same as obverse. Plain edge. (Ulex 2087; Clark 160)

GRAN HOTEL

Rulau	Date	Metal	Size	VG	F	VF	Unc
Gtm 34	ND	Brass	19mm	8.00	—	15.00	—

GRAN HOTEL / 2 R in beaded circle / . GUATE-MALA . Rv: Same as obverse. (Clark 158)

Gtm35	ND	Brass	17mm	8.00	—	15.00	—

As last, but 1 R. (Clark 157; Jason 13-A)

HIPODROMO DEL HOSPITAL GENERAL

Rulau	Date	Metal	Size	VG	F	VF	Unc
Gtm37	ND	Brass	34mm	8.00	11.00	15.00	—

HIPODROMO / DEL / HOSPITAL / GENERAL / DE / GUATEMALA. Rv: 50 / CENTAVOS. (Ulex 2085; Clark 188)

Gtm38	ND	Brass	26mm	6.00	9.00	12.00	—

As last, but 25 / CENTAOVS. (Clark 187; Ulex 2085)

Gtm39	ND	Brass	22mm	—	—	Scarce	—

As last, but 10 / CENTAVOS. (Ulex 2085)

HOTEL GRAN CENTRAL

Rulau	Date	Metal	Size	VG	F	VF	Unc
Gtm41	ND	CN	29.5mm	9.00	—	18.00	—

HOTEL / GRAN CENTRAL / GUATEMALA. Rv: !oo. Plain edge. (Clark 156)

Gtm42	ND	CN	29mm	9.00	—	18.00	—

Obverse as last. Rv: VALE POR / 1.00 / CANTINA. Plain edge. (Clark 155)

Gtm43	—	CN	Oct 25mm	8.00	—	16.00	—

Obverse as last. Rv: Numeral 50 within beaded circle. (Clark 154)

Gtm44	ND	CN	Scal 29mm	6.00	9.00	14.00	—

As last, but 25. (Ulex 2087; Clark 153)

Rulau	Date	Metal	Size	VG	F	VF	Unc
Gtm45	ND	CN	19.5mm	6.00	9.00	14.00	—

As last but 12½. (Ulex 2087; Clark 152; Jason 14-A)

Gtm47	ND	CN	24mm	—	—	14.00	—

GRAN CENTRAL / 25 / ALBERTO NIQUET. Rv: HOTEL / RESTAURANTE . / CANTINA. / BIL-LARES. / CONFITERIA. (Jason 14-C)

JOSE L. RIVERA

Rulau	Date	Metal	Size	VG	F	VF	Unc
Gtm50	ND	Brass	22mm	—	—	9.00	—

Rabbit. Around: EL ANTIGUA CONEJO / (ornament). Rv: JOSE L. RIVERA / 2 RLS / (ornaments). (Ulex 2088; Eklund 869)

Georg Ulex-Hamburg in 1908 listed this under Guatemala City.

J. RUFINO BARRIOS

Rulau	Date	Metal	Size	F	VF	EF	Unc
Gtm52	1884	Silver	20.6mm	—	—	25.00	35.00

Locomotive right. Around: J. RUFINO BARRIOS A. S. GUATEMALTECOS / (small anchor). Rv: 1a. LOCOMOTORA EN LA CAPITAL / 19 / DE JULIO / 1884 / (ornament. Plain edge. (Dick Grinolds collection)

Justo Rufino Barrios was president of Guatemala 1873-85.

ZAPOTE

Rulau	Date	Metal	Size	VG	F	VF	Unc
Gtm55	ND	Brass	27mm	—	5.00	9.50	15.00

(Scrollwork) / ZAPOTE / (scrollwork). Rv: (Ornaments) / -UN- / REAL / (ornaments). (Clark 473; Jason 127-A)

Gtm56	ND	CN	19mm	—	5.00	9.50	15.00

As last, but UN / QUARTILLO.

Gtm58	ND	Steel	20mm	—	—	6.00	10.00

ZAPOTE / F. S. A. / ctsp * (asterisk). Rv: 1/2 / REAL. (Clark 472)

Gtm59	ND	Brass	23.5mm	—	—	—	—

Tree. Rv: HACIENDA / DEL (in shield) / * ZAPOTE *. (Clark 475; Jason 127-B)

Finca Zapote was owned by the brothers Rafael and Mariano Castillo, at Guatemala City's northern edge. In 1886 they founded on the finca grounds a brewery, Cerveceria Centroamericana, which employed 500 workers.

It is not certain that all the tokens above are connected with this Finca Zapote.

HUEHUETENANGO DEPARTMENT

Barillas
JESUS AGUIRRE
Finca La Providencia

Rulau	Date	Metal	Size	VG	F	VF	Unc
Hve1	ND	Brass	25mm	—	—	7.00	—

FINCA "LA PROVIDENCIA" / (ornament) / SAN RAFAEL / -.- / (tiny) L. H. MOISE. S. F. Rv: JESUS AGUIRRE / 1 / * DIA *. Plain edge. (Clark 330)

LA PROVIDENCIA

Rulau	Date	Metal	Size	VG	F	VF	Unc
Hve3	ND	CN	22mm	—	—	6.00	—

LA PROVIDENCIA / . CAFE TAREA . Rv: Ctsp P within relief laurel wreath. (Clark 326)

IZABAL DEPARTMENT

Izabal
CHALMERS GUTHRIE & CO.

Rulau	Date	Metal	Size	VG	F	VF	Unc
Iza3	ND	CN	24mm	—	17.00	20.00	—

CHALMERS, GUTHRIE & CO. * / (ornament) / YZABAL / (ornament). Rv: 2 / REALES. Plain edge.

Iza4	ND	CN	21mm	—	14.00	17.50	—

Similar to last, but 1 / REAL.

Iza5	ND	CN	19.5mm	—	—	7.00	10.00

Similar to last, but 1/2 / REAL. (Jason 2-A)

Livingston
JOSE MICHOVSKY

Rulau	Date	Metal	Size	VG	F	VF	Unc
Iza8	ND	Aluminum	23mm	—	—	12.00	—

JOSE MICHOVSKY / (ornaments) / LIVINGSTON, / -GUA. -. Rv: PAGARA / 25 / AL PORTADOR. Plain edge.

J. C. NORICH

Rulau	Date	Metal	Size	VG	F	VF	Unc
Iza11	(1890's)	Brass	28mm	35.00	42.50	50.00	—

(All incused) J. C. NORICH / 6 1/4 C / LIVINGSTON. Rv: Blank. Beaded, incised rim on each side. Plain edge. (Rulau E10; TAMS Maverick 9034; Oct. 1979)

Rulau	Date	Metal	Size	VG	F	VF	Unc
Iza12	(1890's)	Brass	Oct 26.5mm	42.50	50.00	70.00	—

(All incused): J. C. NORICH. / 25 C / LIVINGSTON. Rv: Blank. Plain edge. Rare. (Rulau coll., ex-Elman)

The Rulau specimen of the 25-centavo token has a monogram AA scratched on the reverse.

Rulau	Date	Metal	Size	VG	F	VF	Unc
Iza14	(1900-10)	Brass	23.5mm	25.00	32.50	40.00	—

J. C. NORICH / (ornament) / LIVINGSTON, / * / GUATEMALA. Rv: 6 1/4. Plain edge. (Rulau coll., ex-Elman)

Iza16	(1910-15)	Aluminum	23mm	—	16.00	20.00	40.00

J. C. NORICH / (ornament) / LIVINGSTON / * / GUATEMALA. Rv: 12 1/2. Plain edge. (Lewis Egnew coll.; Rulau E11)

Livingston is a port city on Bahia de Amatique on Guatemala's Caribbean Sea coast.

The Norich tokens escaped cataloging by Weyl, Ulex, Prober, Jason, Clark and others. They were issued well after Fonrobert's time.

The tokens of J. C. Norich have been claimed at various times for the Livingstons in South Carolina, Texas, Montana and California.

Puerto Barrios
HOTEL DEL NORTE

Rulau	Date	Metal	Size	VG	F	VF	Unc
Iza18	ND	Brass	21mm	—	50.00	80.00	—

HOTEL DEL NORTE / PUERTO BARRIOS. Rv: 25. Plain edge.

JALAPA DEPARTMENT

Mataquescuintla
G. S.
Finca Concepcion

Rulau	Date	Metal	Size	VG	F	VF	Unc
Jlp4	ND	Brass	21mm	—	—	12.50	—

MATAQUESCUINTLA / G . S / - + -. Rv: FINCA / 2 / CONCEPCION. Plain edge. (Jason 19-B)

Jlp5	ND	Brass	19mm	—	—	12.50	—

As last, but 1 (real). (Jason 19-A)

G. S.
Finca Vizcaya

Rulau	Date	Metal	Size	VG	F	VF	Unc
Jlp7	ND	GS	21mm	—	8.25	—	—
		MATAQUESCUINTLA / G . S / - + -. Rv: FINCA / VIZCAYA / 2. Plain edge.					
Jlp8	ND	GS	19mm	—	8.25	—	—
		As last, but 1 (real).					
Jlp9	ND	GS	17mm	—	9.75	—	—
		As last, but 1/2. (Clark 462). This token may also exist in brass.					

Finca Vizcaya = Basque coffee estate.

QUEZALTENANGO DEPARTMENT

Colomba
MARIANO DE J. ANGUIANO
El Rosario Bola de Oro

Rulau	Date	Metal	Size	VG	F	VF	Unc
Quz 3	1872	CN	28mm	—	—	12.50	17.50
		EL ROSARIO BOLA DE ORO / (tree) / 1872 / COSTA CUCA. Rv: MARIANO DE J. ANGUIANO / 2 / . GUATEMALA . Plain edge. (Clark 355)					

Quz 5	1872	CN	21mm	—	4.00	10.00	15.00
		As last, but 1/2. (Clark 353)					
Quz 6	1872	CN	16mm	—	4.00	10.00	15.00
		As last, but 1/4 (real). (Clark 352)					

Quz 8	1872	CN	21mm	—	8.00	15.00	25.00
		As the ½-real token above, but diesinker's error renders surname as ANGUIANA. (Eklund 843; Jason 80-B)					

This series occurs bearing counterstamped initials. Incuse initials H and K are known on separate specimen (illustrations are typical).

ENRIQUE HERMAN
Finca Colomba

Rulau	Date	Metal	Size	VG	F	VF	Unc
Quz 9	ND	Brass	25mm	—	—	12.00	—
		ENRIQUE HERMAN / 4 / * COLOMBA GUATE-MALA *. Rv: Same as obverse. Plain edge. (Rulau coll.; Clark 182)					
Quz 10	ND	Brass	20mm	—	—	10.00	—
		As last, but 1. (Clark 180; Zaffern coll.)					

Enrique Herman was part of the wave of German immigrants which came to Guatemala in the late 19th century and once dominated a good part of the nation's plantation structure. In addition to Finca Colomba, he owned Finca Esmeralda in Costa Cuca, San Marcos Dept.

A. C. JAMES
Finca La Moka

Rulau	Date	Metal	Size	VG	F	VF	Unc
Quz 13	ND	Aluminum	32mm	—	—	11.00	—
		A. C. JAMES / (ornament) / * GUATEMALA * / (tiny) L. H. MOISE S.F. Rv: REALES on ribbon across large numeral 2. Around: LA MOKA / CHUVA. (Eklund 2228)					
Quz 14	ND	Aluminum	32mm	—	—	11.00	—
		As last, ctsp S B on obverse. (Clark 262)					

Similar aluminum tokens for 1-real, 28mm; 1/2-real, 23mm, and 1/4-real, 20mm, are reported. Some are counterstamped MOKA, S B, or 2 4 / MOKA.

J. MARIANO MOLINA
San Carlos Miramar

Rulau	Date	Metal	Size	VG	F	VF	Unc
Quz 17	ND	CN	31mm	6.00	8.00	14.00	—
		SAN CARLOS MIRAMAR / 4 / . COSTA CUCA, J. M. MOLINA. Rv: Same as obverse. This token occurs ctsp O. (Clark 372)					
Quz 18	ND	CN	29mm	—	—	14.00	—
		As last, but 3.					
Quz 19	ND	CN	26mm	4.00	6.00	10.00	—
		As last, but 2. (Jason 90-C)					
Quz 20	ND	CN	26mm	—	—	10.00	—
		As last, but J. MARIANO MOLINA. (2 reales). (Clark 371)					
Quz 21	ND	CN	24mm	3.00	—	8.00	—
		As last (J. MARIANO MOLINA), but 1. (Eklund 2375; Clark 370; Jason 90-B)					

LUCIANO R. MONZON E HIJOS
Finca La Florida

Rulau	Date	Metal	Size	VG	F	VF	Unc
Quz 22	(1893-97)	Brass	38mm	—	—	50.00	70.00

Within wreath: * / LUCIANO R. MONZON E HIJOS. / (starburst) / *. Rv: FINCA / UN / PESO / * LA FLOR-IDA * / (tiny) L. H. MOISE S.F. Plain edge. (Eklund 2133; Pesant 111; ANS coll.)

Brass 4 and 1-real tokens were also issued; all are scarce. The Monzon tokens have been attributed erroneously to Cuba. The finca was located near Colomba in Quezaltenango Dept.

JOSE PACHECO MONTEROS
La Bolsa

Rulau	Date	Metal	Size	VG	F	VF	Unc
Quz 23	1880	CN	19mm	2.50	4.00	6.50	14.00

JOSE PACHECO MONTEROS / 1 / REAL / * 1880 *. Rv: LA BOLSA / COSTA CUCA. Plain edge. (Clark 51; Jason 11-A)

TEOFILO PALACIOS
Jardin de Acultzingo

Rulau	Date	Metal	Size	VG	F	VF	Unc
Quz 26	1888	CN	16mm	4.00	6.50	10.00	—

Within beaded circles: 1/2. Around: TEOFILO PALA-CIOS / . GUATEMALA . Rv: Tree over 1888 within beaded circle. Around: JARDIN DE ACULTZINGO / . COSTA CUCA. Plain edge. (Clark 1; Jason 18-A)

Rulau	Date	Metal	Size	VG	F	VF	Unc
Quz 27	1888	CN	21mm	4.00	6.50	10.00	—

As last, but 1. Plain edge (Clark 2; Jason 18-B)

CARLOS QUEZADA
La Vicha

Rulau	Date	Metal	Size	VG	F	VF	Unc
Quz 30	ND	Copper	25mm	—	7.50	12.50	

CARLOS QUEZADA / (Quatrefoil) / LA VICHA. Rv: VALE / 1 (in circle) / *** REAL ***. (Ulex 3617; Eklund 1440; Clark 459; Jason 125-B)

Rulau	Date	Metal	Size	VG	F	VF	Unc
Quz 31	ND	Copper	20mm	—	—	8.00	

As last, but 1/4 / REAL. (Eklund 1439; Clark 457)

ARSENIO SUAREZ
San Francisco Buena Vista

Rulau	Date	Metal	Size	VG	F	VF	Unc
Quz 33	(1893-97)	CN	30mm	8.00	15.00	30.00	

Coffee branch at center. Around: ARSENIO SUAREZ. / * GUATEMALA. *. Rv: SAN FRAN'CO BUENA VISTA. / 3 / COSTA CUCA / (tiny) KLINKNER & CO. S.F. Plain edge. (Clark 378)

Rulau	Date	Metal	Size	VG	F	VF	Unc
Quz 34	ND	CN	24mm	5.00	9.00	20.00	—

As last, but 2. (Clark 377)

Rulau	Date	Metal	Size	VG	F	VF	Unc
Quz 35	ND	CN	21mm	3.50	6.50	12.00	—

As last, but 1/2. (Clark 375; Brunk coll.)

El Palmar
MONTE CRISTO

Rulau	Date	Metal	Size	VG	F	VF	Unc
Quz 38	ND	Brass	20mm	—	—	6.00	—

MONTE CRISTO / (8-pointed star). Rv: *** / 1 / REAL. Plain edge. (Clark 264)

Xolhuitz
EDUARDO MORA
Fincas Montemaria y La Palmera

Rulau	Date	Metal	Size	VG	F	VF	Unc
Quz 40	ND	Brass	32mm	5.00	7.00	9.50	—

(All incused) FINCAS / MONTEMARIA / Y / LA PALMERA / XOLHUITZ C. C. Rv: EDUARDO MORA / 4 / (round leaf) / REALES. Plain edge. (Clark 266)

This token has been reported only with counterstamp '2' above the word REALES, and the numeral 4 obscured.

Xolhuitz
FINCA LIRIA

Rulau	Date	Metal	Size	VG	F	VF	Unc
Quz 43	(1893-97)	Aluminum	25mm	—	—	15.00	25.00

Radiant double bordered star. Around: FINCA LIRIA / XOLHUITZ / (tiny) L. H. MOISE S.F. (this line broken on die). Rv: Ornate shaded 1 in wreath. Around: VALE / * TAREA *. Plain edge. (Zaffern coll.; Clark N/L; Jason N/L)

M. A. L.
Finca Aliansa

Rulau	Date	Metal	Size	VG	F	VF	Unc
Quz 46	ND	Brass	25mm	3.00	5.00	12.00	—

FINCA / ALIANSA / M. A. L. Rv: SAN JOSE / 1 / XOLHUITZ. Plain edge. Ctsp large M on reverse. Plain edge. (Clark 8)

TADEO PACHECO

Rulau	Date	Metal	Size	VG	F	VF	Unc
Quz 49	ND	Brass	20.5mm	—	—	35.00	—

TADEO PACHECO *. Rv: QUEZALTENANGO / I / *. Plain edge. (Fonrobert 7290; Weyl 1752; Ulex 2101; Eklund 917; Clark 290)

There are two varieties of this token's reverse.

Rulau	Date	Metal	Size	VG	F	VF	Unc
Quz 51	ND	Brass	20.5mm	—	—	Rare	—

TADEO PACHECO *. Rv: LIMPIA / CAFETAL / SHOLWITZ. (Fon. 8271; Eklund 918)

This is a muling. The reverse is from a token of Francisco Sanchez e Hijos. Sholwitz = Xolhuitz.

G .G. S.
San Ygnacio

Rulau	Date	Metal	Size	VG	F	VF	Unc
Quz 53	ND	CN	27.3mm	—	—	10.00	20.00

SAN YGNACIO / (ornament) / * XOLHUITZ. *. Rv: G.G.S. / 2 / ** REALES ** / (tiny) KLINKNER & CO. S.F. Plain edge. (Zaffern coll.; Clark N/L; Jason 104-A)

FRANCISCO SANCHEZ
E HIJOS

NOTE: This entire series was issued before 1878, and the tokens seem to have been made in the United States. Some present locations of Sanchez' plantations have been discovered.

Rulau	Date	Metal	Size	VG	F	VF	Unc
Quz 55	ND	Brass	24.5mm	25.00	35.00	55.00	—

Indian head left, LIBERTY on headband. Around: FRANCISCO SANCHEZ E HIJOS. Rv: III in wreath. (Fonrobert 8265; Ulex 2241; Eklund 1088)

| Quz 56 | ND | Brass | 22mm | 25.00 | 35.00 | 55.00 | — |

As last, but II. (Fon. 8266; Eklund 1087)

| Quz 57 | ND | Brass | 20.5mm | 25.00 | 35.00 | 55.00 | — |

As last, but I. (Fon. 8267; Eklund 1086)

I, II and III apparently indicate 1, 2 or 3 reales. Though there was an abortive attempt to decimalize in 1869-71, Guatemala's coins were not regularly issued in centavo denominations until 1881.

| Quz 59 | ND | Brass | 20.5mm | 30.00 | 40.00 | 60.00 | — |

Obverse as last (Indian head left, etc.). Rv: DIA in wreath. (Fonrobert 8268; Eklund 1082; Clark 374)

Dia = Day. This token was for one day's labor.

| Quz 61 | ND | Brass | 20.5mm | 30.00 | 40.00 | 60.00 | — |

Obverse as last. Rv: LIMPIA / CAFETAL / BOLIVAR. (Fon. 8269)

| Quz 62 | ND | Brass | 20.5mm | 30.00 | 40.00 | 60.00 | — |

Similar, but LIMPIA / CAFETAL / DOLORES. (Fon. 8270)

| Quz 63 | ND | Brass | 20.5mm | 25.00 | 35.00 | 55.00 | — |

Similar, but LIMPIA / CAFETAL / SHOLWITZ. This plantation was at Xolhuitz in Quezaltenango Dept., the usual spelling for Sholwitz. (Fon. 8271; Rulau coll.)

The last three token types were issued for Sanchez and Sons' cafetales named Bolivar, Dolores and Sholwitz, respectively. Some specimens occur ctsp 9 or Radiant Sun.

Fonrobert assigned these tokens to Panama or Colombia; Clark first called one of them Guatemalan. Limpia Cafetal = Honorable coffee estate.

| Quz 65 | ND | Brass | 20.5mm | 15.00 | 20.00 | 35.00 | 50.00 |

Obverse as last. Rv: QUEZALTENANGO / (5-pointed Star) / - * -. Plain edge. (Schimmel & Garretson reports)

Discovery of the above token in 1982 removes whatever doubt might remain that the Sanchez pieces are indeed from Quezaltenango Department, Guatemala, and may be among the earliest and most desirable of such tokens.

| Quz 67 | ND | Brass | 24mm | — | — | 50.00 | 75.00 |

Obverse as last (Indian head left, etc.). Rv: Blank. This token also exists in 22 and 20 mm sizes.

RETALHULEU DEPARTMENT

Champerico
COMPANIA DE AGENCIAS

Rulau	Date	Metal	Size	VG	F	VF	Unc
Ret 3	ND	Brass	26mm	—	—	14.00	—

COMPANIA DE AGENCIAS / (ornament) / CHAMPERICO / (ornament) / .*. Rv: VALE / 1 / * REAL *. Plain edge. (Clark 3)

Rulau	Date	Metal	Size	VG	F	VF	Unc
Ret 4	ND	Brass	Oct 28mm	—	—	17.50	—

As last, but 2 / * REAL *. (James King report)

Rulau	Date	Metal	Size	VG	F	VF	Unc
Ret 6	ND	Brass	Oct 26mm				

Cia. DE AGENCIAS DE CHAMPERICO / C de A / C. de L. (on anchor) / * LIMITADA. Rv: CONTROL DE TRABAJO / VALE / 2 / REALES / MOISE.

Champerico is a Pacific Ocean port city. There are other tokens of this company.

San Felipe
ARIAS HERMANOS
Plantacion Los Encuentros

Rulau	Date	Metal	Size	VG	F	VF	Unc
Ret 9	ND	Brass	21mm	3.00	5.00	7.50	—

ARIAS. Rv: 2 (incused) / ENCUENTROS. Plain edge. (Clark 15)

Rulau	Date	Metal	Size	VG	F	VF	Unc
Ret 11	ND	Brass	26mm	4.00	6.00	9.00	—

Petal at center of circle of leaves. Around: ARIAS HERMANOS / *.* SAN FELIPE *.*. Rv: Numeral 2 on circular checkered field. Around: PLANTACIONES DE / CAFE Y CANA. Plain edge. (Clark 16)

Cafe y Cana = Coffee and (Sugar) Cane.

AUGENER & WITTIG

Rulau	Date	Metal	Size	VG	F	VF	Unc
Ret 13	ND	Brass	22mm	4.00	6.50	10.00	—

Ornate key, ward upward. Rv: AUGENER & WITTIG / 2 / . SAN FELIPE. Plain edge. (Clark 22)

MATEO GOMES M.

Rulau	Date	Metal	Size	VG	F	VF	Unc
Ret 16	ND	Brass	25mm	—	3.50	5.50	—

MATEO GOMES M. / * SANTA ELVIRA * around an empty circle. Rv: 2 / REALES. Plain edge. (Clark 406)

San Sebastian
GREGORIO MUÑOZ

Rulau	Date	Metal	Size	VG	F	VF	Unc
Ret 20	ND	Copper	21mm	—	—	—	—

GREGORIO MUÑOZ / SAN SEBASTIAN. Rv: 2 REALES. (Weyl 1764; Eklund 942; Clark 281)

Rulau	Date	Metal	Size	VG	F	VF	Unc
Ret 21	ND	Brass	21mm	—	—	—	—

As last.

Rulau	Date	Metal	Size	VG	F	VF	Unc
Ret 22	ND	Copper	21mm	—	—	—	—

As last, but 1 1/2 REALES. (W. 1764; Eklund 941; Clark 280)

Rulau	Date	Metal	Size	VG	F	VF	Unc
Ret 23	ND	Brass	21mm	—	—	—	—

As last.

SACATEPEQUEZ DEPARTMENT

Antigua Guatemala
O. BLEULER & CO.

Rulau	Date	Metal	Size	VG	F	VF	Unc
Spq 1	ND	Brass	22mm	—	—	30.00	—

O. BLEULER & Co. / 1/4 R / * ANTIGUA G. *. Plain edge. (Weyl 1700)

Issued in the 19th century. The Weyl sale took place in April, 1899. Also see the Bleuler tokens under Miramar and Morelia in Guatemala.

Rulau	Date	Metal	Size	VG	F	VF	Unc
Spq 3	ND	Copper	22mm	—	—	30.00	—

O. BLEULER & Co. / 1/4 / * ANTIGUA G. *. Rv: Arms of Costa Rica. Around: HACIENDA DEL PATALILLO * / AMERICA CENTRAL (on band). (Weyl 1701)

A muling. Hacienda del Patalillo is in Costa Rica, while Bleuler operated in Guatemala.

MANUEL M. HERRERA
Finca El Portal

Rulau	Date	Metal	Size	VG	F	VF	Unc
Spq 6	1871	Brass	18mm	—	—	30.00	—

MANUEL M. / 1871 / HERRERA. Rv: FINCA "EL PORTAL" / (plow with two wheels) / ANTIGUA GUATEMALA. (Fonrobert 7289; Ulex 2090; Weyl 1701; Clark 318)

This is one of the "classic" tokens of Central America, owned by all the major 19th century European collectors of hacienda pieces.

Rulau	Date	Metal	Size	VG	F	VF	Unc
Spq 8	ND	Brass	15mm	—	—	30.00	—

MANUEL M. HERRERA / (ornamentation). Rv: PORTAL / (guns) / ANTIGUA GUATEMALA. (Garretson report)

SAN MARCOS DEPARTMENT

El Quetzal
HAWLEY HERMANOS
Finca Ona

Rulau	Date	Metal	Size	VG	F	VF	Unc
Smc 3	ND	Brass	38mm	9.00	15.00	30.00	—

FINCA ONA / (ornament) / HAWLEY / (ornament) / COSTA DE CUCHO. Rv: (ornament) / UN PESO / (ornament). The numeral '2' has been stamped over UN to raise the value to two pesos. Plain edge. (Clark 288)

Rulau	Date	Metal	Size	VG	F	VF	Unc
Smc 5	ND	Aluminum	28mm	—	4.50	8.00	—

HAWLEY HERMANOS / UN / PESO / FINCA ONA. Rv: Large open numeral 1, radiate, with rays in all directions. Plain edge. (Clark 289)

ELIAS TOLEDO
Finca Matasano

Rulau	Date	Metal	Size	VG	F	VF	Unc
Smc 8	ND	CN	26mm	—	—	11.00	—

ELIAS TOLEDO / ... / FINCA / ... / . MATASANO . Rv: COSTA DE CUCHO / ... / 1 CAJON / 2 REALES / ... / *. Plain edge. (Clark 226)

Rulau	Date	Metal	Size	VG	F	VF	Unc
Smc 10	ND	CN	17mm	—	—	—	—

ELIAS TOLEDO / * / FINCA / * / . MATASANO . Rv: COSTA DE CUCHO / 1/4 / CAJON / MEDIA / *. (Eklund 895)

These pieces give comparative values of labor. A full cajon (box) picked by a worker was worth 2 reales, or about 25 cents, while a quarter box was worth 1/2 real (media), or 6 1/4 cents. The product, or box size, are not known.

El Tumbador
CAFETAL DOS MARIAS

Rulau	Date	Metal	Size	VG	F	VF	Unc
Smc 13	ND	Brass	22mm	—	—	Scarce	—

CAFETAL DOS MARIAS / COSTA DE CUCHO / SAN MARCOS. Rv: 4 REALES. (Weyl 1704: Eklund 813; Clark 124)

Rulau	Date	Metal	Size	VG	F	VF	Unc
Smc 14	ND	Brass	19mm	—	—	Scarce	—

As last, but 2 REALES. (Weyl 1704; Eklund 812; Clark 124)

N. DE LA CERDA E HIJO

Rulau	Date	Metal	Size	VG	F	VF	Unc
Smc 17	ND	CN	26mm	—	—	15.00	—

N DE LA CERDA E HIJO / 2 / *. Rv: BOLA DE ORO / TUMBADOR. (Ulex 2104; Eklund 951; Clark 50)

Rulau	Date	Metal	Size	VG	F	VF	Unc
Smc 18	ND	CN	18mm	—	—	15.00	—

As last, but 1/2. (Ulex 2104; Eklund 950)

J. D. ESPINOSA Y CO.
Cafetal Las Cruces

Rulau	Date	Metal	Size	VG	F	VF	Unc
Smc 20	(1893-97)	Brass	23mm	—	—	8.00	—

J. D. ESPINOSA Y Co- / DOS / -.- / REALES / -*- TUMBADOR -*-. Rv: CAFETAL LAS CRUCES / DOS / -.- / REALES / -*- / (tiny) L. H. MOISE S.F. Plain edge. (Clark 106; Jason 22-A)

JACINTO GUILLEN
Finca San Isidro

Rulau	Date	Metal	Size	VG	F	VF	Unc
Smc 23	ND	Aluminum	23mm	3.00	4.50	6.00	11.00

FINCA / DE / CAFE / Y CANA / SAN ISIDRO / (tiny) L. H. MOISE, S.F. Rv: *** / JACINTO / GUILLEN / TUMBADOR. Plain edge. (Clark 59; Eklund 956)

JUAN LŪTTMANN
Nahuatancillo

Rulau	Date	Metal	Size	VG	F	VF	Unc
Smc 26	ND	Copper	20.5mm	—	—	25.00	—

JUAN LŪTTMANN / 2 / REALES. Rv: NAHUA-TANCILLO / 2 / TUMBADOR. Plain edge. (Weyl 1748; Eklund 912; Clark 218)

Rulau	Date	Metal	Size	VG	F	VF	Unc
Smc 27	ND	Copper	20mm	—	—	25.00	—

As last, but 1 / REAL. (Weyl 1749; Eklund 911)

Rulau	Date	Metal	Size	VG	F	VF	Unc
Smc 28	ND	Copper	14mm	—	—	—	—

As last, but 1/4. (Weyl 1749; Eklund 910)

Both Weyl and Prober rendered the surname as Leuttmann. The U of the surname on the tokens has an umlaut (..) above it; its diphthong rendition should have been Luettmann.

RODRIGUEZ HERMANOS
Cafetal Luarca

Rulau	Date	Metal	Size	VG	F	VF	Unc
Smc 31	(1893-97)	Brass	38mm	—	—	—	35.00

CAFETAL : LUARCA / 1 / TAREA / 1 / : RODRI-GUEZ : HERMANOS : / (tiny) L. H. MOISE. S.F. Rv: Same as obverse. (Eklund 2079)

Rulau	Date	Metal	Size	VG	F	VF	Unc
Smc 32	ND	Brass	32mm	10.00	15.00	—	—

As last, but 2 / REALES / 2. (Eklund 2078; Clark 213; Jason 43-B). This piece occurs ctsp L / 43.

Rulau	Date	Metal	Size	VG	F	VF	Unc
Smc 33	ND	Brass	23.5mm	4.00	6.00	—	—

As last, but 1 / REAL / 1. (Clark 212; Jason 43-A)

Rulau	Date	Metal	Size	VG	F	VF	Unc
Smc 34	ND	Brass	19mm	—	15.00	—	—

As last, but 1/2 / REAL / 1/2.

SANTA ELENA

Rulau	Date	Metal	Size	VG	F	VF	Unc
Smc 37	ND	Copper	Rect 28x18mm	30.00	40.00	—	—

SANTA ELENA / TUMBADOR. Rv: * / UNA / TAREA / (tiny) L. H. MOISE S.F. (Schrotter 83; Eklund 953)

Rulau	Date	Metal	Size	VG	F	VF	Unc
Smc 38	ND	Aluminum	Rect 27x18mm	10.00	20.00	—	—

As last. (Clark 403)

Rulau	Date	Metal	Size	VG	F	VF	Unc
Smc 39	ND	Copper	Oct 22.5mm	—	15.00	30.00	—

SANTA ELENA / -*- / TUMBADOR / (tiny) MOISE S. F. Rv: DOS / (ornament) / REALES. (Clark 402; Eklund 952)

Rulau	Date	Metal	Size	VG	F	VF	Unc
Smc 40	ND	Aluminum	21mm	—	5.00	8.00	15.00

As last, but UN / REAL. (Clark 401; Eklund 952a)

UNA TAREA = One Task. A tarea was a task performed by a worker, formerly based on measurement or by a specified period of time. It can also indicate one day's labor.

El Tumbador = The Forest Clearer.

Schrotter and other European writers assigned these pieces to Mexico, but Clark straightened this out in the 1970's after consulting a roster of Guatemala coffee producers and devoting much effort toward geographical research.

Esmeralda
ENRIQUE HERMAN

Rulau	Date	Metal	Size	VG	F	VF	Unc
Smc43	ND	Brass	28mm	6.00	10.00	15.00	—

ENRIQUE HERMAN / 2 / *. Rv: ESMERALDA / 2 / * COSTA CUCA *. (Weyl 1719; Clark 179; Eklund 849)

Rulau	Date	Metal	Size	VG	F	VF	Unc
Smc 44	ND	Copper	23mm	—	—	15.00	20.00

As last, but 1. (Weyl 1720; Eklund 848; Randel coll.)

Rulau	Date	Metal	Size	VG	F	VF	Unc
Smc 45	ND	Brass	16mm	—	—	15.00	20.00

As last, but 1/4. (Randel coll.; Eklund 846; Weyl 1720)

This hacienda also issued copper 1/2 real, 18mm.

La Reforma
CAFETAL EL BALUARTE

Rulau	Date	Metal	Size	VG	F	VF	Unc
Smc 48	ND	Brass	22mm	—	—	—	—

CAFETAL EL BALUARTE. Rv: 3 REALES. (Weyl 1705; Eklund 815; Clark 26)

Rulau	Date	Metal	Size	VG	F	VF	Unc
Smc 49	ND	Brass	19mm	—	—	—	—

As last, but 1 REAL. (Weyl 1705; Eklund 814; Clark 24)

In the Costa de Cucho coffee-growing region.

La Ygualdad
ALVARO SIMEON MUNOZ

Rulau	Date	Metal	Size	VG	F	VF	Unc
Smc 52	ND	Copper	20mm	3.00	5.00	9.00	—

ALVARO SIMEON / 2 / * MUNOZ *. Rv: CENTRO AMERICA / LA / * YGUALDAD *. (Weyl 1741; Eklund 895; Clark 470)

Rulau	Date	Metal	Size	VG	F	VF	Unc
Smc 53	ND	Brass	20mm	—	—	—	—

As last, but 1 (real). (Weyl 1741; Eklund 893; Clark 469)

Nuevo Progresso
FINCA J. C.
(Jesus de Candelaria)

Rulau	Date	Metal	Size	VG	F	VF	Unc
Smc 55	ND	Copper	**	—	10.00	15.00	—

** Diamond-shaped flan, 42x25mm. * FINCA * / J. C. Rv: Blank. (Clark 191)

This token has been attributed to the finca (plantation) of Jesus de Candelaria at Nuevo Progresso.

Ocos
J. L.
(J. Luria)

Rulau	Date	Metal	Size	VG	F	VF	Unc
Smc 58	ND	Copper	Oct 15x18mm	—	—	100.	—

J. L. / 1/2 REAL / OCOS. Rv: Blank. (Ulex 2095; Eklund 915)

Ocos is a Pacific Ocean port just inside Guatemala's frontier with Mexico.

San Cristobal Cucho
LAS CASAS CUCHO

Rulau	Date	Metal	Size	VG	F	VF	Unc
Smc 61	(1893-97)	Brass	18mm	—	—	8.00	—

Quetzal on pillar, tiny L. H. MOISE S.F. below. Rv: LAS CASAS / 1 / CUCHO. (Clark 68)

San Pablo
CAFETAL CHIBUJ

Rulau	Date	Metal	Size	VG	F	VF	Unc
Smc 64	ND	Brass	19mm	—	—	Scarce	—

CAFETAL CHIBUJ / SAN PABLO / SAN MARCOS. Rv: 1 REAL. (Weyl 1703; Eklund 811; Clark 74)

Cafetal Chibuj was owned by Eusebio M. Rosal.

PORFIRIO DE LEON
Finca Valdemar

Rulau	Date	Metal	Size	VG	F	VF	Unc
Smc 67	ND	Copper	21mm	—	—	—	—

PORFIRIO DE LEON / SAN PABLO / SAN MARCOS. Rv: 2 REALES. (Weyl 1768; Eklund 960; Clark 115)

Rulau	Date	Metal	Size	VG	F	VF	Unc
Smc 68	ND	Brass	21mm	—	—	—	—

As last, but 1 REAL. (Eklund 959; Clark 114)

Struck for De Leon's Finca Valdemar.

CAFETAL VENEZUELA

Rulau	Date	Metal	Size	VG	F	VF	Unc
Smc 70	ND	Copper	22mm	—	—	—	—

CAFETAL VENEZUELA/ 1 / * COSTA DE CUCHO *. Rv: 1. (W. 1711; Eklund 824; Clark 453)

Rulau	Date	Metal	Size	VG	F	VF	Unc
Smc 71	ND	Brass	22mm	—	—	—	—

As last. (W. 1712; Eklund 824; Clark 455)

Rulau	Date	Metal	Size	VG	F	VF	Unc
Smc 72	ND	Copper	18mm	—	—	—	—

As last, but 1/2 REAL. (Weyl 1711; Eklund 823; Clark 452)

Rulau	Date	Metal	Size	VG	F	VF	Unc
Smc 73	ND	Brass	18mm	—	—	—	—

As last. (W. 1712; Clark 454)

SANTA ROSA DEPARTMENT

Pueblo Nuevo Vinos
J. ZENON POSADAS
Hacienda El Ciprez

Rulau	Date	Metal	Size	VG	F	VF	Unc
SR 3	1887	Brass	23mm	7.00	12.00	18.00	—

J. ZENON POSADAS / -.- / 1887 / -.- / * UN REAL *. Rv: HACIENDA / -.- / EL / CIPREZ / -.- / CORTE DE CAFE. Counterstamped slanting Z P on reverse. Plain edge. (Clark 86)

Santa Cruz Naranjo
J. A.
Agua Blanca

Rulau	Date	Metal	Size	VG	F	VF	Unc
SR 6	ND	Brass	Oct 31mm	—	—	—	—

J.A. Rv: 2 R. (Weyl 1699; Eklund 803)

Rulau	Date	Metal	Size	VG	F	VF	Unc
SR 7	ND	Brass	Oct 22mm	—	—	—	—

As last, but 1. (Eklund 804)

Rulau	Date	Metal	Size	VG	F	VF	Unc
SR 8	ND	Brass	Oct 16mm	—	—	—	—

As last, but 1/4. (W. 1699; Eklund 803)

J. A. = Jose Aguiar.

SOLOLA DEPARTMENT

RODRIGO GARAVITO
Finca "La Patria"

Rulau	Date	Metal	Size	VG	F	VF	Unc
Sll1	(1893-97)	Brass	25mm	—	—	9.50	

FINCA / -*- / "LA PATRIA" / -*- / DEP. DE SOLOLA. / (tiny) L. H. MOISE. S.F. Rv: RODRIGO GARA-VITO / (ornament). Obverse ctsp shield outline. Reverse ctsp F with 5-point star. (Clark 306)

SUCHITEPEQUEZ DEPARTMENT

Chicacao
JUAN APARICIO E HIJOS
Los Castaños

Rulau	Date	Metal	Size	VG	F	VF	Unc
Stz 3	ND	Brass	21mm	3.00	4.50	6.00	11.00

LOS CASTAÑOS (ornament) / PAMAXAN / (ornament) / JUAN APARICIO E HIJOS. Rv: 1/2 / REAL within laurel wreath. At bottom: (tiny) L. H. Moise S.F. Plain edge. (Clark 69)

THEILHEIMER Y MATHIEU
Las Harmonias

Rulau	Date	Metal	Size	VG	F	VF	Unc
Stz 6	ND	CN/Zinc	21mm	—	—	15.00	

THEILHEIMER Y MATHIEU / LAS / HARMONIAS / CHICACAO / * GUATEMALA *. Rv: 1 / REAL. (Weyl 1734; Eklund 878; Clark 19)

Stz 7	ND	CN/Zinc	21mm	—	—	17.50	

As last, but 2 / REALES.

Filadelfia
FLORENCIO CALDERON

Rulau	Date	Metal	Size	VG	F	VF	Unc
Stz 10	ND	GS	21mm	—	—	20.00	

FLORENCIO CALDERON. FILADELFIA PAMAXAN. 2 REALES. (W. 1721; U. 2093; Eklund 850; Jason I-62)

Jocopilas
CHOCOLA
PLANTAGEN-GESELL.

Rulau	Date	Metal	Size	VG	F	VF	Unc
Stz 13	ND	Copper	10-sided 26mm	10.00	12.50	18.00	—

CHOCOLA PLANTAGEN-GESELLSCHAFT / HAM-BURG /. Rv: VALE POR / LA FAENA . (Weyl 1713; Clark 82)

La Faena = One day's work.

Stz 15	ND	Copper	25.5mm	10.00	15.00	20.00	—

Obverse as last. Rv: VALE POR / UN REAL / MAIZ. (value one real of corn. (W. 1714; Clark 81)

Stz 17	ND	Copper	20mm	10.00	15.00	20.00	—

Obverse as last. Rv: VALE POR / UN REAL / DE CARNE. (value one real of meat. (W. 1715; Clark 83)

This plantation used value-systems quite different from other Guatemalan haciendas, probably due to its foreign ownership. The maiz and carne tokens apparently were exchangeable only at the hacienda store.

This plantation was confiscated by the government as an enemy asset after Guatemala entered World War I. In the 1970's it still belonged to the government.

Eklund reported the Faena token was for ship board work.

HACIENDA CHOCOLA

Rulau	Date	Metal	Size	VG	F	VF	Unc
Stz 19	ND	Brass	29mm	2.50	4.00	6.50	—

HACIENDA / CHOCOLA. Rv: VALE POR / 1 / * REAL *. Plain edge. (Clark 80; Jason 16-A)

Pamaxan
BALBINO DELEON

 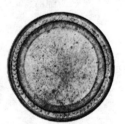

Rulau	Date	Metal	Size	VG	F	VF	Unc
Stz 22	(1893-97)	CN	29mm	—	—	15.00	25.00

BALBINO DELEON / * / PAMAXAN / * / BOLIVIA. / (tiny) L. H. MOISE. S.F. Rv: Blank. Incised beaded rim on each side. Plain edge. (Zaffern coll.; Eklund 2264)

Finca Bolivia.

ALBERTO FUHLROTT
Finca Madrid

Rulau	Date	Metal	Size	VG	F	VF	Unc
Stz 25	ND	Nic	40mm	—	8.50	15.00	35.00

1 / PESO in beaded central circle. Around: ALBERTO FUHLROTT FINCA MADRID PAMAXAN / *. Rv: 1 / PESO. Plain edge. (Clark 140)

Rulau	Date	Metal	Size	VG	F	VF	Unc
Stz 27	ND	Nic	20mm	—	5.00	10.00	20.00

As last, but 1 / REAL. Plain edge. (Clark 139)

8 Reales = 1 Peso.

LAUREANO URRUTIA
Santa Ynes

Rulau	Date	Metal	Size	VG	F	VF	Unc
Stz 29	(1893-97)	Brass	24mm	—	—	15.00	22.50

LAUREANO URRUTIA / (four stars around radiant cross) / * / (tiny) L. H. MOISE S.F. Rv: SANTA YNES / 2 / * PAMAXAN *. Plain edge. (Zaffern coll.)

Pueblo Nuevo
ASTURIAS

Rulau	Date	Metal	Size	VG	F	VF	Unc
Stz 32	ND	Brass	26mm	—	6.50	14.00	—

(Ornament) / ASTURIAS / (ornament). Rv: TRA-BAJOS / (Radiant star) / * TAREA *. Plain edge. (Clark 20)

San Antonio
DIEGO L. ARIZA
Finca El Arco

Rulau	Date	Metal	Size	VG	F	VF	Unc
Stz 35	ND	CN	20mm	4.00	6.50	11.00	—

FINCA / EL ARCO / PAMAXAN. Rv: DIEGO L. ARIZA / 1 / CAJA. Plain edge. (Clark 11)

ROSENDO DE LEON
Basilea

Rulau	Date	Metal	Size	VG	F	VF	Unc
Stz 38	ND	Brass	23.5mm	5.00	7.50	10.00	

ROSENDO DE LEON / (flowers in cross form) / * BASILEA *. Rv: 1/2 / CAJA within wreath. Plain edge (Clark 34)

Rulau	Date	Metal	Size	VG	F	VF	Unc
Stz 40	ND	CN	23mm	5.00	7.50	10.00	—

Flowers in cross form at center, BASILEA / SUCHITE-PEQUEZ / (tiny) MOISE S.F. around. Rv: MEDIA / -+- / CAJA. Plain edge. (Clark 35)

Rulau	Date	Metal	Size	VG	F	VF	Unc
Stz 41	ND	Brass	28mm	6.00	9.00	12.00	—

As last, but UNA / CAJA. (Clark 36)

JOSE MA. MOTA
Finca Bella Isla

Rulau	Date	Metal	Size	VG	F	VF	Unc
Stz 44	ND	CN	24mm	3.00	4.50	7.00	15.00

JOSE Ma. MOTA / (ornament) / BELLA ISLA. Rv: SAN ANTONIO / (divisor sign) / SUCHITEPEQUEZ. Plain edge. (Clark 41)

Rulau	Date	Metal	Size	VG	F	VF	Unc
Stz 45	ND	CN	21mm	3.00	4.50	7.00	15.00

As last, but smaller. (Clark 40)

This finca was owned by in-laws of President Arana of Guatemala.

GIRONDINA
San Francisco Zapotitlan

Rulau	Date	Metal	Size	VG	F	VF	Unc
Stz 50	ND	CN	27.5mm	4.00	6.00	11.00	20.00

(Radiant star) / GIRONDINA / (ornament) / GUATE-MALA, / x C.A. x. Rv: Large 1 (shaded) / TAREA / (tiny) KLINKNER & CO. S.F. Plain edge. (Zaffern coll.; Clark N/L)

Rulau	Date	Metal	Size	VG	F	VF	Unc
Stz 51	ND	CN	20mm	3.00	5.00	10.00	18.00

As last, but 1/4 / TAREA. (Clark 147)

Struck before 1897, when Moise and Klinkner diecutting firms merged. Probably struck in the 1890's.

Santo Tomas La Union
S. J. Y CIA
Finca La Primavera

Rulau	Date	Metal	Size	VG	F	VF	Unc
Stz 54	ND	CN	27.5mm	—	—	7.50	—

S. J. y CIA / (ornament). Rv: FINCA / * / LA PRIMA-VERA / * / XOLHUITZ. Plain edge. (Clark 325; Jason 72-A)

Uncertain
ARCADIA M. DE LEON

Rulau	Date	Metal	Size	VG	F	VF	Unc
Stz 57	ND	Brass	Scal				
			28mm	3.00	5.00	7.00	—

ARCADIA M. DE LEON / (cross-shaped ornament) / SUCHITEPEQUEZ. Rv: DOS / -*- / REALES. Plain edge. (Clark 111)

Stz 59	ND	Brass	34mm	4.75	7.00	9.00	—

ARCADIA M. DE LEON / (floreate ornament) / + SUCHITEPEQUEZ +. Rv: CUATRO / (ornament) / + REALES +. Plain edge. (Clark 112)

Stz 60	ND	Brass	Oct 19mm	—	—	7.00	12.00

As last, but MEDIO / * / REAL. (Zaffern coll.; Eklund 2233)

ZACAPA DEPARTMENT

El Amparo
VICTOR MATHEU Z.

Rulau	Date	Metal	Size	VG	F	VF	Unc
Zcp 3	(1893-97)	Brass	Oct 30.5mm	7.50	12.50	—	—

VICTOR MATHEU Z. * / (ornament) / ctsp R. Rv: ******* / 3 / EL AMPARO / (tiny) L. H. MOISE. S.F. This is usually ctsp M / M / M on reverse.

Zcp 4	(1893-97)	Aluminum	Pentag				
			23mm	—	—	—	—

Similar, but 1. (Eklund 2229)

RICARDO VILLAFRANCA

Rulau	Date	Metal	Size	VG	F	VF	Unc
Zcp 7	ND	Bronze	22mm	—	16.00	—	—

Phoenix rising from ashes. Around: FINCA "VILLA-FRANCA" / DPO. DE ZACAPA. Rv: RICARDO VIL-LAFRANCA / 1 / REAL / * DPO. DE IZABAL *.

Zcp 8	ND	Bronze	22mm	—	15.00	—	—

As last, but 1/2 / REAL. Plain edge.

Used in Zacapa and Izabal departments.

UNCERTAIN LOCALE

El Paraiso
LUIS AGUILAR

Rulau	Date	Metal	Size	VG	F	VF	Unc
Gma 1	ND	Brass	21mm	—	—	—	—

LUIS AGUILAR. EL PARAISO. 2 REALES. (Weyl 1717; Clark 299; Eklund 838)

Gma 2	ND	Copper	21mm	7.50	—	—	—

As last, but 1 REAL. (W. 1717; Clark 298; Eklund 837)

Santa Sofia
F. ALBUREZ

Rulau	Date	Metal	Size	VG	F	VF	Unc
Gma 4	(1893-97)	Brass	29mm	3.50	6.00	10.00	—

SANTA SOFIA / * / BUENA / * / ESPERANZA. Rv: F. ALBUREZ / Large 1 / **** / (tiny) L. H. MOISE S.F. (Clark 411; Eklund 2176)

Gma 5	(1893-97)	Brass	25mm	3.00	5.50	9.00	—

As last, but 1/2. (Clark 410)

Gma 6	(1893-97)	Brass	21mm	3.00	5.50	9.00	—

As last, but 1/4 (real). (Clark 409)

This issue of tokens is found heavily mutilated — counterstamped F-in-star outline on obverse and shield outline on reverse, and sometimes hole-cancelled as well. The illustrations are of typical specimens. Prices are for mutilated specimens; perfect specimens would be worth at least double.

JUAN AMBROSY
Finca Colombia

Rulau	Date	Metal	Size	VG	F	VF	Unc
Gma 8	ND	Brass	20mm	—	—	—	Scarce

JUAN AMBROSY. / COLOMBIA. Rv: 1 REAL. (Weyl 1716; Eklund 832; Clark 91)

This issuer also used brass 1/2 real, 18mm, and 1/4 real, 15mm tokens.

JUAN APARICIO
Finca Palmira

Rulau	Date	Metal	Size	VG	F	VF	Unc
Gma 10	ND	Brass	21mm	—	—	8.50	—

* / APARICIO / -.- / "PALMIRA" / -*-. Rv: 1/2 / REAL within a wreath. Reeded edge. (Clark 291; Rulau coll.)

Gma 11	ND	Brass	19mm	—	—	8.50	—

FINCA PALMIRA / Tree. Rv: JUAN APARICIO / 1/2 / REAL / *. (Clark 292)

Gma 12	ND	Brass	22mm	—	4.00	6.50	—

As last, but UN / REAL. (Clark 293)

Gma 14	ND	Brass	24mm	—	—	8.50	—

* APARICIO / FINCA / "PALMIRA" / *. Rv: DOS / REALES within wreath. Reeded edge. (Clark 294; Jason 62-F)

Gma 16	ND	Brass	25.5mm	—	—	10.00	—

Same as last, but ctsp E P on obverse and P R on reverse. The stamping is crude and has flattened the token to a wider diameter. (Clark 295)

NOTE: Counterstamps are frequent on this series. The first type of 1/2 real (21mm) is known with large C counterstamped on obverse. The second 1/2 real (19mm) occurs with triangular mark counterstamped over the numeral on obverse.

Other known stamps: G, J, G and triangle, Li monogram, 7.

JUAN APARICIO E HIJOS
Cafetal Chile

Rulau	Date	Metal	Size	VG	F	VF	Unc
Gma 18	ND	Brass	29mm	3.00	5.00	7.00	15.00

CAFETAL CHILE / -.- / COSTA / GRANDE / -.- / JUAN APARICIO E HIJOS. Rv: 1 / REAL within oak wreath. Plain edge. (Clark 76)

Gma 19	ND	Brass	31mm	4.50	6.50	9.00	18.00

As last, but 2 / REALES. (Clark 77)

ARMENIA

Rulau	Date	Metal	Size	VG	F	VF	Unc
Gma 21	ND	CN	29mm	—	18.50	—	—

ARMENIA / 2 / * REALES *. Rv: Same as obverse. Beaded border on each side.

Rulau	Date	Metal	Size	VG	F	VF	Unc
Gma 22	ND	Brass	22mm	—	15.00	—	—

ARMENIA / 1 / * REAL *. Rv: Same as obverse. (Weyl 1702; Eklund 810; Clark 18)

Gma 23	ND	Brass	18mm	—	15.00	—	—

As last, but 1/2 / * REAL *. (Eklund 809; Clark 17)

Hacienda Armenia.

ROSENDO AUYON
Finca Sta. Elisa

Rulau	Date	Metal	Size	VG	F	VF	Unc
Gma 25	(1893-97)	Brass	28.5mm	—	—	10.00	15.00

FINCA / -*- / Sta/ ELISA / R.A. / COSTA CUCA. Rv: Large 2 (pebbled) within wreath / (tiny) L. H. MOISE S. F. Plain edge. (Zaffern coll.; Clark N/L)

Gma 27	ND	Brass	28mm				

ROSENDO AUYON / (ornament) / SANTA ELISA / (ornaments). Rv: 2 / REALES within wreath. Plain edge. (Clark 405)

M. L. B.
Finca El Pensamiento

Rulau	Date	Metal	Size	VG	F	VF	Unc
Gma 30	1886	Brass	20mm	—	—	15.00	—

Palm tree. Around: PENSAMIENTO / FINCA. Star ctsp. Rv: (Wreath) / M. L. B. / 1886. Crossed hatchets ctsp. (Clark 309; Eklund 916)

Gma 32	ND	Brass	27mm	—	—	25.00	—

Palm tree. Around: EL PENSAMIENTO / .*. Star ctsp. Rv: (Wreath) / M. L. B. / * / (wreath). Crossed hatchets ctsp. (Clark 311)

Gma 33	ND	Brass	20mm	—	—	15.00	—

Similar to last. (Clark 310)

M. L. B. = Manuel L. Barrillas.

LAUREANO BERMUDEZ

Rulau	Date	Metal	Size	VG	F	VF	Unc
Gma 25	ND	Brass	29mm	6.00	8.50	11.00	—

LAUREANO BERMUDEZ / 1/2 / 1 Caja / SAN / CAYETANO / (illegible line). Rv: Large incused letter C. Plain edge. (Clark 44; Jason 91-A)

BERTHOLIN HS.

Rulau	Date	Metal	Size	VG	F	VF	Unc
Gma 37	ND	Brass	21mm	—	—	10.00	—

BERTHOLIN HS. / S. PEDRO / 1/2. (Ulex 2088; Eklund 864)

Miramar
O. BLEULER & CA.

Rulau	Date	Metal	Size	F	VF	EF	Unc
Gma 40	ND	Brass	24mm	—	10.00	12.00	16.00

2 / * / 0. BLEULER & Ca-. Rv: 2 / MIRAMAR / -.-. (Weyl 1743; Eklund 904)

Gma 41	ND	Copper	24mm	—	10.00	12.00	16.00

As last, but 1. (Weyl 1744; Eklund 903; Rulau coll.)

Gma 42	ND	Brass	20mm	—	10.00	12.00	16.00

As last, but 1/2.

Gma 43	ND	Copper	18mm	—	10.00	12.00	16.00

As last, but 1/4.

Also in this series are 1/2 real copper, 20mm, and 1/4 real brass, 18mm. All struck in Europe, along with other Bleuler tokens for other haciendas.

Morelia
O. BLEULER & CO.

Rulau	Date	Metal	Size	F	VF	EF	Unc
Gma 45	ND	Brass	24mm	—	10.00	12.00	16.00

O. BLEULER & Co= / 1 / *. Rv: 1 / MORELIA / -.-. Plain edge. (Weyl 1746; Eklund 907; Clark 273; Jason 57-B)

Rulau	Date	Metal	Size	F	VF	EF	Unc
Gma 46	ND	Copper	20mm	—	10.00	12.00	16.00

As last, but 1/2. (Weyl 1745)

Gma 47	ND	Brass	20mm	—	10.00	12.00	16.00

As last, but in brass. (Weyl 1746; Eklund 906; Clark 272)

Gma 48	ND	Brass	18mm	—	10.00	12.00	16.00

As last, but 1/4. (Weyl 1746)

Also in this series is 1/4 real copper, 18mm. As all Bleuler pieces, these were struck in Europe in the 1890's or earlier. Also struck in Europe at the same time were tokens of Boy, Koch Hagmann, etc.

San Diego
O. BLEULER & CO.

Rulau	Date	Metal	Size	F	VF	EF	Unc
Gma 50	ND	Copper	27mm	—	—	—	—

O. BLEULER & CO. / 3 / *. Rv: 3 / SAN DIEGO / ***. (Weyl 1755; Eklund 987)

Gma 51	ND	Copper	24mm	—	—	—	—

As last, but 1 (real). (W. 1755; Eklund 927)

Gma 52	ND	Copper	20mm	—	—	—	—

As last, but 1/2 (real). W. 1755; Eklund 926)

Gma 53	ND	Copper	18mm	—	—	—	—

As last, but 1/4. (W. 1755; Eklund 925)

This series was also issued in Brass (Weyl 1756-57). Costa Cuca region.

FINCA DE LAS NUBES
(G. Boy)

Rulau	Date	Metal	Size	VG	F	VF	Unc
Gma 55	ND	Brass	25mm	—	—	—	—

Crescent and star. Around: FINCA DE LAS NUBES. Rv: VALE POR / 2 / REALES. (Weyl 1736; Eklund 886; Clark 285)

Gma 56	ND	Brass	20mm	—	—	—	Rare

Similar, but 1 / REAL. (W. 1737; Clark 286)

Gma 57	ND	Brass	18mm	—	—	14.00	—

Similar, but 1/4 / DE REAL. (W. 1738; Clark 287)

Costa Grande region.

San Jsidro
G. BOY

Rulau	Date	Metal	Size	F	VF	EF	Unc
Gma 60	ND	Brass	30mm	—	—	Rare	—

G. BOY / SAN JSIDRO / * COSTA GRANDE / $1. Rv: Same as obverse. (Weyl 1761; Eklund 938; Clark 52)

Rulau	Date	Metal	Size	F	VF	EF	Unc
Gma 61	ND	Brass	25mm	—	—	—	—
		As last, but 2 REALES. (W. 1762)					
Gma 62	ND	Brass	20mm	—	—	—	—
		As last, but 1 REAL. (W. 1763)					
Gma 63	ND	Brass	18mm	—	—	—	20.00
		As last, but 1/4 REAL. (Weyl 1763)					

Prober calls the first token above a "Dolar". Costa Grande.

Zambo
G. BOY

Rulau	Date	Metal	Size	F	VF	EF	Unc
Gma 65	ND	Brass	30mm	—	—	Rare	—
		ZAMBO / G. BOY / COSTA GRANDE. Rv: 1 DOLAR. (Weyl 1770; Eklund 966; Clark 471)					
Gma 66	ND	Brass	25mm	—	—	—	—
		As last, but 2 REALES. (W. 1771)					
Gma 67	ND	Brass	20mm	—	—	—	—
		As last, but 1 REAL.					
Gma 68	ND	Brass	18mm	—	—	—	—
		As last, but 1/4 REAL. (Weyl 1771)					

Costa Grande region.

BUSTAMANTE

Rulau	Date	Metal	Size	VG	F	VF	Unc
Gma 70	ND	Copper	25mm	—	—	15.00	—
		BUSTAMANTE. Rv: 1 / PESO / -.-. Plain edge. (Clark 53)					

Santa Margarita
H. C.

Rulau	Date	Metal	Size	VG	F	VF	Unc
Gma 72	ND	Brass	Oct 24mm	—	7.00	11.50	—
		H . C within octagonal border. Rv: Sta. / MARGARITA within octagonal border. Plain edge. (Clark 413)					

P. C. C.

Rulau	Date	Metal	Size	VG	F	VF	Unc
Gma 74	1895	Aluminum	20mm	—	—	35.00	50.00
		Volcano. Above: P. C. C. 1895. Rv: (tiny) L. H. MOISE. S.F. (Eklund 2153)					

LAS CAMELIAS

Rulau	Date	Metal	Size	VG	F	VF	Unc
Gma 76	(1893-97)	Aluminum	xx	—	—	17.50	25.00
		xx Triangular flan, 29x32mm. LAS / CAMELIAS. Rv: 1 / DIA / (tiny) L. H. MOISE. S.F. Wide pebbled border on each side. (Zaffern coll.; Eklund 2138)					
Gma 77	(1893-97)	Copper	xx	—	—	—	Rare
		As last. Pattern by Moise.					
Gma 79	ND	Aluminum	Rect 48x15mm	—	—	—	—
		LAS CAMELIAS. Rv: VALE UNA TAREA / (tiny) L. H. MOISE S.F. (Eklund 2139)					
Gma 80	ND	Copper	Rect 48x15mm	—	—	—	Rare
		As last. Pattern by Moise.					

Some collectors attribute these pieces to Mexico.

COMPAÑIA HAMBURGUESA
DE PLANTACIONES
San Andres Osuna Estate

Rulau	Date	Metal	Size	VG	F	VF	Unc
Gma 90	ND	Brass	30mm	3.00	4.50	6.00	15.00
		Inscription in two concentric circles around beaded central circle: COMPAÑIA HAMBURGUESA DE PLANTACIONES EN GUATEMALA * / "OSUNA ROCHELA" SAN ANDRES-OSUNA. within circle: 2. Rv: Same as obverse. Plain edge. (Clark 164; Rulau coll.)					
Gma 91	ND	Brass	Hexag 30mm	—	—	6.00	15.00
		As last, but T (for Tarea) at center. (Clark 165)					
Gma 92	ND	Brass	Hexag 30mm	—	—	6.00	15.00
		As last, but R at center. (Clark 166)					
Gma 93	ND	Brass	30mm	—	—	10.00	20.00
		As last, but 8 (for 8 reales) at center.					

Rulau	Date	Metal	Size	VG	F	VF	Unc
Gma 95	ND	Brass	Oct 30mm	—	—	6.00	15.00
		As last, but CAPORAL (Foreman) at center. (Clark 167; Rulau coll.)					

Rulau	Date	Metal	Size	VG	F	VF	Unc
Gma 96	ND	Brass	Oct 25mm	—	—	6.00	15.00
		As last, but MAIS (corn) at center. (Clark 168)					
Gma 97	ND	Brass	Oct 25mm	—	—	25.00	—
		As last (MAIS), but ctsp 3 over MAIS (for 3 reales). (Rulau coll.)					
Gma 98	ND	Brass	Hexag 25mm	—	—	8.00	17.00
		As last, but LENA (firewood) at center. (Clark 169)					

Numerals 2, 3, 8 = 2, 3 or 8 reales. T = Tarea (task).

La Rochela Estate

Rulau	Date	Metal	Size	VG	F	VF	Unc
Gma 100	(1895)	Zinc	30mm	—	—	11.00	—
		Similar to last series, but innermost of the concentric legends reads: "OSUNA ROCHELA" LA ROCHELA. Large 2 (for 2 reales) in center. Reeded edge. (Clark 170)					
Gma 101	(1895)	Zinc	30mm	—	—	20.00	—
		As last, but 8 (for 8 reales) in center. (Clark 171; Rulau coll.)					

Rulau	Date	Metal	Size	VG	F	VF	Unc
Gma 102	ND	Zinc	Hexag 30.5mm	—	—	6.00 11.00	—
		As last, but T (for Tarea) in center. (Clark 172; Rulau coll.)					
Gma 103	ND	Zinc	Hexag 25mm	—	—	6.00 11.00	—
		As last, smaller. Reeded edge. (Clark 173; Rulau coll.)					
Gma 104	ND	Zinc	Hexag 30mm	—	—	11.00	—
		As last, but R in center. (Clark 174; Rulau coll.)					
Gma 105	ND	Zinc	Hexag 25mm	—	—	11.00	—
		As last, but smaller. Reeded edge. (Clark 175)					
Gma 106	ND	Zinc	Hexag 25mm	—	—	11.00	—
		As last, but large P in center. Reeded edge. (Clark 176; Rulau coll.)					
Gma 107	ND	Zinc	Oct. 25mm	—	—	11.00	—
		As last, but FAINA (Overtime work) in center. (Clark 177; Rulau coll.)					

Rulau	Date	Metal	Size	VG	F	VF	Unc
Gma 108	ND	Zinc	Oct 25mm	—	—	11.00	—
		As last, but MAIS (Corn) in center. (Reeded edge. (Clark 178; Rulau coll.)					

Compañia Hamburguesa de Plantaciones en Guatemala = Hamburg Company of Plantations in Guatemala, a German firm with its offices in Hamburg in north Germany.

After Guatemala declared war on Germany in 1918, the company's assets in Guatemala were seized as enemy property. This is one of the most interesting of all Guatemalan token series, smybolizing as it does the extent of German penetration of Central America before World War I.

The zinc tokens are especially interesting. Each is made from a zinc blank which has been silvered (that is, a coating of silvery metal has been applied) before striking. Each zinc piece also has a reeded edge — even the hexagonal and octagonal tokens! Such metallic technology about 1895 indicates striking in Germany, possibly at the government's Hamburg Mint. We know of no other token series using silvered-zinc, reeded-edge blanks.

Despite considerable usage, the silvered-zinc tokens retain much of their original attractiveness. Dark zinc oxide spots appear where silvering has flaked off.

AVELINO DE LEON LOPEZ
Santa Rita Miramar

Rulau	Date	Metal	Size	VG	F	VF	Unc
Gma 111	ND	Copper	20mm	—	—	—	—
		SANTA RITA MIRAMAR / AVELINO DE LEON LOPEZ. Rv:2 REALES. (Weyl 1765; Eklund 94					
Gma 112	ND	Brass	20mm	—	—	—	—
		As last, but 1 1/2 REALES. (Weyl 1765)					

AVELINO DE LEON MUÑOZ
Tanenburgo

Rulau	Date	Metal	Size	VG	F	VF	Unc
Gma 114	ND	Copper	21mm	—	—	—	—
		AVELINO DE LEON MUÑOZ. TANENBURGO. 2 REALES. (Weyl 1767)					
Gma 115	ND	Copper	21mm	—	—	—	—
		As last, but 1 REAL.					

These tokens also exist in Brass.

ESTEBAN DELEON
Hacienda Belize ?

Rulau	Date	Metal	Size	VG	F	VF	Unc
Gma 117	(1893-97)	Brass	28mm	—	300.	—	—
		ESTEBAN . DELEON / (ornament) / . BELIZE ./ (tiny) L. H. MOISE. S.F. Rv: 3 / REALES. Beaded border on each side. (Christensen March 1973 sale, lot 726; *TAMS Journal* for Dec. 1972, pg. 247)					

This token is almost certainly Guatemalan in origin, not Belizean, despite its legend. A fine piece fetched $325 in 1973 because of the word BELIZE on it.

See Hacienda Armenia under Guatemala for very similar tokens. The real was not legal tender in Belize in the 1890's.

JUAN N. DE LEON

Rulau	Date	Metal	Size	VG	F	VF	Unc
Gma 119	(1893-97)	GS	29mm	—	7.50	11.00	13.00
		JUAN N. DELEON / * / PANAN / * / BARCELONA. / (tiny) L. H. MOISE. S.F. Rv: Blank. Incised beaded rim on each side. Plain edge. (Clark 113; Zaffern coll.)					

EL DELIRIO

Rulau	Date	Metal	Size	VG	F	VF	Unc
Gma 121	ND	Brass	25mm	—	—	9.00	—

Coffee bush. Rv: EL DELIRIO/ 25. Plain edge. (Clark N/L; Rulau coll.)

DOLORES

Rulau	Date	Metal	Size	VG	F	VF	Unc
Gma 123	ND	Brass	31mm	—	—	8.50	—

DOLORES. Rv: 2. Plain edge. (Clark 122)

FINCA DOLORES

Rulau	Date	Metal	Size	VG	F	VF	Unc
Gma 124	ND	Brass	26mm	—	—	6.00	—

FINCA DOLORES. Rv: 1. (Jason 27-A)

This piece occurs counterstamped 7 5.

La Asuncion
JUAN ESCOBAR

Rulau	Date	Metal	Size	VG	F	VF	Unc
Gma 126	ND	Copper	22mm	—	—	—	—

LA ASUNCION / JUAN ESCOBAR / COSTA CUCA. Rv: 1 REAL. (Weyl 1728; Eklund 870)

La Candelaria
MANUEL LOPEZ BARRIOS

Rulau	Date	Metal	Size	VG	F	VF	Unc
Gma 127	ND	Brass	Rect 26x31mm	—	—	—	—

2 / MANUEL LOPEZ BARRIOS. Rv: 2 / LA CANDE-LARIA. (Weyl 1729; Eklund 874; Clark 63)

| Gma 128 | ND | Brass | 23mm | — | — | — | — |

Similar, but round and * / 1 (real). Weyl 1730; Eklund 873; Clark 62)

| Gma 129 | ND | Brass | 20mm | — | — | — | — |

Similar, but 1/2 real. (Clark 61)

| Gma 130 | ND | Brass | 18mm | — | — | — | — |

Similar, but 1/4 real. (Weyl 1730; Eklund 871; Clark 60; Ulloa L12.1)

San Diego
FLORES HERMANOS

Rulau	Date	Metal	Size	VG	F	VF	Unc
Gma 132	ND	Copper	26mm	—	—	—	—

FLORES HERMANOS. REAL. (Weyl 1758)

| Gma 133 | ND | Brass | 26mm | — | — | — | — |

As last. (Weyl 1759)

| Gma 134 | ND | Copper | 21mm | — | — | — | — |

As last, but CENTAVO. (Weyl 1758)

| Gma 135 | ND | Brass | 21mm | — | — | — | — |

As last. (Weyl 1759)

Costa Cuca region.

ALBERTO FLORES
Guadalupe La Ceiba

Rulau	Date	Metal	Size	VG	F	VF	Unc
Gma 138	1886	Copper	24mm	—	—	15.00	25.00

Tree above 1886. Around: GUADALUPE LA CEIBA / * COSTA CUCA *. Rv: ALBERTO FLORES / 2 / REALES /. Repub. De Guat. (Weyl 1722; Randel coll.)

| Gma 139 | 1886 | Brass | 24mm | — | — | — | 25.00 |

As last. (Weyl 1724)

| Gma 140 | 1886 | Silver | 24mm | — | — | Rare | — |

As last. Weight 5.5 grams. Pattern for the regular issue tokens. (Weyl 1723; Ulloa 2094)

| Gma 141 | 1886 | Silver | 20mm | — | — | Rare | — |

Similar to last, but 1 REAL. Pattern for 1-real token which was not made. Weyl 1723; Randel coll.)

FURRER HASTEDT & CIA.

Rulau	Date	Metal	Size	VG	F	VF	Unc
Gma 143	1854	CN	22mm	—	—	30.00	—

Radiant sun above three volcanos, FURRER HAS-TEDT & CIA. around, 1854 in exergue. Rv: Large 2. Plain edge. (Clark 143; Jason 6-C)

Rulau	Date	Metal	Size	VG	F	VF	Unc
Gma 144	1854	CN	18mm	—	—	25.00	—
		As last, but 1. (Clark 142; Jason 6-B)					
Gma 145	1854	CN	13mm	—	—	35.00	—
		As last, but 1/2. (Clark 141; Jason 6-A)					

The three volcanos motif is borrowed from the Central American coinage design. These pieces occur with various counterstamps.

The date 1854 could be a date of issue or it could be a founding date for the Furrer Hastedt agribusiness. Most German immigrants in Guatemala arrived later than 1854.

Morelia
MATEO GOMES M.

Rulau	Date	Metal	Size	VG	F	VF	Unc
Gma 147	ND	Brass	25mm	—	—	—	—
		MATEO GOMES M. / (empty circle) / * MORELIA *. Rv: 2 REALES. Plain edge. (Clark 279)					
Gma 148	ND	Brass	23mm	—	—	—	—
		As last, but 1 / REAL. (Clark 278)					

Also see Mateo Gomes M. under Retalhuleu Dept. (Finca Santa Elvira.)

HACIENDA MODELA

Rulau	Date	Metal	Size	VG	F	VF	Unc
Gma 150	ND	Brass	24mm	—	10.00	—	—
		Plow right. Around: HACIENDA / MODELA. Rv: 1 / REAL / LARRAVE. Plain edge. (Clark 258)					
Gma 151	ND	Brass	19mm	—	—	—	—
		As last, but 1/2.					

HANSEAT. PLANTAGEN GES.

Rulau	Date	Metal	Size	VG	F	VF	Unc
Gma 153	ND	Brass	21.5mm	—	17.50	—	—
		*. HANSEAT. / PLANTAGEN / GES. / *. Rv: VIÑAS / 1 R. Plain edge.					

Rulau	Date	Metal	Size	VG	F	VF	Unc
Gma 154	ND	Brass	28mm	—	7.50	9.50	—
		VIÑAS / 2 R. Rv: Blank. (Clark 461)					

Hanseatische Plantagen Gesellschaft = Hanseatic Plantation Co.

HERRERA FAMILY HOLDINGS

The Herreras have been called "the wealthiest of all the Guatemala oligarchs." Followers of the dictator Justo Rufino Barrios (1873-85), they gained Catholic Church lands which had been confiscated, to become the nation's richest landowners, and built their agricultural empire on coffee and sugar.

By the mid-1960's. when Don Rafael Herrera dominated the plantation empire from posh Guatemala City offices, the Herreras were indeed the top landowning family in the country.

Don Manuel M. Herrera issued his first tokens in 1871 and adopted the bee (for its industriousness) as the family symbol. He had his attractive tokens made in Paris and in San Francisco.

Thus far we have cataloged nine separate token issues of the Herreras, for seven different estates.

Name on Token	Estate	Dates(s)
Manuel M. Herrera	Finca El Portal	1871
Manuel M. Herrera	Ingenio de Penavista	1871
Manuel Herrera Hijo	Finca La Rochela	1878
H. & Ca.	Finca La Rochela	1893-97
Herrera & Ca.	Finca El Potrero	1880's
Herrera y Ca.	Finca San Luis	?
H. y C.	La Soledad	Before 1899
Herrera y Chacon	San Andres Osuna	1878
Herrera & Ca.	San Andres Osuna	1880's

Two of the estates, La Rochela and San Andres Osuna, may have been sold or leased to a German firm, Compania Hamburguesa de Plantaciones, about the turn of the century.

MANUEL M. HERRERA
Ingenio de Penavista

Rulau	Date	Metal	Size	VG	F	VF	Unc
Gma 160	1871	Brass	Oct 20mm	12.00	20.00	—	—
		Bee. Around: INGENIO DE / PENAVISTA. Rv: MANUEL M. / 1871 / HERRERA. (Jason 34-A)					

MANUEL HERRERA HIJO
Finca La Rochela

Rulau	Date	Metal	Size	VG	F	VF	Unc
Gma 162	1878	Brass	Scal 27mm	—	10.00	20.00	—
		Bee within beaded circle. Around: MANUEL HERRERA HIJO / * 1878 *. Rv: 4 within beaded circle. Around: LA ROCHELA / ...***... Plain edge. (Clark 345)					
Gma 163	1878	Brass	Scal 24mm	—	10.00	20.00	—
		As last, but 2. (Clark 344)					

H. & CA.
Rochela

Rulau	Date	Metal	Size	VG	F	VF	Unc
Gma 165	(1893-97)	Brass	28.5mm	—	8.50	11.50	—
		H. & CA / (ornament) / * ROCHELA *. Rv: Within wreath: 4. At bottom: (tiny) L. H. MOISE. S.F. Plain edge. (Eklund 2159; Clark 343)					
Gma 166	(1893-97)	Brass	23mm	—	—	11.00	—
		As last, but 2 (reales). (Clark 342; Rulau coll.)					
Gma 167	(1893-97)	Brass	17mm	—	—	8.00	—
		As last, but 1 (real). (Clark 341)					

Herrera & Compania were successors to Manuel Herrera Son at Finca La Rochela.

HERRERA & CA.
Finca El Potrero

Rulau	Date	Metal	Size	VG	F	VF	Unc
Gma 169	(1880's)	Brass	25mm	6.00	—	15.00	—
		Plow right in beaded circle. Rv: * EL POTRERO * / 4 / (tiny) A. POPERT PARIS / HERRERA & CA. Plain edge.					
Gma 170	ND	Brass	23.5mm	8.00	—	17.50	—
		As last, but 2 (reales).					
Gma 171	ND	Brass	19mm	6.00	—	15.00	—
		As last, but 1 (real)					

HERRERA Y CA.
Finca San Luis

Rulau	Date	Metal	Size	VG	F	VF	Unc
Gma 173	ND	Bronze	26mm	—	—	20.00	—

HERRERA Y Ca. - FINCA / SAN LUIS. Rv: 2 REALES.

H. y C.
(Herrera y Compania)
La Soledad

Rulau	Date	Metal	Size	VG	F	VF	Unc
Gma 175	ND	Copper	28mm	—	—	—	—

H y C. LA SOLEDAD. 2 REALES. (Weyl 1739; Clark 431; Eklund 890)

| Gma 176 | ND | Copper | 18mm | — | — | — | — |

As last, but 1 REAL. (Weyl 1739; Clark 430; Eklund 889)

HERRERA Y CHACON
San Andres Osuna

Rulau	Date	Metal	Size	VG	F	VF	Unc
Gma 178	1878	Copper	27mm	—	—	20.00	—

Bee within beaded circle. Around: HERRERA Y CHACON / * 1878 *. Rv: In beaded circle: 4. Around: SAN ANDRES OSUNA / ...***... Plain edge (Clark 186)

| Gma 179 | 1878 | Copper | 23mm | — | — | 18.00 | — |

As last, but 2. (Clark 185)

HERRERA & CA.
San Andres Osuna

Rulau	Date	Metal	Size	VG	F	VF	Unc
Gma 181	(1880's)	Brass	Oct 28mm	—	—	20.00	—

Bee within beaded circle. Around: HERRERA & CA- / * / (tiny) A. POPERT PARIS. Rv: 6 in beaded circle. Around: SAN ANDRES / * OSUNA *. Plain edge. (Clark 184; Jason 85-D)

Rulau	Date	Metal	Size	VG	F	VF	Unc
Gma 182	(1880's)	Brass	Oct 25mm	—	—	20.00	—

As last, but 5. (Clark 183; Jason 85-C)

| Gma 183 | (1880's) | Brass | Oct 21.5mm | — | — | 33.00 | — |

As last, but 3. (Rulau coll.)

This set of tokens is quite scarce. The 3-reales token has never been reported before now.

FLORENCIO JUAREZ E HIJOS
Finca San Antonio La Union

Rulau	Date	Metal	Size	VG	F	VF	Unc
Gma 190	ND	CN	24.5mm	—	4.00	6.00	—

FINCA / SAN ANTONIO / LA UNION / COSTA CUCA. Rv: FLORENCIO JUAREZ E HIJOS / 2 / REALES. Plain edge. (Clark 366; Jason 87-B)

| Gma 191 | ND | CN | 20mm | — | — | 7.50 | — |

As last, but MEDIO / 1/2 / REAL. (Clark 365; Jason 87-A)

| Gma 193 | ND | Bronze | 25mm | — | — | — | — |

SAN ANTONIO LA UNION / COSTA / CUCA. Rv: MEDIO REAL. (Garretson report)

Costa Cuca region.

Miramar
KOCH, HAGMANN Y CA.

Rulau	Date	Metal	Size	VG	F	VF	Unc
Gma 195	ND	Brass	33mm	—	—	15.00	—

! / PESO / KOCH, HAGMANN Y CA. Rv: 1 / PESO / MIRAMAR. Plain edge. (Clark 254; Rulau coll.)

| Gma 196 | ND | Brass | 20mm | — | — | 8.50 | — |

KOCH, HAGMANN Y CA. / 1/4. Rv: 1/4 / MIRAMAR. (Clark 252)

Also reported is a 1/2, which may not exist.

Morelia
KOCH, HAGMANN & CO.

Rulau	Date	Metal	Size	VG	F	VF	Unc
Gma 198	ND	Brass	24mm	—	—	15.00	—

KOCH HAGMANN & CO. / 1 / (star). Rv: 1 / MORELIA / -.-. Plain edge. (Weyl 1747; Eklund 909; Clark 275; Rulau coll.)

| Gma 199 | ND | Brass | 20mm | — | — | 15.00 | — |

As last, but 1/2 (real). (Weyl 1747; Eklund 908; Rulau coll.)

San Diego
KOCH, HAGMANN & CO.

Rulau	Date	Metal	Size	VG	F	VF	Unc
Gma 201	ND	Brass	27mm	—	—	Scarce	—
		KOCH, HAGMANN & CO. 3 REALES. (Weyl 1760)					
Gma 202	ND	Brass	24mm	—	—	—	—
		As last, but 1 REAL.					
Gma 203	ND	Brass	19mm	—	—	—	—
		As last, but 1/4 REAL. (Weyl 1760)					

Costa Cuca.

KRAUSS SCHROEDER Y CA.

Rulau	Date	Metal	Size	VG	F	VF	Unc
Gma 206	ND	Brass	27.5mm	—	—	—	15.00
		KRAUSS, SHCROEDER Y Ca / 3 (in circle) / (6-pointed star). Rv: 3 / SAN DIEGO / ***. Plain edge.					
Gma 207	ND	Brass	20.5mm	—	7.00	—	—
		As last, but 1/2.					
Gma 208	ND	Brass	19.5mm	—	—	—	12.00
		As last, but 1/4.					

LA LIBERTAD

Rulau	Date	Metal	Size	VG	F	VF	Unc
Gma 210	ND	Brass	27.5mm	—	—	5.00	11.00
		(Ornament) / LA / LIBERTAD / (ornament). Rv: 2 / REALES. Plain edge. (Clark 205; Jason 41-B)					
Gma 211	ND	Brass	24mm	—	—	5.00	9.00
		As last, but 1 / REAL. (Clark 204; Jason 41-A)					

Other Guatemalan tokens of Finca La Libertad owned by Manuel L. Barillas, circa 1886-1900, may be connected. They are listed separately.

LA TRINIDAD

Rulau	Date	Metal	Size	VG	F	VF	Unc
Gma 213	ND	CN	28mm	—	12.50	—	—
		Bull's head left. Rv: LA TRINIDAD / P. (Clark 443)					
Gma 214	ND	CN	28mm	—	25.00	—	—
		As last, but the large P on reverse is retrograde! Error die. (Alpert 1980 report)					

LECHERIA HOLANDESA

Rulau	Date	Metal	Size	VG	F	VF	Unc
Gma 216	1900	Brass	17mm	3.50	5.00	7.00	—
		1900 within circular wreath. Around: LECHERIA HOLANDESA / *. Rv: 1/2. Plain edge. (Clark 189)					

Lecheria Holandesa = Dutch dairy.

M.A.M.
(Mariano A. Morales)
La Delicia

Rulau	Date	Metal	Size	VG	F	VF	Unc
Gma 218	ND	Brass	19mm	—	—	—	—
		M.A.M. 2 CORTES DE CAFE. (Weyl 1731; Clark 120)					
Gma 219	ND	Brass	19mm	—	—	—	—
		MARIANO A. MORALES. 1 TAREA. (Weyl 1732; Clark 119)					

CORTES DE CAFE = Cuttings of coffee. TAREA = Task.

Chiquila
P. M.

Rulau	Date	Metal	Size	VG	F	VF	Unc
Gma 221	ND	Brass	24mm	—	6.00	11.00	—
		Ornate monogram PM. Rv: CHIQUILA / 1 (on scrollwork) / GUATEMALA / C.A. Plain edge. (Clark 79)					

C.A. = Centro America (Central America)

JUAN MATHEU

Rulau	Date	Metal	Size	VG	F	VF	Unc
Gma 223	ND	Brass	22mm	—	—	10.00	—
		A plant. Rv: JUAN MATHEU / DE GUATEMALA / PLANTA DE NOPAL. (Ulex 2088; Eklund 866)					

LAS MERCEDES

Rulau	Date	Metal	Size	VG	F	VF	Unc
Gma 225	ND	Aluminum	Scal				
			29mm	—	—	12.00	—
		LAS MERCEDES / COSTA CUCA. Rv: Same as obverse. (All capital letters). (Clark 242.1)					

Rulau	Date	Metal	Size	VG	F	VF	Unc
Gma 226	ND	Aluminum	Sq 27mm	—	—	12.00	—
		As last (capital letters). (Clark 242)					
Gma 227	ND	Aluminum	Sq 27mm	—	—	12.00	—
		Las Mercedes / Costa Cuca (capital and lower case letters). Rv: Same as obverse. (Clark 241; Rulau coll.)					

Rulau	Date	Metal	Size	VG	F	VF	Unc
Gma 228	ND	Aluminum	Sq 18mm	—	—	10.00	—

As last (upper and lower case letters). (Clark 240)

SIMONA DE MERIDA
Cafetal Los Cipreses

Rulau	Date	Metal	Size	VG	F	VF	Unc
Gma 230	ND	Brass	19mm	—	—	—	—

SIMONA DE MERIDA. CAFETAL LOS CIPRESES. 1 REAL. (Weyl 1708)

Rulau	Date	Metal	Size	VG	F	VF	Unc
Gma 231	ND	Brass	13mm				

As last, but 1/2 REAL. (Weyl 1708; Eklund 819)

GENERAL M. SOTO
Cafetal Platanillo

Rulau	Date	Metal	Size	VG	F	VF	Unc
Gma 233	ND	Brass	19mm	—	—	—	—

GENERAL M. SOTO. CAFETAL PLATANILLO. 1 REAL. (Weyl 1709; Eklund 820; Clark 317)

There is a scarce variety with the hacienda name spelled PLATAUILLO. (Eklund 821)

F. SANCHEZ
Cafetal Siltepec

Rulau	Date	Metal	Size	VG	F	VF	Unc
Gma 234	ND	Brass	22mm	—	—	—	—

F. SANCHEZ. CAFETAL SILTEPEC. 1 REAL. (Weyl 1710; Eklund 822; Clark 427)

A. MERO
Finca Argentina

Rulau	Date	Metal	Size	VG	F	VF	Unc
Gma 236	(1890-97)	Aluminum	24.7mm	2.00	5.00	9.00	15.00

Quetzal perched on a column, wreath below. Along bottom: (tiny) KLINKNER & CO. S.F. Rv: A. MERO / VALE / 1 / *** CAJA *** / FINCA ARGENTINA. Plain edge. (Zaffern coll.; Clark 12)

Rulau	Date	Metal	Size	VG	F	VF	Unc
Gma 237	(1890-97)	Aluminum	24.7mm	3.00	6.00	13.00	20.00

As last, but 1 / TAREA. (Clark 13)

Rulau	Date	Metal	Size	VG	F	VF	Unc
Gma 238	(1890-97)	Aluminum	24.7mm	3.00	6.00	13.00	20.00

As last, but 1 / DIA. (Clark 14)

Caja = Box. Tarea = Task. Dia = Day.
The quetzal on a pillar is adopted from the coat of arms of Guatemala. There is also a 1/2 Caja aluminum, 17.5mm.

MAX MEYER

Rulau	Date	Metal	Size	VG	F	VF	Unc
Gma 240	ND	—	—mm	—	—	—	—

MAX MEYER. (Ulex 2088; Eklund 867)

Guatemala City?

MIRAMAR

Rulau	Date	Metal	Size	VG	F	VF	Unc
Gma 242	ND	Aluminum	41mm	—	—	15.00	—

4- leaf clover outline has P at center, and Z - A - G - A clockwise in each arm. Rv: 4 / PESOS / MIRAMAR. Plain edge. (Clark 251)

Rulau	Date	Metal	Size	VG	F	VF	Unc
Gma 243	ND	Aluminum	Scal 38mm	—	—	10.00	—

As last, but 2 / PESOS. (Clark 250)

Rulau	Date	Metal	Size	VG	F	VF	Unc
Gma 244	ND	Brass	Oval 29.5x20mm	—	4.00	6.50	—

MIRAMAR. Rv: Large 2. (Clark 249)

The brass 2-peso is known ctsp B or 2M and the aluminum 2-peso ctsp Arrow. No satisfactory explanation has yet been offered for the initials ZAPAG.

PASCUAL MONTERROSA
Finca Mujulia

Rulau	Date	Metal	Size	VG	F	VF	Unc
Gma 246	1895	Brass	29mm	—	—	20.00	30.00

FINCA MUJULIA / + / 1895 / + / * COSTA CUCA *. Rv: PASCUAL MONTERROSA / 1 / CAJON / * C.A. * / (tiny) L. H. MOISE. S.F. (See *TAMS Journal* for Aug. 1985, pages 134-135)

Costa Cuca was a coffee-growing region near the Pacific coast of Guatemala; the term is not used any longer. Cajon = Box (of about 25 pounds of coffee beans).

MANUEL MORALES T.
Finca Nueva Americana

Rulau	Date	Metal	Size	VG	F	VF	Unc
Gma 250	ND	Aluminum	4-Scal 28.5mm	—	—	15.00	20.00

MANUEL MORALES T / . FINCA . / * / NUEVA /
AMERICANA / .*. Rv: 1/2 / CAJA / (tiny) L. H.
MOISE S.F. (Zaffern coll.; Clark N/L)

MORELIA

Rulau	Date	Metal	Size	VG	F	VF	Unc
Gma 252	ND	Brass	Oct 27mm	6.50	9.00	15.00	20.00

* / MORELIA / -.-. Rv: 4. (Clark 270; Rulau coll.)

Rulau	Date	Metal	Size	VG	F	VF	Unc
Gma 253	ND	Brass	Oval 29x20mm	—	—	12.50	17.50

As last, but 2 (reales). (Clark 269; Rulau coll.)

Gma 254	ND	Brass	24mm	—	—	15.00	20.00

As last, but 1 (real). (Clark 268)

Gma 255	ND	Brass	20mm	—	—	12.50	17.50

As last, but 1/2 (real). (Clark 267)

Yodostan
LEANDRO MUÑOZ

Rulau	Date	Metal	Size	VG	F	VF	Unc
Gma 257	ND	Copper	21mm	—	—	Scarce	—

LEANDRO MUÑOZ / YODOSTAN. Rv: 2 REALES.
(Weyl 1769; Eklund 962; Clark 283)

Gma 258	ND	Copper	21mm	—	—	—	—

As last, but 1 REAL. (Eklund 961; Clark 282)

These tokens were also issued in Brass.

M. N.
Finca Asuncion

Rulau	Date	Metal	Size	VG	F	VF	Unc
Gma 260	ND	Brass	22mm	—	—	11.00	—

FINCA ASUNCION / M. N. / (wreath). Rv: Numeral
1, wreath below. Plain edge. (Clark 21)

R.O.
Cafetal Las Chicharras

Rulau	Date	Metal	Size	VG	F	VF	Unc
Gma 262	(1890's)	Brass	28.5mm	—	—	10.00	15.00

CAFETAL LAS CHICHARRAS / R. O. / *. Rv: Ornate
1 (pebbled) / CAJA within wreath. Below: (tiny) C. A.
KLINKNER & CO. Incised beaded rim on each side.
Plain edge. (Zaffern coll.; Clark N/L)

Gma 263	ND	Brass	23mm	5.00	7.50	10.00	—

CAFETAL LAS CHICHARRAS / R. O. / *. Rv: 1/2 /
CAJA within wreath. Signature along bottom edge.
(Clark 75)

San Diego
OCHAVADOS

Rulau	Date	Metal	Size	VG	F	VF	Unc
Gma 265	ND	Brass	31mm	—	—	—	—

OCHAVADOS. 4 REALES. (Weyl 1754)

Gma 266	ND	Brass	29mm	—	—	—	—

As last, but 2 REALES.

Gma 267	ND	Brass	Hexag 18mm	—	—	—	—

As last, but 1/2 REAL. (Weyl 1754)

Costa Cuca region.

MARIANO LOPEZ PACHECO
Finca San Antonio Morazan

Rulau	Date	Metal	Size	VG	F	VF	Unc
Gma 269	ND	CN	25mm	—	—	8.00	

FINCA / SAN ANTONIO / MORAZAN / COSTA
CUCA. Rv: MARIANO LOPEZ PACHECO / 1 /
TAREA. Plain edge. (Clark 367). This token occurs ctsp
4 4.

PEDRETTI Y TONEL
Cafetal de la Virgen Petapa

Rulau	Date	Metal	Size	VG	F	VF	Unc
Gma 271	1866	Copper	22mm	—	—	Rare	—

Statue of robed female. Around: CAFETAL DE LA
VIRGEN PETAPA. Rv: PEDRETTI / Y / TONEL /
1866. Plain edge. (Behringer coll.; Clark N/L)

Probably a pattern by Scovill Mfg. Co., Waterbury, Conn.

Rulau	Date	Metal	Size	VG	F	VF	Unc
Gma 272	1867	Copper	22mm	5.00	8.75	20.00	32.50

As last, but 1867. Regular token issue (Clark 314;
Rulau coll.; Jason 68-A)

PELUQUERIA DE LONDRES

Rulau	Date	Metal	Size	VG	F	VF	Unc
Gma 274	(1893-97)	Aluminum	29mm	—	—	—	20.00

PELUQUERIA DE LONDRES / * / 1876 / * / GUA-TEMALA. C.A. / (tiny) L. H. MOISE. S.F. Rv: ESTAB-LECIMIENTO / 4 / REALES / DE PRIMERA. Plain edge. (Zaffern coll.; Clark N/L)

Struck 1893-97 by the Moise firm. The 1876 date is a founding date of the enterprise. Peluqueria de Londres = London barber salon.

FINCA "EL PENSAMIENTO"

Rulau	Date	Metal	Size	VG	F	VF	Unc
Gma 276	ND	Brass	24mm	—	—	6.00	—

FINCA "EL PENSAMIENTO" / 1 / *. Rv: Similar to obverse, from different die. Each side ctsp 88 crudely. (Clark N/L; Zaffern coll.)

E.R.
Cafetal La Esperanza

Rulau	Date	Metal	Size	VG	F	VF	Unc
Gma 278	1878	CN	22mm	5.00	9.00	15.00	—

(Ornament) / ER monogram / 1878. Rv: (Ornament) / CAFETAL / * LA * / ESPERANZA / (rosette). Plain edge. (Clark 126)

Cafetal La Esperanza = Hope coffee plantation. In 1963 there were 37 fincas with this name. An early (pre-1890) directory of coffee growers, if such exists, is needed to positively attribute many of these Guatemalan tokens.

Patria
F. R. R.

Rulau	Date	Metal	Size	VG	F	VF	Unc
Gma 280	ND	Copper	Rect 70x40mm	—	—	25.00	—

F.R.R. at left, MAIZ at top, PATRIA at right, LIBRAS at bottom. At center is large cut-out numeral 12. Rv: Blank. Rectangular flan with cut corners. (Clark 301)

This check was for 12 pounds (libras) of corn (maiz).

EDWIN ROCKSTROH

Rulau	Date	Metal	Size	VG	F	VF	Unc
Gma 283	ND	Brass	xx	—	—	15.00	20.00

xx Diamond-shaped flan, 24x43mm.
(In circular indent): EDWIN ROCKSTROH / *. Rv: (In circular indent): 1 R. (ANS coll.)

Florencia
RODRIGO ROBLES

Rulau	Date	Metal	Size	VG	F	VF	Unc
Gma 282	ND	CN	29mm	4.00	7.00	11.00	20.00

RODRIGO ROBLES / - 3 - / FLORENCIA / COSTA CUCA / -*-. Rv: RODRIGO ROBLES / FLORENCIA / COSTA CUCA / -*-. Dentilated rim on each side. Plain edge. (Clark 339)

DOCTOR ELIAS ROJAS
Hacienda de la Sabanilla

Rulau	Date	Metal	Size	VG	F	VF	Unc
Gma 284	ND	Brass	26mm	—	—	—	—

DOCTOR ELIAS ROJAS. HACIENDA DE LA SABANILLA. 2 REALES. (Weyl 1726; Clark 358)

| Gma 285 | ND | Brass | 18mm | — | — | — | — |

As last, but 1/2 REAL. (Weyl 1726; Clark 356)

VICENTE HERMIDA
Hacienda Matilde Pepino

Rulau	Date	Metal	Size	VG	F	VF	Unc
Gma 287	ND	CN	19mm	—	—	—	—

VICENTE HERMIDA. HACIENDA MATILDE PEPINO. 2 REALES. (Weyl 1727; Clark 313)

| Gma 288 | ND | CN | 16mm | — | — | — | — |

Similar, but 5 CENTAVOS. (Weyl 1727; Clark 312)

FERMIN ROMERO
Cafetal Vergel de Mala

Rulau	Date	Metal	Size	F	VF	EF	Unc
Gma 290	(1893-97)	Brass	Oct 26.5mm	—	8.00	10.00	20.00

CAFETAL / FERMIN / * / ROMERO / * VERGEL DE MALA *. Rv: Large 2 within laurel wreath. (Clark 456; Zaffern coll.)

| Gma 291 | (1893-97) | Brass | Scal 26mm | 16.00 | — | 22.50 | 30.00 |

As last, but 1 within laurel wreath / (tiny) L. H. MOISE. S.F.

RUBIO Y ZIRION

Rulau	Date	Metal	Size	VG	F	VF	Unc
Gma 293	ND	Copper	21mm	—	4.00	8.00	—

RUBIO / Y / ZIRION. Rv: 1 / REAL within wreath. Plain edge. (Clark 477)

La Lima
C.H.S.
(C.H. Salas)

Rulau	Date	Metal	Size	VG	F	VF	Unc
Gma 295	ND	Bronze	20mm	—	—	—	—

C.H.S. 1 REAL. LA LIMA. (Weyl 1733; Clark 209)

Barcena
J. M. S.

Rulau	Date	Metal	Size	VG	F	VF	Unc
Gma 297	ND	Brass	21mm	5.00	7.50	10.00	—

J. M. S. / (ornament) / BARCENA. Rv: Large 1/4, radiant, within semicircle of small o's. Below: (tiny) L. H. MOISE S.F. Plain edge. (Zaffern coll.; Clark 27)

| Gma 298 | ND | Brass | 25mm | — | — | — | — |

As last, but 1/2. (Clark 28)

| Gma 299 | ND | Brass | 29mm | — | — | — | — |

As last, but 1 (real). (Clark 29)

SACHAL

Rulau	Date	Metal	Size	VG	F	VF	EF
Gma 303	ND	Copper	18mm	—	14.00	—	22.50

SACHAL ctsp on German Empire 1-pfennig coins of 1873-99 (KM 1 or 10). (Brunk 60810 and 53920; Clark 580) Examined: 1898-J

This Guatemala hacienda mark is found only on German coins brought in by 19th century German immigrants.

F. SANCHEZ A.
Cafetal El Zapote

Rulau	Date	Metal	Size	VG	F	VF	Unc
Gma 305	ND	Brass	22mm	—	—	—	—

F. SANCHEZ A. / 1 / * REAL. Rv: CAFETAL EL ZAPOTE. (Weyl 1706; Eklund 816; Clark 474)

F. SANCHEZ A.
Cafetal Las Cruces

Rulau	Date	Metal	Size	VG	F	VF	Unc
Gma 307	ND	Brass	22mm	9.00	15.00	17.50	—

CAFETAL / LAS / CRUCES. Rv: F. SANCHEZ A. / 1 / REAL. (Weyl 1707; Eklund 817; Clark 105)

SAN GERONIMO

Rulau	Date	Metal	Size	VG	F	VF	Unc
Gma 309	ND	CN	31mm	3.00	5.00	8.00	—

Coffee tree. Around: SAN GERONIMO / * COSTA-CUCA *. Rv: Large 4. Plain edge. (Clark 385)

| Gma 310 | ND | CN | 18mm | — | — | 8.00 | — |

As last, but 1/2 (real). (Eklund 934)

| Gma 311 | ND | CN | 17mm | — | — | 8.00 | — |

As last, but 1/4. (Jason 94-A)

| Gma 313 | ND | Brass | 17mm | — | — | — | — |

HACIENDA / DE / * SAN GERONIMO *. Rv: 1/4 / REAL. Plain edge. (Jason 94-B)

| Gma 314 | ND | Brass | 22mm | — | — | — | — |

As last, but UN / REAL / (ornament). (Jason 94-C)

STO. DOMINGO

Rulau	Date	Metal	Size	VG	F	VF	Unc
Gma 316	ND	Aluminum	35mm	—	—	20.00	—

STo. DOMINGO / (circle of vetical lines) / * COSTA CUCA *. Rv: Same as obverse. (Clark 417)

| Gma 317 | ND | Aluminum | Scal 27mm | — | — | 9.50 | — |

As last. (Clark 415)

| Gma 318 | ND | Aluminum | 24mm | — | — | 9.50 | — |

As last. (Clark 416; Rulau coll.)

| Gma 319 | ND | Aluminum | 20mm | — | — | 8.00 | — |

As last. (Clark 414)

SAXOC

Rulau	Date	Metal	Size	VG	F	VF	EF
Gma 320	ND	Copper	18mm	—	9.00	—	15.00

SAXOC ctsp on German Empire 1-pfennig coins of 1873-99 period (KM 1 or 10). Examined: 1897-J, 1898-J. (Brunk 60820 and 53995)

| Gma 321 | ND | Copper | 20mm | — | 15.00 | — | 22.50 |

Similar ctsp on German Empire 2-pfennig coins of same issue. Examined: 1876-B. (Clark 591)

| Gma 322 | ND | Copper | 30mm | — | 15.00 | - | 22.50 |

Similar ctsp on France 10-centimes of 1870-98 type, KM 44. (Brunk 53995)

See next entry under C. Trawitz.

C. TRAWITZ
Finca Saxoc-Hainstadt

Rulau	Date	Metal	Size	VG	F	VF	Unc
Gma 324	(1890's)	CN	23.5mm	—	—	25.00	—

* FINCA * / -+- / C. TRAWITZ / -+- / SAXOC-HAINSTADT. Rv: VALE / 1/2 * REAL * / (tiny) KLINKNER & CO. S.F. (ANS coll.)

The ANS collection also has a CN 1/4-real of this issuer. Apparently Trawitz imported German Imperial coins for use on his finca before he ordered special tokens from San Francisco. The German coins were counterstamped SAXOC.

TALLERES "AYAU"

Rulau	Date	Metal	Size	VG	F	VF	Unc
Gma 326	ND	CN	38mm	—	8.00	12.50	—

Anvil mounted on block; broom behind it. Ornamentation around. Rv: TALLERES "AYAU" / (incused numeral) / * GUATEMALA. *. Plain edge. Issued holed. (Clark 23)

Talleres "Ayau" = Ayau Mechanical Shops. The incused numeral on the Clark specimen is 59. Work check?

UNITED FRUIT CO.

Rulau	Date	Metal	Size	VG	F	VF	Unc
Gma 330	ND	Brass	24mm	8.00	12.00	17.00	—

UNITED FRUIT CO. / (Quatrefoil) / (rosette). Rv: Blank. (Clark 448; Rulau coll.)

Rulau	Date	Metal	Size	VG	F	VF	Unc
Gma 331	ND	Brass	24.5mm	8.00	12.00	17.00	—

UNITED FRUIT CO. / ... / ONE / STEM / ... / GUATEMALA / DIVISION. Rv: Same as obverse. (Clark 449)

Die varieties of the first token above were used in Jamaica also.

Rulau	Date	Metal	Size	VG	F	VF	EF
Gma 333	ND	Brass	26.5mm	90.00	—	200.	—

UNITED FRUIT CO. (circular) ctsp on San Agustin 2-real token. Plain edge. (Eklund 2317; Clark 362; Jason 82-C; Rulau coll.; Brunk 54590)

Gma 334	ND	Bronze	23mm	90.00	—	200.	—

Similar ctsp on Guatemala provisional 1915 25-centavos, KM 231. (Brunk 54590)

Gma 335	ND	Bronze	20mm	90.00	—	200.	—

Similar ctsp on Guatemala provisional 1915 12½-centavo coin, KM 230.

This American firm, founded in 1899, is a major exporter of bananas and other fruits from Guatemala, Honduras, Jamaica and other countries. The term "banana republic" seems to have originated from its earlier activities. It's tokens are popular and expensive.

The counterstamped token prepared from a San Agustin hacienda piece in VF fetched $195 in an April 1983 Carol Plante sale in Quebec, and another in just VG realized $90 in a March 1988 Jerry Schimmel sale.

V. i J.
(Vargas y Juarez ?)
Las Mercedes

Rulau	Date	Metal	Size	VG	F	VF	Unc
Gma 337	ND	Copper	25mm	—	12.50	20.00	—

LAS MERCEDES / 39 (incuse) / *. Rv: V i J. Reeded edge. (Clark 238; Rulau coll.; Weyl 1735)

Rulau	Date	Metal	Size	VG	F	VF	Unc
Gma 338	ND	Copper	17mm	—	11.00	18.00	—

As last, smaller. No ctsp. (Clark 235)

Gma 340	ND	Copper	20mm	—	11.00	18.00	—

LAS MERCEDES / (rosette). Rv: V i J. Toothed edge. (Clark 236; Prober 1735; Jason 48-B)

This token is known bearing counterstamp F.

Gma 341	ND	Aluminum	20mm	—	3.00	5.00	—

As last.

Gma 342	ND	Aluminum	26mm	—	5.00	8.00	—

Similar to last. Plain edge. (Clark 239)

The latter token is known with counterstamp 5 (value 8.00 VF) or 39 (value 11.00 VF). The hacienda has not been located.

S. VELASQUEZ

Rulau	Date	Metal	Size	VG	F	VF	Unc
Gma 344	ND	Copper	26mm	—	—	15.00	—

S. VELASQUEZ / (floreate device) / (laurel branches). Rv: 1 / PESO / (ornament). (Clark 451)

F. W.
(F. Weiss)
Hacienda Marzill

Rulau	Date	Metal	Size	VG	F	VF	Unc
Gma 346	ND	Brass	21mm	—	—	—	—

HACIENDA MARZILL / F. W. Rv: IV CENTAVOS. (Weyl 1742; Eklund 900; Clark 225)

Gma 347	ND	Brass	21mm	—	—	—	—

As last, but III. (Eklund 899; Clark 224)

Gma 348	ND	Brass	21mm	—	—	—	—

As last, but II. (Eklund 898)

Gma 349	ND	Brass	21mm	—	—	—	—

As last, but I. (Weyl 1742; Clark 223)

Prober, repeating Weyl, called this "Marzill Farm." The tokens were issued before 1899, since Weyl listed them.

EUGENIO WENK Y CIA.
Valle de Oro

Rulau	Date	Metal	Size	VG	F	VF	Unc
Gma 351	ND	Brass	19mm	—	—	8.00	—

EUGENIO WENK Y CIA. / UN / REAL / . VALLE DE ORO . Rv: Blank. Plain edge. (Clark 464; Rulau coll.)

Gma 352	ND	Steel	19mm	—	—	10.00	—

As last. (Clark 463; Jason 9-A)

WILCHES HERMANOS
La Suiza

Rulau	Date	Metal	Size	VG	F	VF	Unc
Gma 354	1894	CN	24mm	—	—	15.00	—

WILCHES HERMANOS / LA SUIZA / 1894. Rv: 10 CENTAVOS. (Weyl 1740; Eklund 892; Clark 435)

La Suiza = The Swiss. Wilches Brothers apparently were Swiss.

ANTONIO ZOLLIKOFER
El Transito

Rulau	Date	Metal	Size	VG	F	VF	Unc
Gma 356	ND	Brass	31mm	—	—	9.00	—

EL TRANSITO / 8 / * ANTONIO ZOLLIKOFER *. Rv: Blank. Plain edge. (Clark 440; Jason 121-A)

III CENTAVO

Rulau	Date	Metal	Size	VG	F	VF	EF
Gma 440	(1871)	Bronze	21mm	—	8.00	—	16.00

I ctsp on Guatemala 1871 1-centavo coin, KM-196. Rv: III / CENTAVO ctsp on reverse of the coin. (Gary Pipher Oct. 1987 sale, lot 2499)

This is, perhaps, a private revaluation from 1 to 3 centavos. Some background explanation is in order:

Guatemala did not finally abandon the real-peso system until 1915, continuing to strike real-denomination coins through 1912. This was despite the fact that decimal system coins had been introduced in 1871, including the host coin for the counterstamp above.

The tiny silver 1/4-real of the government was struck through 1899 (and then in cupronickel to 1901). Upon the introduction of the bronze centavo of 1871, it was the only copper coin of the nation! The popular silver 1/4-real was valued at 3.125 centavos. There may be a connection between that fact and the counterstamp reported above.

Guatemala did not produce another bronze centavo until 1881, and after that not another until 1925!

The currency of Guatemala in the second half of the 19th century consisted of government silver and gold coins and a plentiful supply of privately issued tokens in base metals.

M.

Rulau	Date	Metal	Size	VG	F	VF	
Gma 402	(?)	Bronze	21mm	—	—	15.00	—

* M (large, script) * ctsp on Guatemala 1881 centavo, KM 202.1. (Georg Forster coll.)

R.S.

Rulau	Date	Metal	Size	VG	F	VF	EF
Gma 404	(?)	Bronze	21mm	—	—	15.00	—

R G (large) ctsp on Guatemala 1881 centavo, KM 202.1. Georg Forster coll.)

Counterstamped 1871 Centavos

A number of maverick counterstamps appear on Guatemala copper 1-centavo coins of 1871. The 21mm coin KM 196 was introduced by the government in an era when reales were the preferred coinage and numbers of these centavos — not wanted in circulation — found themselves marked for use as hacienda tokens. Most 1871 centavos were EF or Unc. when counterstamped. The marks usually are placed over the UN on reverse.

Counterstamp	Catalog No.	EF
Castle turret (chessman)	Brunk 61060	15.00
Crown	Brunk 61080	15.00
Tree	Clark 541; Brunk 61130	15.00
Bow tie	Clark 540	15.00
Signature (in rectangle)	Brunk 61120	15.00
D B	—	7.00
E 98	—	7.00
G&A	Clark 497	7.00
J	—	7.00
M	Clark 499	7.00
J M	Brunk 60455	7.00
MA monogram	—	9.00
P (inverted) plus other symbol	Clark 501	7.00
Q E H	—	7.00
R.C. (relief, in oval depression)	Brunk 60710	15.00
R	Clark 515	7.00
L B / R / I	—	7.00
S / 2	Brunk 60790	7.00
S. D.	Clark 529	7.00
L U	—	7.00
VZ	Forster coll.	7.00
R / H	—	10.00
F E	—	10.00

HONDURAS

ATLANTIDA DEPARTMENT

Bonito
E. P. DUTU

Rulau	Date	Metal	Size	VG	F	VF	Unc
Atl 3	ND	Brass	23.5mm	—	—	15.00	—

E. P. DUTU / BONITO / (ornament) / PORVENIR / o HONDURAS o. Rv: o SE RECIBE o / * / POR MEDIO / -*- / REAL.

JOSE RUIZ Y CA

Rulau	Date	Metal	Size	VG	F	VF	Unc
Atl 5	ND	Brass	22mm	—	—	20.00	—

JOSE RUIZ / BONITO, / HONDURAS. Rv: SE RECIBE POR / ½ / * REAL *.

Rulau	Date	Metal	Size	VG	F	VF	Unc
Atl 6	ND	Brass	20mm	—	—	20.00	—

JOSE RUIZ Y Ca. / (rosette) / . BONITO . Rv: BUENO POR / ½ / * REAL *. (Eklund 1244)

These tokens have been claimed as Peru.

La Ceiba
MUNICIPALIDAD CEIBA

Municiplos

Rulau	Date	Metal	Size	VG	F	VF	Unc
Atl 7	(1880 ?)	Brass	27.3mm	—	—	500.	—

MUNICIPALIDAD / (starburst) / * DE LA CEIBA *. Rv: REPUBLICA MAYOR ESTADO / 1 / REAL. / -*- / * HONDURAS. *. Incised, beaded rim on each side. Plain edge. (Rulau coll.)

This city notgeld piece is missing from both the ANS and Smithsonian collections and from all private collections surveyed for the preparation of this catalog. The only known specimen, illustrated, reposed in Germany for about a century, unpublished in all traceable references. It surfaced only in 1992.

Rulau	Date	Metal	Size	VG	F	VF	Unc
Atl 8	1911	Brass	21mm	—	15.00	40.00	70.00

MUNICIPALIDAD / ½ / REAL / CEIBA. Rv: 1911. Plain edge. (*TAMS Journal* for Aug. 1985, page 135)

La Ceiba is a banana company town near the Caribbean seacoast in the north. This piece is town notgeld, issued at a time of shortage of small change.

Other towns which issued notgeld coins were Tela (Atlantida Dept.), Olanchito (Yoro Dept.) and El Paraiso (El Paraiso Dept.).

BAZAR ITALIANO

Rulau	Date	Metal	Size	VG	F	VF	Unc
Atl 10	1909	Copper	23mm	—	—	40.00	—

BAZAR ITALIANO / ½ / REAL / CEIBA. Rv: 1909. (ANS coll.)

P. DE VAUX Y CA.

Rulau	Date	Metal	Size	VG	F	VF	Unc
Atl 12	ND	Brass	24mm	—	—	40.00	—

P. DE VAUX Y Ca / (Star) / CEIBA / (Star) / * HONDURAS *. Rv: SE RECIBE POR / ½ / REAL. Plain edge. (Eklund 971)

Se recibe por = Accepted at.

E. P. DUTU

Rulau	Date	Metal	Size	VG	F	VF	Unc
Atl 13	ND	Brass	23mm	—	—	25.00	—

E. P. DUTU / HONDURAS / LA CEIBA / EL PORVENIR. Rv: SE RECIBE / POR MEDIO / REAL. (Zaika coll.)

LAFFITE Y ALVAREZ

Rulau	Date	Metal	Size	VG	F	VF	Unc
Atl 14	ND	Brass	24mm	—	—	25.00	—

LAFFITE Y ALVAREZ * / CEIBA, / (Star) / HONDURAS. Rv: SE RECIBE. / .*. / POR MEDIO / -.- / REAL. Plain edge. (Eklund 972)

LAFFITE Y DEVAUX

Rulau	Date	Metal	Size	VG	F	VF	Unc
Atl 16	ND	Brass	29mm	—	20.00	—	—

LAFFITE . Y . DEVAUX / ***** / LA CEIBA / * / HONDURAS / --*--. Rv: DEBEMOS AL PORTADOR / ½ / REAL. Plain edge. (Henkle report)

M. MEJIA Y H.

Rulau	Date	Metal	Size	VG	F	VF	Unc
Atl 18	ND	Brass	21mm	—	—	40.00	—

M. MEJIA Y H. / ½ / REAL / CEIBA. Rv: Blank. Plain edge. (Eklund 973)

This token in 17mm size is in the ANS collection.

LOUIS NAVES

Rulau	Date	Metal	Size	VG	F	VF	Unc
Atl 20	ND	Brass	25mm	—	—	25.00	—

LOUIS NAVES. / (Radiant star) / CEIBA / (Radiant star) / HONDURAS. Rv: VALE -*- / ½ / REAL -*-. (Eklund 2378; Zaika coll.)

Rulau	Date	Metal	Size	VG	F	VF	Unc
Atl 21	ND	Brass	23.5mm	—	—	25.00	—

Similar to last, from different dies, smaller. (Dana Roberts report)

R. RODRIGUEZ

Rulau	Date	Metal	Size	VG	F	VF	Unc
Atl 23	ND	Brass	23mm	—	—	15.00	—

R. RODRIGUEZ / (ornament) / CEIBA / . HONDURAS . Rv: SE RECIBE POR / ½ / REAL. (Schimmel report)

VACCARO BROS. & CO.

Rulau	Date	Metal	Size	VG	F	VF	Unc
Atl 25	1904	Brass	21mm	—	—	20.00	—

VACCARO BROS. & Co. / ½ / REAL / CEIBA. Rv: 1904. Plain edge. (Schimmel coll.)

Rulau	Date	Metal	Size	VG	F	VF	Unc
Atl 27	1906	Brass	21mm	—	—	20.00	—

As last, but 1906. (Zaika coll.)

D. WARREN & CO.

Rulau	Date	Metal	Size	VG	F	VF	Unc
Atl 29	ND	Brass	24mm	—	—	30.00	—

D. WARREN & CO. / LA CEIBA HONDURAS. Rv: DEBEMOS AL PORTADOR / ½ / REAL. (ANS coll.)

Salado Barra
J. HIRIGOYEN

Rulau	Date	Metal	Size	VG	F	VF	Unc
Atl 33	ND	Brass	21mm	—	14.00	25.00	—

J. HIRIGOYEN / -.- / HONDURAS / * SALADO *. Rv: SE RECIBE / (sailboat left) / *** / POR ½ REAL. Plain edge. (Schimmel report)

Rulau	Date	Metal	Size	VG	F	VF	Unc
Atl 35	ND	Copper	--mm	—	—	22.00	—

½ RIAL J. R. HIRIGOYEN / (incuse) S. H. K. Rv: No. descr. available. (CCE report, not verified)

Tela
MUNICIPALIDAD DE TELA

Municipios

Rulau	Date	Metal	Size	VG	F	VF	Unc
Atl 40	1912	Brass	21mm	—	15.00	40.00	—

MUNICIPALIDAD / ½ / REAL / DE TELA. Rv: 1912. Plain edge. (*The Numismatist* for May 1942, pg. 376; Rulau coll.)

J. W. GRACE
La Esperanza

Rulau	Date	Metal	Size	VG	F	VF	Unc
Atl 42	ND	Brass	23mm	—	—	20.00	—

LA ESPERANZA / * (Anchor) * / J. W. GRACE / TELA HUND. Rv: BUENO POR / 1 / * REAL *. Plain edge.

"Hund." is probably a misspelling for Hond(uras)".

BOTICA ATLANTIDA

Rulau	Date	Metal	Size	VG	F	VF	Unc
Atl 50	1909	Brass	23mm	—	—	15.00	—

BOTICA ATLANTIDA / ½ / REAL. Rv: 1909.

COLON DEPARTMENT
Trujillo
JUAN LAFFITE

Rulau	Date	Metal	Size	VG	F	VF	Unc
Con 5	ND	Brass	24mm	—	—	30.00	—

JUAN / LAFFITE / TRUXILLO. Rv: SE RECIBE / (ornament) / POR / (ornament) / (rosette) ½ REAL (rosette). Plain edge. (Eklund 1395)

This token has in the past been considered Peruvian. Trujillo is the present name for Truxillo, a Caribbean Sea port in Colon Department, Honduras.

Juan Laffite is probably related to the Laffite token issuers of La Ceiba, Atlantida Dept.

CORTES DEPARTMENT
Cofradia
COFRADIA

Municipios

Rulau	Date	Metal	Size	VG	F	VF	Unc
Crt 3	ND	CN	18mm	—	10.00	15.00	—

* / COFRADIA / *. Rv: Un / CUARTILLO / -.-.

Rulau	Date	Metal	Size	VG	F	VF	Unc
Crt 5	ND	Brass	18mm	—	10.00	15.00	—

COFRADIA. Rv: A star.

These tokens have been claimed as Guatemala.

Cuyamel
CUYAMEL FRUIT CO.

Rulau	Date	Metal	Size	VG	F	VF	Unc
Crt 7	ND	Aluminum	32mm	—	—	80.00	—

CUYAMEL FRUIT CO. VALE POR UN REAL. Rv:
12½ CENT.

Cuyamel Fruit Co. was incorporated in South Dakota in 1911 and bought out
by the United Fruit Co. in 1929. It had operations also in Jamaica.

PLANTACION CUYAMEL

Rulau	Date	Metal	Size	VG	F	VF	Unc
Crt 9	ND	--	28mm	—	—	—	—

PLANTACION CUYAMEL * / VALE / UN MEDIO.
Rv: No descr. available. (Utberg H14)

The Plantacion Cuyamel piece may be Mexican.

Puerto Cortes
J. A. AYBAR

Rulau	Date	Metal	Size	VG	F	VF	Unc
Crt 15	1898	CN	24mm	—	—	15.00	22.00

J. A. AYBAR / 12½ / CENTAVOS / PUERTO
CORTES / HONDURAS. Rv: SE RECIBE POR / 12½
/ CENTAVOS / 1898. Plain edge. (Eklund 2380)

Crt 16	1898	CN	20mm	—	—	10.00	17.00

As last, but 6¼. (Eklund 978; Zaika coll.)

Crt 18	ND	CN	19mm	—	—	—	20.00

Obverse similar to last, but from different die. Rv: SE
RECIBE POR / 6¼ / CENTAVOS. Plain edge. (Eklund
2248)

Se recibe por 12½ centavos = Accepted at 12½ centavos.

THE CORTEZ COMPANY

Rulau	Date	Metal	Size	VG	F	VF	Unc
Crt 20	ND	Brass	23mm	—	—	11.00	—

THE CORTEZ COMPANY / PUERTO CORTEZ. Rv:
No descr. available.

VICTOR KUYLEN

Rulau	Date	Metal	Size	VG	F	VF	Unc
Crt 25	ND	CN	20mm	—	—	30.00	—

VICTOR KUYLEN / (Cross-shaped ornament) / *
PTO. CORTEZ *. Rv: 1 / UN REAL within wreath.
Plain edge. (Eklund 979)

Crt 26	ND	CN	14.5mm	—	—	30.00	—

As last, but ½ in wreath. (Smithsonian coll.)

GEO. LEFEBVRE

Rulau	Date	Metal	Size	VG	F	VF	Unc
Crt 28	ND	Brass	38mm	—	—	30.00	—

WITH / - GEO. - / LEFEBVRE / PUERTO CORTES. /
HOND. Rv: GOOD FOR / 25 C / IN TRADE. Plain
edge. (Eklund 2249; Zaika coll.)

Zaika says copper.

PITTSBURGH &
HONDURAS CO.

Rulau	Date	Metal	Size	VG	F	VF	Unc
Crt 33	ND	Brass Oval 33.5x20mm		—	20.00	—	—

PITTSBURGH / *** / HONDURAS CO. / *** /
PUERTO CORTEZ. Rv: SE RECIBE / POR / - 1 - / *
REAL *. Plain edge.

Crt 34	ND	Brass Oval 26x18mm		—	—	—	—

As last, but - ½ / REAL.

San Pedro Sula
BAZAR FRANCES

Rulau	Date	Metal	Size	VG	F	VF	Unc
Crt 39	ND	Brass	20mm	—	20.00	30.00	45.00

BAZAR FRANCES / ½ / REAL / SAN PEDRO SULA.
Rv: SE RECIBE / -.- / * POR UN * / -.- / MEDIO. (Holsen-Zelaya pg. 33; Zaika coll.)

A. MEJIA

Rulau	Date	Metal	Size	VG	F	VF	Unc
Crt 45	1893	Brass	23.5mm	20.00	25.00	40.00	—

+ A. MEJIA, + / ½ / REAL / COMERCIANTE EN
GENERAL. Rv: * SAN PEDRO SULA, * / 6¼ C /
HONDURAS / 1893 (?) / ctsp V. Plain edge. Rare. (Ted
Uhl report)

LEONARD WALDEN

Rulau	Date	Metal	Size	VG	F	VF	Unc
Crt 49	ND	Brass	23.5mm	15.00	20.00	35.00	—

LEONARD WALDEN / ½ / REAL / COMERCIANTE
EN GENERAL. Rv: SAN PEDRO SULA / 6¼ C across
large V/ * HONDURAS *. Plain edge.

EL PARAISO
DEPARTMENT

El Paraiso

Municipios

Rulau	Date	Metal	Size	VG	F	VF	Unc
ELP 3	ND	Brass	21mm	—	35.00	50.00	—

EL PARAISO / 6¼ / * HONDURAS *. Rv: Same as
obverse. Plain edge. (Eklund 974; ANS coll.)

ARCADIA COBAS

Rulau	Date	Metal	Size	VG	F	VF	Unc
ELP 7	ND	Brass	24mm	—	—	30.00	—

EL PARAISO / 1 / REAL / HONDURAS. Rv: SE
RECIBE / POR UN / REAL / ARCADIA COBAS.
Plain edge. Varieties?

ELP 8	ND	Brass	20mm	—	—	30.00	—

As last, but POR UN / MEDIO. (ANS coll.)

ELP 10	ND	Brass	20.5mm	—	—	30.00	—

ARCADIA COBOS / (arc of 13 stars) / (hexagram) / EL
/ * PARAISO. *. Plain edge. (Smithsonian coll.)

FRANCISCO MORAZAN DEPARTMENT

Tegucigalpa
BANCO ATLANTIDA

Rulau	Date	Metal	Size	F	VF	EF	Unc
FM 20	1963	Gilt/B	31mm	—	—	4.00	8.00

Modernistic building; script Banco Atlantida near its top. Around: BANCO ATLANTIDA / TEGUCI-GALPA. Rv: ANIVERSARIO / 50 / AÑOS / 1913-1963 / (stylized wreath). Plain edge. (Brunk coll.)

ISLAS DE LA BAHIA DEPARTMENT

Guanaja, Isla de Guanaja
SALVADOR BALDERRAMOS

Rulau	Date	Metal	Size	F	VF	EF	Unc
ILB 5	ND	Aluminum	24mm	—	—	—	35.00

LA HONDURENA / DE / SALVADOR / BALDER-RAMOS / VALE / 12. Rv: GUANAJA DPTO / DE / ISLAS DE / LA BAHIA / HONDURAS, C.A. Plain edge.

Roatan, Isla de Roatan
F. O. McN. & BROS.

Rulau	Date	Metal	Size	VG	F	VF	Unc
ILB 9	ND	Brass	23mm	—	20.00	35.00	—

P. O. McN & BROS RUATAN . Rv: DEBEMOS AL PORTADOR / ½ R.

D. WARREN

Rulau	Date	Metal	Size	VG	F	VF	Unc
ILB 12	ND	Brass	23.5mm	—	20.00	35.00	—

D. WARREN / (ornament) / * RUATAN *. Rv: DEBEMOS AL PORTADOR / ½ / REAL / -*-. Plain edge. (ANS coll.)

WARREN & SONS

Rulau	Date	Metal	Size	VG	F	VF	Unc
ILB 14	ND	Copper	23mm	—	20.00	35.00	—

WARREN & SONS / RUATAN / ctsp M. Rv: ½ REAL MDSE.

Utila, Isla de Utila
D. WARREN & CO.

Rulau	Date	Metal	Size	VG	F	VF	Unc
ILB 20	ND	Copper	20mm	—	20.00	35.00	—

D. WARREN & CO. / UTILLA HONDURAS. Rv: DEBEMOS AL PORTADOR / ½ / REAL. (ANS coll.)

R. WOODVILLE & SON

Rulau	Date	Metal	Size	VG	F	VF	Unc
ILB 23	ND	Brass	Oct--mm	—	25.00	40.00	—

UTILA, HONDURAS/ R. WOODVILLE & SON. Rv: 6¼. Scarce.

French Harbor
R. O. McNAB

Rulau	Date	Metal	Size	VG	F	VF	Unc
ILB 28	1901	Brass	23mm	45.00	70.00	—	—

R. O. McNAB / (ornament) / 1901 / (ornament) / FRENCH HARBOR. Rv: DEBEMOS AL PORTA-DOR / ½ / REAL / -.-. Plain edge. (Schimmel report)

YORO DEPARTMENT

Olanchito
MUNICIPIO DE OLANCHITO

Municipios

Rulau	Date	Metal	Size	VG	F	VF	Unc
Yor 6	1910	Brass	21mm	—	25.00	50.00	—

MUNICIPIO DE OLANCHITO ANO / 1910. Rv: VALE AL PORTADOR / 6¼ / * MEDIO REAL *. Plain edge. (Schimmel report)

UNATTRIBUTED HONDURAS

Cayo Indes
P. A. BETANCOURT

Rulau	Date	Metal	Size	VG	F	VF	Unc
Hon 3	ND	Brass	24mm	—	12.50	20.00	—

P. A. BETANCOURT. / CAYO INDES, HONDURAS . Rv: ½ REAL. (Holsen-Zelaya pg. 33)

BURCHARD HOND. FRUIT CO.

Rulau	Date	Metal	Size	VG	F	VF	Unc
Hon 5	ND	Brass	23mm	—	30.00	—	—

BURCHARD / (Pineapple) / HOND. FRUIT CO. Rv: 12½. (Eklund 2237)

Rulau	Date	Metal	Size	VG	F	VF	Unc
Hon 6	ND	Brass	20mm	—	30.00	—	—

BURCHARD / (Stalk of bananas) / HOND. FRUIT CO. Rv: 6¼.

GEO. D. EMERY

Rulau	Date	Metal	Size	VG	F	VF	Unc
Hon 9	ND	Brass	Oct 26 mm	—	—	20.00	—

GEO. D. EMERY / (ornaments) / HONDURAS. Rv: SE RECIBE / POR / UN / REAL.

Rulau	Date	Metal	Size	VG	F	VF	Unc
Hon 10	ND	Brass	Oct 26mm	—	—	18.00	30.00

GEO. D. EMERY / (ornaments) / * HONDURAS *. Rv: SE RECIBE / POR / * * * / * UN * / MEDIO. (ANS coll.)

GRAND HOTEL GODDERIS

Rulau	Date	Metal	Size	VG	F	VF	Unc
Hon 15	ND	Copper	Oct 23mm	—	—	30.00	—

GRAND HOTEL GODDERIS / A. DE VOS / (Rosette). Rv: Large 45. Plain borders. (Eklund 2240)

Rulau	Date	Metal	Size	VG	F	VF	Unc
Hon 16	ND	WM	24mm	—	—	30.00	—

As last, but 40. Beaded border on each side. (Eklund 2239)

Rulau	Date	Metal	Size	VG	F	VF	Unc
Hon 18	ND	Copper	24mm	—	—	30.00	—

As last, but 25. Beaded borders. (Eklund 2238)

P.K.

Rulau	Date	Metal	Size	VG	F	VF	Unc
Hon 20	(?)	CN	20mm	—	—	15.00	—

P K ctsp on Honduras 1869-A ¼ real, KM 31. (Georg Forster coll.)

ZELAYA I DIAZ
La Hondureña

Rulau	Date	Metal	Size	VG	F	VF	Unc
Hon 30	1877	Brass	23mm	—	—	50.00	—

REPUBLICA DE HONDURAS / (Tree) / 1877. Rv: * LA HONDUREÑA * / 25 / ZELAYA I DIAZ. Plain edge. (Eklund 977)

Rulau	Date	Metal	Size	VG	F	VF	Unc
Hon 31	1877	Brass	20mm	—	—	30.00	—

As last, but 10 (centavos). (Ulex 2208; Eklund 976; Zaika coll.)

Rulau	Date	Metal	Size	VG	F	VF	Unc
Hon 32	1877	Brass	18mm	—	—	30.00	—

As last, but 5. (Eklund 2379; Zaika coll.)

J. Zelaya ?

6¼

Rulau	Date	Metal	Size	VG	F	VF	Unc
Hon 40	1898	Silver	19mm	—	—	25.00	—

Legend within border of dashes. 11/41/4. Rv: 6¼ / 1898 in border of dashes. (ANS coll.)

NICARAGUA

CARAZO DEPARTMENT

Diriamba
CRISANTO BRISEÑA

Rulau	Date	Metal	Size	VG	F	VF	Unc
Czo 1	ND	Brass	20mm	—	17.50	—	—

CRISANTO / (ornament) / BRISEÑA / (ornament) / DIRIAMBA. Rv: ¼ / REAL. Plain edge.

Briseña is a spelling error for Briceño, according to specialist Alan Luedeking.

LA TIENDA DEL PUEBLO

Rulau	Date	Metal	Size	VG	F	VF	Unc
Czo 4	ND	Copper	17mm	—	—	40.00	—

LA / TIENDA / DEL / PUEBLO / DIRIAMBA. Rv: ¼ / REAL. Plain edge.

Jinotepe
DESIDERIO ROMAN
Hacienda La Guinea

Rulau	Date	Metal	Size	VG	F	VF	Unc
Czo 6	ND	Brass	22mm	—	—	20.00	35.00

Broad tree. Around: HACIENDA LA GUINEA / . JINOTEPE . Rv: Basket. Around: UNA TAREA / . DESIDERIO ROMAN . Plain edge. (Eklund 1010.1; Rulau coll.)

Czo 7	ND	Brass	22mm	—	—	—	35.00

Similar to last, but tall, full-branched tree. Basket on reverse slightly different. Plain edge. (Luedeking coll.)

FERNANDO CHAMORRO Y HNO.

Rulau	Date	Metal	Size	VG	F	VF	Unc
Czo 10	ND	Brass	24mm	—	—	Rare	—

HACIENDAS DE CAFE / DE / FERNANDO / CHAMORRO Y Hno. Rv: 10 / MEDIOS. Plain edge.

Czo 11	ND	Brass	24mm	—	—	V.Rare	—

As last, but 5 / MEDIOS. (Luedeking coll.)

HACIENDA ELVIRA

Rulau	Date	Metal	Size	VG	F	VF	Unc
Czo 13	ND	CN	19.5mm	—	15.00	30.00	—

Coffee tree. Rv: HACIENDA ELVIRA / . SAN MARCOS . Plain edge. (Randel coll.; Luedeking coll.)

LEON DEPARTMENT

Leon
MERCADO DE LEON

Rulau	Date	Metal	Size	VG	F	VF	Unc
Leo 5	(1859)	Copper	27mm	—	—	250.	500.

MERCADO DE LEON. Rv: Within laural wreath: 1/12 / DIME. (Eklund 1013; Luedeking coll.)

Rulau	Date	Metal	Size	VG	F	VF	Unc
Leo 6	(1859)	Copper	20.5mm	—	—	300.	650.

As last, but 1/24 / DIME. (Eklund 1012; NASCA Dec. 1979 sale, lot 2288). Weight 3.89 grams.

Rulau	Date	Metal	Size	VG	F	VF	Unc
Leo 7	ND	Copper	27mm	—	—	—	Unique

As the 1/12 dime token, but ctsp S incuse.

Mercado = Market. Eklund erroneously used the name Cojutepeque (a town in El Salvador) in connection with this issue. The token has also been claimed as Mexican.

COMPANIA AGUADORA DE LEON

Rulau	Date	Metal	Size	VG	F	VF	Unc
Leo 9	(1885)	Copper	19mm	—	25.00	40.00	70.00

Nicaraguan arms in triangle, cannon below. Rv: COMPANIA AGUADORA DE LEON NICA. / 1½ / CENTAVOS. (Eklund 1014)

Compania Aguadora de Leon = Leon Water Co. This token was struck by Scovill Mfg. Co., Waterbury, Conn. (referred to as "Waterbury Mint" by Robert A. Lamb.)

This piece had official government sanction to circulate as a coin. (See *Numismatic Scrapbook Magazine* for July 1968, page 1120).

MANAGUA DEPARTMENT

Managua
FERNANDO Y MANUEL LACAYO
Hacienda Del Carmen

Rulau	Date	Metal	Size	VG	F	VF	Unc
Mga 7	ND	Brass	21mm	—	20.00	40.00	—

HACIENDA DEL CARMEN / (Palm tree) / * MANAGUA *. Rv: FERNANDO Y MANUEL LACAYO + + / DE / GRANADA / (Double fleur de lis). (Eklund 1015; ANS coll.)

MASAYA DEPARTMENT

Masatepe
NAPOLEON TAPIA

Rulau	Date	Metal	Size	VG	F	VF	Unc
Mya 5	1895	Zinc	21.3mm	—	—	150.	—

NAPOLEON TAPIA / *. Rv: MASATEPE NICARAGUA / 1895 / *. Plain edge. (Robert A. Lamb report; Alan Luedeking coll.)

Extremely rare.

RIO SAN JUAN DEPARTMENT

San Juan del Norte
C. F. BERGMANN

Rulau	Date	Metal	Size	VG	F	VF	Unc
RSJ 1	ND	CN	21mm	—	—	200.	—

(All incuse): C. F. BERGMANN / 5 C / GREYTOWN. Rv: Blank. (Eklund 2109; ANS coll.)

San Juan del Norte is the present name for Greytown, the only Nicaraguan Caribbean port not in Zelaya Department. Greytown was a British-oriented city (like Bluefields to its north) during the 19th century.

RIVAS DEPARTMENT

Rivas
LOPEZ I MALIAÑO

Rulau	Date	Metal	Size	VG	F	VF	Unc
Riv 5	ND	Brass	20mm	—	15.00	30.00	—

LOPEZ I MALIAÑO / 5 / CINCO / * CENTAVOS *. Rv: REPUBLICA DE NICARAGUA / * RIVAS *. (Eklund 1016)

Lopez i Maliaño = Lopez and Maliaño.

Rulau	Date	Metal	Size	VG	F	VF	Unc
Riv 6	ND	Brass	24mm	—	—	35.00	—

Coffee tree. Around: VALE POR UN CELEMIN CAFE / . * . Rv: -.- / H. PRADO / DE / Y. MALIAÑO / —.—. Plain edge. (Luedeking coll.)

It is uncertain whether Riv 6 preceded Riv 5 or followed it. Hacienda Prado was owned by Y. Maliaño on 6 and by Lopez and Maliaño on 5.

DAVID MORICE

Rulau	Date	Metal	Size	F	VF	EF	Unc
Riv 8	1925	Brass	31mm	—	9.00	20.00	25.00

INGENIO DOLORES / 25 / RIVAS NICARAGUA. Rv: DAVID MORICE / (ornament) / 1925. Plain edge. (See *TAMS Journal* for Aug. 1985, page 135)

Ingenio Dolores was a sugar plantation and mill near the west shore of Lake Nicaragua, in a mainly coffee-growing area. Jerry Schimmel reports this token was struck by Meyer & Wenthe Co. of Chicago.

Other denominations in brass in this series exist: 2, 19.5mm; 5, 21mm; 10, 24mm; 20, 27mm. All in Alan Luedeking coll.

ZELAYA DEPARTMENT

Zelaya is easily the largest department in Nicaragua, extending from the Honduran frontier almost to the Costa Rican border along the Caribbean seacoast and inland to the central mountain ranges. This area has a special history quite apart from the rest of Nicaragua.

From 1655 through 1850 the British claimed sovereignty over the Miskito Indians of the Mosquito Coast of Nicaragua and Honduras. They exercised this sovereignty mostly through the port of Bluefields and several other ports. The British did not completely surrender their claims until 1860.

In 1860, with the extinguishing of the British claims, Nicaragua granted autonomy to the Miskito Indian tribes, who were largely self-governing from 1860 to 1894. In 1894 the tribes voluntarily surrendered their autonomy, and their territories in Nicaragua were included in the new Departamento de Zelaya.

Most of the British-oriented tokens were issued before 1895.

Zelaya includes the Caribbean ports (north to south) of: Cabo Gracias a Dios, Puerto Cabezas, Huaunta, Prinzapolca, Rio Grande, Bluefields and Punta Gorda.

Bluefields
BLUEFIELDS BOTTLING CO.

Rulau	Date	Metal	Size	VG	F	VF	Unc
Zel 2	ND	Brass	24mm	—	—	—	—

Nicaraguan coat of arms. Around: BLUEFIELDS BOTTLING CO. *. Rv: BLUEFIELDS BOTTLING CO. / 5 / CENTS / *. (Eklund 1007)

CHOW WING SING & CO.

Rulau	Date	Metal	Size	VG	F	VF	Unc
Zel 4	ND	Brass	23mm	—	—	100.	—

CHOW-WING SING & CO. / 5 CTS. / BLUEFIELDS / NIC. Rv: Same as obverse. On the obverse, below NIC., is an incuse ctsp in Chinese which means: WING / SING. Plain edge. Very rare. (Luedeking coll.)

H. EBENSPERGER

Rulau	Date	Metal	Size	VG	F	VF	Unc
Zel 6	ND	Brass	23mm	—	—	—	—

(All incused): H. EBENSPERGER. 5 CENTAVOS. BLUEFIELDS. (Eklund 1008, from 1899 Weyl catalog.)

H. C. INGRAM

Rulau	Date	Metal	Size	VG	F	VF	Unc
Zel 8	ND	Brass	23mm	—	—	—	—

(All incused): H. C. INGRAM, 5 CENTAVOS. BLUE-FIELDS. (Eklund 1009)

S. PARSONS

Rulau	Date	Metal	Size	VG	F	VF	Unc
Zel 10	1878	Brass	20mm	—	—	—	—

S. PARSONS / BLUEFIELDS / 1878. Rv: TOKEN / 2½ / CENTS. (Eklund 1011; ANS coll.)

WILSON & BELANGER

Rulau	Date	Metal	Size	VG	F	VF	Unc
Zel 12	ND	CN	20mm	—	—	—	—

(All incused): WILSON & BELANGER. 5 CENTAVOS. BLUEFIELDS. (Eklund 1010)

A 10-centavos has been reported.

Huaunta
G. S. & S.

Rulau	Date	Metal	Size	VG	F	VF	Unc
Zel 16	ND	CN	24mm	—	—	—	—

G.S. & S. / (Palm tree) / * WOUNTA *. Rv: EXCHANGE / 10 / * CENTS *. (Eklund 1022)

Rulau	Date	Metal	Size	VG	F	VF	Unc
Zel 17	ND	CN	21mm	—	—	—	—

As last, but 5. (Eklund 1021; ANS coll.)

Wounta = Huaunta, on Laguna Huaunta, an arm of the Caribbean sea on the Mosquito Coast of Nicaragua.

UNATTRIBUTED NICARAGUA

BERNARDINO CIFUENTES
Finca El Peten

Rulau	Date	Metal	Size	VG	F	VF	Unc
Nic 6	(1893-97)	Brass	25mm	—	—	—	—

FINCA EL PETEN / (Tree) / BERNARDINO CIFUENTES. Rv: 2 (in circle of 8 stars) / (tiny) L. H. MOISE, S. F. Plain edge. (ANS coll.)

Rulau	Date	Metal	Size	VG	F	VF	Unc
Nic 7	(1893-97)	Brass	21mm	—	—	—	—

As last, but 1 (real). (ANS coll.)

The American Numismatic Society attributes these to Nicaragua, but the basis is unknown. David Henkle also prefers Nicaragua. They could be from Guatemala, where there is a Peten Dept.

R.G.L.

Rulau	Date	Metal	Size	VG	F	VF	EF
Nic 10	1899	CN	19.5mm	—	—	45.00	—

R G L (script initials) ctsp on Nicaragua 1899 5-centavos coin, KM-9. Very Scarce.

The author has examined three different specimens of this token. Each piece had a fair amount of wear before the counterstamp was applied to turn the coin into a hacienda token.

D. R. DE F.

Rulau	Date	Metal	Size	VG	F	VF	Unc
Nic 14	ND	Silver	23mm	—	—	35.00	—

D. R./ DE. F. ctsp on reverse of Nicaragua 1887-H 20-centavos, KM-7. Center of the reverse within wreath had been shaved smooth to accommodate the stamp. Ex. rare. (Rulau coll., ex-Fauver)

All privately counterstamped Nicaraguan coins are scarce to rare, but those on silver coins especially so.

ARTURO VAUGHAN
Hacienda San Francisco

Rulau	Date	Metal	Size	VG	F	VF	Unc
Nic 15	ND	Brass	25mm	—	—	60.00	—

Hc. da SAN FRANCISCO / (crosslike ornament) / . SAN MARCOS / Rv: ARTURO / VAUGHAN around illegible central device. Plain edge. Rare. (Luedeking coll.)

Araguito
F. MARVEZ

Rulau	Date	Metal	Size	VG	F	VF	Unc
Nic 16	1867	Lead	—	—	—	—	—

F. MARVEZ / ¼ REAL / 1867. Rv: Blank. Pattern by LORENZ of Hamburg, Germany. (Ulex 2169; Eklund 1006)

Eklund said Nicaragua. Henkle suggests Mexico.

Counterstamped Nicaraguan Centavos
On CN 1 Centavo, 1878, 21mm

Stamp	VG-F
Nic 20 A.O.	15.00
Nic 21 B A	—
Nic 22 B F in circle of rings	35.00
Nic 23 E B	5.00
Nic 24 E H	15.00
Nic 25 F / * / * * / F	15.00
Nic 26 F M	5.00
Nic 27 F S	5.00
Nic 28 G S	5.00
Nic 29 J C (in border of 8 U-shaped ornaments)	Rare
Nic 30 J R	20.00
Nic 32 L	5.00
Nic 34 R	—
Nic 35 R D	5.00
Nic 36 S	5.00
Nic 37 S. L.	5.00
Nic 38 T. A.	15.00
Nic 40 V.	5.00
Nic 42 3	5.00
Nic 44 (Spread eagle) / 2 (obv); 2 (rev)	35.00
Nic 46 B F (in border of 14 circles - on shaved coin)	Unique

(Smithsonian Inst.)

On CN 5 Centavos, 1898 or 1899, 20mm

Stamp	VG-F
Nic 50 MF monogram 1899	15.00
Nic 51 N (outlined) 1898	25.00
Nic 53 R C 1898	20.00
Nic 54 R C (obv.); S. R. (rev.) 1898	30.00
Nic 55 S / P 1898	—
Nic 60 (bird shaped outline) 1899	35.00

PANAMA

BOCAS DEL TORO PROVINCE

Bocas del Toro
WILSON & FITZGERALD

Rulau	Date	Metal	Size	VG	F	VF	Unc
BDT 6	ND	CN	23.5mm	—	—	50.00	—

WILSON & FITZGERALD/BOCAS DEL TORO. Rv: 5 CENTS. (Plumer pg. 10; King coll.)

M.

Rulau	Date	Metal	Size	VG	F	VF	Unc
BDT 3	ND	—	—mm	—	—	—	—

M. Rv: Blank. (Plumer pg.7)

Plumer reported this item was found in use on Isla Colon, the offshore island on which the city of Bocas del Toro is located in the Caribbean Sea. This city was formerly known as Punta Toro.

CHIRIQUI PROVINCE

Boquete
CAROLIN, SUTTON & CASTILLO

Rulau	Date	Metal	Size	VG	F	VF	Unc
Chq 1	ND	Copper	28.5mm	—	—	45.00	—

- CAROLIN - / BOQUETE / SUTTON & CASTILLO. Rv: VALE POR UNA LATA DE CAFE / 1. Plain edge. Scarce. (King coll.)

Vale por una lata de cafe = Good for one tin can of coffee.

EMILIO C. KANT
El Progreso

Rulau	Date	Metal	Size	VG	F	VF	Unc
Chq 3	ND	Brass	28mm	—	—	45.00	—

EL PROGRESO / BOQUETE / EMILIO C. KANT. Rv: VALE POR UNA LATA DE CAFE / 1. Plain edge. (Plumer N/L; Kirtley April 1989 sale, lot 421; King coll.)

Una lata de cafe = One tin can of coffee. In the Kirtley sale of Oct. 1990, a VF specimen made $45.00.

NEMESIO LEDESMA

Rulau	Date	Metal	Size	VG	F	VF	Unc
Chq 5	ND	Brass	28.5mm	7.00	13.00	20.00	—

LA ESPERANZA / * / BOQUETE / * / NEMESIO LEDESMA. Rv: VALE POR UNA LATA DE CAFE / 1 / -.-. Plain edge. (King coll.; Plumer pg. 6; Rulau coll.)

A. D. MACINTYRE

Rulau	Date	Metal	Size	VF	F	VF	Unc
Chq 6	ND	Aluminum	30mm	—	—	75.00	—

Radiant star. Around: A. D. MACINTYRE / * BOQUETE *. Rv: GOOD FOR - / 50 C / - IN TRADE. Plain edge. (King coll.)

Rulau	Date	Metal	Size	VG	F	VF	Unc
Chq 7	ND	Aluminum	24.5mm	—	—	50.00	—

As last, but * 25 C.

Rulau	Date	Metal	Size	VG	F	VF	Unc
Chq 7A	ND	Aluminum	18mm	—	—	30.00	—

As last, but 10 C.

Rulau	Date	Metal	Size	VG	F	VF	Unc
Chq 7B	ND	Aluminum	21mm	—	—	30.00	—

As last, but 5 C. (King coll.)

J. Conte Porras called these *fincas cafeteras* (coffee estate tokens) in 1982. Supposedly only 5 sets exist.

AURELIO ROVIRA

Rulau	Date	Metal	Size	VG	F	VF	Unc
Chq 8	ND	Copper	28.5mm	—	—	—	—

LA PANDURA / BOQUETE / -AURELIO ROVIRA-. Rv: VALE POR UNA LATA DE CAFE / 1 -.-. (Peters Jan. 1975 sale, lot 201)

ENRIQUE VASQUEZ

Rulau	Date	Metal	Size	VG	F	VF	Unc
Chq 11	ND	Aluminum	25mm	—	—	30.00	—

FINCA JARAMILLO / ENRIQUE VASQUEZ. S / BOQUETE. Rv: Blank. (Peters Jan. 1975 sale, lot 225)

Chiriqui Plantation
SNYDER BROS.

Rulau	Date	Metal	Size	VG	F	VF	Unc
Chq 18	ND	Copper	35mm	—	—	—	—

SNYDER BROS. / (incuse) 21 / o CHIRIQUI PLTN. o.
Rv: Blank. Plain edge. Issued holed. Very rare. (Jess
Peters Jan. 1975 sale, lot 217)

This was called a "slave token" in the Jess Peters 1975 sale of a major collection of Panamanian coins and tokens. Warren Plumer first used this description.

David
JUAN ARIAS

Rulau	Date	Metal	Size	VG	F	VF	Unc
Chq 21	ND	CN	24.5mm	—	8.50	16.00	35.00

On folds of ribbon: JUAN / ARIAS / DAVID. Rv:
VALE / 5 / CENTAVOS. Plain edge. (Plumer N/L;
Kirtley April 1989 sale, lot 419; King coll.)

| Chq 22 | ND | CN | 24.5mm | — | — | — | — |

As last, but with center hole over the denomination, as
issued. (King coll.; Kirtley April 1989 sale, lot 420)

F.
(FRANK TEDMAN)

𝔽

Rulau	Date	Metal	Size	VG	F	VF	Unc
Chq 24	(1930's)	CN	24.5mm	—	—	45.00	—

As the first Arias token above, but ctsp F on either
obverse or reverse. (King coll.)

Frank Tedman purchased the plantation near David from Juan Arias in the 1930's, according to King.

CARLOS MILLINGEN

Rulau	Date	Metal	Size	VG	F	VF	Unc
Chq 27	ND	CN	24.5mm	—	25.00	40.00	—

CARLOS / MILLINGEN / DAVID (all on folds of a
ribbon). Rv: VALE / 5 / CENTAVOS. Plain edge. (King
coll.)

COCLE PROVINCE

Agua Dulce
MARIO A. RAMIREZ

Rulau	Date	Metal	Size	VG	F	VF	Unc
Coc 1	ND	Copper	25mm	—	—	—	—

LA VIOLETA (etc.). Rv: MARIO A. RAMIREZ / 10
(in circle) / * AGUA DULCE *. (Conte-Porras report)

COLON PROVINCE

Cativa
LAM HING CO. STORES

Rulau	Date	Metal	Size	VG	F	VF	Unc
Col 3	1912	Aluminum	20mm	—	—	—	—

LAM HING CO. / GOOD FOR / 5 CENTS / SILVER /
STORES. Rv: THE PANAMA DEV. & MFG. CO. /
CATIVA / 1912. Rare. (Peters Jan. 1975 sale, lot 209)

| Col 5 | 1912 | Aluminum | 24mm | — | — | — | — |

As last, but 20. (King coll.)

Colon (City)
G.A.

Rulau	Date	Metal	Size	VG	F	VF	Unc
Col 20	1884	Copper	20mm	—	42.50	—	—

* / G.A. / 1884 / COLON. Rv: VALUE / Radiant 5 /
CENTS. Plain edge. (Peters Jan. 1975 sale, lot 210)

COLL BRANDON & CO.

Rulau	Date	Metal	Size	VG	F	VF	Unc
Col 22	ND	Copper	28mm	—	—	60.00	100.

Train right, palm tree behind. Rv: COLL BRANDON
& CO. / 2½ Cts.. (in beaded circle) / COLON, (ASPIN-
WALL). Plain edge. (Eklund 1054)

This token also occurs in Brass, same valuations.

Rulau	Date	Metal	Size	VG	F	VF	Unc
Col 23	ND	Copper	29mm	—	—	175.	

Same, but struck over U.S. 1851 Large cent. (Bill Randel coll.)

Rulau	Date	Metal	Size	VG	F	VF	Unc
Col 24	ND	Copper	28mm	—	-	175.	

Same, but struck over New York Civil War store card of John Matthews, 1863 (Fuld NY 523). (Bill Randel coll.)

Since the discovery of the overstrikes listed above, it may be assumed these tokens were issued after 1863.

CHARLES COURTNEY

Rulau	Date	Metal	Size	VG	F	VF	Unc
Col 26	ND	CN	20mm	—	—	25.00	

(All incused): CHARLES COURTNEY / COLON. Rv: DEBO / 5 / CENTAVOS. (Eklund 1057; Weyl 1899 listing)

HENRY DE LISSER

Rulau	Date	Metal	Size	VG	F	VF	Unc
Col 28	ND	CN	20mm	—	—	—	—

HENRY DE LISSER / -o- / COLON / -o- / (ornament). Rv: (Ornament) 5 (ornament) / CENTS. Plain edge (Randel coll.)

The Randel collection contains three specimens of this previously unpublished token.

H. GANS

Rulau	Date	Metal	Size	VG	F	VF	Unc
Col 31	ND	Copper	23mm	—	—	50.00	

. JOYERIA Y RELOJERIA . / H. / GANS / COLON / . Rv: Fasces and bow-and-arrows within cornucopia wreath. Plain edge. Rare. (Eklund 1060)

Rulau	Date	Metal	Size	VG	F	VF	Unc
Col 32	ND	Copper	24mm	—	—	50.00	

Similar. 10 CENT. (Eklund 1061)

SANTIAGO GARCIA

Rulau	Date	Metal	Size	VG	F	VF	Unc
Col 34	ND	CN	20mm	—	—	45.00	

SANTIAGO GARCIA / (ornament) / COLON / .*. Rv: 5 between scrolls / CENTS. Plain edge. (Wright 1425; Peters Jan. 1975 sale, lot 206; Eklund 2387)

GRAND HOTEL INTERNATL.

Rulau	Date	Metal	Size	VG	F	VF	Unc
Col 36	ND	CN	23mm	—	—	30.00	65.00

GRAND HOTEL INTERNATL / 5 Cvos / COLON. Rv: Same as obverse. (Rulau coll.)

Rulau	Date	Metal	Size	VG	F	VF	Unc
Col 37	ND	Brass	23mm	—	15.00	22.50	50.00

As last. Plain edge. (Eklund 1062; Rulau coll.)

Struck by Scovill Mfg. Co., Waterbury, Conn.

A. GROSSO

Rulau	Date	Metal	Size	VG	F	VF	Unc
Col 39	ND	CN	20mm	—	—	50.00	—

(All incuse): COLON Y CARGRE around A. GROSSO. Rv: Blank. (King coll.; Plumer pg. 1)

Plumer described CARGRE as CHAGATE, but said he never saw the piece.

E. B. HEALEY

Rulau	Date	Metal	Size	VG	F	VF	Unc
Col 40	ND	Aluminum	23mm	—	—	60.00	
Col 40A	ND	Aluminum	19mm	—	—	50.00	

E. B. HEALEY / EAGLE / . - . / BAR / COLON, R. DE P. Rv: GOOD FOR / 10 / IN / MERCHANDISE. Plain edge. (King coll.)

As last, but 5. (Two die varieties are known). (J. Conte Porras report)

HENRIQUES E HIJO

Rulau	Date	Metal	Size	VG	F	VF	Unc
Col 41	ND	CN	20mm	—	20.00	50.00	—

(All incused): HENRIQUES E. HIJO / 5 C (slanted) / . COLON . Rv: Blank. (Peters Jan. 1975 sale, lot 215; King coll., ex-Randel)

HOTEL INTEROCEANIQUE

Rulau	Date	Metal	Size	VG	F	VF	Unc
Col 43	ND	CN	19mm	—	—	60.00	—

HOTEL INTEROCEANIQUE / Radiant 5 / * COLON *. Rv: Blank. (Eklund 1063)

C. JACKSON

Rulau	Date	Metal	Size	VG	F	VF	Unc
Col 47	ND	CN	20mm	—	—	—	—

C. JACKSON / (ornament) / COLON / .*. / 18 (incuse). Rv: (Ornament) / 5 / (ornament) / CENTS. Plain edge. (Eklund 1065; 1899 Weyl listing)

JOSE MONTEVERDE

Rulau	Date	Metal	Size	VG	F	VF	Unc
Col 50	ND	CN	20mm	—	—	—	—

(All incuse): JOSE MONTEVERDE / 5 C / COLON. Rv: Blank.

SAVINGS BANK OF COLON

Rulau	Date	Metal	Size	VG	F	VF	Unc
Col 60	1885	Silver	20mm	—	—	50.00	125.

SAVINGS BANK OF COLON / 10 / CENTS / (small) B. Rv: FIELD BRODIE & CO. / 10 / CENTS / 1885. Reeded edge. (Eklund 1069)

Col 61	1885	Silver	16mm	—	—	50.00	125.

As last, but 5 / CENTS. Reeded edge. Weight 1.25 grams. (Eklund 1068)

B = Bogota Mint, most likely. The weight of the 5-centavo token is the same as the Colombia 5-centavo coin of the period (KM 174a.1), and this may be struck on the regular .667 fine coin planchets. Colon was a Colombian port city in 1885.

G. M. SOLLAS

Rulau	Date	Metal	Size	VG	F	VF	Unc
Col 63	ND	CN	20mm	—	—	50.00	—

G. M. SOLLAS / (ornament) / * COLON *. Rv: .o. / (ornaments) 5 (ornaments) / CENTS. (King coll.; Bosco sale of Nov. 1985)

S. SORACCO

Rulau	Date	Metal	Size	VG	F	VF	Unc
Col 65	ND	CN	20mm	—	—	35.00	—

S. SORACCO / (ornament) / COLON / .*. Rv: 5 between ornate scrolls / CENTS. Plain edge. Rare. (Ulex 2241; Eklund 1070; Bernal 376; Scott)

J. SUCRE

Rulau	Date	Metal	Size	VG	F	VF	Unc
Col 67	ND	CN	20mm	—	23.00	50.00	—

VALE AL PORTADOR / 5 C / COLON / . J. SUCRE. Rv: Same as obverse. (Peters Jan. 1975 sale, lot 228)

WING CHONG YUEN & CO.

Rulau	Date	Metal	Size	VG	F	VF	Unc
Col 69	ND	CN	20mm	—	—	70.00	—

WING CHONG YUEN & CO. / Radiant 5 / * COLON *. Rv: Blank. Rare. (Eklund 1071; Peters Jan. 1975 sale, lot 194)

Rulau	Date	Metal	Size	VG	F	VF	Unc
Col 70	ND	CN	20mm	—	—	40.00	—

WING CHONG / YUEN & CO. / COLON. Rv: Radiant 5, VALUE / CENTS around. (Ulex 2241; Eklund 1072; Bernal 377)

Rulau	Date	Metal	Size	VG	F	VF	Unc
Col 71	ND	CN	20mm	12.50	20.00	35.00	—

(All incused) WING CHUNG YUEN / 5 / CENT. VALE. Rv: Blank. (Peters Jan. 1975 sale, lot 208)

WING TAI LONG & CO.

Rulau	Date	Metal	Size	VG	F	VF	Unc
Col 73	ND	CN	20mm	—	40.00	60.00	—

(All incused): WING TAI LONG & Co. / 5 / CENT VALE. Rv: Blank. (Peters Jan. 1975 sale, lot 214)

DARIEN PROVINCE

Cana
THE DARIEN GOLD MINING COMPANY LIMITED

1st Series

Rulau	Date	Metal	Size	VG	F	VF	Unc
Dar 1	1894	Brass	Oct 31.5mm	—	60.00	100.	—

Gold miner with pick stands left. Around: THE DARIEN GOLD MINING COMPANY / -LIMITED-. Rv: LA-MINAS-DE-ORO-DARIEN-A-CANA / 50 C / - / 1894 -. Plain edge. (*SIN Journal* for Jan. 1969; Plumer pg. 9)

Rulau	Date	Metal	Size	VG	F	VF	Unc
Dar 2	1894	Brass	Oct 27mm	—	—	100.	—

As last, but 25 C.

Rulau	Date	Metal	Size	VG	F	VF	Unc
Dar 3	1894	Brass	Oct 31mm	—	50.00	75.00	—

As last, but 20 C.

Tokens in this series are frequently found counterstamped with numerals 3, 4, 5 or 6 on reverse. It is believed these were camp numbers.

2nd Series

Rulau	Date	Metal	Size	VG	F	VF	Unc
Dar 5	ND	Brass	Sq 33mm	—	80.00	150.	RR

Obverse similar to last series. Rv: PARA SIMPLIFI-CAR LAS CUENTAS / $1 / NADA MAS / *. Plain edge. (Plumer pg. 9)

Rulau	Date	Metal	Size	VG	F	VF	Unc
Dar 6	ND	Brass	Oct 31.5mm	—	60.00	—	—

As last, but 50 C.

Rulau	Date	Metal	Size	VG	F	VF	Unc
Dar 7	ND	Brass	Oct 31.5mm	—	—	125.	—

As last, but 20 C.

Rulau	Date	Metal	Size	VG	F	VF	Unc
Dar 8	ND	Brass	Oct 24mm	—	35.00	50.00	80.00

As last, but 10 C. (Bernal 395; Plumer pg. 9; Randel coll.)

Tokens in this series are reported with or without counterstamped numeral 3, possibly a camp number.

Para simplificar las cuentas, nada mas = To simplify accounting, nothing more. Apparently an evasion of laws against creating private money.

3rd Series

Rulau	Date	Metal	Size	VG	F	VF	Unc
Dar 10	(1905)	Brass	31mm	—	—	—	—

As next, but 50 C.

Rulau	Date	Metal	Size	VG	F	VF	Unc
Dar 11	ND	Brass	Sq 23.5mm	—	—	100.	—

At center: 20 C in circle above mine headgear. Around: THE DAIREN / GOLD / MINING COMy. / LIMITED. Rv: Large 20 C/ (tiny) G. Y. ILIFFE BIRM within center. Around: PARA SIMPL / IFICARLAS / CUENTAS / NADA MAS. Plain edge. Rare. (Peters Jan. 1975 sale, lot 200)

Rulau	Date	Metal	Size	VG	F	VF	Unc
Dar 12	ND	Brass	Oct 24mm	—	—	—	125.

As last, but 10 C. (Eklund 1073)

Para simplificar las cuentas, nada mas = To simplify accounting, nothing more. A transparent method of evading the laws against paying wages in currency tokens.

Struck by George Yorke Iliffe, the tokenmaker of Birmingham, England (in business 1875-1934).

There is also a rare $1 token, square, brass, 34.5mm, and an extremely rare $5 token, triangular, 35x41mm, which bears a 1905 date. The latter carries the signature G. Y. ILIFFE, ENG.

PANAMA PROVINCE

Panama (City)
CESARIO CELIS

Rulau	Date	Metal	Size	VG	F	VF	Unc
Pma 5	ND	CN	20mm	—	—	50.00	—

CESARIO CELIS / PANAMA. Rv: DEBO / 2 ½ / CENTAVOS. Plain edge. (Ulex 2241; Eklund 1076; King coll.)

Supposedly only 2 known.

THE MADURO—LUPI CO.

Rulau	Date	Metal	Size	VG	F	VF	Unc
Pma 10	(1900-15)	Brass	32mm	—	—	50.00	—

In central circle: EMPORIUM / OF / FASHION. Around: GOOD VALUE & GOOD LUCK / ALWAYS AT THE / PANAMA / o THE MADURO-LUPI Co. o. Rv: Reverse swastika and good luck symbols. Around: MEMBERSHIP EMBLEM OF THE GOOD VALUE CLUB / GOOD LUCK. Plain edge.

J. DEL C. MEJIA

Rulau	Date	Metal	Size	VG	F	VF	Unc
Pma 12	ND	CN	20mm	—	—	25.00	—

(All incused): J. DEL C. MEJIA / PANAMA. Rv: DEBO / 5 / CENTAVOS. Plain edge. (Ulex 2241; Eklund 1075)

| Pma 13 | ND | CN | 20mm | — | — | 25.00 | — |

As last, but 2½. (*World Coins* for Sept. 1970, pg. 1184)

Jose del C. Mejia, according to the late Ted Uhl of Auburndale, Florida.

SAN BLAS TERRITORY
SAN BLAS ISLANDS

Rulau	Date	Metal	Size	F	VF	EF	Unc
SB 1	(1971)	Brass	29mm	—	—	—	9.00

Sailboat left, man at tiller. Around: SAN BLAS ISLANDS. Rv: Palm tree, SIABIBI at right. Tiny CQP in right field. Plain edge. Mintage: 5000. (Rulau coll.)

CQP = Charlie Q. Peters, the designer. Struck by Wendell-Northwestern medallic firm in Minnesota, U.S.A. Supposedly valued in 1971 at 5 coconuts, or 50 cents.

| SB 3 | (1977) | Brass | 29mm | — | — | — | 7.00 |

Obverse similar to last, but 5-pointed star added at right of sailboat, and initials J.A.M. added. Rv: As last. Plain edge.

Rulau	Date	Metal	Size	F	VF	EF	Unc
SB 5	(19)78	Brass	26mm	—	—	—	8.00

San Blas Indian woman's head half left, a large flat disc pendant dangling from her earring. On the disc is: 78. She also wears a nose ring. At right: SAN BLAS . PANAMA. Rv: Palm tree in reversed-motif, tiny CQP near its base. At right: SIABIBI. Plain edge. (Lauren Benson report)

| SB 6 | (1)979 | Brass | 26mm | — | — | — | 8.00 |

As last, but inscription on earring pendant reads: 979 / 78.

| SB 7 | (19)80 | Brass | 26mm | — | — | — | 8.00 |

As last, but inscription on earring reads: 80 /979 /78.

| SB 9 | 1986 | CN | 26mm | — | — | — | 5.00 |

As last, but inscription on earring pendant reads: 1986 / 80 / 979 / 78. (Henkle report)

The Gulf of San Blas lies off Panama's northern (Caribbean) coast. The two ports serving the gulf's mainland are Mandinga and Ustupo. Inland from the gulf, on the mainland, a mountain range parallels the shoreline, the Cordillera de San Blas.

The Comarca (Territory) of San Blas is, administratively, part of Colon Provincia. The territory has 1,238 square miles and a 1970 population of 25,000.

The Cuna Indians live in the 375 islands of the Archipielago de las Mulatas (San Blas Islands) and the nearby coast of the Golfo de San Blas, and along the shores of the Rio Tuira and its tributaries. They speak the Cuna language and are relatively primitive. In 1990 there were an estimated 40,000 Cunas living in the islands or on the mainland.

Relations between the Republic of Panama and the Cunas are regulated by a 1953 treaty which prohibits any non-Cuna Panamanian from owning land, starting a business or building a house in San Blas Territory without permission from the Cuna Congress, a legislative body with at least five representatives from each of the 52 inhabited islands.

The American invasion of Panama in December, 1989, briefly dragged the Cunas back into the 20th century. The Cunas usually support the U.S., though a few had accommodated themselves to the corrupt Noriega regime. Leonidas Valdes, cacique (chief) of all the Cunas, gave his permission Jan. 30, 1990 to American troops to hunt for Noriega guerrillas in the jungles of San Blas. Valdes hoped the U.S. would provide aid in return.

Coconuts are a medium of exchange among the San Blas Indians. Each coconut is worth about 10 cents.

UNATTRIBUTED PANAMA

BARROWS PANAMA COFFEE LANDS

Rulau	Date	Metal	Size	VG	F	VF	Unc
Pan 1	ND	Brass	33.5mm	—	—	45.00	—

BARROWS PANAMA COFFEE LANDS. Rv: GOOD FOR / 50 / IN TRADE. Scarce (King coll.)

25, 10, 5 and 2½-centavo tokens also are known.

JAMES CHONG & CO.

Rulau	Date	Metal	Size	F	VF	EF	Unc
Pan 6	ND	Copper	35mm	—	—	—	—

JAMES CHONG & CO. / (ornament) / GENERAL / MERCHANDISE / (ornament). Rv: GOOD FOR / $1oo / IN MERCHANDISE. Beaded border on each side. (Peters Jan. 1975 sale, lot 218)

Horqueta
SEGUNDO DIAZ

Rulau	Date	Metal	Size	VG	F	VF	Unc
Pan 7	ND	Brass	28.5mm	—	10.00	17.50	—

LA BERLINA / HORQUETA / SEGUNDO DIAZ. Rv: VALE POR UNA LATA DE CAFE / 1. (King coll.)

There is a locale in the Canal Zone called Palo Horqueta on Gatun Lake. However, this is likely Panama outside the Zone.

ELISEO DE LEON

Rulau	Date	Metal	Size	VG	F	VF	Unc
Pan 8	ND	CN	20mm	—	—	50.00	—

(All incuse: ELISEO DE LEON / 5 / CENT . VALE. Rv: Blank. (Plumer pg. 3; King coll.)

S.L. ISAACS & ASCH

Rulau	Date	Metal	Size	VG	F	VF	Unc
Pan 12	ND	CN	20mm	—	45.00	—	—

(All incused): S.L. ISAACS & ASCH / 5 / CENTAVOS. Rv: Blank. (Eklund 1064 and 2311; 1899 Weyl listing)

LUM. CHANG. LONG & CO.

Rulau	Date	Metal	Size	VG	F	VF	Unc
Pan 14	ND	CN	20mm	—	—	40.00	—

LUM. CHANG. LONG & Co / 5 / CENT. VALE. Rv: Blank. Rare. (Peters Jan. 1975 sale, lot 222)

OSORIO

Rulau	Date	Metal	Size	VG	F	VF	Unc
Pan 16	ND	Brass	27mm	—	12.50	20.00	30.00

FINCA DE CAFE / * / OSORIO / *. Rv: VALE POR / * / 1 LATA / *. Plain edge. Scarce. (Peters Jan. 1975 sale, lot 212)

Rulau	Date	Metal	Size	VG	F	VF	Unc
Pan 17	ND	Brass	25mm	—	12.50	20.00	—

FINCA DE CAFE / * / OSORIO / *. Rv: VALE POR / * / ½ LATA / *. Plain edge. Holed after issue, for stringing. (Rulau coll.)

Rulau	Date	Metal	Size	VG	F	VF	Unc
Pan 18	ND	Brass	20mm	—	—	—	—

As last, but ¼. (King coll.)

PIZA, LINDO & BAUDOUIN

Rulau	Date	Metal	Size	VG	F	VF	Unc
Pan 20	ND	CN	32mm	—	—	—	—

(All inclused): PIZA, LINDO & BAUDOUIN / 50 / CENTAVOS / +. Rv: Blank. (Peters Jan. 1975 sale, lot 197)

FINCA SANTO DOMINGO

Rulau	Date	Metal	Size	VG	F	VF	EF
Pan 24	1924	Aluminum	28.5mm	—	—	40.00	90.00

FINCA SANTO DOMINGO / -.- / E. PANAMA / 1924 / ____. Rv: VALE / 25 / * CENTAVOS *. Plain edge. (Plumer pg. 4; King coll.)

VENEZUELA PANAMA LIMITED

Rulau	Date	Metal	Size	VG	F	VF	Unc
Pan 30	ND	Brass	Hexag 27mm	—	—	—	—

VENEZUELA PANAMA / GOLD / MINE / Co. / . LIMITED . Rv: Blank. (Peters Jan. 1975 sale, lot 221)

PANAMA CANAL ZONE

Ancon
ALEXANDER HOSKINS

Rulau	Date	Metal	Size	VG	F	VF	Unc
CZ 2	ND	CN	24mm	—	—	—	—

ALEXANDER HOSKINS / -.- / ANCON / -.-. Rv: VALE UN CIGARRO / 5 (on ornate circle) / CTVOS. Plain edge. (Plumer pg 1)

Rulau	Date	Metal	Size	VG	F	VF	Unc
CZ 3	ND	Bronze	25.5mm	—	—	—	—

Obverse as reverse of last token. Rv: Same as obverse. Plain edge. (Smithsonian Institute coll.)

There is no name on the second token above.

Bajo Obispo
J. DE LA PEÑA & CO.

Rulau	Date	Metal	Size	VG	F	VF	Unc
CZ 4	(1905-15)	CN	20mm	—	—	—	—

(All incused): J DE LA PEÑA & CO./ BAJO OBISPO. Rv: VALE / 5 / CENTAVOS. Plain edge. (See TAMS *Journal* for Aug. 1985, page 136)

This was a canal construction token for laborers. Bajo Obispo is a location on the south shore of Gatun Lake, on the west side of the Panama Canal.

PEÑA HERMANOS

Rulau	Date	Metal	Size	VG	F	VF	Unc
CZ 6	(1905-15)	CN	20mm	—	—	—	—

(All incused): PEÑA HERMANOS / BAJO OBISPO. Rv: VALE / 5 / CENTAVOS. (Jess Peters Jan. 1975 sale, lot 216)

Culebra
B. B. BRYAN

Rulau	Date	Metal	Size	VG	F	VF	Unc
CZ 9	ND	CN	20mm	—	—	—	—

(All incused): B. B. BRYAN CULEBRA / 5 / CENT - VALE. Rv: Blank. (Eklund 1028)

ANJEL OVALLEP

Rulau	Date	Metal	Size	VG	F	VF	Unc
CZ 12	ND	xx	32mm	—	—	100.	

ANJEL OVALLEP / JAMAICA / BAZAAR / CULE-BRA. Rv: VALE / 5 / CENTAVOS. (Plumer pg. 1)

xx Black vulcanite.

F.M.PIERRA & CO.

Rulau	Date	Metal	Size	VG	F	VF	Unc
CZ 14	1883	xx	32mm	—	60.00	100.	

xx Red vulcanite. F.M. PIERRA & CO. / 5 / CULE-BRA I COLON. Rv: VALE CINCO CENTAVOS / 5 / 1883. (Eklund 1067; Randel coll.; King coll.)

Rulau	Date	Metal	Size	VG	F	VF	Unc
CZ 15	1883	vv	32mm	—	—	75.00	

vv Black vulcanite. F.M. PIERRA & CO. 5 CEN-TAVOS. CULEBRA. (Eklund 1029)

The second piece has not been examined. CZ 14 also occurs in black vulcanite.

ANTONIO ZUBIETA

Rulau	Date	Metal	Size	VG	F	VF	Unc
CZ 17	ND	CN	20.5mm	—	—	50.00	—

(All incuse) ANTONIO ZUBIETA / CULEBRA. Rv: (All incuse) VALE / 5 / CENTAVOS . Plain edge. (Plumer pg. 1)

| CZ 18 | ND | CN | 20.5mm | — | — | — | — |

As last, but ctsp 7 on obverse. (Plumer pg. 1)

This token has also been reported ctsp V instead of 7.

ZUBIETA & PASOS

Rulau	Date	Metal	Size	VG	F	VF	Unc
CZ 20	(1870)	CN	20mm	—	8.00	11.00	20.00

Cross made up of floreate devices. Around: ZUBIETA & PASOS / .CULEBRA. Rv: VALE / 5 (radiant) / CENTAVOS. Plain edge. (Ulex 3352; Bernal 374; Rulau coll.)

Culebra is a city in Panama on the west bank of the Panama Canal. When this token was issued it was long before the canal was begun and long before there was a Canal Zone.

Panama was a Colombian department before its independence in 1903.

There is a port of Culebra in Peru, and some authorities ascribe this token there. Author Bernal claims it for Colombia. The reverse device, however, is typical of Panama tokens of this period. (Antonio Zubieta.)

El Canal
RONCALLO Y CA.

Rulau	Date	Metal	Size	VG	F	VF	Unc
CZ 25	ND	CN	20mm	—	—	50.00	—

(All incused): EL CANAL / 5 / CENTS / RONCALLO Y CA. Rv: Blank. Plain edge. (Ulex 2241; Eklund 1074; King coll.)

The reference to "the canal" on this piece probably refers to the French canal company, though it could have been issued as late as about 1907 under the American enterprise.

| CZ 26 | ND | CN | 20mm | — | — | — | — |

As last, but ctsp with rayed device. (Zaika coll.)

Emperador
R. A. AROSEMENA & CO.

Rulau	Date	Metal	Size	VG	F	VF	Unc
CZ 28	ND	CN	20.5mm	—	—	75.00	—

R.A. AROSEMENA & CO. / EMPERADOR. Rv: VALE / 5 / CENTAVOS. (Plumer pg. 8). All inscriptions on this token are incused. The token has been reported seen counterstamped, but no description of the stamp was given.

RODRIGUEZ Y R.....OB

Rulau	Date	Metal	Size	VG	F	VF	Unc
CZ 29	1887	**	31mm	—	—	75.00	—

** Purple vulcanite, lettering enameled white. RODRIGUEZ Y R.....OB (second name partially erased) / CINCO / VA 5 LE / CENTAVOS / EMPERADOR. Rv: VALE CINCO CENTAVOS / Y / R. 5. R. / EMPERADOR / - 1887 -. (Bob Lyall coll.)

Unpublished. Until another specimen surfaces, we cannot know the second partner's name. ** Possibly celluloid.

SANTIAGO SAMUDIO

Rulau	Date	Metal	Size	VG	F	VF	Unc
CZ 30	1886	Vulcanite	31mm	—	—	100.	—

SANTIAGO SAMUDIO / 5 / EMPERADOR. Rv: VALE CINCO CENTAVOS / 5 / 1886. Rare. (Peters Jan. 1975 sale, lot 207; Eklund 1512; King coll.)

| CZ 32 | ND | CN | 20mm | — | — | 60.00 | — |

(All incused): S. SAMUDIO / 5 C / EMPIRE. Rv: Blank. (Peters Jan. 1975 sale, lot 196)

Emperador is on the west side of Culebra Cut, between Culebra and Bajo Obispo.

Gatun
GATUN GOLF CLUB

Rulau	Date	Metal	Size	F	VF	EF	Unc
CZ 34	ND	Brass	20mm	—	—	—	—

GATUN GOLF CLUB / GATUN, CANAL ZONE / CLAIM CHECK. Rv: No descr. available.

Gorgona
NORZA & CO.

Rulau	Date	Metal	Size	VG	F	VF	Unc
CZ 37	ND	CN	20mm	—	—	—	—

(All incused): NORZA & Co. GORGONA / 5 / CENT - VALE. Rv: Blank. (Peters Jan. 1975 sale, lot 204)

Gorgona is on Gatun Lake, north of Bajo Obispo.

Mount Hope
ISTHMIAN TRADING & CONTRACTING CO.

Rulau	Date	Metal	Size	VG	F	VF	Unc
CZ 44	ND	Brass	32mm	—	—	—	—

ISTHMIAN TRADING & CONTRACTING CO. / -.- / 1 QT. / -.- / MT. HOEP. C. Z. Rv: Blank. Plain edge. (Eklund 1090; Plumer pg. 6)

Rulau	Date	Metal	Size	VG	F	VF	Unc
CZ 45	ND	Brass		—	—	—	—

As last, but 1 PT. (Plumer pg. 6)

The spelling Hoep appears on both tokens. It is believed it should have read Hope. These are, possibly, milk tokens.

Paraiso
COMPAGNIE UNIVERSELLE DU CANAL INTEROCEANIQUE D. PANAMA

Rulau	Date	Metal	Size	VG	F	VF	Unc
CZ 50	(1881-88)	++	32mm	—	125.	275.	800.

++ Red vulcanite. COMPAGNIE UNIVERSELLE DU CANAL INTEROCEANIQUE DE PANAMA / 5. Rv: SECTION DE PARAISO / 5 / CANTINES. (Eklund 1091; *World Coins* for May 1971, pg. 669; Randel coll.; King coll.; Gadoury-Elie 1.1)

This was the French company headed by Ferdinand de Lesseps, builder of the Suez Canal, which secured the rights in 1880 to build the canal across the Panama isthmus. The company was bankrupt and in scandal by 1889.

Paraiso was later, under the Americans, to become the site for the north entrance to the huge Pedro Miguel Locks on the Panama Canal.

PANAMA

Rulau	Date	Metal	Size	VG	F	VF	EF
CZ 52	(1887)	Bronze	30mm	—	—	Rare	—

PANAMA ctsp on France 1887-A 10-centime coin, Yeoman-44.1. Specimens examined have had the incuse stamp applied on obverse.

James E. Lorah of Oakland Park, Fla. reported in 1984 that a very limited number of French 10-centime coins were counterstamped by De Lesseps' company for use in the company store or redeemed in silver.

Tavernilla
L. CHACON

Rulau	Date	Metal	Size	VG	F	VF	Unc
CZ 55	ND	CN	20mm	—	—	—	—

L. CHACON. 10 CENT. (Eklund 1056, from 1899 Weyl listing)

This token also occurs in Brass.

CZ 57	ND	CN		—	—	—	50.00	—

(All incuse): L. CHACON TABERNILLA / 5 / CENT - VALE. Rv: Blank. Plain edge. (King coll.)

Tavernilla is a location on the Panama Canal, between Gorgona and Bohio Soldado.

ISTHMIAN CANAL COMMISSION

Rulau	Date	Metal	Size	VG	F	VF	EF
CZ 69	(1904)	Brass	46mm	—	180.	—	—

(All incused): A / 138 (or another number) / I.C.C. Rv: Blank. (A = American. Made with single-letter punches.)

Rulau	Date	Metal	Size	F	VF	EF	Unc
CZ 70	(1905-09)	Brass	++		37.50	70.00	—

++ Diamond-shaped flan, 35x53mm. ISTHMIAN CANAL / 37145 / COMMISSION. Rv: Blank. Issued holed for suspension. (Kirtley Nov. 1988 sale no. 28, lot 41)

Identification check. Another specimen is numbered 53584.

Rulau	Date	Metal	Size	F	VF	EF	Unc
CZ 72	(1905-09)	Brass	++		75.00	—	—

++ Diamond shaped flan, 38x59mm. All letters and numerals are enameled black. (All incused): ISTHMIAN -CANAL- / 72622 (or another number) / COMMISSION. Rv: Blank. Plain edge. (Rulau coll., ex-Randel)

Rulau	Date	Metal	Size	F	VF	EF	Unc
CZ 73	(?)	Brass	vv	—	75.00	—	—

vv Hexagonal flan, size not known, black enameled letters and digits. ISTHMIAN CANAL COMMISSION / 53584 (or another number). Rv: Blank. (Plumer report, Sept. 1985)

Rulau	Date	Metal	Size	F	VF	EF	Unc
CZ 74	(1909-14)	Brass	35.5mm	—	—	50.00	—

(Tiny) AM. RY. S. CO. / (tiny) NEW YORK / 46890 (or another number) / I. C. C. Rv: Blank. 180,000 pieces were made in two varieties, plus a nickel-plated version. Numbers examined: 38888, 46890, 179974.

Rulau	Date	Metal	Size	F	VF	EF	Unc
CZ 75	(1919-38)	Brass	Oct 38mm	35.00	—	—	—

(Tiny) AM. RY. S. CO. / (tiny) N. Y. / PANAMA / (number) / CANAL. Rv: Blank. Planchet slotted for strap. Numbers examined: 226, 229, 5905.

Struck by American Railway Supply Co. of New York, which was active in supplying tokens and tags to Mexico and Central America in the 1908-14 period. They also supplied caps, uniforms etc. during the construction days on the Panama Canal through the Isthmian Canal Commission.

The tag above is an identification tag for workers on the canal, issued by the Isthmian Canal Commission.

Rulau	Date	Metal	Size	F	VF	EF	Unc
CZ 77	(1914)	Brass	Sq 43x37mm	—	35.00	—	—

PANAMA / 8830 / CANAL (all incuse). Rv: Blank. Also seen: 8339, 11111, 63994.

When the Panama Canal Zone was established in 1903, the U.S. opened a chain of commissaries and hotels for civilian employees and contract workers. Cash was not used, but scrip in coupon books. Only persons with a brass "check" could present scrip.

The "check" was an Isthmian Canal Commission numbered badge, now a very rare and eminently collectible item. I.C.C.-labeled checks were used 1904-14 and Panama Canal-labeled checks after that until the system ended in 1938. As earlier badges were replaced with those of different shape (as a control measure), they were turned in and destroyed; thus the earliest brass checks are quite rare and probably underpriced on today's market.

Besides the types cataloged here, there are special checks in triangular, oval, 8-point star and other shapes. Some round checks labeled P.R.R. were issued by the Panama Rail Road for dock laborers before 1915.

PANAMA CANAL

Rulau	Date	Metal	Size	VG	F	VF	EF
CZ 79	1907	Silver	30mm	—	275.	—	375.

PANAMA (curved) / 1907 / CANAL (curved) ctsp on shaved reverse of Panama 1904 silver 25-centesimos, KM-4. Shaving of the reverse left the dentilated rim reasonably intact. Reeded edge. (Georg Forster coll., Ludwigshafen, Germany)

Nothing is known of this unpublished counterstamp. The incusing on reverse seems to come from a prepared die, possibly designed for another use than marking coins.

ZONE
(Lucien Wyse)

Rulau	Date	Metal	Size	VG	F	VF	Unc
CZ 80	1878	Bronze	20.5mm	—	25.00	—	—

Crossed hammers above 1878. Rv: (Rosette) * ZONE * (rosette) / ** ½ *. Plain edge.

In 1878 the Colombian government granted a concession to Lucien N. B. Wyse of the Societe Civile Internationale du Canal Interoceanique du Darien.

PART IV
SOUTH AMERICA

ARGENTINA

The word *estancia* — Argentine for a large ranch or estate — was coined in 1514 to indicate a "stay", that is, an amount of time spent in one place. In Argentine usage it came to indicate an estate devoted to animal husbandry, especially cattle raising.

By the late 19th century it expanded loosely to include farms of all types, though the terms *finca, vinedo* etc. were also used.

Branding of cattle was practiced from earliest times. The *cabildo* of Buenos Aires adopted an ordinance in 1589 for the branding of livestock and registration of the brands.

Cataloging of Argentina's tokens includes a good many previously unpublished pieces, and is due to assistance from Roberto E. Diaz, Salta, Argentina; George Lill III, La Paz, Bolivia.

BUENOS AIRES PROVINCE

Chascomus
LA ALAMEDA

Rulau	Date	Metal	Size	VG	F	VF	Unc
Bue 3	1899	Brass	21.5mm	—	10.00	15.00	—

(A-shaped cattle brand) / "LA ALAMEDA" / 1789. Rv: 1 / CHASCOMUS / 1899. Plain edge. (Rulau coll.)

This token is quite scarce and very popular. The date 1789 refers to the year the estancia was founded. 1 = 1 centavo.

Signed by BELLAGAMBA Y ROSSI, a Buenos Aires diesinking firm.

See the *TAMS Journal* for Feb. 1986, page 13.

Dolores
CIRCULO DE OBREROS

Rulau	Date	Metal	Size	VG	F	VF	Unc
Bue 5	1898	Silv/Bs	30.5mm	—	—	15.00	—

Radiant cross, IN HOC / SIGNO VINCES on ribbons. Around: CIRCULO DE OBREROS / DOLORES - (Bs As). Tiny ORZALI B. Y C. (?) below cross. Rv: RECUERDO DE SU INAUGURACION / 21 / DE AGOSTO / 1898 / (on scroll) ORA ET LABORA. Plain edge. Issued looped for suspension.

Catholic Workers Party. Struck by Orzali Bellagamba & Co., Buenos Aires.

Guamini
ARTAGAVEYTIA

Rulau	Date	Metal	Size	VG	F	VF	Unc
Bue 8	ND	Brass	23mm	—	—	7.50	—

ARTAGAVEYTIA / 1 / * GUAMINI *. Rv: Blank. Plain edge. (Eklund 2110)

Necochea
IBRAHIM, SARAN Y CIA.

Rulau	Date	Metal	Size	VG	F	VF	Unc
Bue 15	ND	Brass	20mm	—	—	7.50	—

IBRAHIM, SARAN Y Cia / (Star and crescent) / * PATAGUA *. Rv: (Pipe) (at left) / & (at right) / (tiny) N. BARES. (Bidone report)

The pipe was the brand mark for Estancia "El Pito" and the ampersand (&) the brand mark for Estancia "La Hebrea."

Rulau	Date	Metal	Size	VG	F	VF	Unc
Bue 17	ND	Brass	27mm	—	—	7.50	—

Obverse as last. Rv: 50 in beaded border. Tiny A.N. BARES below. (Bidone report)

| Bue 18 | ND | Brass | 24mm | — | — | 7.50 | — |

As last, but 10 in laurel wreath.

LA OTOMANA

Rulau	Date	Metal	Size	VG	F	VF	Unc
Bue 20	ND	Brass	25mm	—	—	10.00	—

LA OTOMANA / (Star and crescent) / * LARRABURU *. Rv: 1 / (tiny) A.N. BARES. Plain edge. (Bidone report)

Salto
EDUARDO KENNY

Rulau	Date	Metal	Size	VG	F	VF	Unc
Bue 25	ND	Brass	27mm	—	—	12.50	—

EDUARDO KENNY / AGENTE / PARA / TODOS LOS / (ornament) / ESPECIFICOS / + SALTO SUIPACHA ROJAS +. Rv: EDUARDO KENNY/ VALE / POR / UN / VELLON / + SALTO +. Plain edge. (Sanz & Sanchez 2306)

Agente para todos los especificos = Agent for all medicines. Vale por un vellon = Good for one fleece. (The word *vellon* also is a West Indian colloquialism for a dime).

San Fernando
MUNICIPALIDAD DE SAN FERNANDO

Rulau	Date	Metal	Size	VG	F	VF	Unc
Bue 28	1888	Bronze	26mm	—	—	25.00	—

MUNICIPALIDAD DE SAN FERNANDO / 1888. Rv: PERMISO DE DISFRAZ. (Sanz & Sanchez 1533)

Permiso de disfraz = License for costume ball. San Fernando is a port city on the Rio de La Plata estuary, north of Buenos Aires.

Zarate
SOCIEDAD ESPAÑOLA DE SOCORROS MUTUOS

Rulau	Date	Metal	Size	VG	F	VF	Unc
Bue 33	1899	Brass	26mm	—	—	7.50	—

Crowned Spanish-Bourbon shield of arms above laurel wreath. Rv: SOCIEDAD ESPAÑOLA / DE / SOCORROS / MUTUOS / -.- / ZARATE / -.- / .4 DE FEBRERO DE 1899. Plain edge. Looped for suspension.

Uncertain
ESQUINA DE LA VICTORIA

Rulau	Date	Metal	Size	VG	FF	VF	Unc
Bue 35	ND	Copper	**	—	—	—	—

** Bell-shaped flan, 18x30mm.
In an oval frame: ESQUINA DE LA VICTORIA. Rv: Blank. (Fonrobert 10198; Eklund 1616)

Fonrobert's cataloger, Weyl, guessed Argentina. Some authorities say Esquina de la Victoria = Victory Corner.

A.R.
(Arthur Rostand)

Rulau	Date	Metal	Size	VG	F	VF	Unc
Bue 40	(1881)	Zinc	40mm	—	—	—	—

Large AR monogram. Rv: Large 25 in laurel wreath closed at top by a 5-pointed star. Plain edge. (Eklund 1609)

| Bue 41 | (1881) | Zinc | 30mm | — | — | — | — |

Ram standing left. Rv: Large 5 in laurel wreath, star at top. (Eklund 1607)

| Bue 42 | (1881) | Brass | 30mm | — | — | — | — |

As last. (Eklund 1608)

| Bue 43 | (1881) | Zinc | 25mm | — | — | — | — |

As last, but 1. (Eklund 1605)

| Bue 44 | (1881) | Brass | 25mm | — | — | — | — |

As last. (Eklund 1606)

| Bue 45 | ND | Brass | 23.5mm | — | 7.50 | — | — |

Laurel wreath encloses empty center, on which is incused A.R. Rv: Large shaded 10 in laurel wreath. Below: (tiny) A N BARES. (Henkle report)

Issued by Arthur Rostand in 1881 to pay for the shearing of sheep. The last token above may not be connected with Rostand.

JUAN SHAW E HIJOS
Estancia Las Marias

Rulau	Date	Metal	Size	VG	F	VF	Unc
Bue 50	ND	Copper	34mm	—	—	6.50	—

ESTANCIA LAS MARIAS / S in diamond / . + . Rv: JUAN SHAW E HIJOS / 20 / + B . A +. (Henkle report)

| Bue 52 | ND | Copper | 22mm | — | — | 6.50 | — |

As last, but 1. (George Lill report)

Buenos Aires (City)
ANEZIN HOS. Y CIA.

Rulau	Date	Metal	Size	VG	F	VF	Unc
Bue 100	(ca 1800-07?)	Silver	28mm	—	—	25.00	—

Charles IV bust right. Around: ANEZIN Hos Y Cia / . ESMERALDA 211 Bs As . Rv: Crowned, pillar-supported Spanish arms. Around: HISPAN ET IND. REX BOT DE PLA. Reeded edge.

Bot. de Pla. = Abbreviation for silver button. A VG specimen of this strange item appeared in a Bob Reis (Lake Oswego, Oregon) sale of Jan. 1968, where it fetched a mere $3. It has no shank, thus can hardly be considered a metal button.

It is reminiscent of the game counter-type store cards of Britain in the 1790's.

ARTYMET VENTAS S.R.L.

Rulau	Date	Metal	Size	VG	F	VF	Unc
Bue 102	ND	Bronze	30.3mm	—	—	12.50	—

Rounded triangle resembling a top, HILLMAN incused above circular depression containing three vertical bars. Rv: ARTYMET VENTAS / S.R.L./ (panel) / AV. DEL LIBERTADOR / GRAL. S. MARTIN 2004 / BUENOS AIRES. Plain edge. Issued looped for suspension.

LA ASOCIACION DE TRAMWAYS

Rulau	Date	Metal	Size	VG	F	VF	Unc
Bue 104	1906	Copper	34.5mm	—	—	18.00	—

Electric streetcar approaching viewer head-on. On folds of a long scroll surrounding: PASE LIBRE / ANGLO ARGENTINO / BUENOS AIRES Y BELGRANO / LA CAPITAL / GRAN NACIONAL / ELECTRICOS DE BUENOS AIRES / METROPOLo. / LA NUEVA / TRAMWAY A QUILMES / LACROZE. Rv: Within wreath: 1906 / LA / ASOCIACION / DE / TRAMWAYS / AL SEÑOR / F. H. CHEVALLIER / BOUTELL. Below wreath: (tiny) GOTTUZZO. Plain edge. Loop removed. (Rulau coll.)

Pase libre = Free pass. Supposedly a tramways pass for a very high official. Scarce.

ROMAN BRAVO & CO.

Rulau	Date	Metal	Size	VG	F	VF	Unc
Bue 106	ND	Copper	30.5mm	—	5.00	—	—

Draped figure stands in 4-horse chariot, ROMAN BRAVO & Co above. Rv: Crossed hammer and banner labeled REMATE. Below: SAN MARTIN / 318 A 326 / BUENOS AIRES.

Remate = Auction sales.

CAFE A MANERA DEL BRASIL

Rulau	Date	Metal	Size	VG	F	VF	Unc
Bue 110	ND	Steel	37mm	—	22.50	—	—

In a triangle: CAFE / A / MANERA / DEL BRASIL. Around: VALE / POR UN / CAFE. Rv: Blank. Thick planchet. Weight 8.22 grams. (There is also a thin planchet variety, weight 5.62 grams, same price). (Bill Judd report)

| Bue 111 | ND | Aluminum | 34mm | — | 15.00 | — | — |

Similar to last. (Ludolph 96; Smithsonian coll.)

CAMPAÑA DEL CHACO

Rulau	Date	Metal	Size	VG	F	VF	Unc
Bue 113	(1890's?)	Copper	30mm	—	—	—	—

Oval arms of Buenos Aires. Above: CAMPAÑA DEL CHACO. Rv: In wreath: LA / NACION / ARGENTINA. (Eklund 1600; Rosa 248)

Campaign medalet. In the 1865-1870 war against Paraguay, Argentina was allied with Brazil and Uruguay.

JOSE CHIEZE

Rulau	Date	Metal	Size	VG	F	VF	Unc
Bue 116	ND	Brass	19mm	—	11.50	—	—

JOSE CHIEZE / . / BUENOS / AIRES / . / A.R. Rv: VALE / 20 C.

COLISEO DE BUENOS AIRES

Rulau	Date	Metal	Size	VG	F	VF	Unc
Bue 118	(1840)	Copper	32.5mm	—	40.00	135.	—

Lyre in front of violin and French horn, at center. Around: COLISEO DE BUENOS AIRES. Rv: (Spray) / ENTRADA / DE / COMEDIA / *. (Ulex 3857; Eklund 1601; Rosa 92/570)

The William Christensen sale of Sept. 9, 1983, lot 282, featured this theater admittance token, one of the most important early Argentine issues.

This token occurs with counterstamped ornate letter P.

This "Comedy ticket" was struck at the Buenos Aires Mint on blanks intended for the 2-real coins of 1840, KM-8.

COLISEO PABELLON DE LAS ROSAS

Rulau	Date	Metal	Size	F	VF	EF	Unc
Bue 120	ND	Aluminum	Oval 30.x14mm	—	—	20.00	35.00

COLISEO / PABELLON DE LAS ROSAS / CASINO SCALA ETC. ETC / -.- / BUENOS AIRES. Rv: 10 / CENTAVOS. Plain edge. (Rulau coll.)

Rulau	Date	Metal	Size	F	VF	EF	Unc
Bue 121	ND	Aluminum	Scal 36mm	—	—	25.00	40.00

COLISEO / PABELLON DE / LAS ROSAS / * CASINO * / SCALA / ETC. ETC. ETC. / BUENOS AIRES / *. Rv: 20 / CENTAVOS. Plain edge. (Rulau coll.)

Rulau	Date	Metal	Size	F	VF	EF	Unc
Bue 122	ND	Brass	Scal 36mm	—	—	30.00	45.00

As last. (Zaika coll.)

Rulau	Date	Metal	Size	F	VF	EF	Unc
Bue 125	ND	Brass	Oval 44x29mm	—	—	40.00	60.00

Similar to last, but 10 / PESOS. (Henkle report)

There is also a round aluminum 21mm 5-centavo token in this series, and a heart-shaped brass 50-centavo token, 34x24mm.

Pabellon de las Rosas = Pavilion of the Roses. These tokens apparently were used in the Coliseum complex, Casino Scala, Pavilion of the Roses, etc.

GARIBALDI CUBELLI

Rulau	Date	Metal	Size	VG	F	VF	Unc
Bue 128	ND	Gilt/Bz	31mm	—	—	—	—

GARIBALDI CUBELLI. DORADOR PLATEADOR NIQUELADOR. CASA FUNDADA EN 1872, CANGALLO 1324. BUENOS AIRES. (Sanz & Sanchez 437)

Dorador plateador niquelador = Gilder, (silver) plater and nickel-plater. Casa fundada en 1872 = House founded in 1872.

ENTRADA AL TEATRO

Rulau	Date	Metal	Size	VG	F	VF	Unc
Bue 130	ND	Copper	32mm	75.00	90.00	125.	240.

Mask, hat, lyre, dagger and other theatrical paraphernalia. Rv: Within wreath: ENTRADA / AL / TEATRO. Plain edge. (Rulau coll., ex-A. H. Baldwin 1992)

This theater pass is found counterstamped POTOSI for use in the Potosi, Bolivia theater (see Bov 13). The token is illustrated at Bov 13. This is one of Argentina's most popular early tokens, always bringing strong prices at auction.

Similarly designed pieces also were used in Lima, Peru and in Havana, Cuba. (See Hav 45 and Per 19, respectively.)

ESMERALDA SKATING-RINK

Rulau	Date	Metal	Size	VG	F	VF	Unc
Bue 131	1879	Copper	mm	—	—	—	—

SKATING-RINK / 2 / * ESMERALDA 149 *. Rv: BUENOS AIRES / J.S. Y D.P. / . 1r ENERO 1879 . Weight 2.1 grams. (Eklund 1604; Rosa 1534)

FONTAN & CAIRO HOS.

Rulau	Date	Metal	Size	VG	F	VF	Unc
Bue 133	ND	Brass	21mm	—	—	10.00	—

FONTAN & CAIRO Hos. / VENTA / DE / MAQUINAS / AUTOMATICAS / -o- / DEAN FUNES 1632. Rv: 20 within ornamental border. Reeded edge. (Zaika coll.)

FERNANDO J. FONTAN

Rulau	Date	Metal	Size	VG	F	VF	Unc
Bue 135	ND	Brass	21.5mm	—	—	10.00	—

Owl. Around: FERNANDO J. FONTAN / DEAN FUNES 1632. Rv: VALE POR / 20 / CENTAVOS / EN CONSUMO. Reeded edge.

Fontan was a seller of automatic machines, and these are most likely modern machine tokens.

LA CIUDAD DE BUENOS AIRES

Rulau	Date	Metal	Size	F	VF	EF	Unc
Bue 140	1903	Silver	30mm	—	15.00	—	—

Train emerges from tunnel at right, toward tree at left bearing shields of Chile and Argentina, small CASANOVAS Y HORTA at lower right rim. Above: AVSPICIVM . MELIORIS . AEVI . Rv: LA CIUDAD / DE / BUENOS-AIRES / A / LOS DELEGADOS / DEL / GOBIERNO DE CHILE / 25 MAYO 1903. Plain edge. (Sanz & Sanchez 252a)

The city of Buenos Aires salutes the peace delegates of the government of Chile. This medalet was also struck in Copper and in Silver-plated Copper.

LA CIUDAD DE LONDRES STORE

Rulau	Date	Metal	Size	VG	F	VF	Unc
Bue 142	ND	Pewter	30mm	—	7.50	—	—

LA CIUDAD DE LONDRES STORE / BUENOS AIRES. Rv: No descr. available.

LA PLATA

Rulau	Date	Metal	Size	F	VF	EF	Unc
Bue 144	1907	Silver	Irreg 33x36mm	—	—	25.00	—

Seated female watches electric tram emerge from tunnel at right. Above: LA PLATA - 29 DECbre 1907 / CALLE 12 / AL SUD. Rv: Raised panel across center (for inscribing name). Above: Shield within wreath. Below: LOS VECINOS FAVORECIDOS / CON EL TRAMWAY / Y EMPEDRADO / OFRECEN. Plain edge. Issued holed for suspension. (Rulau coll.)

L. MORALES

Rulau	Date	Metal	Size	F	VF	EF	Unc
Bue 148	1893	Bronze	38mm	—	—	25.00	—

Fancy shirt. Rv: L. MORALES, BUENOS AIRES, 10 MAYO 1893. APERTURA DE LA GRAN FABRICA DE CAMISAS. Plain edge.

Advertising token for the opening of the Morales Shirt Factory.

MUNICIPALIDAD DE LA CAPITAL

Rulau	Date	Metal	Size	VG	F	VF	Unc
Bue 150	1883	Copper Rect 29x24mm		—	—	30.00	—

MUNICIPALIDAD DE LA CAPITAL. Rv: BAILES DE DISFRAZ / . 1883 . Weight 6.2 grams. (Eklund 1603; Rosa 1529; Sanz & Sanchez 1532)

Bailes de Disfraz = Costume balls. Medallic issue. Also issued in Silver-plated Copper.

Rulau	Date	Metal	Size	F	VF	EF	Unc
Bue 152	1901	S/Brass	26mm	—	—	10.00	—

Male bust left. Around: 8mo ANIVERSARIO DE SU NATALICIO / * 26 JUNIO 1901 *. Rv: Shield of arms. Tiny J. GOTUZZO at lower right. Around: HOMENAJE DE LA / . MUNICIPALIDAD DE LA CAPITAL . Plain edge.

ORZALI BELLAGAMBA Y CA.

Rulau	Date	Metal	Size	F	VF	EF	Unc
Bue 155	1894	Aluminum	30mm	—	—	8.50	11.00

FABRICA NACIONAL DE MEDALLAS . ORZALI BELLAGAMBA Y CA. Rv: INAUGURACION OFICIAL DEL GRAN TALLER ARGENTINO DE GRABADOS Y ACUÑACION. 10 JUNIO 1894. Plain edge. (Sanz & Sanchez 429)

Gran taller Argentino de grabados y acuñacion = Great Argentine workshop of engraving and minting.

Bue 156	1895	Copper	30mm	—	—	8.50	11.00

FELIZ AÑO NUEVO, 1o ENERO 1895. FABRICA NACIONAL DE MEDALLAS DE ORZALI, BELLAGAMBA Y CA. RIVADAVIA 1637. BUENOS AIRES. (Sanz & Sanchez 432)

The first item above is a commemorative token honoring the launch of the "National Medal Factory" by the united Orzali and Bellagamba diesinking interests. The second is a New Year's token for advertising purposes. Both were struck in fairly large quantities as giveaways.

PARQUE JAPONES

Rulau	Date	Metal	Size	F	VF	EF	Unc
Bue 159	(1960)	Aluminum	Oval 35x44.5mm	—	17.50	—	—

PARQUE JAPONES / * PALACIO DEL BAILE * . Rv: 20 (large, shaded) / PESOS / (tiny) A. N. BARES. Plain edge.

Amusement park token, now obsolete. Parque Japones, Palacio del Baile = Japanese park, dance palace.

PETIT CAFE

Rulau	Date	Metal	Size	VG	F	VF	Unc
Bue 161	ND	Brass	35mm	12.50	17.50	—	—

Circle of stars, tiny E. BARES below. Ctsp in center: Petit Cafe (script). Rv: 500 (shaded) in triple circle border.

Bue 162	ND	Aluminum	Rect 36x26mm	—	20.00	—	—

(All incused): Petit Cafe (script). Rv: 100.

Bue 164	ND	Aluminum	45mm	—	17.50	—	—

50 (shaded) in triple circle border. Ctsp Petit Cafe (script). Rv: Blank.

Bue 165	ND	Brass	39mm	—	22.50	—	—

Similar to last, but 10.

RESTAURANT JARDINES JAPONESES

Rulau	Date	Metal	Size	VG	F	VF	Unc
Bue 170	ND	Brass	35mm	10.00	20.00	30.00	40.00

RESTAURANT JARDINES JAPONESES / 10 / PESOS / * / (tiny) A. N. BARES. Rv: 10 / PESOS. Plain edge. (Rulau coll.)

Restaurant Jardines Japaneses + Japanese Gardens Restaurant. There are also 31mm brass 100 (centavos) and 28mm brass 50 (centavos). Both latter signed **A BARES** for diesinker A. N. Bares.

RIVERA & GUERRERO

Rulau	Date	Metal	Size	F	VF	EF	Unc
Bue 172	(1890's)	Bronze	22mm	—	—	15.00	—

Imitation of reverse of Argentina 5-peso gold coin of 1884, KM-5 (Liberty head). Rv: Within wreath: RIVERA & GUERRERO. Around: CASA INTRODUCTORA. PARIS. BUENOS AIRES. Plain edge. (Sanz & Sanchez 444)

VAUXHALL

Rulau	Date	Metal	Size	VG	F	VF	Unc
Bue 180	1828	Copper	32mm	—	80.00	125.	—

Harp within oak wreath. Around: PARQUE / ARGENTINO. Rv: VAUXHALL / 1828 within surrounding floreate wreaths. Plain edge. (Ulex 3888; Eklund 1602; Rosa 571; Sanz & Sanchez 1160)

Struck in England for the park's inauguration in 1828 and used as an admission check. Santiago Wilde owned the park, located along Cordoba Avenue, Uruguay and Viamonte Streets. This is Argentina's oldest token.

CORDOBA PROVINCE

Cordoba
B. LLERENA
Establecimiento "Jesus Maria"

Rulau	Date	Metal	Size	VG	F	VF	Unc
Cdb 3	ND	Brass	20mm	—	10.00	—	—

B. LLERENA / -.- / VALE / 800 Gr. Rv: ESTABLECIMIENTO "JESUS MARIA" / 5 /. CORDOBA .

ENTRE RIOS PROVINCE

VAPOR NEPTUNO

Rulau	Date	Metal	Size	F	VF	EF	Unc
ER 7	1892	Silv/Cop	26mm	—	—	—	—

VAPOR NEPTUNO CTAN. BASILI PESSOA. 1er. VIAJE POR EL RIO IBICUY. 28 DE JUNIO 1892. (Tiny) ORZALI B y C. (Sanz & Sanchez 428)

Vapor Neptuno (steamship Neptune) under Capt. Basili Pessoa made its first voyage up the River Ibicuy on June 28, 1892. The Ibicuy is a tributary of the Parana, flowing through Entre Rios province. The city of Ibicuy is in Entre Rios.

JUJUY PROVINCE

El Carmen
FIGUEROA HNOS.
Finca San Juan

Rulau	Date	Metal	Size	VG	F	VF	Unc
Juj 9	(ca 1912)	Brass	38mm	—	—	12.50	

FIGUEROA Hnos / -.- / FINCA / SAN JUAN / (brand mark resembling B lying sideways). Rv: 100 (open numerals) on shaded circle. Plain edge.

Rulau	Date	Metal	Size	VG	F	VF	Unc
Juj 10	(1912)	Brass	30.5mm	—	—	12.50	

As last, but 50.

Rulau	Date	Metal	Size	VG	F	VF	Unc
Juj 11	ND	Brass	28.4mm	—	—	10.00	—

As last, but 20.

Rulau	Date	Metal	Size	VG	F	VF	Unc
Juj 12	ND	Brass	23mm	—	—	10.00	—

As last, but 5. (Almanzar report)

The reverses are identical to the 1912-dated Paraguay Land Cattle Co. tokens of Paraguay, which reportedly were struck in England.

Finca San Juan is in Jujuy province but is large enough to overlap into Salta province. It was devoted to agriculture and cattle raising.

Ledesma
INGENIO DE LEDESMA

Rulau	Date	Metal	Size	VG	F	VF	Unc
Juj 15	(1889)	CN	25mm	5.00	7.00	—	—

INGENIO LEDESMA. Rv: 20 (open). Plain edge.

Rulau	Date	Metal	Size	VG	F	VF	Unc
Juj 16	(1889)	CN	23mm	—	—	16.00	—

As last, but 10. (Roberto Diaz coll.)

Alcedo Almanzar noted that this is the world's largest privately-owned sugar plantation. These tokens have been claimed without evidence for Domican Rep.
There is a city of Pueblo Ledesma in Jujuy Prov., southeastern part. There is also a CN 5, 20mm.

San Pedro
L. H. Y CIA.

Rulau	Date	Metal	Size	VG	F	VF	Unc
Juj 18	(1890)	Brass	22.5mm	7.50	12.00	18.00	—

(Ornaments) / L. H y Cia. / (ornaments). Rv: 14.

Alcedo Almanzar reports these were used at a sugar refinery of Leach Brothers Ingenio La Esperanza, founded in the mid-19th century. San Pedro is in southeastern Jujuy Province. L.H. y Cia = Leach Hermanos & Co.

ALVARADO HNOS. & MULLER

Rulau	Date	Metal	Size	VG	F	VF	Unc
Juj 23	1894	Copper	24.5mm	7.50	12.00	20.00	—

INGENIO EL PORVENIR / 1894 / * JUJUY *. Rv: ALVARADO Hnos & MÜLLER / 2 / R. Plain edge.

Rulau	Date	Metal	Size	VG	F	VF	Unc
Juj 24	1894	Copper	20mm	—	—	15.00	—

INGENIO EL PORVENIR / 1894 / * JUJUY *. Rv: * ALVARADO Hnos & MÜLLER * / R. Plain edge.

Rulau	Date	Metal	Size	VG	F	VF	Unc
Juj 26	1894	Brass	29.6mm	—	—	18.00	—

INGENIO EL PORVENIR / JUJUY / - / 1894 / + ALVARADO Hnos & MÜLLER +. Rv: DINERO EN TRABAJO / 25 / * Cvos *. Plain edge.

Wage tokens for sugar refinery workers at Ingenio el Porvenir, at La Mendieta, San Pedro Dept., according to Roberto Diaz.

Establecimiento "Pampa Blanca"

Rulau	Date	Metal	Size	VG	F	VF	Unc
Juj 29	ND	Brass	20mm	—	8.00	—	—

. ESTABLECIMIENTO . / 10 / b y r / "PAMPA BLANCA". Rv: * VALE * / 10 / PARA EL ALMACEN.

Leach Brothers store, says Alcedo Almanzar. Struck by Bellagamba y Rossi, Buenos Aires.

R.C.L.

Rulau	Date	Metal	Size	VG	F	VF	Unc
Juj 35	ND	Brass	16.1mm	—	—	10.00	—

R.C.L. Rv: 3½. Plain edge.

R.C.L. = Rogelio C. Leach. 3½ = 3½ days' work. A 19mm 7 is known.

Zapla
MATEO C. CORDOVA

Rulau	Date	Metal	Size	VG	F	VF	Unc
Juj 50	ND	Brass	21.3mm	—	—	10.00	—

MATEO C CORDOVA / (ornaments) / ZAPLA. Rv: 0.20 (large, shaded) / (tiny) BELLAGAMBAYROSSI. (Roberto Diaz coll.)

Struck by Bellagamba y Rossi, Buenos Aires

MENDOZA PROVINCE

Canada Seca
JOSE H. RUIZ Y ZUEL

Rulau	Date	Metal	Size	F	VF	EF	Unc
Mnz 4	ND	Aluminum	18mm	—	—	5.00	7.00

JOSE H. RUIZ Y ZUEL / (bunch of grapes) / CANADA / * SECA *. Rv: Large shaded 1; small LUPPOLI at right.

Grape picker's check in a vineyard. Canada Seca is in Maipu Dept., Mendoza Prov.

Caucete
FINCA SAN ANTONIO

Rulau	Date	Metal	Size	F	VF	EF	Unc
Mnz 6	ND	Aluminum	Hexag 23mm	—	—	5.00	8.00

FINCA / SAN / ANTONIO / CAUCETE. Rv: NO NEGOCIABLE / 1 (large) superimposed over ripe grape stem / (tiny) TM monogram (Rulau coll.)

Grape picker's chit.

Guaymallen
MATEO LONCHARICH

Rulau	Date	Metal	Size	VG	F	VF	Unc
Mnz 9	(1930)	Aluminum	18.7mm	—	—	5.00	7.00

MATEO LONCHARICH / (roped circle) / * GUAY-MALLEN *. Large 1 (shaded) within wreath circle. Plain edge.

Grape pickers chit for one basket. The Loncharich enterprise was located in Guaymallen department, Mendoza province.

Junin
BLAS RUSSO
Finca "La Perla"

Rulau	Date	Metal	Size	F	VF	EF	Unc
Mnz 12	ND	Aluminum	21mm	—	—	5.00	7.00

BLAS RUSSO / FINCA / "LA PERLA" / B.R. / *JUNIN *. Rv: Large shaded 1 within thick circular wreath: small LUPPOLI at left.

Finca = Vineyard. 1 = One basket of grapes picked. Struck by A. Luppoli of Mendoza, Argentina.

Lucan
AMBROSIO BERTONA

Rulau	Date	Metal	Size	VG	F	VF	Unc
Mnz 17	ND	Aluminum	21mm	—	—	5.00	7.00

AMBROSIO BERTONA / AB monogram / - LUCAN. MZA. -. Rv: Large shaded 1 within thick circular wreath; small LUPPOLI at left.

Struck by A. Luppoli of Mendoza, Argentina. Vineyard check. Lucan is in Lujan Dept.

Lujan
FIESTA PATRIOTICA

Rulau	Date	Metal	Size	F	VF	EF	Unc
Mnz 15	1898	Copper	27mm	—	—	9.00	—

Warship steams right as sun rises over mountains in background. Tiny ORZALI B. Y CA. at lower left. Above: REPUBLICA ARGENTINA / MENDOZA. Rv: FIESTA PATRIOTICA / 1898 (in circle) / -LUJAN -. Plain edge. Issued with loop. (Zaffern coll.)

Struck by Orzali Bellagamba & Co., Buenos Aires.

ELISERIO S. MOYANO

Rulau	Date	Metal	Size	F	VF	EF	Unc
Mnz 22	ND	Aluminum	Oct 23mm	—	—	—	8.00

ELISERIO S. MOYANO / VIÑEDOS LA AURORA / (scriptlike) M / ..*.. / * LUJAN (MENDOZA) *. Rv: 20 (large, shaded) in beaded circle. Plain edge. (Henkle N/L)

For picking 20 baskets of grapes.

Maipu
BODEGAS EL GLOBO

Rulau	Date	Metal	Size	VG	F	VF	Unc
Mnz 20	ND	Aluminum	21mm	—	—	7.50	—

BODEGAS EL GLOBO / NO NEGOCIABLE / * MENDOZA *. Rv: Large shaded 1; small LUPPOLI at lower right.

Bodega = winery. A winery worker's chit.

Mendoza
CLUB MENDOZA

Rulau	Date	Metal	Size	VG	F	VF	Unc
Mnz 25	ND	Silver	29mm	—	—	—	—

TIRO NACIONAL / (Building) / CLUB MENDOZA. Rv: Liberty caps, cross etc. Plain edge. (Kirtley Dec. 1988 sale, lot 1110)

Tiro Nacional = National Shooting Festival.

E. PAULLADA

Rulau	Date	Metal	Size	VG	F	VF	Unc
Mnz 28	1873	Brass	24mm	—	—	25.00	—

E. PAULLADA / 1873. Rv: DOS / REALES / -.-. Plain edge. (Zaffern coll.; Plante 1992 stocklist, lot 609)

Nueva California
GABRIEL HERNANDEZ
MARCIANO

Rulau	Date	Metal	Size	VG	F	VF	Unc
Mnz 30	ND	Aluminum	22mm	—	—	6.50	—

-*- GABRIEL HERNANDEZ -*- MARCIANO / NUEVA CALIFORNIA / MZA / *. Rv: Large shaded 1 within circular wreath; small LUPPOLI at left.

Vineyard worker's chit.

Rivadavia
DI LORENZO HNOS.

Rulau	Date	Metal	Size	F	VF	EF	Unc
Mnz 35	ND	Aluminum	Sq 21mm	—	6.00	—	—

DI LORENZO / HNOS. / RVIA. / LA CENTRAL. Rv: NO NEGOCIABLE / 1 (shaded) superimposed over basket / (tiny) TM monogram. (Rulau coll.)

Grape picker's chit for 1 basket.

Uncertain
ESTANCIA USPALLATA

Rulau	Date	Metal	Size	VG	F	VF	Unc
Mnz 40	ND	Bronze	23.5mm	—	7.00	—	—

ESTANCIA USPALLATA / (snowflake ornament) / *. VALE / POR / 20 CENTAVOS. Plain edge.

Uspallata Pass is through the Andes into Mendoza Province.

OCTAVIO R. FALASCO
E HIJOS

Rulau	Date	Metal	Size	F	VF	EF	Unc
Mnz 42	ND	Aluminum	23mm	—	6.00	—	—

OCTAVIO / R. / FALASCO / E / HIJOS. Rv: NO NEGOCIABLE / 1 (large) superimposed over ripe grape stem / (tiny) TM monogram. (Rulau coll.)

Grape picker's chit.

HOSPITAL PROVINCIAL

Rulau	Date	Metal	Size	F	VF	EF	Unc
Mnz 44	1907	Silver	31mm	—	16.00	—	—

Shield of arms in laurel wreath. Around: PROVINCIA DE MENDOZA / . OBRAS PUBLICAS . Rv: * / HOSPITAL PROVINCIAL / INAUGURADO / EL 24 FEBRERO 1907 / - / GOBERNADOR / Dr / C. GALIGNIANA SEGURA / *. Plain edge. (Rulau coll.)

VICTORIANO SOTTANO
Y HNOS.

Rulau	Date	Metal	Size	F	VF	EF	Unc
Mnz 48	ND	Aluminum	18mm	—	—	8.00	—

VICTORIANO SOTTANO / Y / HNOS. / (ornament) / . NO NEGOCIABLE . Rv: Large shaded 1; small LUPPOLI at right.

Grape picker's chit in a vineyard; the numeral 1 was for a basket of grapes picked.

MISIONES PROVINCE

Puerto Iguazu
IGUAZU

Rulau	Date	Metal	Size	VG	F	VF	Unc
Mis 3	ND	Aluminum	Oval 28x36mm	—	6.00	15.00	—

IGUAZU incused vertically within struck laurel wreath. Below: (tiny) E. BARES. Rv: Large 5 in beaded necklace border. Plain edge.

Rulau	Date	Metal	Size	VG	F	VF	Unc
Mis 4	ND	Aluminum	30mm	—	6.00	15.00	—

Similar, but 1.

SALTA PROVINCE

Animana
VDOS. Y BGAS. COLL

Rulau	Date	Metal	Size	VG	F	VF	Unc
Sal 1	(1940)	Aluminum	Sq 23mm	—	—	5.00	—

VDOS. Y BGAS. / COLL / -.- / ANIMANA/ SALTA. Rv: 10 (large) within wreath, TM monogram above. Raised rims.

These are grape pickers chits used on the farm, vineyard and winery of the Coll family near Animana, San Carlos Dept., Salta Province.

Vdos (Viñedos) y Bgas (Bodegas) = Vineyards and wine cellars.

Anta
PAULINO ECHAZU
Estancia Nueva Poblacion

Rulau	Date	Metal	Size	VG	F	VF	Unc
Sal 4	(1897)	Brass	25.5mm	—	—	10.00	—

PAULINO ECHAZU / F.S. (script, large) / (tiny) B.Y.R. / * NUEVA POBLACION *. Rv: CONTRA-SEÑA / * 25 * / ANTA.

B y R = Bellagamba & Rossi, Buenos Aires. Nueva poblacion = New town. Contra-seña = Check. Probably struck about 1897.

Echazu's cattle ranch and farm was in Anta Department, in eastern Salta Province, centered around the city of Joaquin V. Gonzalez. He also issued tokens for his Estancia Palermo in Anta department.

PAULINO ECHAZU
Estancia Palermo

Rulau	Date	Metal	Size	VG	F	VF	Unc
Sal 6	(1900)	Brass	19.6mm	—	—	10.00	—

Within beaded borders: PAULINO ECHAZU / Script JF monogram in beaded circle / * PALERMO *. Rv: Within beaded borders: 10 (large, shaded).

See also Echazu's estancia Nueva Poblacion in Anta department. Estancia Palermo was a cattle ranch. The monogram is their brand mark.

FINCA DE LA LAGHIGNANA

Rulau	Date	Metal	Size	VG	F	VF	Unc
Sal 8	(1890)	Brass	28.3mm	—	—	10.00	—

FINCA DE LA LAGHIGNANA / -.- / . Rv: FABRICA NACIONAL DE MEDALLAS . .ORZALI, BELLA-GAMBA Y Ca. / 50 / Bs As / . RIVADAVIA 1837. .

The name is spelled incorrectly on the token. It should be LACHIGUANA. This finca was devoted to agriculture and cattle raising in Anta department, eastern Salta province.

The tokens were used to pay daily workers, who could shop with them at the company store and grocery. Struck ca 1890-1905.

Campo Santo
C.U.
Ingenio San Ysidro

Rulau	Date	Metal	Size	VG	F	VF	Unc
Sal 12	(1880)	Copper	21.5mm	—	—	20.00	—

C.U. / SAN YSIDRO. Rv: 14 (large, shaded). Reeded edge.

Rulau	Date	Metal	Size	VG	F	VF	Unc
Sal 13	(1880)	Copper	19.3mm	—	—	12.50	—

As last, but 7. Reeded edge.

San Ysidro was a sugar plantation and farming estate. Campo Santo is located in Grl. Guemes Dept., Salta Province, east of the city of Salta. The department formerly was called Campo Santo also, but has been renamed after General Martin Guemes, hero of the war against Spain.

Roberto Diaz says the '7' and '14' stand for days' work.

This is "the oldest sugar cane factory" in Argentina, founded 1760 by Juan Adrian Fernandez Carnejo y Rendon.

Rulau	Date	Metal	Size	VG	F	VF	Unc
Sal 15	(1920)	Copper	18mm	—	—	15.00	—

INGENIO SAN ISIDRO / CAMPO SANTO. Rv: VALE / 10 / PARA EL ALMACEN. (Louis Hudson report)

Type Sal 12 with plain edge and unshaded 14 was issued about 1860 and fetches $30 in VF. Type Sal 15 is known with 20.

Rio Piedras
J. GUICHARD

Rulau	Date	Metal	Size	VG	F	VF	Unc
Sal 19	(1900)	Brass	25mm	—	—	8.00	—

J. GUICHARD / (brand mark) / RIO PIEDRAS. Rv: ESTANCIA / 50 / DEL VALLE QUIETO.

Sal 20	ND	Brass	20mm	—	—	8.00	—

As last, but 10. (Eklund 506)

Rio Piedras is southeast of the Salta provincial capital of Salta, and near Metan. The finca was devoted to agriculture and cattle raising.

Rosario de Lerma Dept.
NAVAMUEL Y CIA.

Rulau	Date	Metal	Size	VG	F	VF	Unc
Sal 22	(1930)	Aluminum	18.5mm	—	—	8.00	—

NAVAMUEL Y Cia. / $0.10 / * SALTA *. Rv: Blank.

Private coinage of the farming and cattle finca of Navamuel & Co.

Salta
FERRO-CARRIL A SALTA

Rulau	Date	Metal	Size	VG	F	VF	Unc
Sal 25	1890	Copper	32mm	—	—	15.00	22.50

Head atop a star. Around: EL PUEBLO DE SALTA / * A LOS TRABAJADORES DEL FERRO-CARRIL *. Rv: Locomotive right. Around: FERRO-CARRIL A SALTA / 1o ENERO 1890. Plain edge. (Eklund 1615)

This medalet is a tribute by the people of Salta to the railway workers on the Salta line.

MOYA HERMANOS

Rulau	Date	Metal	Size	VG	F	VF	Unc
Sal 30	(1930)	Brass	22.5mm	—	—	19.00	—

MOYA HERMANOS / M . H in beaded circle / + SALTA +. Rv: 25.

Sal 31	ND	Brass	20mm	—	—	20.00	—

As last, but 10. (Al Zaika coll.)

San Lorenzo
HACIENDA DE SAN LORENZO

Rulau	Date	Metal	Size	VG	F	VF	Unc
Sal 35	ND	Copper	14mm	—	—	40.00	—

MEDIO in circle. Around: HACIENDA DE S. LORENZO. Rv: Blank. Crude beaded rim around obverse.

Sal 36	(1850)	Copper	18mm	—	—	40.00	—

As last, but REAL in circle.

Sal 37	(1850)	Copper	18mm	—	—	60.00	—

REAL in circle. Around: HACIENDA DE SAN LORENZO. Rv: Beaded outline of a 6-pointed star, circular wreath around. Crude.

San Lorenzo is 12 kilometers west of Salta in the Capital Dept. of Salta Province. The hacienda was devoted to farming and cattle raising.

These tokens were used in the 19th century to pay wages to workers. They must predate 1882.

Medio = Half real, or 6¼ cents. Real = ⅛ peso, or 12½ cents.

Yuchan
FINCA ANAMABEA

Rulau	Date	Metal	Size	VG	F	VF	Unc
Sal 40	(1930)	Brass	30mm	—	—	10.00	—

FINCA ANAMABEA / . YUCHAN . incused within wide dentilated border in relief. Rv: Large shaded 1 within wide dentilated border. Plain edge.

1 = One day's work? Yuchan is in the northern department of Oran in Salta Province. Anamabea was a farming estate.

Uncertain
FINCA RURAL

Rulau	Date	Metal	Size	VG	F	VF	Unc
Sal 50	(1890)	CN	25mm	—	—	16.00	—

JORNAL DE PEONES / (Ram) / * FINCA RURAL *. Rv: 20. Plain edge.

Attribution by Alcedo Almanzar. The term "finca" for a plantation is generally Central American, but is also used by western Argentina.

SANTA FE PROVINCE

Rosario
ERNESTO HERRMANN Y CIA.

Rulau	Date	Metal	Size	VG	F	VF	Unc
STF 4	ND	Brass	Oval 43x33mm	—	—	—	—

ERNESTO HERRMANN Y Cia. Rv: Blank. (Ulex 3888; Eklund 1613)

ROSARIO JOCKEY CLUB

Rulau	Date	Metal	Size	F	VF	EF	Unc
STF 7	1907	Bronze	34mm	—	—	25.00	—

Horse head facing ¾ left from within a horseshoe frame. Around: JOCKEY CLUB ROSARIO / (wreath). Rv: No. descr. available. (Kirtley Jan. 1991 sale, lot T011)

Rulau	Date	Metal	Size	F	VF	EF	Unc
STF 10	1913	Silv/Bz	**	—	—	30.00	—

** Triangular with curved sides, 55x57mm. Building with five pennons flying. Around: JOCKEY CLUB / ROSARIO between branches. Rv: Jockey club seal amid branches at top. Below: INAUGURACION / DE . LAS . OBRAS . DEL . EDIFICIO / SOCIAL / PRESIDENCIA / ALFREDO J. ROUILLON / DICIEMBRE . 1913. In tiny letters at lower right: J. GOTUZZO. Plain edge. (Rulau coll.)

FELIX WOELFLIN

Rulau	Date	Metal	Size	VG	F	VF	Unc
STF 15	ND	Copper	30mm	—	—	—	—

FELIX WOELFLIN . LITOGRAFO . 184 SANTE FE . ROSARIO / (Arms). Rv: No description available. (Ulex 3888; Eklund 1614)

Santa Fe
MARIA EUGENIA SARALEGUI

Rulau	Date	Metal	Size	F	VF	EF	Unc
STF 18	1894	Sil/Bz	34mm	—	—	—	—

FIESTA DEDICADA A MARIA EUGENIA SARALEGUI / EL DIA DE SU NATALICIO / 1a. Rv: MISA CELEBRADA EL 28 DE DICIEMBRE DE 1894 EN EL RINCON DE SAN ANTONIO / SANTA FE. (Sanz & Sanchez 659)

Baptismal token of the Saralegui family.

TUCUMAN PROVINCE

San Miguel de Tucuman
SERAFIN ANTONIETTI

Rulau	Date	Metal	Size	VG	F	VF	Unc
Tcu 1	ND	Brass	31mm	—	—	—	—

ASERRADERO / SUIZO / ARGENTINO / DE / SERAFIN ANTONIETTI / H. & C. / TUCUMAN. Rv: 100. (Zaika coll.)

TIERRA DEL FUEGO TERRITORY

El Paramo
POPPER

Gold 1 and 5-gramo pieces dated 1889 issued by Julio Popper, though a token issue, have long been cataloged as coins. They are listed in Krause-Mishler as numbers Tn1 and 2, worth $600 and $2500 respectively in EF.

Punta Arenas
ESTANCIAS PRA. Y SDA. ARGENTINA

Rulau	Date	Metal	Size	VG	F	VF	EF
TDF 5	(1898)	xx	35mm	—	—	—	—

xx Black vulcanite.
ESTANCIAS PRIMERA Y SEGUNDA ARGENTINA / TIERRA / (Radiant sun) / DEL FUEGO / (ornament). Rv: PAGADERO EN MERCADERIAS EN PUNTA ARENAS / $1 / 205096 (mfr. no.) / (ornament). (TAMS Journal for Oct. 1971, pg. 175)

TDF 6	(1898)	vv	31mm	—	—	—	—

vv Red vulcanite.
Similar, but 50 C / . + . and no mfr. number.

TDF 7	(1898)	gg	26mm	—	—	—	—

gg Tan-black-tan vulcanite.
Similar, but abbreviations Pra, Sda and MERCas replace full words in the legend.

Estancias primera y segunda Argentina = Estates first and second Argentine.

UNATTRIBUTED ARGENTINA

AERO COM. 34.9964

Rulau	Date	Metal	Size	F	VF	EF	Unc
Arg 1	ND	Nickel	31mm	—	—	15.00	—

Airplane in flight, AVIONES PIPER CUB around. Rv: AERO COM. 34.9964 / AV. R. S. PENA 730. (Plante 1992 stocklist, lot M3)

Probably Buenos Aires.

Finca "La Cañada" ARIAS HERMANOS

Rulau	Date	Metal	Size	VG	F	VF	Unc
Arg 2	ND	Brass	30.8mm	—	—	—	—

* ARIAS HERMANOS * / (ornament) / FINCA / "LA CAÑADA". Rv: 1 / UN PESO. Plain edge.

CIGARILLOS HABANOS MONTERREY

Rulau	Date	Metal	Size	F	VF	EF	Unc
Arg 7	1810	Silv/Bz	25.5mm	12.50	14.50	17.00	—

Liberty head left, 1810 to left, 1910 to right, all within central beaded circle. Around: 1r. CENTENARIO DE LA INDEPENDENCIA DE LA REPUBLICA ARGENTINA / * / (tiny) VANZO. Rv: 20 / CENTAVOS / -.- in beaded circle. Around: CIGARRILLOS HABANOS MONTERREY / *. Plain edge. (Rulau coll.)

Arg 8	1910	Silv/Bz	25.5mm	12.50	—	—	—

Similar to last, but maker's signature M. VANZO at bottom of obverse. (Eklund 1612)

These tokens are close imitations of the regular coinage 20-centavo cupronickel coins of 1896-1942, KM-11, struck by M. VANZO.

Piedra Parada G. E. COX

Rulau	Date	Metal	Size	F	VF	EF	Unc
Arg 11	ND	rr	25.5mm	—	18.50	25.00	30.00

rr. Black vulcanite. G.E. COX / 10 / CENTS / * PIEDRA PARADA *. Rv: G. E. COX / 10 / CENTS/ * CUCHA CUCHA *. (Christensen Oct. 1975 sale, lot 21; David Harrison report)

Also claimed as Chile.

EL COLOSO

Rulau	Date	Metal	Size	F	VF	EF	Unc
Arg 14	ND	Aluminum	Oval 29x36mm	—	10.00	—	—

EL COLOSO / - incused at center of chain oval in relief, tiny relief E. BARES below. Rv: Shaded 5 in beaded wreath. Plain edge. Arranged vertically. (Rulau coll.; Henkle N/L)

ESPARTILLAR

Rulau	Date	Metal	Size	VG	F	VF	Unc
Arg 16	ND	Copper	38mm	—	—	10.00	—

ESPARTILLAR / 100 / * * *. Rv: FAIR. Plain edge.

| Arg 17 | ND | Copper | 32.5mm | — | — | 10.00 | — |

As last, but 50. (Schimmel June 1989 sale)

| Arg 18 | ND | Copper | 29mm | — | — | 10.00 | — |

As last, but 25.

According to James Lorah, this was a maker of esparto (feather grass) items. In that event, Fair may be a surname.

ESPECHE HERMANOS

Rulau	Date	Metal	Size	VG	F	VF	Unc
Arg 20	ND	Copper	39mm	—	12.00	—	—

HE monogram / (tiny) BELLAGAMBA Y ROSSI. Incuse number stamped below monogram. Rv: * ESPECHE HERMANOS * / 3 (large, shaded) / (tiny) BELLAGAMBA Y ROSSI / VALE POR JORNAL. Numbers examined: 46, 241.

| Arg 21 | ND | Copper | 34.5mm | — | 10.00 | — | — |

As last, but 2. (Numbers: 208)

| Arg 23 | ND | Copper | 31mm | — | 10.00 | — | — |

As last, but 1. (Numbers: 232)

Corrales
LUIS I. GARCIA

Rulau	Date	Metal	Size	VG	F	VF	Unc
Arg 28	1913	Brass	24.5mm	—	10.00	—	—

LUIS I. GARCIA / V (outline) / * 1913 *. Rv: ESTAN-CIA DE ASON / 1 (outline) / . CORRALES .

Cachari
JOSE MENENDES

Rulau	Date	Metal	Size	VG	F	VF	Unc
Arg 36	ND	Brass	27.5mm	—	—	25.00	—

JOSE MENENDES / (acorn brand mark) / * CACHARI *. Rv: VALE POR / 25 / * VEINTICINCO OVEJAS *. (Zaika coll.; Clark 234)

Veinticinco ovejas = 25 ewes (shorn). Also claimed as Guatemala.

Garabato
EDWARD MULLER

Rulau	Date	Metal	Size	VG	F	VF	Unc
Arg 40	ND	Copper	31mm	—	—	—	—

Three men standing. Around: EDWARD MULLER / . GARABATO . Rv: 50 CENTAVOS. (Eklund 1611)

PATENTE DE AMBULANTE

Bronze 37mm tokens bearing the words PATENTE DE AMBULANTE (ped-dler's license) and dated 1895, 1897, 1898, 1902, 1902 or 1904 have been cataloged as transportation tokens by the American Vecturist Association writers. These all bear the denomination 10 pesos.

Ten pesos in this period was the equal of 10 U.S. silver dollars, far too high a price for any transport fee but about right for an annual licensing fee. Patente de ambulante = Peddler's license.

The 1902 example shown is typical of the series. Such tokens are worth $17.50 in Fine or $28 in VF condition. They are not cataloged here as the dispute about their status needs resolution: this catalog does not cover transportation tokens.

F. POBLET Y CA.

Rulau	Date	Metal	Size	VG	F	VF	Unc
Arg 50	ND	Brass	20mm	—	—	—	—

Snowflake-like ornament. Around: CANTERA LA CONCORDIA / F. POBLET Y Ca. Rv: 5. (Zaika coll.)

Cantera = Quarry.

REID Y PEREIRA

Rulau	Date	Metal	Size	VG	F	VF	Unc
Arg 54	ND	—	26mm?	—	—	—	—

Ram left. REID Y PEREIRA above. Rv: No descr. available.

Sheep shearing token.

F. SEMPE Y S. CANALE

Rulau	Date	Metal	Size	VG	F	VF	Unc
Arg 56	ND	Brass	Rect 32x40mm	—	—	10.00	—

(All incused): F. SEMPE Y S. CANALE / - / 1 Ps / - / X. Rv: Blank. Arranged vertically. (Rulau coll.)

P. ULACCO

Rulau	Date	Metal	Size	VG	F	VF	Unc
Arg 60	ND	Bronze	31mm	—	—	15.00	—

P. ULACCO ctsp on Argentina 1883 2-centavos coin, KM-8.

FCO. URIBURU
Establecimiento Viti Vinicola

Rulau	Date	Metal	Size	VG	F	VF	Unc
Arg 62	ND	CN	19mm	—	—	10.00	—

Wine press within oval frame. Around: ESTABLECI-MIENTO VITI VINICOLA / (tiny) H... STRADA / * Fco URIBURU *. Rv: 1 (ornamental) / CAJON. Plain edge. (Bill Judd report)

Grape picker's chit. Cajon = Box.

Belgrano
V. & C.

Rulau	Date	Metal	Size	VG	F	VF	Unc
Arg 64	(1930)	Brass	25.5mm	—	—	10.00	—

BELGRANO / (beaded circle) / (rosette) V & C (rosette). Rv: A G in rectangle ctsp on blank reverse.

Tandil
P.F. VICUNA

Rulau	Date	Metal	Size	VG	F	VF	Unc
Arg 66	ND	Brass	20.5mm	—	—	—	—

CANTERA DE P. F. VICUNA / TANDIL. Rv: 5. (Zaika coll.)

Cantera = Quarry.

JOSE... VILLAP.

Rulau	Date	Metal	Size	VG	F	VF	Unc
Arg 68	(1850)	Copper	22.5mm	—	—	60.00	—

JOSE... / VILLAP. in relief within double-bordered oval ctsp twice on blank planchet. Rv: Blank.

BAPTISMAL TOKENS

Rulau	Date	Metal	Size	F	VF	EF	Unc
Arg 80	ND	Copper	24mm	—	—	15.00	—

MARIA SIN PECADO CONCEBIDA ROGAD POR NOSOTROS. Rv: RECUERDO DE MI PRIMERA COMUNION. (Sanz & Sanchez 662)

First communion token.

Rulau	Date	Metal	Size	F	VF	EF	Unc
Arg 81	(1890-94)	Sil/Bz	19mm	—	—	15.00	—

Argentina shield. Around: RECUERDO DE BAU-TISMO / (arc of 4 stars and 5 dots). Rv: Radiant sun. Around: REPUBLICA ARGENTINA / ROSARIO GRANDE VICTORIA 120. (Sanz & Sanchez 655)

Diesinker Rosario Grande was active in Buenos Aires 1873-1901.

Rulau	Date	Metal	Size	F	VF	EF	Unc
Arg 83	ND	Sil/Bz	13mm	—	—	10.00	—

Radiant star contains: VIRTUD / FELICIDAD. Rv: RECUERDO / DE / BAUTISMO in starred and floreate field. (Sanz & Sanchez 656)

| Arg 85 | ND | Sil/Bz | 17mm | — | — | 10.00 | — |

Baptism of Christ in the Jordan by St. John the Baptist. Rv: RECUERDO / DE / BAUTISMO in floreate field. (Sanz & Sanchez 657)

83 and 85 are general-purpose baptismal tokens which could be used by Argentine families.

BOLIVIA

COCHABAMBA DEPARTMENT

Cochabamba
GUILLERMO GAINSBORG Y CIA.

Rulau	Date	Metal	Size	VG	F	VF	Unc
Coc 3	1877	Brass	16mm	3.50	5.50	8.50	17.00

Llama right, DEPARTAMENTO DE COCHABAMBA / + around. Rv: PAGARA A LA VISTA GUILLERMO GAINSBORG Y Cia. / CINCO / * / CENT. / 1877 within laurel wreath. Reeded edge. (Eklund 1415; Rulau coll.)

Rulau	Date	Metal	Size	VG	F	VF	Unc
Coc 4	1877	Silver	16mm	—	—	35.00	50.00

As last, struck in silver. Reeded edge. Weight 1.67 grams.

Rulau	Date	Metal	Size	VG	F	VF	Unc
Coc 5	1877	CN	16mm	2.50	3.50	4.50	9.00

As last, struck in cuni. Reeded edge.

A hoard of the brass tokens surfaced in 1980 in grades VG through VF, depressing prices for most of the decade which followed. The hoard was dispersed by NASCA and Paul Bosco, eastern U.S. dealers. Pieces are readily available in 1992 in La Paz.

NICASIO DE GUMUCIO

Rulau	Date	Metal	Size	VG	F	VF	Unc
Coc 6	1876	WM	16mm	—	6.00	8.50	12.50

Lion reclining under tree left. Around: DEPARTAMENTO DE COCHABAMBA / **. Rv: PAGARA A LA VISTA NICASIO DE GUMUCIO / CINCO / . / CENT /. 1876. Reeded edge. (Ulex 3596; Eklund 1416)

Rulau	Date	Metal	Size	VG	F	VF	Unc
Coc 7	ND	WM	12.5mm	—	10.00	15.00	—

Lion reclining left, ECONOMIA ES RIQUEZA / ** around. Rv: PAGARA NICASIO DE GUMUCIO / DOS / 1 / MEDIO / CENT. Reeded edge. (*TAMS Journal* for June 1974)

Struck at Heaton Mint, Birmingham, England. A small hoard of silver-washed pieces entered U.S. in 1990.

PIL

Rulau	Date	Metal	Size	F	VF	EF	Unc
Coc 9	(?)	Brass	25mm	—	2.00	3.00	5.00

Triangular logo shows outline cow's head facing above PIL. Rv: FICHA CONTROL / 2 Litros / COCHABAMBA-BOLIVIA. Plain edge.

Rulau	Date	Metal	Size	F	VF	EF	Unc
	(?)	Brass	18mm	—	2.00	3.00	5.00

As last, but 1 Litro.

Modern milk tokens.

DANIEL M. QUIROGA

Rulau	Date	Metal	Size	F	VF	EF	Unc
Coc 11	(1876)	CN	16mm	—	—	5.50	8.50

Eagle-topped fountain, DEPARTAMENTO DE COCHABAMBA around. Rv: Within wreath at center: CINCO / CENTA- / VOS. Around: PAGARA A LA VISTA DANIEL M. QUIROGA / . Reeded edge. (Zaffern coll.)

These are gold dollar-sized tokens of excellent workmanship, struck at Heaton Mint, Birmingham, England. A large hoard of both types was dispersed by a Houston, Texas dealer in 1988, depressing prices.

TORRES Y HERMANO

Rulau	Date	Metal	Size	VG	F	VF	EF
Coc 14	ND	**	24mm	12.50	—	20.00	50.00

** Red vulcanite. TORRES Y HERMANO . / 1 R. Rv: COCHABAMBA Y SANTA CRUZ. / 10 / Ctos. (Eklund 1418; Asbun-Karmy T4)

Rulau	Date	Metal	Size	VG	F	VF	EF
Coc 15	ND	**	21mm	8.00	—	15.00	40.00

TORRES Y HERMANO . / 1/2 R. Rv: COCHABAMBA Y SANTA CRUZ . / 5 / Ctos. (Eklund 2258; Asbun-Karmy T5(R))

Rulau	Date	Metal	Size	VG	F	VF	EF
Coc 16	ND	**	24mm	—	—	25.00	—

TORRES Y HERMANO / 1 R /. Rv: COCHABAMBA Y SANTA CRUZ / 10 / Ctos / *. (Lill coll.)

This firm operated in Cochabamba and Santa Cruz departments.

EL BENI DEPARTMENT

Trinidad
FRANCISCO SUAREZ

Rulau	Date	Metal	Size	VG	F	VF	Unc
EB 2	ND	Gilt/B	19mm	3.00	5.00	9.50	—

Sailing ship left within circular laurel wreath. Around: DEPARTAMENTO DEL BENI / * BOLIVIA *. Rv: FRANCISCO SUAREZ / VALOR / 10 / CENTAVOS / + TRINIDAD +. Reeded edge. (Asbun-Karmy T9)

Rulau	Date	Metal	Size	VG	F	VF	Unc
EB 3	ND	Gilt/B	16.5mm	—	—	20.00	30.00

As last, but 5. Reeded edge. (Asbun-Karmy T10)

Rulau	Date	Metal	Size	VG	F	VF	Unc
EB 4	ND	Gilt/B	13.5mm	—	—	20.00	27.50

As last, but 2 1/2. Reeded edge. (Asbun-Karmy N/L)

LA PAZ DEPARTMENT

Corocoro
CASA DE GRIFES

Rulau	Date	Metal	Size	VG	F	VF	Unc
Lpz 3	ND	Brass	22mm	—	—	12.50	—

CASA DE GRIFES / (Pentagram) / * COROCORO *. Rv: Crossed hammer and chisel in circular wreath. Plain edge.

COMPANIA COROCORO DE BOLIVIA

Rulau	Date	Metal	Size	VG	F	VF	Unc
Lpz 6	1877	++	35mm	—	—	18.00	—

++ Vulcanite. Specimens are known in red, brown or black, about equally scarce. COMPANIA CORO-CORO DE BOLIVIA / COROCORO / - 1877 -. Rv: VALE / 4 / REALES. (Asbun-Karmy T15)

Lpz 7	1877	**	28.5mm	8.00	—	—	30.00

** Vulcanite, black.
As last, but 2 / REALES. (Asbun-Karmy T16)

Lpz 8	1877	xx	22mm	—	—	20.00	—

xx Vulcanite, red. As last, but 1 / REAL.

Lpz 9	1877	**	19mm	—	16.50	—	—

** Vulcanite, black.
As last, but 1/2 / REAL.

Lpz 11	ND	Brass	18.5mm	—	—	16.50	—

COMPANIA COROCORO DE BOLIVIA / (pentagram in beaded circle) / . COROCORO. Rv: Crossed hammer and chisel within circular laurel wreath. (Asbun-Karmy T22)

ENRIQUE HERTZOG

Rulau	Date	Metal	Size	VG	F	VF	Unc
Lpz 14	ND	Brass	22mm	—	—	10.00	—

Crossed hammer and chisel in circular wreath. Rv: ENRIQUE HERTZOG / COROCORO.

La Paz
LUIS AMPUERO

Rulau	Date	Metal	Size	VG	F	VF	Unc
Lpz 18	1863	Brass	Scal 27mm	—	—	22.50	—

Condor sits atop tall column. Around: PARA LA COLUMNA DE ORO EN LA PAZ / 1863. Rv: Within wreath: DOS REALES / LUIS AMPUERO / LA PAZ. (Eklund 1437; Asbun-Karmy T6)

Rulau	Date	Metal	Size	VG	F	VF	Unc
Lpz 19	1863	Brass	Scal 22.5mm	—	—	20.00	30.00

As last, but UN REAL. (Eklund 1436; Asbun-Karmy T7; Rulau coll.)

Rulau	Date	Metal	Size	VG	F	VF	Unc
Lpz 20	1863	Brass	Scal 19mm	—	17.50	25.00	—

As last, but MEDIO REAL. (Eklund 1435; Asbun-Karmy T8)

These tokens occasionally are found counterstamped E. S. flanking the column. These are worth a premium of about $10 over prices quoted.

WENCESLAO ARGOTE

Rulau	Date	Metal	Size	F	VF	EF	Unc
Lpz 23	ND	Copper	20mm	4.00	8.00	17.50	25.00

Cornucopia. Around: BAZAR DE WENCESLAO ARGOTE / *. Rv: LA PAZ. / 1/2 / (wreath). Plain edge. (Asbun-Karmy T19; Brunk coll.; Rulau coll.)

Rulau	Date	Metal	Size	VG	F	VF	Unc
Lpz 24	ND	Brass	25mm	—	9.00	20.00	30.00

Similar to last, but 1. Two stars under cornucopia. (Eklund 1438; Scott; Rulau coll.)

A small hoard of choice EF to Unc. specimens of the 1-real token surfaced in 1990 and was dispersed by Louis Hudson of North Carolina. The Brunk collection contains two red Unc. specimens of the 1/2-real token.

BISHOP'S BORATERA CHILCAVA

Rulau	Date	Metal	Size	VG	F	VF	Unc
Lpz 26	1900	Brass	24mm	—	—	15.00	—

BORATERA CHILCAVA / BISHOP'S / . 1900 . Rv: 50 / CENTS. (Also known in CN, same prices)

Lpz 27	1900	CN	24mm	—	—	—	—

As last, but $1oo. (Zaika coll.)

Doubtful attribution. A similar $1 has been attributed to a boratera (borax mine) in Chile. Attributions to Peru also are reported.

GRAND HOTEL GUIBERT & C.

Rulau	Date	Metal	Size	VG	F	VF	Unc
Lpz 29	(?)	Brass	25mm	—	—	—	—

GRAND HOTEL GUIBERT & C. / 20 / . LA PAZ . Rv: Same as obverse. Plain edge..

PELUQUERIA ESCALANTE

Rulau	Date	Metal	Size	VG	F	VF	Unc
Lpz 31	(?)	Aluminum	Oct 26mm	—	—	15.00	—

PELUQUERIA ESCALANTE / (ornament) / * LA PAZ *. Rv: Bs 1oo within circle of alternating stars and rings. (George Lill coll.)

PRIMER CENTENARIO DE LA REVOLUCION

Rulau	Date	Metal	Size	F	VF	EF	Unc
Lpz 33	1909	Bronze	26.3mm	—	7.50	—	—

Sun rises over moutain in background, city view in foreground, within circle. Around: PRIMER CENTENARIO DE LA REVOLUCION DE JULIO 1809 / . LA PAZ BOLIVIA 1909. Rv: Tall monument in center circle; tiny HORTA. (last letter illegible) at lower left. Around: LA TEA QUE DEJO ENCENDIDA. NADIE LA PODRA APAGAR / *. Plain edge. Looped for suspension. (Rulau coll.)

A. A. SHAW

Rulau	Date	Metal	Size	F	VF	EF	Unc
Lpz 35	(1930's)	Brass	25mm	—	—	8.00	12.00

A.A. SHAW / (ornament) / LA PAZ / (ornament) / * REP . DE BOLIVIA * / (tiny) L. A. RUB. STAMP CO. Rv: VALOR / * 25 * / CENTAVOS.

Rulau	Date	Metal	Size	F	VF	EF	Unc
Lpz 36	(1930's)	Brass	21mm	—	—	7.00	11.00

As last, but 5.

ORURO DEPARTMENT

Oruro
FEDERICO BELTRAN

Rulau	Date	Metal	Size	VG	F	VF	Unc
Oru 1	ND	Brass	20mm	—	—	8.00	—

Eagle on perch. Around: SENA / ORURO. Rv: * FEDERICO BELTRAN * / 1 / -*-. (Ulex 3611; Eklund 1442; Scott; Asbun-Karmy T11)

Rulau	Date	Metal	Size	VG	F	VF	Unc
Oru 2	ND	Brass	15mm	—	—	12.00	—

As last, but 1/2. (Zaika coll.)

Rulau	Date	Metal	Size	VG	F	VF	Unc
Oru 3	ND	Brass	15mm	—	—	10.00	—

As last (1/2), but ornament in place of ORURO. (Schiaffino 260)

BLONDEL & CIE.

Rulau	Date	Metal	Size	VG	F	VF	Unc
Oru 5	ND	CN	24mm	—	—	10.00	—

Male bust 3/4 right. Rv: + / BLONDEL & Cie / +. Plain edge. (Eklund 1444 & 2263)

Rulau	Date	Metal	Size	VG	F	VF	Unc
Oru 6	ND	CN	18.5mm	—	—	—	30.00

As last, smaller. (Lill coll.)

Oruro silver mine tokens, according to Ole P. Eklund.

Toledo
HACIENDA DE STA. ROSA

Rulau	Date	Metal	Size	VG	F	VF	Unc
Oru 9	1864	Brass	24mm	—	25.00	—	—

Tree on grassy mound. Around: HACIENDA DE Sta. ROSA. Rv: TOLEDO AND DE 1864 / 1 R. Plain edge.

Rulau	Date	Metal	Size	VG	F	VF	Unc
Oru 10	1864	Brass	20mm	—	—	20.00	—

As last, but 3/4 R. Plain edge. (Fonrobert 7171; Scott)

The 3/4-real token has also been claimed for Mexico, Costa Rica, Colombia and other countries. Its attribution here is doubtful.

The denomination 3/4-real was unusual, equaling 9.375 centavos. It must have had some special purpose on the hacienda.

Toledo is the capital of Saucari province, Oruro department.

PANDO DEPARTMENT

Orton Barraca
ANTONIO VACA DIEZ

Rulau	Date	Metal	Size	VG	F	VF	Unc
Pdo 4	1889	CN	24mm	—	15.00	20.00	—

FICHAS PARA EL ESTABLECIMIENTO DE ORTON / 20 / CENTAVOS / 1889. Rv: ANTONIO VACA DIEZ / 20 / CENTAVOS / ORTON. Reeded edge. Scarce.

This rubber-producing barraca (establishment) was located on the Orton River near its confluence with the Beni River.

Vaca Diez was a pioneer in the area of dense jungle, where rubber trees had grown naturally before man discovered them. There is a governmental unit in Beni Department named Vaca Diez after him.

At the time these tokens were issued, the area was Colonias Territory, part of the huge El Beni.

CN 10 and 5-centavo tokens, 19.5 and 17mm, are in the George Lill collection.

Valparaiso Barraca
AUGUSTO ROCA Y HNO.

Rulau	Date	Metal	Size	VG	F	VF	Unc
Pdo 7	1890	CN	24mm	—	15.00	20.00	—

Rubber plant divides 18 -- 90, in central circle. Around: FICHAS PARA EL ESTABLECIMIENTO DE VALPARAISO. Rv: 20 in central circle. Around: AUGUSTO ROCA Y Hno / Rio MADRE de DIOS. Reeded edge. Scarce.

This barraca (rubber establishment) was located on the north bank of Madre de Dios River, across the river from the present town of Las Piedras.

At the time this token was issued, the area was Colonias Territory, part of the huge El Beni. The barracas of Orton and Valparaiso were near the present city of Riberalta in El Beni Department, which had been founded in 1885 on the east bank of the Beni River.

POTOSI DEPARTMENT

Huanchaca
EMPRESA HUANCHACA

1st Series

Rulau	Date	Metal	Size	VG	F	VF	Unc
Psi	(1874)	**	25mm	—	—	20.00	30.00

** Beige vulcanite. EMPRESA HUANCHACA / (arabesque ornament) / . DE BOLIVIA . Rv: VALE EN MONEDA CORRIENTE / CINCO / CENTAVOS / DE / BOLIVIANO. Plain edge.

Rulau	Date	Metal	Size	VG	F	VF	Unc
Psi 4	(1874)	++	—mm	—	—	20.00	30.00

++ Green vulcanite. As last, but CINCUENTA / CENTAVOS.

Rulau	Date	Metal	Size	VG	F	VF	Unc
Psi 5	(1874)	++	45mm	—	—	60.00	75.00

++ Green vulcanite. As last, but UN / BOLIVIANO. (Eklund 1434; Rulau coll.; Lill coll.)

See *TAMS Journal* for June 1972, pages 106-111, and *TAMS Journal* for Feb. 1986, page 13.

2nd Series

Rulau	Date	Metal	Size	VG	F	VF	Unc
Psi 7	(1879)	XX	—mm	—	—	—	—

XX Black vulcanite. Obverse as last. Rv: VALE EN MERCADERIAS / DIEZ / CENTAVOS / DE / BOLIVIANO / +.

Rulau	Date	Metal	Size	VG	F	VF	Unc
Psi 8	(1879)	XX	31mm	—	—	—	—

As last, but VEINTE / CENTAVOS. (Eklund 1433)

Pulacayo (P)
COMPANIA HUANCHACA

3rd Series

Rulau	Date	Metal	Size	VG	F	VF	Unc
Psi 11	(1880's)	XX	26mm	—	—	—	—

XX Black vulcanite. P on ornamented circle. Around: COMPANIA . HUANCHACA / + DE . BOLIVIA +. Rv: VALE . EN . MERCADERIAS / 10 / CENTAVOS / DE / BOLIVIANO / . / + PULACAYO +. (Eklund 1431)

Rulau	Date	Metal	Size	VG	F	VF	Unc
Psi 12	ND	XX	28mm	—	—	—	—

As last, but 20. (Eklund 1432)

Rulau	Date	Metal	Size	VG	F	VF	Unc
Psi 13	ND	XX	34mm	—	—	—	—

As last, but 50. (Eklund 1432A; Zaika coll.)

Huanchaca (H)

3rd Series

Rulau	Date	Metal	Size	VG	F	VF	Unc
Psi 15	(1880's)	**	26mm	—	—	—	—

** Beige vulcanite. Similar to (P) issues, but H on obverse and + HUANCHACA + on reverse. 10 / CENTAVOS. (Eklund 1426)

Rulau	Date	Metal	Size	VG	F	VF	Unc
Psi 16	ND	**	29mm	—	—	—	—

** Beige vulcanite. As last, but 20. (Eklund 1427)

Rulau	Date	Metal	Size	VG	F	VF	Unc
Psi 17	ND	**	34mm	—	—	—	—

As last, but 50. (Eklund 1428)

Rulau	Date	Metal	Size	VG	F	VF	Unc
Psi 18	ND	**	39mm	—	—	—	—

As last, but UN / BOLIVIANO. (Eklund 1429)

Asiento (A)

3rd Series

Rulau	Date	Metal	Size	VG	F	VF	Unc
Psi 17	(1880's)	&&	34mm	—	—	—	—

&& Red vulcanite. Similar to (P) issues, but A on obverse and + ASIENTO + on reverse. 50 / CENTAVOS.

Rulau	Date	Metal	Size	VG	F	VF	Unc
Psi 18	ND	&&	39mm	—	—	—	—

As last, but UN / BOLIVIANO. (Eklund 1430)

Prospector Mariano Ramirez discovered silver at Pulacayo in 1837 but it could not be mined until 35 years later, by others. In 1872 the Compania Huanchaca de Bolivia was established, with most shares held in France. The capitalization was trebled in 1890.

Pulacayo mines yielded 5,000 tons of silver in the 1875-1900 period, when it was the second richest silver district on earth.

The Pulacayo group of mines was located 6½ miles south of another group of silver mines at Huanchaca, with a mountain between them. A third group was at Asiento, about 18½ miles north of Huanchaca.

The company began issuing tokens to pay its workers about 1874 titled EMPRESA HUANCHACA (Huanchaca Enterprise) and bearing the redemption phrase VALE EN MONEDA CORRIENTE (worth in current money). A second series in the late 1870's read VALE EN MERCADERIAS (worth in merchandise). These two series were for use at all company mines in the company stores, and the vulcanite tokens were most likely made in France.

A third series was for use at each of the locations: Huanchaca, Pulacayo and Asiento, each so designated on the tokens themselves. Differing colors of vulcanite were used for each mine.

A related series of vulcanite tokens was issued by EMPRESA PACHECO at Portugalete, 150 miles southeast of Huanchaca.

About 1914 the company's silver ores were largely played out and the firm shifted to increased output of lead, zinc, antimony and wolfram. In 1952 the Huanchaca mines and railway were nationalized and in 1961 they were operated at a loss. The mines ceased production in the 1960's.

The Huanchaca Co. also issued vulcanite tokens in its name for the Playa Blanca smelting plant near Antofagasta. Antofagasta had been ceded by Bolivia to Chile after the War of the Pacific (1879-1883), so these tokens, released in the early 1900's, are actually Chilean pieces (see under Chile).

Dr. Asbun-Karmy says there is no actual evidence these tokens were used at the sites named. Most specimens seen are in excellent condition.

LIPEZ

Rulau	Date	Metal	Size	VG	F	VF	Unc
Psi 22	ND	Vulcanite	—mm	—	—	8.00	—

LIPEZ. HUANCHACA. (Ulex 3598; Eklund 1441)

Portugalete
EMPRESA PACHECO

Rulau	Date	Metal	Size	VG	F	VF	Unc
Psi 25	(1879)	*	25mm	—	—	—	—

* Green vulcanite. EMPRESA PACHECO / (ornamented circle) / + PORTUGALETE +. Rv: VALE EN MERCADERIAS / DIEZ / CENTAVOS / DE / BOLI-VIANO. (Ulex 3613; Eklund 1445)

Rulau	Date	Metal	Size	VG	F	VF	Unc
Psi 26	ND	+	34mm	—	—	—	—

+ Black vulcanite.
As last, but CINCUETNA / CENTAVOS.

Rulau	Date	Metal	Size	VG	F	VF	Unc
Psi 27	ND	X	39mm	—	—	—	—

X Yellow vulcanite.
As lst, but UN / BOLIVIANO. (*TAMS Journal* for June 1972, page 111)

This mining enterprise apparently had its tokens made in France. They greatly resemble those of Compania Huanchaca, also in Potosi Dept.

Potosi
JERMAN FRICKE Y CA.

Rulau	Date	Metal	Size	VG	F	VF	Unc
Psi 33	ND	Brass	23.2mm	—	—	20.00	—

JERMAN FRICKE Y Ca - BOLIVIA / 1 R (shaded) / .*. Rv: JERMAN FRICKE Y. Ca - BOLIVIA / 10 (shaded) / Cvos = / .*. Plain edge. (Eklund 1449; Ulex 3582; Asbun-Karmy T14; Rulau coll.; Lill coll.)

Rulau	Date	Metal	Size	VG	F	VF	Unc
Psi 34	ND	Brass	18mm	—	—	9.00	—

As last, but 1/2 R and 5 / Cvos. (Eklund 1448; Ulex 3582)

These tokens were also listed in the 1899 Weyl catalog. George Lill assigns them to Cochahamba and Oruro rather than Potosi. Fricke was an importer-exporter in 1880.

INAUGURACION DEL FERRO CARRIL

Rulau	Date	Metal	Size	F	VF	EF	Unc
Psi 37	1912	Silver	26mm	—	—	30.00	—

Train entering Potosi. Looped for suspension. (Hudson April 1990 sale, lot 757)

Rulau	Date	Metal	Size	F	VF	EF	Unc
Psi 38	1912	Silver	Rect 26.5mm	—	—	25.00	—

Similar. (Hudson April 1990 sale, lot 758)

P.P. LOUREIRO I CIA.

Rulau	Date	Metal	Size	F	VF	EF	Unc
Psi 40	(1876?)	CN	16.5mm	8.00	10.00	25.00	

Eagle displayed, above arc of 9 stars. Around: EL VALOR DE MEDIO REAL / . (the value of half real). Rv: Within wreath: P. P. / LOUREIRO / I Cia-. Around: PAGARAN A LA VISTA AL PORTADOR /. (P. P. Loureiro and Co. will pay on sight to the bearer). Reeded edge. (Ulex 3582; Eklund 1450; Asbun-Karmy T3; Brunk coll.; Zaika coll.)

Struck at Heaton Mint, Birmingham.

HOTEL COLON

Rulau	Date	Metal	Size	VG	F	VF	Unc
Psi 42	1877	Bronze	22mm	—	30.00	40.00	55.00

HOTEL COLON / (circular wreath) / * POTOSI *. Rv: POTOSI AGOSTO 30 / 10 / CENT. / . 1877 . Plain edge. (ANS coll.)

SOCIEDAD POTOSINA

Rulau	Date	Metal	Size	VG	F	VF	Unc
Psi 43	1876	Copper	18mm	—	—	25.00	—

Mercury bust in winged cap left. SOCIEDAD POTO-SINA around. Rv: 1/8 / FICHA / 1876. (Eklund 1451)

UNATTRIBUTED BOLIVIA

EMPRESA NACIONAL DE BOLIVIA

Rulau	Date	Metal	Size	VG	F	VF	Unc
Bov 1	1885	Brass	24mm	—	10.00	15.00	35.00

EMPRESA / (ornaments) / NACIONAL / (9 stars) / DE BOLIVIA. Rv: FICHA POR / 10 (in floreate circle) / . CENTAVOS . 1885. Plain edge. (Zaika coll.)

Rulau	Date	Metal	Size	VG	F	VF	Unc
Bov 2	1885	Brass	19mm	7.50	10.00	15.00	35.00

As last, but 5. (Asbun-Karmy T21)

Kenneth Smith is in error when he says these may be transportation tokens. Empresa Nacional de Bolivia = Bolivian National Enterprise. It operated in Santa Cruz Dept. during construction of Puerto Pacheco, George Lill reports.

Miscellaneous Bolivian Counterstamps

Rulau	Stamp	Host coin	Value in VF
Bov 4	EA	on Bolivia 1864 copper 2-centecimos, 27mm, reeded edge	75.00
Bov 5	*F. G* (in relief within beaded oval)	on France 1841-A silver 1/2 franc, 18mm, reeded edge	75.00
Bov 6	-do-	on France 1841-A silver ¼-franc, 15mm, reeded edge (Lill coll.)	75.00

Rulau	Stamp	Host coin	Value in VF
Bov 7	-do-	on Chile 1851-59 worn silver 1/2-decimo	75.00

All the F.G. pieces were found in La Paz markets.

Rulau	Stamp	Host coin	Value in VF
Bov 9	Serif R (retrograde)	On 1/5 segment of Bolivia 8-soles of type used 1827-63. May be a brand mark. (Krueger 1991 sale, lot 1606)	100.
Bov 11	3	on Bolivia 1951 copper 1 boliviano, 18mm reeded edge.	60.00

Bov 13 POTOSI — on Argentina Buenos Aires copper 33mm Entrada al Teatro token. (Lill coll.) — 125.

BRAZIL

About Brazilian Tokens

Though Brazil is the largest nation in Latin America and it is known to have produced a very large number of tokens, they are uniformly scarce in numismatic hands except in Brazil itself. Only the modern tokens of post-World War II Brazil, mostly in plastic, bakelite and similar sustances are encountered in any quantity in 1992.

Thus pricing in this series is especially difficult. The tokens bring high prices in Brazil yet are little known elsewhere.

Only a fraction of the nation's token coinage can be catalogued here.

Slavery in Brazil

Slavery was abolished in Brazil very late. It was the last nation in the Western Hemisphere to tolerate official slavery. Even Spanish Cuba had outlawed slavery in 1883.

Emancipation in Brazil came in steps. In 1871 the Rio Branco law provided that children of slaves should be free. In 1885, all slaves over 60 years of age were freed by the imperial government and two states — Ceara and Amazonas — freed all slaves within their boundaries.

Ultimately, on May 13, 1888, total emancipation *without compensation to owners* was declared.

The emancipation led to the alienation of the landed aristocracy against the emperor and contributed to the military overthrow of the empire in Nov. 1889. (There had been 2.5 million slaves in 1850, decreasing to 1.5 million in 1872.)

It also led to the introduction of fazenda tokens on those plantations where former slaves became wage earners.

Coffee production became important in the 1880's, as did rubber production in the Amazon basin, and stock raising in the south continued important. By 1925 coffee production comprised 4/5 of the entire world's supply! After 1910 rubber production declined.

Sao Paulo became the leading coffee state, while cotton and cocoa became important along the coast north of Rio de Janeiro.

Kilo Denominations

Rulau	Date	Metal	Size	VG	F	VF	Unc
Ags 17	(1894)	Copper	40mm	—	—	—	—
		Sugar cane refining engine. Rv: USINA LEAO UTINGA ALAGOAS * / 2000 / KILOS. Plain edge. (Eklund 1639; Ludolph 9; Meili 193)					
Ags 18	(1894)	Copper	35mm	—	—	—	—
		As last, but 1000 / KILOS. (Eklund 1638)					
Ags 19	(1894)	Copper	29mm	—	—	—	—
		As last, but 500 / KILOS. (Eklund 1637)					
Ags 20	(1894)	Copper	25mm	—	—	—	—
		As last, but 200 / KILOS. (Eklund 1636)					
Ags 21	(1894)	Copper	20mm	—	—	—	—
		As last, but 100 / KILOS. (Eklund 1635; Ludolph 13)					

Struck in Germany in 1894, these carried the word "Kilos" but this had to be translated as "Reis." The sugar company wanted to evade the law which prohibited the private issue of coins.

ALAGOAS STATE

Jaragua
USINA LEAO UTINGA

Reis Denominations

Rulau	Date	Metal	Size	VG	F	VF	Unc
Ags 4	1893	CN	26mm	—	—	—	—
		USINA LEAO / 1893 / BRAZIL / JARAGUA ALAGOAS. Rv: USINA LEAO / 090 (in circle) / 090 (in circle) / UTINGA. Plain edge. Centrally holed flan. (Ludolph 8)					

Sugar mill token for 90 reis.

Rulau	Date	Metal	Size	VG	F	VF	Unc
Ags 7	1907	Aluminum	30mm	—	—	—	—
		Head left of Luiz de Anorim Leao. Around: L. A. LEAO 1856-1907. Rv: USINA LEAO * / 2 / 000 / UTINGA - ALAGOAS. (Ludolph 14)					
Ags 8	1907	Aluminum	Triang 29x25mm	—	—	—	—
		As last, but 9 / 00. (Ludolph 15)					
Ags 9	1907	Aluminum	Hexag 21mm	—	—	—	—
		As last, but 8 / 00. (Ludolph 16)					
Ags 10	1907	Aluminum	25mm	—	—	—	—
		As last, but 7 / 00. (Ludolph 17)					
Ags 11	1907	Aluminum	22mm	—	—	—	—
		As last, but 5 / 00. (Ludolph 18)					
Ags 12	1907	Aluminum	Rect 23x20mm	—	—	—	—
		As last, but 4 / 00. (Ludolph 19)					
Ags 13	1907	Aluminum	20mm	—	—	—	—
		As last, but 2 / 00. (Ludolph 20)					
Ags 14	1907	Aluminum	18mm	—	—	—	—
		As last, but 1 / 00. (Ludolph 21; Eklund 2283)					

Luiz de Anorim Leao founded the sugar mill firm Usina Leao Utinga in 1893, and died in 1907. The 1907 token issue memorializing the founder, denominated in reis, were in use until about 1909.

8 / 00 = 800 reis. 2 / 000 = 2000 reis (etc.).

Uncertain
I. T. A.

Rulau	Date	Metal	Size	VG	F	VF	EF
Ags 25	ND	CN/Cop	40mm	—	—	—	—
		ITA . & within octagonal frame ctsp on plated Brazil copper 80-reis coin, 1830-R (Rio), KM-366.1 Rv: VALE / ITA 40 & / REIS ctsp on opposite side. (Wes Scharlow coll.)					

Rulau	Date	Metal	Size	VG	F	VF	Unc
Ags 26	ND	CN/Cop	40mm	—	—	—	—

Similar ctsp on plated Brazil copper 40-reis revalued coin, 1831-R (Rio), KM-441.1 Rv: Similar to last reverse stamp, but no 40 stamped since govt. ctmk 40 in shaded oval is in place (Wes Scharlow coll.)

ITA . & = Industrias Tabacos Arapiraca Cia. In each case the coin was cupronickel-plated before counterstamping.

It is possible that Ags 25 & 26 are fantasy concoctions made by an entrepreneur in Texas 40 years ago. Research is needed.

BAHIA STATE

Caldo do Cipo
BODEGA DO MEGADO

Rulau	Date	Metal	Size	VG	F	VF	EF
Baa 3	ND	Copper	40mm	—	—	—	—

x BODEGA DO MEGADO x / C. CIPO BAHIA ctsp on Brazil revalued 40-reis, date worn, KM-441. Rv: + VALE + / EM GENEROS around 4 S's in cross form, all ctsp on opposite side of the coin. (Wes Scharlow coll.)

Salvador
COMPANHIA DO QUEIMADO

Rulau	Date	Metal	Size	VG	F	VF	Unc
Baa 6	ND	Zinc	32mm	—	—	—	—

Fountain. Around: COMPANHIA DO QUEIMADO / BAHIA. Rv: VALE / UM BARRIL / D'AGOA. (Eklund 1640; Ludolph 27)

Companhia do Queimado, founded in 1853, furnished drinking water to the city of Bahia. Vale um barril d'agoa = Good for a barrel of water. Bahia is now known as Salvador.

Dulce Ludolph reports minor varieties of this token.

CEARA STATE

Baturite
MANOEL JOSE D'OLIVEIRA FIGUEIREDO
Fazenda Bom Successo

Rulau	Date	Metal	Size	VG	F	VF	Unc
Cea 1	1895	Brass	30mm	—	—	—	—

MANOEL JOSE D'OLIVEIRA FIGUEIREDO / *.* / ESCRIPTORIO / FAZENDA / BOM SUCCESSO / BATURITE / *.* / (diamond). Rv: Bar across center interrupts circular wreath; on bar: . ALQUEIRE . 1 above, 1895 below (Ludolph 52)

| Cea 2 | 1895 | Brass | 26mm | — | — | — | — |

As last, but . QUARTA . on the bar. (Ludolph 53)

| Cea 3 | 1895 | Brass | 23.5mm | — | — | — | — |

As last, but . TERCA . on the bar.

The Terca token passed at 120 reis, the Quarta piece at 500 reis. The Alqueire piece passed at 2000 reis, according to Rocha, but Prober says 800 reis.

Fortaleza
B. A.

Rulau	Date	Metal	Size	VG	F	VF	EF
Cea 6	ND	Brass	Oct 31x26mm	—	—	—	—

(All incused): B. A. / 1.000. Rv: Blank. (Scharlow coll.)

MARANHAO STATE

Brejo
ARAUJO & BRAGA

Rulau	Date	Metal	Size	VG	F	VF	Unc
Mnh 1	ND	Bronze	33mm	—	—	—	—

ARAUJO & BRAGA. BREJO. (Weyl 3035; Eklund 1642)

MINAS GERAIS STATE

Belo Horizonte
MORRO VELHO

First Issue - Raised Letters

Rulau	Date	Metal	Size	VG	F	VF	Unc
MG 1	1848	Zinc	44mm	—	50.00	70.00	—

MORRO / VELHO / 1848 within double circle. Outside circle; Continuous leaf tips to rim. (Same wide border on each side). Rv: 320 / REIS. Reeded edge. (Ludolph 227-234; Meili 126-130). Many minor varieties. Also known in antimony.

MG 2	1848	Zinc	44mm	—	300.	500.	—

As last, ctsp C. Varieties. (Ludolph 228)

MG 3	1848	Zinc	42mm	30.00	50.00	70.00	—

As first token, smaller. Reeded edge. (Ludolph 233)

MG 4	1848	Zinc	37.5mm	30.00	50.00	70.00	—

As last, but 80 / REIS. Reeded edge. Thick and thin planchet varieties. (Ludolph 236-236A)

MG 5	1848	Zinc	37mm	—	—	—	—

As last, but ctsp C. (Ludolph 238)

Rulau	Date	Metal	Size	VG	F	VF	Unc
MG 6	1848	Zinc	37mm	—	500.	—	—

As last, but the ctsp is now Vo. (Ludolph 238)

MG 7	1848	Zinc	37mm	—	500.	Rare	—

Obverse as last. Rv: Plain center within leaf circle. (Ludolph 239)

MG 8	1848	Zinc	37mm	—	—	—	—

As last (plain reverse), but ctsp C. (Meili 132)

MG 8A	1848	Zinc	37mm	500.	650.	—	—

MG 4 with reverse ctsp with large numeral. Numbers reported: 20, 29, 31, 56, 188. All ex. rare. (Alan York coll.)

MG 9	1848	Zinc	28mm	—	—	40.00	—

As last, but 40 / REIS. Raised letters. Reeded edge. (Ludolph 243)

MG 10	1848	Zinc	28mm	—	—	—	—

As last, but ctsp Mo. (Ludolph 244-245)

MG 11	1848	Zinc	28mm	—	—	—	—

As last, but ctsp is now C. (Ludolph 246)

Third Issue

MG 12	ND	Zinc	38mm	—	—	Rare	—

Star on a radiant pentagram, all within wreath. Rv: (Incused) Mo Vo / 1½. Reeded edge. Rare. (Ludolph 247-248). These are known ctsp with numerals, e.g. 143.

MG 13	ND	Zinc	37mm	—	400.	—	—

As last, but 1¼. Reeded edge. Rare. (Ludolph 250). These are known with incused numerals, e.g. 43.

MG 14	ND	Zinc	37mm	—	500.	—	—

As last, but 1¾. Reeded edge. (Ludolph 251-252). These are known with ctsp numerals, e.g. 30.

MG 15	ND	Zinc	38mm	—	500.	—	—

As last, but 1. Reeded edge. (Ludolph 253-255). These are known with ctsp numerals, e.g. 12.

MG 16	ND	Zinc	38mm	—	600.	—	—

As last, but ¾. Reeded edge. (Ludolph 256-257). These are known with ctsp numerals, e.g. 147.

Rulau	Date	Metal	Size	VG	F	VF	Unc
MG 17	ND	Zinc	38mm	—	500.	—	—

As last, but ¼. Reeded edge. (Ludolph 258-259). Known with ctsp numerals, e.g. 49.

Rulau	Date	Metal	Size	VG	F	VF	Unc
MG 18	ND	Zinc	38mm	—	500.	—	—

As last, but ½. Reeded edge. (Ludolph 260-261). Known with ctsp numeras, e.g. 15.

Rulau	Date	Metal	Size	VG	F	VF	Unc
MG 20	ND	Zinc	31mm	200.	500.	—	—

(All incused): Mo Vo. Rv: 1¾. Very rare. (Ludolph 262; Souza-Lobo 61)

This type is also reported with reverse ½ or 1½ in 31mm zinc format, both very rare.

Rulau	Date	Metal	Size	VG	F	VF	Unc
MG 22	ND	Zinc	44mm	500.	—	—	—

* / Mo. Vo. / * radiant, all in circle of crosses and stars. Rv: 320 / R / (ornament) radiant, all in circle of crosses and stars. Reeded edge. Varieties. (Ludolph 265-266; Meili 142-143)

These pieces are struck over 320 reis tokens of 1848.

Rulau	Date	Metal	Size	VG	F	VF	Unc
MG 23	ND	Zinc	44mm	500.	—	—	—

As last, ctsp C. (Ludolph 267)

Morro Velho, near Belo Horizonte, is one of the oldest and richest gold mines in Brazil, opened in 1725.

Morro Velho is located in the municipio of Sabara. Its tokens were issued by the Saint John d'El Rey Mining Company Ltd., a British firm. This firm was succeeded by Companhia Inglesa de Mineracao do Morro Velho, later known as Villa Nova de Lima.

The first issue of tokens uses raised letters and digits. The second issue has the denominations in incuse letters. The third issue is denominated all in "units".

According to Dr. Alan York, who has researched this series, the Morro Velho mines used the tokens to pay the slaves who worked the gold mines. It was possible in 19th century Brazil for slaves to earn money with which to purchase their freedom. Upon presentation of a sufficient number of these tokens, they were presented a tin medal to wear about the neck.

After a further period of good conduct and sufficient output of gold, the slave was presented with a silver medal, which if worn for a prescribed period of time could earn the slave his freedom. All the Morro Velho tokens were used prior to 1888, the year slavery was finally abolished in Brazil.

York says "These may be considered 'anti-slavery tokens' in the truest sense of the word."

Diamantina
VIDIGAL

Rulau	Date	Metal	Size	VG	F	VF	Unc
MG 27	ND	CN	Oval 48x34mm	—	—	—	—

(All incused): F L / VIDIGAL. Rv: Blank. (Ludolph 385; Meili 174)

Leopoldina
C. E. F. L.
(Companhia de Estrada de Ferro Leopoldina)

Rulau	Date	Metal	Size	VG	F	VF	Unc
MG 30	ND	Brass	36mm	—	—	—	—

N 58 / C E F L / BICAS / N 58. Rv: Blank. Issued holed. (Ludolph 386)

Rulau	Date	Metal	Size	VG	F	VF	Unc
MG 31	ND	Brass	38mm	—	—	—	—

N 58 / C E F L / N 58. Rv: Blank. Issued holed. (Meili 166c)

Bicas = Water spout. These checks were given, apparently, for supplying water to trains of the C.E.F.L. line.

Mar de Espanha
B. J.
(Fazenda Bom Jardin)

Rulau	Date	Metal	Size	VG	F	VF	Unc
MG 34	ND	Zinc	Oct 32mm	—	—	—	—

B J. Rv: Blank. Issued holed. (Ludolph 350-352)

This token was valued at 500 reis. Bom Jardin estate was owned by Viuva Saldanha & Filhos, who also owned fazendas Providencia, Floresta and Tucaia.

A. A. P. S.
(Antonio A. P. Saldanha)

Rulau	Date	Metal	Size	VG	F	VF	Unc
MG 36	ND	Zinc	Oct 32mm	—	—	—	—

A A P S / B J / 1000. Rv: Blank. Issued holed. (Ludolph 353-354)

A A P S / B J = Antonio Augusto Pereira Saldanha, owner of Fazenda Bom Jardin.

s B s J s
(Fazenda Bom Jardin)

Rulau	Date	Metal	Size	VG	F	VF	Unc
MG 38	1899	Zinc	Rect 50x38mm	—	—	—	—

s B s J s. Rv: 1 8 9 9 (one numeral in each corner) / 94 / 99. Issued holed. (Museu-Rocha 576)

Worth one day's work or 1 alquiere de trabajo.

Rulau	Date	Metal	Size	VG	F	VF	Unc
MG 40	1899	Zinc	Rect 50x38mm	—	—	—	—

990 / 800 / s B s J s / 94. Rv: 1899. (Ludolph 356)

Dulce Ludolph says this was worth 1 alquiere or 800 reis at Fazenda Bom Jardin.

There are many more similar varieties of this estate's tokens, Ludolph numbers 357 to 364.

I. C.
(Ivo de Carvalho)

Rulau	Date	Metal	Size	VG	F	VF	EF
MG 43	ND	Copper	36mm	—	35.00	—	—

I . C within rectangle ctsp on Brazil copper 40-reis coins of Portuguese rule 1802-23 or empire 1823-32 (KM 234, 363 etc.). (Prober 111)

Rulau	Date	Metal	Size	VG	F	VF	EF
MG 45	ND	Copper	40mm	—	—	—	—

I . C within rectangle ctsp on Brazil copper 80-reis coins of Portuguese rule 1811-23 or empire 1823-32 (KM 342, 366 etc.).

Sometime in the 1849-71 time period a good number of ranchers, commercial firms and others who provided wages to a work force, began counterstamping the old, heavy 40 and 80-reis copper pieces still in circulation, to revalidate them in the more convenient decimal denominations. By the Law of 1837 such coins produced before the copper coinage weight was reduced by 50 percent in 1834 were to be valued at their old face value — so that there were two completely different size-and-weight coins for these denominations.

Ivo de Carvalho counterstamped the Brazilian coppers for use on his fazenda, guaranteeing acceptance at the higher values within his area of control, including the company store. (Research courtesy Kurt Prober)

Mar de Espanha is near Juiz de Fora, about 96 miles north of Rio de Janeiro.

CONCEICAO
(Fazenda da Conceicao)

Rulau	Date	Metal	Size	VG	F	VF	Unc
MG 48	ND	WM	27mm	—			

MAR / DE / ESPANHA (ornament) / CONCEICAO /
(ornament). Rv: (Ornament) / BRITO / (ornament).
Plain edge. (Ludolph 339-341)

Brito = Gravel?

GUARANY
(Fazenda Guarani)

Rulau	Date	Metal	Size	VG	F	VF	Unc
MG 51	ND	Zinc	Rect 51x25mm	—	—	—	—

(Incuse): GUARANY. Rv: Blank. (Ludolph 368-369)

Worth 500 reis on the estate.

Mariana
N. D. R.
(North d'El Rey Gold Mining)

Rulau	Date	Metal	Size	VG	F	VF	EF
MG 53	ND	Copper	34mm	—	450.	—	—

(All incused): N D R in circle made up of squarish dots.
Rv: 500. Plain edge. (Meili 146; Ludolph 274-275;
Souza-Lobo 7)

MG 54	ND	Copper	31mm	—	350.	—	—

As last, but 320 (reis). (Meili 154-155; Ludolph 284-
286)

MG 54A	ND	Copper	24mm	—	—	—	—

As 54 (320) in smaller size. (Ludolph 288-289)

MG 55	ND	Copper	28mm	—	250.	—	—

As last, but 160. (Ludolph 290-291)

MG 56	ND	Copper	25mm	—	250.	—	—

As last, but 80. (Meili 151)

MG 57	ND	Copper	23mm	—	150.	—	—

As last, but 40 (reis). (Meili 152; Ludolph 297-298;
Souza-Lobo 11)

N D R = Dom Pedro North d'El Rey Gold Mining Co. Ltd., organized in
1862. The 500-reis tokens occur ctsp 3, 7, 27, 34, 39, etc.
A number of these tokens in Fine were sold in the United States in 1986 at $45
apiece. All the above are known on planchets of varying thicknesses and weights.

Santa Barbara
P. M.
(Pari Mines)

Rulau	Date	Metal	Size	VG	F	VF	Unc
MG 58	ND	Brass	31mm	—	800.	—	—

Miner with pick shovel and lamp working in mine pas-
sageway. Rv: P. M / 10. Reeded edge. (Ludolph 271;
Alan York coll.)

Rulau	Date	Metal	Size	VG	F	VF	Unc
MG 58A	ND	Zinc	31mm	—	400.		

As last, but 5 (tostoes). Reeded edge. (Meili 144; Souza-
Lobo 13; Ludolph 272). Henkle reports this in brass.

MG 59	ND	Brass	31mm	—	350.	—	—

As last, but 2. Reeded edge. (Meili 145; Souza-Lobo 12;
Ludolph 273; Alan York coll.)

Issued by Santa Barbara Gold Mining Company Ltd. in the minicipio of Santa
Barbara for the Pari Mines. The company was organized 1862. Values are given
in tostoes (2 tostoes = 200 reis, etc.). All tokens are rare and eagerly sought.

Uncertain
GENERAL BRAZILIAN
COMPANY

Rulau	Date	Metal	Size	VG	F	VF	Unc
MG 60	ND	Brass	31mm	—	—	—	—

GENERAL / -.- / BRAZILIAN / -.- / COMPANY. Rv:
80 RS.. in multilobed circle. Plain edge. (Meili 72)

MG 61	ND	Brass	25.5mm	—	—	—	—

As last, but 40 RS.. (Ludolph 268)

USINA WIGG

Rulau	Date	Metal	Size	VG	F	VF	Unc
MG 64	ND	Brass	31mm	—	—	—	—

USINA WIGG / (empty circle) / +MINAS +. Rv:
Blank. Issued holed. Plain edge. (Ludolph 317-318)

This is the basic Usina Wigg token. It is found with numbers incused in the
circle, such as 563 or 569.
These tokens also occur with numerals stamped on reverse; e.g. ¼, ½, ¾ (for
portions of a day's work).

MG 66	ND	WM	24mm	—	—	—	—

Obverse similar to last. Rv: Blank, but with incused
number (such as 250). (Ludolph 325)

PARA STATE

Belem
ANTONIO ABEL
AFFONSO & CIA.

Rulau	Date	Metal	Size	VG	F	VF	Unc
Par 1	ND	Brass	35mm				

ANTONIO ABEL AFFONSO & CIA. / 1000 (reis). Rv:
Quatrefoil in circle of 16 stars. (Eklund 1643; Ludolph
395)

Para is now known as Belem.

ALVES MAGALHAES & CA.

Rulau	Date	Metal	Size	VG	F	VF	Unc
Par 6	ND	Brass	28mm	—	—	—	—

ALVES MAGALHAES & Ca / TRAVESSA / MAR-QUEZ / DE POMBAL / * PARA *. Rv: *** / 1000 / ***. (Eklund 1646; Ludolph 396)

| Par 7 | ND | Brass | 28mm | — | 15.00 | — | — |

As last, but 800 (reis). (Eklund 1645)

| Par 8 | ND | Brass | 28mm | — | — | — | — |

As last, but 500 (reis). (Eklund 1644)

CARDOSO DANIN & CA.

Rulau	Date	Metal	Size	VG	F	VF	Unc
Par 12	ND	Brass	Oval 48x32mm	—	—	20.00	—

CARDOSO DANIN & Ca / (ornament) / ESTIVAS E COMISSOES / RUA DE IMPERATRIZ . 20 / PARA. Rv: 1000. Plain edge. (Eklund 1649; Ludolph 399)

| Par 13 | ND | Brass | Oval 48x32mm | — | — | — | — |

As last, but 800. (Eklund 1648; Ludolph 400)

| Par 14 | ND | Brass | Oval 48x32mm | — | — | 20.00 | — |

As last, but 500. (Eklund 1647; Ludolph 401; Meili 213)

All struck in Germany.

COMPANHIA DE REBOCADORES DO PARA

Rulau	Date	Metal	Size	VG	F	VF	Unc
Par 17	ND	Brass	**	—	—	—	—

** Diamond-shaped flan, 55x33mm. COMPANHIA DE REBOCADORES / DO / PARA. Rv: DIA / 4000. (Eklund 1652; Ludolph 406)

| Par 18 | ND | Brass | Oval 47x32mm | — | — | — | — |

COMPANHIA / DE / REBOCADORES / DO / PARA. Rv: MEIA NOITE / 2500. (Eklund 1651; Ludolph 408)

| Par 19 | ND | Brass | xx | — | — | — | — |

xx Vertical diamond-shaped flan, 33x55mm. COMPANHIA DE REBOCADORES / DO / PARA. Rv: MEIO DIA / 2000. (Eklund 1650; Ludolph 407)

Dia = Day's work, 4,000 reis (about $2 U.S.) Meia noite = Half a night's work, 2,500 reis. Meia dia = Half a day's work. 2,000 reis. Used as payment for labor in the harbor of Para (now Belem).
These tokens were struck in Germany.

CUNHA & BASTOS

Rulau	Date	Metal	Size	VG	F	VF	Unc
Par 22	ND	Brass	28mm	—	—	15.00	25.00

CUNHA & BASTOS / 800 / -***- / * PARA *. Rv: ARMAZEM DE ESTIVAS / 800 -***- / * PARA *. (Eklund 1653; Ludolph 409)

A cargo warehouse.

JGNACIO JOSE DA SILVA & CIA

Rulau	Date	Metal	Size	VG	F	VF	Unc
Par 25	(1880-1910)	Brass	28mm	—	15.00	20.00	—

CASA DE COMISSOES / 1000 / (ornament) / * PARA *. Rv: JGNACIO JOSE DA SILVA & Cia. / 1000 / (ornament) / * PARA *. (Eklund 1656; Meili 216; ANS coll.; Ludolph 412)

Rulau	Date	Metal	Size	VG	F	VF	Unc
Par 26	(1880-1910)	Brass	28mm	—	11.00	15.00	40.00

As last, but 800. (Eklund 1655; Meili 217; Ludolph 413)

| Par 27 | (1880-1910) | Brass | 28mm | — | 13.00 | 20.00 | — |

ARMAZEM DE ESTIVAS / 500 / (ornament) / * PARA *. Rv: As last, but 500 (reis). (Eklund 1657; Ludolph 410)

MAGALHAES & SANTOS

Rulau	Date	Metal	Size	VG	F	VF	Unc
Par 30	1903	Tin ?	--mm	—	—	—	—

N. Sa.DE NASARETH / LOJA DE MILAGRES / DE / MAGALHAES & SANTOS / RUA CONSELHEIRO JOAO ALFREDO / N. 106 / BELEM DO PARA / BRAZIL. Rv: BRINDE / DE / LOJA DOS MILAGRES / 1903 / BELEM DO PARA / BRAZIL. Plain edge. (Museu-Rocha 607)

PESCARIA PARAENSE

Rulau	Date	Metal	Size	VG	F	VF	Unc
Par 33	ND	Brass	Sq 25mm	—	—	—	—

Fish right. Rv: PESCARIA / 200 / PARAENSE. (Eklund 1662; Ludolph 416)

| Par 34 | ND | Brass | ** | — | — | — | — |

** Lozenge-shaped flan, 35x21mm. Fish right. Rv: * PESCARIA * / 50 / PARAENSE. (Eklund 1661; Meili 204)

| Par 35 | ND | WM | --mm | — | — | — | — |

As last, but 500. (Eklund 1662A)

| Par 36 | ND | Zinc | 27.5mm | — | — | — | — |

As last, but 20 (reis). (Eklund 1660)

Pescaria Paraense = Para fish market. This market was established in 1857. The city of Para is now known as Belem.
The pescaria tokens were struck in Germany, according to Eklund.

PARAIBA STATE

Areia
ENGENHO BRUXAXA

Rulau	Date	Metal	Size	VG	F	VF	EF
Pba 3	(1898-1910)	Copper	42mm	—	—	—	—

ENGENHO BRUXAXA . / VALE UMA ARROBA ASSUCAR MAS ctsp around rim of Brazil counterfeit Pedro I or II 40-reis coin obverse. Rv: BRUXAXA / P. B. ctsp at center of reverse. Plain edge. Weight: 23.9 grams.

Uma arroba assucar mas(cava) = One arroba (about 4 gallons) of molasses. A sugar plantation token.
The old city of Bruxaxa no longer stands. The city of Areia was built approximately on its site.

N. N. F.
(Nicodemos N. Figueiredo)

Rulau	Date	Metal	Size	VG	F	VF	EF
Pba 6	ND	Aluminum	Rect 50x30mm	—	—	—	—

(All incused): P. BRASIL / N. N. F. Rv: TROCO / CR. $ 0.50. (Scharlow coll.)

Nicodemos Nunes Figueiredo owned and operated Panificadora Brasil, a bakery, in which these tokens were used to represent the value of one-half cruzeiro. A counterfeit detection system was implemented with these pieces, Scharlow assserts.

The cruzeiro currency was adopted by Brazil in 1942.

PARANA STATE

Campo do Tenente
J. BETTEGA & CIA.

Rulau	Date	Metal	Size	VG	F	VF	Unc
Pna 1	1926	Aluminum	30mm	—	—	—	—

Ornate B is pierced by stylized pine tree, all in a circle. Around: J. BETTEGA & Cia / . CAMPO DO TENENTE . Rv: Q / (ornament) / 500 (large, shaded) / (ornament) / 1926. Plain edge. (Ludolph note 452; Wes Scharlow coll.)

Rulau	Date	Metal	Size	VG	F	VF	Unc
Pna 2	1926	Aluminum	28mm	—	—	—	—

Obverse similar to last, but ornate B is *before* tree. Rv: B / (ornament) / 200 (shaded) / (ornament) / 1926. Plain edge. (Ludolph note 452; Scharlow coll.)

Dulce Ludolph mentions 100, 1,000, 5,000 and 10,000-reis tokens in this series, the last with letter D atop reverse.

Curitiba
CASA JOSE NABO

Rulau	Date	Metal	Size	VG	F	VF	EF
Pna 4	ND	Copper	30mm	—	—	—	—

(All incused): CASA JOSE NABO / C / + CURITYBA +. Rv: Blank. (Ludolph 425; Scharlow coll.)

Also known WM-plated before striking.

E. DE FERRO DO PARANA
(Parana Railways)

Rulau	Date	Metal	Size	VG	F	VF	Unc
Pna 8	ND	Brass	Sq 36.5mm	—	—	75.00	—

E.(strada) DE FERRO / DO / PARANA. Rv: FORNECIMENTOS / 10000. Plain edge. (Eklund 1670; Meili 83)

Rulau	Date	Metal	Size	VG	F	VF	Unc
Pna 9	ND	Brass	Sq 36.5mm	—	75.00	—	—

As last, but ctsp EPF at top of reverse. (Ludolph 433 and 446)

Fornecimentos = Merchandise. These are not transportation tokens; they were used to pay railway employees who in turn paid grocers, bakers, butchers, etc. with them as small change. They found ready acceptance by merchants in the interior as well as with the urban populace, as small change was always in short supply.

Rulau	Date	Metal	Size	VG	F	VF	Unc
Pna 10	ND	Brass	Oct 34mm	—	—	—	—

As the first token, but 5000 (reis). (Eklund 1669; Meili 84; Ludolph 434)

Rulau	Date	Metal	Size	VG	F	VF	Unc
Pna 11	ND	Brass	Oct 34mm	—	—	—	—

As last, but ctsp EPF at top of reverse. (Ludolph 435 and 436)

This series was also issued in brass 1000, 500, 100, 50 and 10 reis denominations, Eklund 1658 to 1664.

PERNAMBUCO STATE

Recife
C. DE DETENCAO

Rulau	Date	Metal	Size	VG	F	VF	EF
Pbc 5	ND	Copper	36mm	—	—	45.00	—

C.DE DETENCAO (curved) / PERNAMBUCO with oval frame ctsp on Brazil 40-reis coins of Colony and Empire. (Prober 54; Brunk 51330)

Rulau	Date	Metal	Size	VG	F	VF	EF
Pbc 6	ND	Copper	40mm	—	—	45.00	—

As last, but on 80-reis coins. The counterstamp measures 21mm in width.

The city of Pernambuco is now called Recife.

AUGUSTO KRUSS SUCCESSORES

Rulau	Date	Metal	Size	VG	F	VF	Unc
Pbc 9	ND	Copper	29mm	—	—	—	—

AUGUSTO KRUSS SUCCESSORES / VALE / O / CONSUMO / DE / 200 REIS /FABRICA DE CERVEJA / . PERNAMBUCO . Rv: Same as obverse. (Ludolph 471; Eklund 1671)

Fabrica de Cerveja = Brewery. This token for 200 Reis would be used to purchase a beer. The Reis was last used as a monetary unit in 1942. The last large cent-sized 200-Reis piece was the CN coin of 1900.

MERCADO SAO JOSE

Rulau	Date	Metal	Size	VG	F	VF	EF
Pbc 10	ND	CN	31mm	—	—	25.00	—

MERCADO SÀO JOSE RECIFE . (circular) ctsp on Brazil 1921 400-reis. KM-520. Rv: VALE ctsp on opposite side of coin. All single letter-punches. (Scharlow coll.)

LA PUERTA DEL SOL

Rulau	Date	Metal	Size	VG	F	VF	Unc
Pbc 12	ND	Copper	27mm	—	16.00	—	—

LA PUERTA DEL SOL PERNAMBUCO * / (The sun of the Argentine). Rv: 500. (Eklund 1674; Ludolph 473)

Rulau	Date	Metal	Size	VG	F	VF	Unc
Pbc 13	ND	Copper	25mm	—	30.00	—	—

As last, but 200 (reis). (Eklund 1673)

Rulau	Date	Metal	Size	VG	F	VF	Unc
Pbc 14	ND	Copper	20mm	—	—	—	—

As last, but 100 (reis). (Eklund 1672)

La Puerta del Sol = Gate of the Sun. This was probably an Argentinian restaurant; the legend is Spanish.

Uncertain
U. C. R.
(or U. R. C. ?)

Rulau	Date	Metal	Size	VG	F	VF	EF
Pbc 17	ND	Copper	Oct 35mm	—	—	—	—

(All incused): U C / R. Rv: Blank. (Scharlow coll.)

Brazilian collectors refer to these pieces as "slave tokens," used to keep track of work accomplished. Wes Scharlow says they resemble picker chits, such as those depicted by Julius Meili in *Brasilianische Geldwesen* (1905) for Minas Gerais coffee pickers.

The true story of their use has not been uncovered.

Rulau	Date	Metal	Size	VG	F	VF	Unc
Pbc 19	ND	CN ?	35mm	—	—	—	—

(All incused): U. C. R. / (ornament). Rv: 200 / REIS.

Rulau	Date	Metal	Size	VG	F	VF	Unc
Pcb 20	ND	Bronze	31mm	—	—	—	—

(All incused): U. C. R / (ornament, different than last). Rv: 100 / REIS / +. (Wes Scharlow coll.)

These handmade tokens were used in northern Brazil, Scharlow says.

UZINA CUCAU

Rulau	Date	Metal	Size	VG	F	VF	Unc
Pbc 30	ND	++	33mm	12.00	16.00	25.00	—

++ Brass with 4-lobed copper insert.
C.G.M. (on ribbon) / UZINA / CUCAU / PERNAMBUCO. Rv: COMPANHIA GERAL DE MELHORAMENTOS * / No / 2ooo / (Hand). Reeded edge.

Sugar plantation. Also reported: 1000 and 500-reis of same basic type; copper inserts cross-shaped and 6-lobed, respectively.

UZINA RIBEIRAO

Rulau	Date	Metal	Size	VG	F	VF	Unc
Pbc 35	ND	++	33mm	12.00	16.00	—	—

++ Brass with 4-lobed copper insert.
C.G.M. (on ribbon) / UZINA / RIBEIRAO / PER-NAMBUCO. Rv: CAMPANHIA GERAL DE MEL-HORAMENTOS . / No / 2ooo / (Hand). Reeded edge. (Ludolph 640)

Sugar plantation. Also known: 1000 and 500-reis of same basic type; cross-shaped and 6-lobed copper inserts, respectively.

UZINA TIUMA

Rulau	Date	Metal	Size	VG	F	VF	Unc
Pbc 40	ND	++	33mm	10.00	15.00	25.00	—

++ Brass with 4-lobed copper insert.
C.U.C.S. (on ribbon) / UZINA / TIUMA / PERNAM-BUCO. Rv: CAMPANHIA UZINA CANSANCAO DE SINIMBU * / 2ooo / (Rising sun). Reeded edge.

Sugar plantation. Also known: 1000, 500 and 200-reis of same basic type, with cross-shaped, 6 lobed and cross-shaped copper inserts, respectively.

PIAU STATE

Floriano
NATAL

Rulau	Date	Metal	Size	F	VF	EF	Unc
Pia 1	(1945)	CN	26.5mm	—	—	10.00	12.50

(Incused): NATAL. Rv: 1000 / No. (Ludolph 476)

Used during a postwar change shortage. Dulce Ludolph reports. The 1000-reis (milreis coins were replaced in 1942, but the old milreis and the new cruzeiro had the same value. Small-size 1-milreis notes printed in 1944 overcame the shortage.

RIO DE JANEIRO STATE

Niteroi
MIRAMAR

Rulau	Date	Metal	Size	VG	F	VF	Unc
RDJ 2	ND	Brass	28mm	—	—	Rare	—

MIRAMAR / -.- / 1000 Rs. / -.- / NICTHEROY. Rv: Blank. Plain edge. (Scharlow coll.)

The Miramar Restaurant was destroyed by fire about 1950. The tokens were in use well before that. Scharlow says the tokens, heretofore unpublished, are very difficult to obtain.

Niteroi is a large city across the bay entrance from Rio de Janeiro.

Rio de Janeiro (City)
AMEDEE CARRUETTE

Rulau	Date	Metal	Size	F	VF	EF	Unc
RDJ 8	ND	Brass	Oct 35mm	—	—	50.00	—

FORNECEDOR DA Sta CASA DE MISERICORDIA / AMEDEE / CARRUETTE / RUA FRESCA / 14 / RIO DE JANEIRO / (rosette). Rv: BREAD BISCUIT / FOUR (in oval) / PAIN BISCUIT / FARINE (in oval) / BROD ZWEIBACK / MEHL (in oval) / PAO BOLO-CHA / FARINHA (in oval) / CONTRACTOR / TO / H.B.M. NAVY. Plain edge.

Carruette was a supply contractor to the Sta. Casa de Misericordia hospital and to Her Britannic Majesty's navy, according to his store card.

CASA AMERICANA

Rulau	Date	Metal	Size	VG	F	VF	Unc
RDJ 11	ND	++	30mm	45.00	—	85.00	—

++ Silver-gilt zinc shell card.
CASA AMERICANA / * / M B & Ca. / -o- / *** RIO ***. Rv: 1000 (in circle). (Ludolph 175; Henkle coll.)

Rulau	Date	Metal	Size	VG	F	VF	Unc
RDJ 12	ND	xx	28mm	—	—	40.00	—

xx Copper-gilt zinc shell card.
As last, but 500 (reis). (Ludolph 176)

In this series are also brass (solid) 200 and 100-reis tokens. A brass 400-reis token does not mention M. B. & Ca. The 1,000-reis token is probably extremely rare. Casa Americana = American House.

CASA CYPRIANO

Rulau	Date	Metal	Size	F	VF	EF	Unc
RDJ 14	1900	Aluminum	29mm	—	—	30.00	40.00

Bust left above crossed laurel branches, PEDRO ALVARES CABRAL around. Rv: 4o CENTENARIO DO DESCOBRIMENTO DO BRASIL / 1000 / PRATA / SERA PAGO / O PORTADOR / NO / 5o CENTENARIO / NA / CASA CYPRIANO / .500 - 1900 . Plain edge. (Ludolph 220; Rulau 'Discovery' P17)

This must be considered one of the most unusual trade tokens ever issued. It promises on reverse (in Portuguese) that "1,000 (reis) silver will be paid to the bearer on the 5th centennial (in A.D. 2000) at Casa Cypriano." Issued in 1900 to honor the 4th centennial of the discovery of Brazil, it carries a payment date a full 100 years into the future!

We know of no other trade token in the world with such a far-reaching payment provision specified. In 1900, 1,000 reis silver was a coin which exchanged at about U.S. 50 cents in silver.

CASA DA MOEDA

Rulau	Date	Metal	Size	VG	F	VF	Unc
RDJ17	ND	Copper	25mm	—	—	40.00	—

CASA DA MOEDA / * REPUBLICA * / DOS / E. U. DO BRASIL within oval frame measuring 17 by 14mm, ctsp on Brazil 40-reis coins dated up to 1832. (Prober 52)

This stamp would appear to be an official countermark of the Rio de Janeiro Mint, but it is not cataloged as such in Brazilian references. So, tentatively, it appears in this reference as a token issue.

Rulau	Date	Metal	Size	VG	F	VF	Unc
RDJ 19	1946	Alum Bz	25mm	—	—	—	8.50

Map of Brazil, BRASIL at left (obverse die of regular 1-cruzeiro coin, KM-558, Y-67) Rv: CASA . DA . MOEDA / 5o C. P. / (an envelope) / 19-IX-1946 / * LEMBRANCA *. Reeded edge.

Struck at the Rio de Janeiro Mint on blanks for the 1-cruzeiro coin of 1946. Lembranca = Souvenir, probably of a postal exhibition.

CASA DO CAFE

Rulau	Date	Metal	Size	VG	F	VF	Unc
RDJ 22	(1870's)	**	27.5mm	—	—	60.00	—

** Black imprint on cream-colored celluloid. Casa / do / Cafe. Rv: E. T. A. / (signature) / ..o - 22 - 9. (Rulau coll., ex-Paul Cunningham)

CASINO DO BALNEARIO DA URCA S.A.

Rulau	Date	Metal	Size	F	VF	EF	Unc
RDJ 25	ND	gg	Oval 54x31mm	—	—	—	10.00

gg White bakelite; black enameled lettering. (All design elements incused, blackened): Inverse triangular logo carrying CBU monogram and word RIO, while below is: CASINO DO BALNE / ARIO DA URCA, S.A. Rv: 50 (scrimshaw style). (Wes Scharlow coll.)

Gambling casinos are no longer legal in Brazil.

CASA SIMPATIA

Rulau	Date	Metal	Size	F	VF	EF	Unc
RDJ 33	(1940's)	xx	Rect				
			49x29mm	—	—	—	—

As next, but 2,00 (2-cruzeiros),

Rulau	Date	Metal	Size	F	VF	EF	Unc
RDJ 33A	(1940's)	xx	Rect				
			37x28mm	—	—	6.00	—

xx Red lettering on cream bakelite, rounded corners. (Script) Casa / Simpatia. Rv: (Script) Cr $ / 1,00. (Scharlow coll.)

Rulau	Date	Metal	Size	F	VF	EF	Unc
RDJ 33B	(1940's)	xx	Sq 24mm	—	—	6.00	—

As last, but 0,50.

The cruzeiro was used in Brazil 1942-1967, and these tokens came in use in the 1940's. The inscriptions are incused and filled in with red ink.

Rulau	Date	Metal	Size	F	VF	EF	Unc
RDJ 34	(1988)	vv	26mm	—	1.50	2.00	—

vv light blue plastic/bakelite. CASA / (tiny) DIRENE / (tiny) RIO / + SIMPATIA +. Rv: CASA / + SIMPATIA +. (Scharlow coll.). A variety lacks the maker's name on either side.

These tokens were used in Casa Simpatia Bar Ltda. at Avenida Rio Branco number 92/4, in the Centro of Rio. This was an old open-air sidewalk cafe and bar, no longer in existence.

This issue is typical of the large number of such ultra-modern Brazilian tokens excluded from this catalog.

CASA CAVE'

Rulau	Date	Metal	Size	VG	F	VF	Unc
RDJ 28	ND	Brass	25mm	—	—	—	—

CONFISERIE / A. CAVE' / ** PARISIENNE **. Rv: 800 on beaded circle. Plain edge.

| RDJ 30 | ND | Brass | Oval 29x23mm | — | — | — | — |

RUA DA CARIOCA / C. CAVE' / (rosette) RIO DE JANEIRO (rosette). Rv: 2000. Plain edge.

Both Cave' pieces above are denominated in reis. Casa Cave' is a very old ice cream parlor in Rio's "Centro."

Rulau	Date	Metal	Size	VG	F	VF	Unc
RDJ 32	ND	**	26mm	—	4.00	—	—

** Brown plastic.
CAVE'. Rv: CAVE'.

A waiter's check for ice cream, used at Casa Cave' through 1985. Paper chits replaced these. There were is use many years.

CONFEITARIA COLOMBO

Rulau	Date	Metal	Size	F	VF	EF	Unc
RDJ 35	ND	Aluminum	Rect	—	—	15.00	—
			50x22mm	—	—	—	—

CONFEITARIA COLOMBO / 100$000. Rv: Blank. Plain edge. (Ludolph 97)

This token is part of a lengthy series of rectangular aluminum pieces in all these denominations: 50,000, 40,000, 30,000, 20,000, 10,000, 9000, 8000, 7000, 6000, 5000, 4000, 3000, 2000, 1900, 1800, 1700, 1600, 1500, 1400, 1300, 1200, 1100, 1000, 900, 800, 700, 600, 500, 400, 300, 200 and 100 reis (Ludolph 65 to 96).

This aluminum issue was preceded by another extensive issue, undated, in blue enameled metal with white numerals.

A round steel series followed, then series in bakelite and plastic.

COPACABANA CASINO

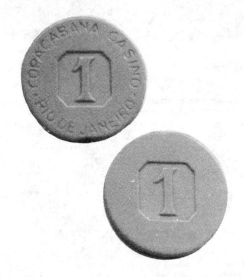

Rulau	Date	Metal	Size	F	VF	EF	Unc
RDJ 38	ND	xx	32mm	—	—	7.00	—

xx Red bakelite.
CASINO COPA CABANA / 5000 REIS. Rv: Same as obverse (1982 report)

| RDJ 39 | ND | vv | 35mm | — | — | 7.00 | — |

vv Red bakelite.
COPACABANA CASINO (incuse) / 1 (relief, in octagonal depression) / . RIO DE JANEIRO . (incuse). Rv: 1 (relief, in oct. depression). (Scharlow coll.)

A. ESPINGARDA INGLEZA

Rulau	Date	Metal	Size	VG	F	VF	Unc
RDJ 42	ND	Copper	35mm	—	—	40.00	60.00

Arms of the Republic of Brazil. Rv: A. ESPINGARDA INGLEZA (rosette) / 102, RUA DA QUITANDA, 102 / (rosette). In field: RIO / DE / JANEIRO / * within circle. (Eklund 1695)

This token also occurs in Cupronickel, Aluminum and Zinc. (Eklund 1696).

FARINHA FERRAZ & CO.

Rulau	Date	Metal	Size	VG	F	VF	Unc
RDJ 45	ND	Copper	33mm	—	—	—	—

FARINHA FERRAZ & Co. / (arms of the company) / MEDICO-PHARMACEUTICOS. Rv: DROGARIA E LABORATORIO DE PRODUCTOS CHIMICOS, PHARMACEUTICOS / RUA DOS OURIVES No 41 / RIO DE JANEIRO. (Eklund 1700; Museo-Rocha 600 in June, 1911)

FARMACIA JARDIM

Rulau	Date	Metal	Size	VG	F	VF	Unc
RDJ 48	ND	Nic/Bs	39mm	—	—	—	—

FARMACIA / 23 (or another number) / JARDIM. Rv: VALE UMA APLICACÃO / &&&. Plain edge. Issued with center hole. (Wes Scharlow coll.)

Vale uma aplicacão = Worth one shot. Customer paid the cashier, a numbered token was issued, and customer went to the area where someone administered the inoculation and collected the token.

The center hole was for stacking the tokens on a long spike, fixed in a turned wooden base with the Farmacia Jardim's name on it. Scharlow reports he examined such a spike holder.

FERREIRA NICOLAO & CIA.

Rulau	Date	Metal	Size	VG	F	VF	Unc
RDJ 51	ND	Brass	30mm	—	—	—	—

* INDUSTRIA NACIONAL * / FERREIRA / NICO-LAO / & Cia / RIO DE JANEIRO. Rv: CALCADO FABRICA A VAPOR / ADAO / Rua d'Alfandega / 137-139 / (rosette). Plain edge. (Eklund 1701; Museu-Rocha 599 in June, 1911.)

FIGNER IRMAOS

Rulau	Date	Metal	Size	VG	F	VF	Unc
RDJ 54	ND	Brass	22mm	4.00	7.00	—	—

-.- / CASA EDISON / FRED FIGNER- / RIO. / -.-. Rv: -.- / CASA EDISON / FIGNER IRMAOS- / SAO PAULO. / -.-. Plain edge. (Rulau coll.)

A dual card, used in Rio and Sao Paulo.

GOMES & MATHIAS

Rulau	Date	Metal	Size	F	VF	EF	Unc
RDJ 57	ND	Brass	33mm	—	12.50	20.00	

CAZA DO CARNEIRO / 30 / (sheep left) / RUA LUZITANA / + GOMES & MATHIAS +. Rv: FAZENDAS MODAS E NOVIDADES / RUA DO / COMMERCIO / 17 / I CAMPINAS I. Plain edge.

E. J. GONDOLO

Rulau	Date	Metal	Size	VG	F	VF	Unc
RDJ 60	ND	Brass	34mm	—	60.00	100.	

Imperial arms of Brazil. Around: RELOJOARIA UNIVERSAL / * AO REGULADOR PUBLICO *. Rv: Watch at center. Around: E. J. GONDOLO. / VALE UM VIDRO / No 12 A RUA DA CANDELARIA / RIO DE JANEIRO. (Eklund 1694; Ludolph 221)

Vale um vidro = Worth one (watch) crystal.

RDJ 61	ND	Brass	Oct 26mm	—	—	35.00	—

As last, on smaller, octagonal flan.

RDJ 63	ND	Brass	34mm	—	—	15.00	—

Obverse at last. Rv: Watch at center. Around: E. J. GONDOLO / ET Cie / VALE UM VIDRO / No 12A RUA DA CANDELARIA / * RIO DE JANEIRO *. (Ludolph 222)

All the Gondolo pieces were issued under the Empire, that is, 1889 or earlier.

GRANADO & CA.

Rulau	Date	Metal	Size	VG	F	VF	Unc
RDJ 66	ND	Copper	28mm	—	—	20.00	

Crowned Brazil arms. Around: FORNEDORES / GRANADO * Ca / * RUA 1o. DEMARCO. No. 12 * / +*+ DA CASA IMPERIAL +*+. Rv: 6-point star labeled MARCA / RETGISTRADA. Around: IMPERIAL DROGARIA / DEPOSITO GERAL AL do LICOR TIBAINA / * RIO DE JANEIRO * / +*+ E PHARMACIA +*+. Plain edge. (Eklund 1704)

M. GRASS & CIA.

Rulau	Date	Metal	Size	VG	F	VF	Unc
RDJ 68	ND	Nic/Bs	Scal 23mm	—	8.00	—	—

Star of David with Hebrew word ZION in center, ornate border around. Rv: M. GRASS & CIA. LTDA. / TEL. / 48-7440 * RIO *. Plain edge. Issued with loop.

HOTEL 7 DE SETEMBRO

Rulau	Date	Metal	Size	VG	F	VF	Unc
RDJ 70	ND	Brass	22mm	—	—	25.00	

HOTEL 7 DE SETEMBRO / - / 100 / - / *. Rv: Blank. (Scharlow coll.)

Unpublished token. Only the 100-reis is known.

M. U. D.

Rulau	Date	Metal	Size	F	VF	EF	Unc
RDJ 75	1968	CN	24mm	—	1.50	2.50	3.50

Statue with outstretched arms above 1968 in foreground. In background are seen the Rio shoreline and Sugar Loaf mountain. Rv: In central circle: mud. in ornate lettering / 2 in circle. Around: EXCLUSIVAMENTE PARA DIVERSAO / - BRASIL -. Plain edge.

Exclusivament para diversao = Exclusively for diversion. A modern gaming activator token which frequently turns up in Brazilian accumulations.

J. B. O.
Fazenda Boa Vista

Rulau	Date	Metal	Size	VG	F	VF	EF
RDJ 80	ND	Copper	Oval 45x53mm	—	—	Rare	

UM DIA DE TRABALHO (circular) / JBO monogram in oval, ctsp on elongated Brazil 80-reis coin. Rv: FAZENDA + BOA VISTA + (circular) ctsp on opposite side of the coin. (Scharlow coll.)

There are varieties in the counterstamp's letter placement.

M. P.

Rulau	Date	Metal	Size	VG	F	VF	Unc
RDJ 83	(ca 1890)	Aluminum	21mm	—	—	—	—

* 6 LARGO DA CARIOCA 6 * / MP monogram (Star) / MARCA REGISTRADA. Rv: Imperial arms of Brazil. (Eklund 1678)

The Empire of Brazil ended in 1889. Similar trademark registration tokens, bearing the coat of arms of various foreign countries were also issued, some in 24mm size.

PASCHOAL

Rulau	Date	Metal	Size	VG	F	VF	Unc
RDJ 84	(1888-89)	Brass	37mm	—	—	200.	—

Mantled imperial arms. Rv: CONFEITARIA IMPE-RIAL / PASCHOAL / RUA / DO OUVIDOR /126 / * RIO-DE-JANEIRO *. Plain edge. (Wes Scharlow coll.)

RDJ 85	(1890-91)	Brass	37mm	—	—	90.00	—

Republican Brazil arms in wreath. Rv: GRANDE CONFEITARIA / PASCHOAL / RUA / DO OUVIDOR / 126 & 128 / * RIO-DE-JANEIRO *. Plain edge. (Eklund 1707; Salgado report)

RDJ 84 is heretofore unpublished. The empire was overthrown Nov. 15, 1889. Confeitaria = Confectionery. These scarce tokens of Rio span the period of the end of the empire.

REI MOMO 1o

Rulau	Date	Metal	Size	F	VF	EF	Unc
RDJ 86	(1940's)	Bronze	--mm	—	—	2.50	3.50

Carnival king bust right. At right: BRASIL / Rei (script) / MOMO / 1o. Rv: Mask, fan etc. Plain edge. (Wes Scharlow coll.)

A generic beer token used in the Largo da Carioca area where the Centro subway station is now located. It was apparently used during carnival time in one establishment and accepted at most surrounding bars as well.

Rei Momo 1o = King Momo I, mythic ruler of the Mardi Gras carnival period.

THEODORO SATTLER & CA.

Rulau	Date	Metal	Size	VG	F	VF	Unc
RDJ 100	ND	Brass	25mm	12.50	—	—	—

THEODORO SATTLER & Ca. / (beaded field in circle) / ***. Rv: 400 on beaded field. (Ludolph 174)

RDJ 101	ND	CN	Oct 19mm	—	—	—	—

THEODORO / SATTLER / & Ca / RIO DE JANEIRO. Rv: 14 (large). (Ludolph 173)

RDJ 102	ND	CN	27mm	—	—	—	—

As last, but 2. (Ludolph 173)

RDJ 103	ND	CN	19mm	—	—	8.00	—

As last, but 1.

Dulce Ludolph says Sattler & Compania preceded the Casa Americana of Rio, whose tokens are listed above. The 400 may indicate 400-reis, but the 14, 2 and 1 may indicate something other than a denomination.

RIO GRANDE DO SUL STATE

Arroio Grande
MANOEL ANNIBAL RIBEIRO

Rulau	Date	Metal	Size	VG	F	VF	Unc
RGS 1	ND	Brass	34.5mm	—	—	—	—

MANOEL ANNIBAL RIBEIRO / 500 / ARROIO GRANDE. Rv: Blank. (Ludolph 511)

Pelotas
HERTEL

Rulau	Date	Metal	Size	VG	F	VF	Unc
RGS 5	ND	Lead	25mm	—	—	—	—

VALE / (beer stein) / 120 / HERTEL. Incused numeral at left: 253. Rv: Blank. (Meili 16)

Hertel was the owner of a brewery and cafe.

Porto Alegre
B (Gothic)

Rulau	Date	Metal	Size	VG	F	VF	Unc
RGS 8	ND	Brass	30mm	—	—	—	—

Large Gothic B. Rv: Blank. (Ludolph 7; Meili 69)

CHAVES & ALMEIDA

Rulau	Date	Metal	Size	VG	F	VF	Unc
RGS 11	ND	Brass	29mm	—	—	—	—

CHAVES & ALMEIDA / (embossed numeral) / * PORTO ALEGRE *. Rv: 1 CARRETO. Reported without control number or with embossed numbers 145 and 388. (Eklund 1676; Ludolph 483)

RGS 12	ND	Brass	24mm	—	—	—	—

As last, but ½ CARRETO. Numbers known: 30, 145, 247. (Ek. 1675; Lud. 485)

1 CARRETO = One cartload. The embossed numeral is apparently a control number for these freight worker checks.

HOTEL PASCAL

Rulau	Date	Metal	Size	VG	F	VF	Unc
RGS 15	ND	CN	28mm	—	—	—	—
		HOTEL PASCAL / RIO GRANDE / DO SUL. Rv: 300 / REIS. Plain edge. (Ludolph 497; Meili 19)					
RGS 16	ND	CN	23mm	—	—	—	—
		As last, but 200.					
RGS 17	ND	CN	23mm	—	—	—	—
		As last, but 160. (Ludolph 499)					
RGS 18	ND	CN	19.5mm	—	—	—	—
		As last, but 100. (Ludolph 500-501; Meili 22)					

In 1865 the owner of Hotel Pascal was Rene Pascal.

JARDIM DO PARQUE

Rulau	Date	Metal	Size	VG	F	VF	Unc
RGS 21	ND	Brass	26mm	—	—	—	—
		JARDIM / DO / PARQUE / -.- / PORTO ALEGRE / -*-. Rv: 500. (Ludolph 504)					
RGS 22	ND	Brass	23mm	—	—	—	—
		As last, but 200. (Ludolph 505)					

Jardim do Parque = Park Garden.

GEORGE ROBINSON

Rulau	Date	Metal	Size	VG	F	VF	Unc
RGS 25	ND	Copper	27mm	—	—	—	—
		GEORGE ROBINSON / GR monogram / * PORTA-LEGRE *. Rv: Blank, but beaded border. (Eklund 1677)					

Quarahy
S. GUERRA

-S.GUERRA-

Rulau	Date	Metal	Size	VG	F	VF	EF
RGS 26	(1920-28)	CN	30mm	-	25.00	—	35.00
		- S. GUERRA - in minute letters ctsp on Brazil 1901 400-reis, KM-505.					
RGS 26A	(1920-28)	CN	31mm	—	25.00	—	35.00
		Similar ctsp on Brazil Empire 200-reis of 1871-1888 types, KM-428, 484,					
RGS 26B	ND	CN	32mm	—	20.00	—	30.00
		- S. GUERRA - in minute letters (shown actual size above) ctsp on Brazil 200-reis of 1889-1900 type, KM-493. (Prober 236; Brunk 51990)					
RGS 26C	(1920-28)	CN	25mm	—	20.00	—	30.00
		Similar ctsp on Brazil 1901 200-reis, KM-504.					
RGS 27	(1920-28)	CN	--mm	—	20.00	—	30.00
		Similar ctsp on Brazil 100-reis coins of 1874 through 1901, KM types 477, 492 and 503.					
RGS 28	(1920-28)	Silver	27mm	—	65.00	—	115.
		Similar ctsp on Brazil 1,000-reis coins of 1907 through 1912, KM-507.					
RGS 28A	(1920-28)	Silver	--mm	—	80.00	—	125.
		Similar ctsp on Brazil 2,000-reis of 1907, KM-508.					
RGS 29	ND	Gold	22mm	—	—	200.	—
		Similar ctsp on Great Britain sovereign of Queen Victoria Jubilee or Veiled head types, KM 767 or 785.					
RGS 29A	ND	Gold	22mm	—	—	200.	—
		Similar ctsp on Great Britain sovereign of King Edward VII type, KM 805.					

Sovereigns with this mark were found in an early 1970's shipment of gold coins from Uruguay to Toronto, Canada. It may have been applied in/after 1930.

The Guerra stamp occurs also on Brazil coppers, according to Wes Scharlow.

Souza Guerra was a fazenda owner in Quarahy, Rio Grande do Sul State, near the Uruguayan border. He was prolific in stamping copper, cupronickel and silver coins for use as tokens on his estate in the 1920-1928 period.

Scharlow feels the gold sovereigns would not have been used on the fazenda, but may either have been applied there for some reason or the stamps could have fallen into the hands of a collector who wanted to make variations of his own.

Rio Grande
HALLAWELL & CIA.

Rulau	Date	Metal	Size	VG	F	VF	Unc
RGS 30	ND	Brass	26mm	—	—	—	—
		HALLAWELL & CIA. / DROGARIA / INGLEZA / . RIO GRANDE . Rv: (Incused) 400. Reeded edge. (Ludolph 492; Meili 23)					
RGS 31	ND	Brass	26mm	—	—	—	—
		As last, but 200. Reeded edge.					
RGS 32	ND	Brass	26mm	—	—	—	—
		As last, but 120 (reis). Reeded edge. (Ludolph 495)					
RGS 33	ND	Brass	26mm	—	—	—	—
		As last, but 100. Reeded edge. (Ludolph 496; Meili 27)					

SAO PAULO STATE

Sao Paulo
ANDRE MURANO & CIA.

Rulau	Date	Metal	Size	VG	F	VF	Unc
Spo 7	ND	Brass	24.5mm	—	—	8.00	12.50
		Columbia / (musical note). Rv: CASA MURANO / -.- / ANDRE MURANO / & CIA., / SAO PAULO / BRAZIL. Plain edge. (Tanenbaum coll.)					

VAUDEVILLE ROYAL

Rulau	Date	Metal	Size	VG	F	VF	Unc
Spo 11	ND	Brass	25mm	—	—	10.00	—
		VAUDEVILLE ROYAL / R & F (on scroll) / SAN PAULO. Rv: VALLE / 200 / REIS / *** / *** EM COMPRAS ***. Plain edge. (Tanenbaum coll.)					
Spo 12	ND	Brass	21mm	—	—	10.00	—
		As last, but 100. (Ludolph 620)					

Both SAO and VALE are misspelled on this token series!

SERGIPE STATE
Uncertain
ENGENHO CENTRAL
RIACHUELO

Rulau	Date	Metal	Size	VG	F	VF	Unc
Ser 20	ND	Brass	25mm	—	—	—	—
		ENGENHO CENTRAL RIACHUELO / (radiant sun-face) / 200. Rv: E. C. R. / ENGENHO CENTRAL / SERGIPE. Plain edge. (Ludolph 639; Scharlow coll.)					
Ser 21	ND	Brass	22mm	—	—	—	—
		As last, but 100. (Ludolph 640)					

Well-made tokens from a sugar refinery. Rio de Janeiro's Sugar Museum (Museu do Azucar) also possesses 500, 1,000 and 2,000-reis tokens of this type.

UNATTRIBUTED BRAZIL

D. A.

Rulau	Date	Metal	Size	VG	F	VF	EF
Brz 1	ND	Copper	36mm	—	—	10.00	—
		D. A. in relief within toothed rect. depression ctsp on Brazil 40-reis coins before 1833. (Prober 279)					

S. T. B.

Rulau	Date	Metal	Size	VG	F	VF	EF
Brz 5	ND	CN	32mm	—	—	25.00	—
		VALE UM DIA DE TRABALHO (circular) / S T B ctsp on Brazil 1899 200-reis, KM 493, Yeoman 4. (Wes Scharlow coll.)					

C. B.

Rulau	Date	Metal	Size	VG	F	VF	EF
Brz 3	ND	Copper	--mm	—	—	10.00	—
		Monogram CB between three dots on left and three dots on right, all within irregular frame, ctsp on various Brazilian coins. (Prober 53)					

C. (in shield)

Rulau	Date	Metal	Size	VG	F	VF	EF
Brz 7	ND	Copper	--mm	—	—	15.00	—
		C in shield-shaped frame ctsp on various Brazilian coins. (Prober 50)					

J. J. G. C.

Rulau	Date	Metal	Size	VG	F	VF	EF
Brz 9	ND	Copper	40mm	—	—	15.00	—

J J G C (straight) ctsp on Brazil 40-reis-revalued 80-reis coin, KM 444, Craig 128a. (Scharlow coll.)

Rulau	Date	Metal	Size	VG	F	VF	EF
Brz 10	ND	Copper	37mm	—	—	15.00	—

J J G C (curved) ctsp on Brazil 1826-R (Rio) 20-reis-revalued 40-reis coin, KM 436.1, Craig 127a.1. (Scharlow coll.)

The official revaluation counterstamps were applied in 1835 but these coins stayed in circulation for many years. The J. J. G. C. private stamps may have been applied up to 50 years later.

K. C.

Rulau	Date	Metal	Size	VG	F	VF	EF
Brz 12	ND	Copper	--mm	—	—	25.00	—

K : C / (bar) / 78. within irregular shaped depression ctsp on various Brazil coins. (Prober 178)

COPA

Rulau	Date	Metal	Size	VG	F	VF	EF
Brz 14	ND	Copper	36mm	—	—	15.00	—

COPA (the A minus its crossbar) within double-lined rect. frame ctsp on Brazil 40-reis coins of Colony and Empire until 1832. (Prober 269)

Crowned E

Rulau	Date	Metal	Size	VG	F	VF	EF
Brz 16	ND	Copper	36mm	—	—	15.00	—

Greek letter Eta within crown shield, ctsp on Brazil 40-reis coin before 1832. (Prober 62)

A. T. E.

ATE 18$

Rulau	Date	Metal	Size	VG	F	VF	EF
Brz 18	ND	Copper	--mm	—	—	15.00	—

ATE 18$ within rect. depression ctsp on various Brazilian coins. (Prober 36)

The denomination 18$ would indicate 18 milreis (18,000 reis). Obviously the stamp has no relation to the *value* of the piece.

Crowned F. E.

Rulau	Date	Metal	Size	VG	F	VF	EF
Brz 20	ND	Copper	--mm	—	—	20.00	—

(Crown) / F. E. within cartouche shaped to fit the devices, ctsp on various Brazil coins. (Prober 78)

ENGENHO CENTRAL DE QUISSAMAN

Rulau	Date	Metal	Size	VG	F	VF	Unc
Brz 21	ND	Aluminum	33mm	—	—	25.00	—

ENGENHO CENTRAL DE / PROVISORIO / B 200 / OPERARIO / QUISSAMAN. Rv: E. C. Q. / SERVICO INTERNO / 610 (or another number, incused). (Scharlow coll.)

Sugar refinery.

A. J. F.

Rulau	Date	Metal	Size	VG	F	VF	EF
Brz 22	ND	Copper	--mm	—	—	15.00	

A J F monogram within irregular cartouche which resembles a heart with a hairdo, ctsp on various Brazil coins. (Prober 26)

V. F.

Rulau	Date	Metal	Size	VG	F	VF	EF
Brz 24	ND	Copper	--mm	—	—	10.00	—

VF monogram within toothed diamond-shaped depression ctsp on various Brazil coins. (Prober 250)

A. FUECHER

Rulau	Date	Metal	Size	VG	F	VF	Unc
Brz 27	ND	Copper	26mm	—	—	—	—

Uniface. No descr. available. (Eklund 1058)

| Brz 28 | ND | Brass | 34mm | — | — | — | — |

Similar? (Eklund 1059; Weyl 1899 listing)

Also claimed as Panama.

PEREGRINO GIMENEZ

Rulau	Date	Metal	Size	VG	F	VF	Unc
Brz 31	1905	Brass	21mm	—	—	10.00	

PEREGRINO GIMENEZ / (G-shaped brand) / * 1905 *. Rv: Large shaded 1. At bottom: (tiny) ORZALI. B. Y CA. Plain edge. (Zaffern coll.)

Possibly Uruguay or Argentina. Orzali Bellagamba y Ca. was a Buenos Aires medallic firm.

C. A. I.

CAI

Rulau	Date	Metal	Size	VG	F	VF	EF
Brz 38	ND	Copper	--mm	—	—	10.00	—

C A I in large thick letters ctsp on various Brazil coins. (Prober 51)

INSPECCAO GERAL DOS INGENDIOS

Rulau	Date	Metal	Size	VG	F	VF	Unc
Brz 40	ND	Brass	26.5mm	—	—	5.00	7.50

Three-masted sailing ship left, flying a royal Portuguese (?) flag at its stern. Rv: INSPECCAO / GERAL / DOS / (rosette) / INGENDIOS (rosette). Plain edge. (Tanenbaum coll.)

This could be Portugal rather than Brazil.

Crowned G. M.

Rulau	Date	Metal	Size	VG	F	VF	Unc
Brz 42	ND	Copper	39mm	—	—	35.00	

(Crown) / G . M within large upright oval (23x26mm) ctsp on various Brazil coins, including 40-reis shown above. (Prober 99)

S. M.

Rulau	Date	Metal	Size	VG	F	VF	EF
Brz 44	ND	Copper	35mm	—	—	10.00	—

S M ctsp on each side of Portugal 1796 10-reis coin, KM 327. (Stanley Steinberg Feb. 1991 price list)

MARCOLINO F.

Rulau	Date	Metal	Size	VG	F	VF	EF
Brz 46	ND	Copper	40mm	—	—	40.00	—

(M)ARCOLINO: F: within rectangular depression ctsp on Brazil 80-reis copper coins issued 1832 or earlier. The full stamp measures 43mm, too wide for the coin, and the M is left off the flan. (Prober 195)

| Brz 47 | ND | Copper | 45mm | — | — | 55.00 | |

As last, but full stamp, ctsp on blank copper disc.

MILBON

Rulau	Date	Metal	Size	VG	F	VF	Unc
Brz 50	ND	CN	21.5mm	1.00	2.00	3.00	4.00

MACHINA AUTHOMATICA PUCK / MILBON / -.
Rv: VALE EM GENEROS / 100 / REIS / (ornament).
Plain edge. (Ludolph 43ND)

MONA

Rulau	Date	Metal	Size	VG	F	VF	Unc
Brz 52	ND	Copper	36m	—	—	100.	—

MONA within rect. depression ctsp on Brazil 40-reis
copper coins. (Prober 210)

It is quite possible this is not Brazilian at all, but intended for Mona Island,
Puerto Rico. See entry under Mona in Puerto Rican section.

B. I. N.

Rulau	Date	Metal	Size	VG	F	VF	Unc
Brz 54	ND	Copper	--mm	—	—	15.00	—

B I N with flourishes above and below, all within dentilated circular frame, ctsp on various Brazilian coins.
(Prober 44)

NONATO

NONATO

Rulau	Date	Metal	Size	VG	F	VF	Unc
Brz 56	ND	Copper	36mm	—	—	25.00	—

NONATO within rect. depression ctsp on Brazil 40-reis
copper coins. (Prober 217)

Crowned A. O.

Rulau	Date	Metal	Size	VG	F	VF	Unc
Brz 58	ND	Copper	36mm	—	—	15.00	—

(Crown) / A O within upright pointed frame, ctsp on
Brazil 40-reis coins before 1833. (Prober 30)

The counterstamp is shown double natural size above.

OLIVEIRA

Rulau	Date	Metal	Size	F	VF	EF	Unc
Brz 59	ND	Brass	24.5mm	—	—	15.00	—

OLIVEIRA. Rv: MERCADORIAS / *** / 200 / *** / *
REIS *. Plain edge. (Rulau coll.)

PONS

Rulau	Date	Metal	Size	VG	F	VF	EF
Brz 60	ND	Copper	--mm	—	—	35.00	—

Script Pons within tiny double-bordered oval ctsp on
various Brazil coins. (Prober 220)

The stamp is shown actual size, as are most line drawings of private counterstamps of Brazil included in this reference.

This stamp is listed by Prober because it occurs on Brazilian coins. However,
it is possible this is a hallmark of goldsmith Thomas Pons who worked in Boston, Mass. 1789-1804 and later as a spectacle maker in Boston 1806-16. According to Gordon (*West Indies Countermarked Gold Coins*, 1987) Pons' normal
assay mark on Brazil gold was T. P and this appears on 6400-reis pieces dated
1733, 1735, 1743, 1753 and 1758.

PROSPERIDADE

Rulau	Date	Metal	Size	VG	F	VF	EF
Brz 61	ND	Leather	40mm	—	—	Rare	—

Serif-type M circled by eight alternating x's and dots.
Around all: PROSPERIDADE x. Rv: Blank. (Wes
Scharlow coll.; Ludolph 6ND; Souza-Lobo 67)

Probably an old fazenda token.

J. T. R.

Rulau	Date	Metal	Size	VG	F	VF	EF
Brz 62	Nd	Copper	--mm	—	—	15.00	—

J T R monogram in shield-shaped cartouche ctsp on
various Brazil coins. (Prober 177)

This counterstamp resembles a "brand" such as that used in marking cattle on
a ranch.

O. H. ROBINSON

Rulau	Date	Metal	Size	VG	F	VF	EF
Brz 64	ND	Copper	40mm	—	25.00	—	40.00

O. H. ROBINSON incuse in prepared punch, ctsp on Brazil 80-reis of 1823-31 type, which had previously been countermarked by the government in 1835 with 40 (reis) in shaded circle, KM-444. Ctsp once on obverse, three times on reverse. Date and mintmark are worn off. (Rulau coll., ex-Kirtley)

The huge Brazilian 80-reis coins, weighing 8 oitavos or 28.69 grams, were privately counterstamped for use as fazenda tokens, etc. The Robinson mark is not listed among the several hundred known stamps in Prober's work.

However, this large copper coin did not fit in the currency systems of any other Latin American country, the United States, or England. In England a good deal of private counterstamping of large Cartwheel 1797 pennies and twopenny pieces was still going on after 1835, and this piece may eventually prove to be British, or from a British-oriented area in Central America.

(See George Robinson under Porto Alegre, Rio Grande do Sul State)

T.

Rulau	Date	Metal	Size	VG	F	VF	EF
Brz 66	ND	—	—mm	—	—	15.00	—

Large serif T . (Star) within rect. frame ctsp on unspecified coins. (Prober 243)

A. T.

Rulau	Date	Metal	Size	VG	F	VF	EF
Brz 68	ND	Copper	36mm	—	—	10.00	—

AT within orante cartouche ctsp on Brazil 40-reis coins of the Empire. (Prober 37)

J. I. V.

Rulau	Date	Metal	Size	VG	F	VF	EF
Brz 70	ND	Copper	35mm	—	—	10.00	—

J. I. V. in relief within irregular rect. depression ctsp on Brazil 40-reis coins dated up to 1832. (Prober 158)

The private validation of these large copper 40-reis coins had the effect of raising their trade value to 100-reis within the plantation, ranch or enterprise which issued them.

120

Rulau	Date	Metal	Size	VG	F	VF	EF
Brz 90	ND	Copper	36mm	—	—	15.00	—

120 within rect. frame ctsp on Brazil 40-reis coins of the Empire until 1832. (Prober 265)

Presumably this stamp raised the value of the underlying 40-reis coin to 120 reis rather than the more standard 100 reis of most private Brazilian counterstampers.

1874

Rulau	Date	Metal	Size	VG	F	VF	EF
Brz 92	1874	Copper	—mm	—	—	15.00	—

1874 within irregular rect. cartouche ctsp on various Brazil coins.

Most of the private counterstamping of old coppers in Brazil was over by 1871. The ungainly large coppers were withdrawn from circulation when the 100-reis cupronickel coins were introduced in 1871, and they were demonetized in 1907.

Other post-1871 dates are known privately stamped, however, including 1876 and 1897.

1876

Rulau	Date	Metal	Size	VG	F	VF	EF
Brz 94	1876	—	—mm	—	—	15.00	—

1876 in rect. frame ctsp on various Brazil coins. (Prober 267)

1897

Rulau	Date	Metal	Size	VG	F	VF	EF
Brz 96	1897	—	—mm	—	—	15.00	—

1897 ctsp on various Brazil coins. (Prober 268)

(Crosses)

Rulau	Date	Metal	Size	VG	F	VF	EF
Brz 100	ND	Copper	20.5mm	—	—	15.00	—

Four square indents ctsp to form cross between them. In each square depression is one diagonal line in relief so arranged that all four diagonals make an interrupted St. Andrews cross (X). The effect is of a British Union Jack. All ctsp on Brazil Empire 1869 10-reis coins, KM-473. (Rulau coll.)

The small bronze 10-reis coin was issued only 1868-1870. Its purchasing power was quite small and it was never very popular. Thereafter, until the reis disappeared as a monetary unit in 1942, no more 10-reis coins were issued in Brazil. Its value in 1868-70 was about that of ½-cent U.S.

Rulau	Stamp	Host Coin	Value in VF
Brz 113	Z in circle of small crosses	on Brazil copper 80-reis	7.50

Miscellaneous Brazil Counterstamps

Rulau	Stamp	Host Coin	Value in VF
Brz 110	. C . (relief, in square depression)	On Brazil 40-reis-revalued copper 80-reis	15.00

Rulau	Stamp	Host Coin	Value in VF
Brz 114	100 / REIS	on Brazil copper 80-reis	10.00

Rulau	Stamp	Host Coin	Value in VF
Brz 111	I W (relief, in toothed rect. depression)	On Brazil copper 20-reis coin	10.00

Rulau	Stamp	Host Coin	Value in VF
Brz 115	8-pointed leaf (relief, in oval depression)	on Brazil 40-reis-revalued copper 80-reis	7.50

Rulau	Stamp	Host Coin	Value in VF
Brz 112	W W (relief, in toothed rect. depression)	on Brazil 1828-R copper 80-reis coin	7.50

Rulau	Stamp	Host Coin	Value in VF
Brz 116	W.D. (relief)	on Brazil 1824-R copper 40-reis coin (ANS coll.)	25.00

CHILE

The word "mitad"·(half) was used by people in Chile in the 1700's to describe the lead, copper, tin and shoe leather tokens which proliferated due to the lack of small change.

In this sense the Chilean mitad was the equal of the Mexican tlaco, also worth one-eighth of a silver real.

About Chilean Tokens

Chile is the only nation in the world which has used hard rubber (vulcanite) tokens in a massive way. Beginning about 1870 and continuing until the 1920's, nitrate mines and other enterprises paid their workers in vulcanite "fichas," often of large diameter.

Two different types of number appear on these tokens.

* Manufacturer's number (abreviated mfr. no.) is a token-making contract number *IN RELIEF* on many of the pieces. The numerals are quite small and are usually the same for each issuing firm. Six-digit numbers are commonest.

* Control number (abbreviated cont. no.) is an **INCUSED** numeral, used by the issuing firm to account for tokens in the hands of mine managers and workers. If sufficient specimens can be examined, an estimate of the mintage of a token can be calculated.

Vulcanite tokens appear in one of three ways:

Solid color. Listed as (e.g.) Red vulcanite.

One color on obverse, different color on reverse. Listed as Red-blue vulcanite.

Color on obverse, bonded to a black core, color on reverse. Listed as (e.g.) Red-black-tan vulcanite. (The black core is all the way through the token, which can be seen when one is cut apart).

Chilean Hoard in Chicago

A South American coin firm was offered a 4,000-piece hoard of Chilean nitrate tokens (including a few other Chilean pieces) in early 1990. This hoard was purchased, and was resold in Chicago, Ill. on March 15, 1990 - primarily to one wholesaler, but 300 typical pieces were purchased first by the author after examination of the intact hoard.

Some 22 pieces were of leather, and another 20-odd pieces were casino gaming pieces of Viña del Mar, etc. The entire remainder, about 4,000 pieces, were of hard rubber (vulcanite), ranging in condition from Very Good to Uncirculated, the average being Very Fine.

Your author personally examined about 60 different tokens, and estimates that the hoard contained no more than 200 *different* tokens. The bulk of the vulcanite pieces were in $2, $1 and 10-centavo denominations, with lesser numbers of 50 and 20-centavo pieces. One token - the C.S. de A. $2 green-black-tan - was represented by as many as 600 specimens! Another, the C. S. de A. $1 blue-black-red, was represented by perhaps 400 specimens.

The South American couple who bought and then resold the hoard asserted that in 22 years in the coin business in South America, this was the only large hoard of Chilean vulcanite tokens they had ever been offered - despite considerable advertising in the lay press which they had placed.

The appearance of this hoard will keep prices depressed on certain vulcanite tokens for perhaps 5 to 10 years, but the author firmly believes the hoard will be beneficial to Latin token collecting. It means some Chilean nitrate pieces can be purchased for as little as $1.50 to $2.50 each for several years, providing an avenue for new collectors to enter the hobby.

The last such vulcanite token hoard discovered - perhaps about the same size - was dispersed in Los Angeles about 1971 by a Bolivian firm and has since been completely absorbed by collectors.

The 1891 Revolution

Forces loyal to the Chilean Congress rose in revolt against President Jose Manuel Balmaceda, who had assumed office in 1886, in January, 1891. The Congressional forces, led by the navy, were victorious everywhere. Balmaceda committed suicide Sept. 19, 1891.

During the revolt, the city of Iquique in Tarapaca Province felt the need for small change and a large number of round cardboard tokens were issued by Iquique merchants. All are rare and seldom obtainable, but a few remainders and/or contemporary reprints came on the numismatic market in 1989. Only these remainders are cataloged in this volume. About 35 of each of the 10 types are in the marketplace, hardly enough to satisfy any demand.

The War of the Pacific and its Territorial Changes

The armed forces of Chile easily defeated the combined armies and navies of Bolivia and Peru, and Chile annexed Bolivia's entire seacoast and Peru's richest mining area as spoils of war. Chile's frontier was pushed far north of the border resulting from its wars of independence against Spain.

How do we treat these territories in this catalog?

The experience of the cataloger is that collectors expect to find Chilean tokens, regardless of when issued, under Chile. So, if the tokens were issued in lands that today are in Chile, they will be found there in this catalog. To reflect historic accuracy, explanatory matter has been placed under each affected issuer something like this: Issued under Bolivian dominion; issued under Peruvian dominion, etc.

The exact date of issue of tokens is seldom known, so these explanatory notes may not always be factual, but we have tried to make a judgement in each case.

The political and territorial changes are briefly summarized below:

1866. By treaty, Bolivia ceded part of its territory in coastal Atacama Department to Chile. This slice of land included all of Atacama south of the 24th Parallel, down to the old border between Bolivian Atacama Dept. and Chilean Atacama Province, the Salado River. This area included the ports of Chañaral, Pan de Azucar, Taltal and Paposo and the towns of Breas, Alemania, Flor de Chile, Catalina, Altamira, Imilac, Neurara, Llanta and Pueblo Hundido.

1879-1884. War of the Pacific between Chile and the allies, Bolivia and Peru. Chilean troops easily mastered their opponents, seizing all the coastal areas as far north as Tacna within the first year. Even Lima fell to Chilean forces in 1881.

Oct. 20, 1883. **Treaty of Ancon.** Peru cedes Tarapaca Department, a prime mineral producer, to Chile. Peru also accedes to Chilean occupation of Tacna and Arica for 10 years, after which a plebiscite is to decide their future.

April 4, 1884. **Treaty of Valparaiso.** Bolivia cedes the department of Atacama north of the 24th Parallel to Chile. This area includes the important port of Antofagasta.

1884. Chile reorganizes part of old Atacama Department of Bolivia as Antofagasta Province. Chile reorganizes Tarapaca Department of Peru as Tarapaca Province.

June 3, 1929. Direct negotiations lead to a settlement of the Tacna-Arica question. Chile reneged on its treaty obligations to hold a plebiscite after 10 years, and international pressures 1910-26 were placed on Chile to settle the matter peacefully. Tacna was returned to Peruvian rule after 50 years of occupation, while Arica was retained and added to Tarapaca Province. Peru was given transit and port facility at Arica. Bolivia also received transit rights to the Pacific coast across Chile.

The old frontier between Bolivian Atacama and Peruvian Tarapaca had been the Loa River.

Interestingly, it was a token-issuing mining firm which precipitated the War of the Pacific. In a boundary settlement between Chile and Bolivia in 1874, the 24th Parallel was reaffirmed as the frontier, and Bolivia said Chileans could engage in mining in Atacama Dept. for 25 years without additional taxation.

In 1878 Pres. Hilarion Daza of Bolivia imposed an additional tax on nitrate exported from the Bolivian coast. The Chilean Nitrate Co. of Antofagasta appealed to Pres. Anibal Pinto of Chile, and during the ensuing negotiations, Bolivia temporarily rescinded the contract of the nitrate company. Chilean troops promptly occupied Antofagasta (on Feb. 14, 1879), opening the war. Peru refused to guarantee neutrality, and Chile declared war on both countries on April 5.

ACONCAGUA PROVINCE

Catemu
C. G. H.
Fundicion de Cobre

Rulau	Date	Metal	Size	VG	F	VF	Unc
Aco 1	ND	CN	25mm	—	—	15.00	

Ornate CGH monogram within rope circle. Rv: FUNDICION DE COBRE / 20 C. / (triangle) CATEMU (rosette). Plain edge. (The triangular mark bears the initials TC). (Rulau coll.)

This copper mine is the only reported token issuer from Aconcagua Province, a small province just north of Valparaiso and Santiago. A 50-centavo is also known.

ANTOFAGASTA PROVINCE

Aguas Blancas
COMPANIA CHILENA DE SALITRES

Rulau	Date	Metal	Size	VG	F	VF	Unc
Ant 2	ND	++	50.5mm	13.50	—	—	—

++ Green-black-green vulcanite.
(All incused): COMPANIA CHILENA DE SALITRES / ROSARIO / *. Rv: $ 3 (large). (Leslie 582e; Chanique 414)

Three pesos token; scarce.

COMPANIA SALITRERA EL BOQUETE

Rulau	Date	Metal	Size	VG	F	VF	Unc
Ant 5	ND	++	40mm	—	—	12.00	15.00

++ Vulcanite; red obverse, green reverse.
COMPANIA SALITRERA / (empty circle) / . EL BOQUETE . Rv: $2 (large, shaded). (Leslie 230b)

CIA. SALITRERA EL PEÑON
Oficina San Gregorio

Rulau	Date	Metal	Size	F	VF	EF	Unc
Ant 8	ND	**	31.3mm	—	8.00	11.00	14.00

** Green-black-green vulcanite.
Cia- SALITRERA EL PEÑON / OFICINA / SAN / GREGORIO / *. Rv: Large $1. (Zaffern coll.; Chanique 445; Rulau coll.; Leslie 633)

Alemania
COMPANIA SALITRERA ALEMANA
Oficina Alemania

Rulau	Date	Metal	Size	VG	F	VF	Unc
Ant 12	ND	Brass	44.5mm	12.00	14.00	—	—

COMPANIA SALITRERA ALEMANA / 1 (large, shaded) / * OFICINA ALEMANA *. Rv: VALE PARA LA PULPERIA / 1 (large, shaded) / (laurel branches). Reeded edge. (Eklund 1468; Leslie 18d; Chanique 18; Schiaffino 174)

OFICINA ALEMANA

Rulau	Date	Metal	Size	F	VF	EF	Unc
Ant 15	(1904)	xx	71mm	—	28.00	40.00	50.00

xx Red vulcanite.
OFICINA ALEMANA / 5 (large, shaded) / .-*-. / (tiny) 241549 (mfr. no.). Incused control no. (Examined: 597, 893, 1437). Rv: VALE PARA LA PULPERIA / 5 (large, shaded) / (ornaments). (Leslie 18k)

This huge piece is normally encountered cracked, chipped or otherwise damaged due to its large diameter and relatively delicate fabric. Specimens in choice condition are scarce!

Antofagasta
M. CY CA.

(Bolivian dominion)

Rulau	Date	Metal	Size	VG	F	VF	Unc
Ant 20	(1870)	xx	37mm	—	—	—	100.

xx Vermilion vulcanite.
M C / 15 (in beaded circle) / * & Co. *. Rv: Blank, but serial no. ctsp. (Eklund 1473 & 1599; Leslie 453b)

Rulau	Date	Metal	Size	VG	F	VF	Unc
Ant 21	(1870)	**	30mm	—	15.00	—	100.

** Black vulcanite.
M. Cy Ca- / UNA BEBIDA / PARA / MULA O CABALLO / ANTOFAGASTA (one drink for mule or horse). Rv: Blank. (Leslie 453c; Smith 50YA)

Rulau	Date	Metal	Size	VG	F	VF	Unc
Ant 22	(1870)	++	30mm	—	15.00	—	100.

++ Red vulcanite.
As last. (Eklund 1472; Leslie 453d)

Kenneth Smith considers the second token above to be a transportation piece, but it seems clearly to be a "good for" for animal watering. Melbourne Clark & Co.

COMPANIA DE SALITRES DE ANTOFAGASTA

Rulau	Date	Metal	Size	VG	F	VF	Unc
Ant 26	(1904-05)	**	40mm	—	2.00	4.00	6.50

** Green-black-tan vulcanite.
COMPANIA DE SALITRES / $2 (large) / 254082 (mfr. no.) / . DE ANTOFAGASTA. Rv: large ornate CSA monogram. Control no. incused above. Control numbers examined: 1358 through 49157. Estimated mintages: 49,000 pieces. (Leslie 51h)

| Ant 27 | (1904-05) | ++ | 40mm | — | 4.00 | 6.50 | 9.00 |

+ Blue-black-blue vulcanite.
As last. Control numbers examined: 2807 through 36646. Estimated mintage: 39,000 pieces. (Leslie 51i)

Rulau	Date	Metal	Size	VG	F	VF	Unc
Ant 28	(ca 1904)	xx	36mm	—	2.00	3.00	5.50

xx Deep blue-black-red vulcanite.
As last, but $1. Numbers examined: 1004 through 96173. Estimated mintage: 98,000 pieces. Leslie 51f)

| Ant 29 | ND | && | 36mm | — | — | 6.00 | 8.00 |

&& Black vulcanite.
As last. Numbers examined: 2535 through 12306. (Leslie 51e)

| Ant 30 | ND | vv | 36mm | — | — | 5.00 | 7.50 |

vv Red vulcanite.
As last. Numbers examined: 21006 through 41365. (Leslie 51d)

| Ant 33 | (1905) | gg | 31mm | — | — | 7.00 | 10.00 |

gg Green-black-green vulcanite.
As last, but 50 C. No control no. (Leslie 51b)

| Ant 34 | (1905) | gg | 31mm | — | — | 7.00 | 10.00 |

As last, but control number incused. Numbers examined: 9845. (Leslie 51c)

Elwin Leslie also reports a black vulcanite 20-centavos, 25mm, as his number 51a, which we have not examined.

Substantial hoards of this company's vulcanite tokens were placed on the numismatic marketplace in 1971 and again in 1990. The author has personally examined about 600 pieces each of the $2 green-black-tan and $1 blue-black-red tokens, but far fewer of the others listed above.

It is likely that no more large hoards of the CSA tokens remain to be dispersed. Prices are quite low for these very attractive vulcanite pieces.

OFICINA BLANCO ENCALADA

Rulau	Date	Metal	Size	F	VF	EF	Unc
Ant 37	ND	xx	36mm	5.00	8.00	11.00	—

xx Red vulcanite.
OFICINA BLANCO ENCALADA / (empty circle) / . ANTOFAGASTA. Rv: . VALE . / $1 (large, shaded) / EN MERCADERIAS. (Leslie 93c; Chanique 77)

This nitrate mine was at 23 degrees 13 minutes South, 69 degrees 37 minutes West.

Caracoles
CARACOLES

(Bolivian dominion)

Rulau	Date	Metal	Size	VG	F	VF	EF
Ant 40	(1870's)	—	41mm	—	—	—	—

CARACOLES / 20. Rv: Blank. (*TAMS Journal* for June 1988, pg. 119)

| Ant 41 | (1870's) | — | Oval 52x34mm | — | — | — | — |

E m e / AGUA. Rv: Blank.

| Ant 42 | (1870's) | — | Oval 52x34mm | — | — | — | — |

D r / CARNE. Rv: Blank.

| Ant 43 | (1870's) | — | Oval 52x34mm | — | — | — | — |

Fr Do / PAN. Rv: Blank. (*TAMS Journal* for June 1988, pg. 119)

Agua = Water. Carne = Meat. Pan = Bread. Caracoles silver mines were owned by Jose Diaz Gana, Baron Arnous Riviere and others. (See *TAMS Journal* for June 1988, pgs. 119-120)

Carmen Alto
CA. DE SALITRES Y F. CARRIL DE ANTOFAGASTA

(Bolivian dominion)

1876 Series

Rulau	Date	Metal	Size	VG	F	VF	Unc
Ant 46	(1876)	vv	33.5mm	—	—	—	—

vv Red vulcanite.
Old locomotive left, above cornucopia, all within circle. Around: Ca. DE SALITRES Y F CARRIL DE ANTOFAGASTA / +. Rv: DESPACHO DE / 10 C / EN / MERCADERIAS / + CARMEN ALTO +. (Leslie 147b)

| Ant 47 | (1876) | vv | 27mm | — | — | — | — |

As last, but 5 C. (Leslie 147a)

C.S.F.A.'s mine was located at 23 degrees 11 minutes south, 69 degrees 41 minutes west. It was later renamed as Oficina Francisco Puelma.

1878 Series

Rulau	Date	Metal	Size	VG	F	VF	Unc
Ant 49	(1878)	**	—mm	—	—	—	—

** Vulcanite; green obverse, tan reverse.
$1 PESO DE MERCADERIAS EN CARMEN ALTO .
/ C. S. F. A. Rv: Ornate border. (Chanique 233)

| Ant 50 | (1878) | vv | 26mm | — | — | — | — |

vv Red vulcanite.
As last, but 50 CENTAVOS. A serial no. is stamped incuse. (Chanique 132)

| Ant 51 | (1878) | + + | 26mm | — | — | — | — |

+ + Tan vulcanite.
As last (50 CENTAVOS). Serial no. stamped incuse (number 5863 examined). (Leslie 114e)

| Ant 52 | (1878) | + + | 18mm | — | — | — | — |

As last, but 20 CENTAVOS. (Leslie 114b)

| Ant 53 | (1878) | @@ | 18mm | — | — | 20.00 | — |

As last (20 CENTAVOS). (Leslie 114b)

C. S. F. A. = Compania de Salitres y Ferrocarril de Antofagasta. In this 1878 series are also 25-centavo tan vulcanite, 21mm; 10-c. tan vulcanite, 24mm; and 10-c. black vulcanite, 24mm.

Cobija
J.L. HERMITE
Mineral de Huanillo de Cobija

Rulau	Date	Metal	Size	VG	F	VF	Unc
Ant 57	ND	xx	36mm	—	7.00	9.00	—

xx Green-black-green vulcanite.
MINERAL DE HUANILLO DE COBIJA / J. L. HER-MITE / . / (stamped control no.) Rv: VALE POR MER-CADERIAS / $2 /.+. Numbers examined: 257, 425. (Zaika coll.)

| Ant 58 | ND | vv | 31mm | — | 5.00 | 7.00 | — |

vv Red vulcanite.
As last, but $1. Numbers examined: 771. (Zaika coll.)

| Ant 59 | ND | @@ | 30.5mm | — | 5.00 | 7.00 | — |

@@ Tan-black-tan vulcanite.
As last, but 50 C. (Zaika coll.)

Collahuasi
THE PODEROSA
MINING COMPANY
LD.

Rulau	Date	Metal	Size	VG	F	VF	Unc
Ant 62	(1908)	**	36mm	5.00	8.50	12.50	—

** Red vulcanite.
THE PODEROSA MINING COMPANY Ld. / 5 (shaded, in circle) / . COLLAHUASI . Rv: THE PODEROSA MINING COMPANY Ld. / VALE SOLO / EN LA / PULPERIA / 333895 (mfr. no.) / . COLLA-HUASI . (TAMS Journal for Dec. 1971, pg. 223)

| Ant 63 | (1908) | xx | 36mm | — | — | 7.50 | — |

xx Green-black-green vulcanite.
As last, but 1.

Fractional vulcanite tokens in 50, 20 and 10-centavo denominations may exist.

MINA PODEROSA

Rulau	Date	Metal	Size	VG	F	VF	Unc
Ant 66	(1908)	Copper	38mm	—	—	—	—

MINA / 50 C / PODEROSA. Rv: PAGADEROS / EN / ARTICULOS / DE LA / DESPENSA. Plain edge. (Schiaffino 722; Zaika coll.)

| Ant 67 | ND | Copper | 28mm | — | — | 8.00 | — |

As last, but 23 C. (Schiaf. 721; Zaika coll.)

| Ant 68 | ND | Copper | 23.5mm | — | — | 8.00 | — |

As last, but 10 C. (Schiaf. 720)

Despensa = Pantry or larder. The Poderosa mine was owned by The Poderosa Mining Co. Ltd., formed in 1905 and reorganized in 1908. This copper mine was at 16,000 feet, near the Bolivian border, and was last worked in 1931.

SINDICATO COLLAHUASI

Rulau	Date	Metal	Size	F	VF	EF	Unc
Ant 71	(1904)	qq	40mm	—	12.50	—	—

qq Tan-black-tan vulcanite.
SINDICATO COLLAHUASI / (upward arc) / 1 (large) / VALE POR / 239560 (mfr no) / MERCADERIAS. Rv: SINDICATO COLLAHUASI / (upward arc) / 1 (large, shaded) / VALE POR / MERCADERIAS.

A red vulcanite 20-centavos, 31mm, is known, and other values may exist. Sindicato Collahuasi (Collahuasi Syndicate) was organized in 1904 but lasted only a year, breaking up into Compania Anglo-Chilena de Collahuasi and Compania Poderosa de Collahuasi (Poderosa Mining Co. Ltd.).

SOCIETE FRANCAISE DES
MINES DE CUIVRE

Rulau	Date	Metal	Size	F	VF	EF	Unc
Ant 74	(1912)	zz	50mm	—	—	—	—

zz Black vulcanite.
As next token, but 5 / PESOS.

| Ant 75 | (1912) | ** | 40mm | 8.00 | 10.00 | 14.00 | — |

** Red vulcanite.
SOCIETE FRANCAISE DES MINES DE CUIVRE / COLLAHUASI / LA GRANDE / .:. Rv: VALE POR UN PESO DE MERCADERIAS / 1 / PESO / . PUL-PERIA. (TAMS Journal for Dec. 1971, pg. 224; Rulau coll.)

| Ant 77 | (1912) | xx | 30mm | — | — | 6.00 | — |

xx Blue-black-blue vulcanite.
As last, but 20 / CENTAVOS. (Zaika coll.)

Collahuasi La Grande was one of the larger copper mines in Chile. Its five main mines were grouped around Collahuasi Hill.

These mines were worked by Indians in pre-Columbian times. Spaniards called the area Peirira. Compania Minera de Collahuasi (organized 1899) took over mine ownership, but in 1912 a French enterprise bought it and changed the company's name as shown on the miners' payment tokens. The Societe Francaise was purchased by Poderosa Mining Co. Ltd. in 1923. The mines were last worked in 1931.

Taltal
COMPANIA SALITRERA ALEMANA
Oficina Moreno

Mejillones
HUANERA DE MEJILLONES

(Bolivian dominion)

Rulau	Date	Metal	Size	VG	F	VF	Unc
Ant 80	1876	Brass	28mm	—	22.50	—	—

HUANERA DE MEJILLONES / DESPACHOS / * BOLIVIA *. Rv: VALE EN MERCADERIAS / VEINTE / 20 / CENTAVOS / ** 1876 **.

M. DEL C.

(Bolivian dominion)

Rulau	Date	Metal	Size	VG	F	VF	Unc
Ant 82	(?)	xx	26mm	—	—	—	60.00

xx Red-orange vulcanite.
MEJILLONES / + / . 2 GALS . / + / DE BOLIVIA. Rv: M. DEL C / 5,000. (Lill coll.)

Playa Blanca
COMPANIA HUANCHACA DE BOLIVIA
Establecimiento de Playa Blanca

Rulau	Date	Metal	Size	VG	F	VF	Unc
Ant 85	(1900-04)	XX	40mm	—	—	—	—

XX Black vulcanite.
COMPANIA HUANCHACA DE BOLIVIA / ESTABLECIMIENTO / DE / PLAYA BLANCA / -.- / 201405 / ANTOFAGASTA / -+. Rv: VALE SEGUN / 1 (large, shaded) / . REGLAMENTO .

Rulau	Date	Metal	Size	VG	F	VF	Unc
Ant 86	(1900-04)	++	25mm	—	—	15.00	—

++ Green-black-green vulcanite.
As last, but ESTABTO and numeral 3.

See the *TAMS Journal* for June, 1972, pages 108-111.
This plant belonged to the Bolivian mining enterprise of Huanchaca. It was set up to process ores near the shipping point. It proved unworkable, however, and was sold to European interests.

Rulau	Date	Metal	Size	VG	F	VF	Unc
Ant 94	ND	Brass	59.2mm	—	35.00	50.00	—

Large numeral 5 in beaded circle. Around: COMPANIA SALITRERA ALEMANA / * OFICINA MORENO *. Rv: Large numeral 5. VALE PARA LA PULPERIA / (laurel wreath). Reeded edge. (Christensen Sept. 9, 1983 sale, lot 326; Chanique 323; Leslie 462 & 463)

Compania Salitrera Alemana = German Saltpeter Co.

Puerto Oliva
KEATING Y QUAET-FASLEM

(Bolivian dominion, Chilean occup.)

Rulau	Date	Metal	Size	VG	F	VF	Unc
Ant 90	(1880)	Copper	29mm	16.50	20.00	25.00	—

KEATING y QUAET-FASLEM / (ornaments) / . PUERTO OLIVA . Rv: VALE EN ARTICULOS DEL DESPACHO / 10 / Cts- / *. (Leslie 348b)

Rulau	Date	Metal	Size	VG	F	VF	Unc
Ant 91	(1880)	Copper	29mm	20.00	22.00	25.00	—

As last, but 5 / Cts-.

This was a nitrate shipping facility north of Taltal, occupied by Chilean troops in 1879. Puerto Oliva passed by treaty from Bolivia to Chile in 1884.

COMPANIA SALITRERA LAUTARO

Rulau	Date	Metal	Size	VG	F	VF	Unc
Ant 97	ND	Brass	35mm	—	14.00	—	—

50 (shaded) in circular wreath. Around: * COMPANIA SALITRERA LAUTARO *. Rv: 50 (shaded) in circular wreath. Around: VALE PARA LA PULPERIA / (wreath). Reeded edge. Issue holed. (Leslie 405c; Rulau coll.)

Rulau	Date	Metal	Size	VG	F	VF	Unc
Ant 98	ND	Brass	30mm	—	11.00	—	—

As last but 20. Reeded edge. (Leslie 405b; Rulau coll.)

10-centavo and 1-peso brass tokens were also issued in this series.

J. C. H. Y CA.

(Bolivian dominion)

Rulau	Date	Metal	Size	VG	F	VF	Unc
Ant 100	1878	Copper	23mm	—	—	15.00	—

FABRICA DE SALITRE / J. C. H Y Ca. / 1878 / * TALTAL *. Rv: VEINTE CENTAVOS / 20 / (ornaments). (Leslie 266c)

Rulau	Date	Metal	Size	VG	F	VF	Unc
Ant 101	1878	Copper	19mm	—	—	15.00	—

As last, but 10. (Eklund 1566; Leslie 266a)

This early elaboration plant was located at 25 degrees 28 minutes south and 70 degrees 28 minutes west. The tokens are met with counterstamped G M.

OFICINA ATACAMA

(Bolivian dominion)

Rulau	Date	Metal	Size	VG	F	VF	Unc
Ant 104	ND	++	30.5mm	—	10.00	30.00	—

++ Red vulcanite.
OFICINA ATACAMA / HP monogram / * TALTAL *. Rv: VALE EN MERCADERIAS / 1 / UN PESO / * DEL DESPACHO *. (Leslie 63b)

Rulau	Date	Metal	Size	VG	F	VF	Unc
Ant 105	ND	++	21mm	—	—	—	—

As last, but 50 / Cts. (Leslie 63a)

HP = Hernan Puelma.

(Chilean dominion)

Rulau	Date	Metal	Size	VG	F	VF	Unc
Ant 107	ND	@@	—mm	—	—	—	—

OFICINA ATACAMA. Rv: 0,10. (Chanique 61)

Rulau	Date	Metal	Size	VG	F	VF	Unc
Ant 109	(1894)	++	36mm	—	—	—	—

++ Red vulcanite.
OFICINA / 190105 (mfrs. no.) / ATACAMA / TALTAL. Rv: VALE UN PESO / $1 / EN MERCADERIAS. (Leslie 63c)

Rulau	Date	Metal	Size	VG	F	VF	Unc
Ant 110	(1900)	++	71mm	—	—	—	—

OFICINA / 227280 (mfrs. no.) / 5. Rv: VALE PARA LA PULPERIA / 5 (pesos). (Leslie 63d)

OFICINA BRITANNIA

Rulau	Date	Metal	Size	VG	F	VF	Unc
Ant 113	ND	Brass	32mm	—	9.00	13.00	40.00

OFICINA BRITANNIA. Rv: MERCADERIAS EN PULPERIA / $1 (in circle). Plain edge. (Leslie 102d; Chanique 91)

Rulau	Date	Metal	Size	VG	F	VF	Unc
Ant 114	ND	CN	31mm	—	—	—	—

As last. (Schiaffino 130)

Rulau	Date	Metal	Size	VG	F	VF	Unc
Ant 115	ND	Brass	27mm	—	—	—	—

As last, but 50 C. (Chanique 90)

Rulau	Date	Metal	Size	VG	F	VF	Unc
Ant 116	ND	CN	27mm	—	5.00	9.00	25.00

As last. (Leslie 102c; Chanique 89; Schiat. 129)

Rulau	Date	Metal	Size	VG	F	VF	Unc
Ant 117	ND	Brass	21mm	—	—	—	—

As last, but 20 C. (Leslie 102b)

Rulau	Date	Metal	Size	VG	F	VF	Unc
Ant 118	ND	Brass	16mm	—	8.00	—	—

As last, but 10 C. (Chanique 88)

Rulau	Date	Metal	Size	VG	F	VF	Unc
Ant 119	ND	CN	16mm	—	10.00	15.00	25.00

As last. (Leslie 102a; Chanique 87; Rulau coll.)

Leslie says this mine was located at 25 degrees 19 minutes South latitude and 69 degrees 52 minutes West longitude.

Toco
A. C. N. & R. CO. LD.

Rulau	Date	Metal	Size	VG	F	VF	Unc
Ant 122	ND	Copper	36mm	—	—	25.00	—

A. C. N. & R. Co. Ld. / COYA / TOCO. Rv: VALE / UN PESO / $1 / EN MERCADERIAS. Plain edge. (Leslie 201c)

Anglo-Chilean Nitrate & Railroad Co. Ltd.

H. B. S. Y CIA.
Oficina Empresa

Rulau	Date	Metal	Size	VG	F	VF	Unc
Ant 124	(1903)	++	45.5mm	—	—	11.00	—

++ Red vulcanite.
ESTE VALE SE CANJEA SOLAMENTE EN LA PULPERIA + / H. B. S. / Y / Cia-. Rv: OFICINA EMPRESA / 1 (large, shaded) / (tiny) 237567 (mfg. no.) / +++. (Leslie 233d var.; Chanique 192 var.)

H. B. S. y Cia. = Compania Salitrera H. B. Sloman y Cia.

Rulau	Date	Metal	Size	VG	F	VF	Unc
Ant 126	(1903)	xx	55mm	—	10.00	20.00	30.00

xx Black vulcanite.
As last, but 5. (Leslie 233c; Chanique 192)

OFICINA EMPRESA

Rulau	Date	Metal	Size	VG	F	VF	Unc
Ant 128	(1903-04)	**	54.5mm	—	—	15.00	—

** Red vulcanite.
OFICINA EMPRESA / 5 (large, shaded) / *** / 237567 (small). Rv: CANJEABLE UNICAMENTE A LOS TRABAJADORES DE LA FIRMA. / (script monogram OE). (Leslie 233d; Rulau coll.)

237567 = Manufacturing number. Token for 5 pesos.
Canjeable unicamente a los trabajadores de la firma = Exchangeable only by the workers of the firm.

Rulau	Date	Metal	Size	F	VF	EF	Unc
Ant 129	(1903-04)	pp	55mm	—	15.00	17.50	22.50

pp Red-black-blue vulcanite.
As last. (Leslie 233e; Harrison coll.)

This token is more scarce than the all-red vulcanite piece.

Tocopilla
SOCIEDAD BENEFICIADORA DE TOCOPILLA

Rulau	Date	Metal	Size	VG	F	VF	Unc
Ant 132	ND	vv	49.5mm	—	—	12.00	—

SOCIEDAD / (beaded arc) / ... / BENEFICIADORA (on panel) / DE / 289,726 (mfr. no.) / (beaded arc) / . TOCOPILLA . Rv: $1 (ornate, shaded).

Rulau	Date	Metal	Size	VG	F	VF	Unc
Ant 133	ND	vv	35.5mm	—	—	11.00	—

vv Tan-black-tan vulcanite.
As last, but 50 C (shaded).

Rulau	Date	Metal	Size	VG	F	VF	Unc
Ant 134	ND	vv	30.5mm	—	—	11.00	—

As last, but 20 C.

Rulau	Date	Metal	Size	VG	F	VF	Unc
Ant 135	ND	vv	21mm	—	—	15.00	—

As last, but 5 C.

BABURIZZA BRUNA Y COMPANIA
Oficina Ausonia

Rulau	Date	Metal	Size	VG	F	VF	Unc
Ant 150	ND	xx	41mm	—	5.00	8.00	—

xx Black vulcanite.
BABURIZZA BRUNA Y COMPANIA / OFICINA / AUSONIA / ..... . Rv: $1 (large, shaded) / (control no. incused). Numbers examined: S2598, S2980, S6666, S7478, 151, 541, 3398, 3851, 4084. (Leslie 78g; Chanique 69)

COMPANIA SALITRERA "EL LOA"
Oficina Angamos

Rulau	Date	Metal	Size	F	VF	EF	Unc
Ant 152	(1909)	xx	41mm	7.00	8.00	9.00	—

xx Blue-black-blue vulcanite.
COMPANIA SALITRERA "EL LOA" / OFICINA / ANGAMOS / 346781 (mfr. no.) / *+* . Rv: $1 (large, shaded). (Leslie 36c; Chanique 40)

COMPANIA SALITRERA "EL LOA"
Oficina Anita

Rulau	Date	Metal	Size	F	VF	EF	Unc
Ant 154	(1912)	xx	46mm	3.00	4.50	6.00	8.00

xx Green-black vulcanite.
COMPANIA SALITRERA "EL LOA" / OFICINA / ANITA / 366474 (mfr. no.) / (3-leaf clover) (5-point star) (3-leaf clover). Rv: $1 (large, shaded). (Leslie 48b; Chanique 44; Rulau & Zaffern colls.)

Rulau	Date	Metal	Size	F	VF	EF	Unc
Ant 155	(1912)	++	46mm	4.00	6.00	—	—

++ Black vulcanite.
As last. (Leslie 48a; Chanique 45)

COMPANIA SALITRERA "EL LOA"
Oficina Curico

Rulau	Date	Metal	Size	F	VF	EF	Unc
Ant 157	(1906-07)	vv	41mm	—	6.00	9.00	

vv Green-black-red vulcanite.
COMPANIA SALITRERA "EL LOA" / OFICINA / CURICO / 299467 (mfr. no.) / ... + ... Rv: $1 (large). (Leslie 210d straight 1; Zaffern coll.)

COMPANIA SALITRERA
EL LOA
Oficina Luisis

Rulau	Date	Metal	Size	F	VF	EF	Unc
Ant 159	ND	**	Oct 42mm	3.00	8.00	11.00	—

** Green-black-green vulcanite.
COMPANIA SALITRERA EL LOA / OFICINA / LUISIS / .. Rv: $1 (large). (Leslie 432c; Chanique 296; Zaffern coll.)

COMPANIA SALITRERA
"ESMERALDA"
Oficina Luisis

Rulau	Date	Metal	Size	VG	F	VF	Unc
Ant 161	ND	++	Oct 42mm	4.00	6.00	8.00	—

++ Green-black-green vulcanite. COMPANIA / "ESMERALDA" / 250486 mfr. no.) / SALITRERA. Rv: OFICINA / $1 (in circle) / "LUISIS". (Leslie 432b; Chanique 297)

OFICINA LINA

Rulau	Date	Metal	Size	VG	F	VF	Unc
Ant 163	ND	Vulcanite*	41mm	5.00	6.00		

* Light brown both sides, clad to black center. OFICINA / (empty circle) / * LINA *. Rv: . VALE . / Large $2 (shaded) / EN MERCADERIAS. (Zaffern coll.; Leslie 423e; Chanique 291)

Rulau	Date	Metal	Size	VG	F	VF	Unc
Ant 164	ND	xx	41mm	5.00	6.00	7.50	

xx Blue-black-blue vulcanite.
As last. (Leslie 423d; Chanique 292; Rulau coll.)

OFICINA MARIA

Rulau	Date	Metal	Size	VG	F	VF	Unc
Ant 170	ND	CN	Oval 39x27mm	11.00	15.00	—	—

OFICINA / MARIA. Rv: 50. Plain edge. (Leslie 438h)

Rulau	Date	Metal	Size	VG	F	VF	Unc
Ant 171	ND	CN	27mm	—	—	—	—

As last, but 20 (centavos). (Leslie 438g)

Rulau	Date	Metal	Size	VG	F	VF	Unc
Ant 172	ND	CN	—mm	—	—	—	—

As last, but 10. (Leslie 438f)

Rulau	Date	Metal	Size	VG	F	VF	Unc
Ant 168	ND	CN	Oct—mm	—	22.50	—	—

As last, but 5 (pesos).

Rulau	Date	Metal	Size	VG	F	VF	Unc
Ant 169	ND	CN	35mm	—	18.00	—	—

As last, but 1 (peso). Plain edge. (Rulau coll.)

This whole issue is scarce and little is known about it.

VALOR A VUELTA INDICADO
(Comercio Antofagasta)

Rulau	Date	Metal	Size	F	VF	EF	Unc
Ant 175	ND	xx	41mm	—	—	8.00	—

xx Red vulcanite.
VALOR A LA VUELTA INDICADO / -+- / CANJE / 303081 (mfr. no.) / .+. Rv: $10 (large, shaded). (David Harrison coll.)

ZANELLI Y SCAGLIA
Oficina Riviera

Rulau	Date	Metal	Size	VG	F	VF	Unc
Ant 178	ND	xx	25mm	10.00	15.00	20.00	—

xx Green-black-tan vulcanite.
(All incused): ZANELLI Y SCAGLIA / 4 (in circle) / +. Rv: OFICINA RIVIERA / 4 (in circle) / +. Scarce. (Chanique 410; Leslie 579h ?)

4 = 4 centavos, probably. This is an odd denomination for the early Chilean vulcanite pieces.

Also in this series are 3, black vulcanite; 5, blue; and 6, red. In larger format, and issued later, are 1 and 2-peso vulcanite pieces.

ARAUCO PROVINCE
Colico
C. A. L.

Rulau	Date	Metal	Size	VG	F	VF	Unc
Ara 3	ND	xx	32mm	—	6.50	8.50	—

xx Tan-black-tan vulcanite.
COLICO / C. A. L. / * MERCADERIAS *. Rv: UNO. (Rulau coll.)

A coal mine. Uno = One. Issued by Arauco Mining Co.?

Curanilahue
CA. CARBONIFERA LOS RIOS DE CURANILAHUE

Rulau	Date	Metal	Size	VG	F	VF	Unc
Ara 8	(1915)	vv	41mm	15.00	20.00	30.00	—

vv Red vulcanite.
Ca. CARBONIFERA / 000898 (mfr. no.) / CURANI-LAHUE / LOS RIOS / DE / . CURANILAHUE . Rv: VALE EN MERCADERIAS / 2 (in circle) / + "QUIN-CENA" +.

Rulau	Date	Metal	Size	VG	F	VF	Unc
Ara 9	(1915)	uu	31mm	—	7.00	—	—

uu Tan-black-tan vulcanite.
Obverse as last, but no mfr. no. Rv: 50 C / .+.

Rulau	Date	Metal	Size	VG	F	VF	Unc
Ara 11	(1915)	ff	31mm	—	10.00	15.00	—

ff Orange-black vulcanite.
Obverse as last. Rv: SECCION CARNICERIA / 50 C / .+. (Harrison coll.)

Coal mine.

Plegarias
C. A. L.

Rulau	Date	Metal	Size	VG	F	VF	Unc
Ara 15	ND	xx	32mm	4.00	6.00	8.00	—

xx Tan-black-tan vulcanite.
PLEGARIAS / C.A.L. /. MERCADERIAS . Rv: UNO. (Rulau coll.)

Rulau	Date	Metal	Size	VG	F	VF	Unc
Ara 16	ND	++	32mm	—	7.00	10.00	—

++ Blue-black-red vulcanite.
As last, but CINCO on reverse. (Rulau coll.)

Rulau	Date	Metal	Size	VG	F	VF	Unc
Ara 17	ND	**	32mm	—	6.50	9.00	—

** Green-black-red vulcanite.
As last.

Rulau	Date	Metal	Size	VG	F	VF	Unc
Ara 19	ND	yy	25mm	—	6.00	8.00	—

yy Black vulcanite.
All incused: PLEGARIAS / C. A. L. / MERCA-DERIAS. Rv: (Relief) 50 C. (D. Harrison coll.)

For a coal mine. Uno = One. Cinco = Five.

ATACAMA PROVINCE
Caldera
MINAS DEL MORADO

Issues of Juan H. Craig

Rulau	Date	Metal	Size	VG	F	VF	Unc
Ata 3	ND	xx	27mm	—	—	—	—

xx Black vulcanite.
MINAS DEL MORADO / + JUAN H. CRAIG +. Rv: VEINTE CENTAVOS / ... / 20 C / ... / + MERCA-DERIAS +. (Eklund 1533)

Rulau	Date	Metal	Size	VG	F	VF	Unc
Ata 4	ND	++	21mm	—	—	—	—

++ Red vulcanite.
As last, but DIEZ CENTAVOS / ... / 10 C. (Eklund 1532)

Issues of C. y C.

Rulau	Date	Metal	Size	VG	F	VF	Unc
Ata 7	1876	Brass	30.5mm	—	17.50	—	—

Crossed hammer and pick separate C -- y -- C, all in central circle. Around: MINAS DEL MORADO / + 1876 +. Rv: VALE EN MERCADERIAS / CIN-CUENTA / 50 / + CENTAVOS + / (ornaments).

Rulau	Date	Metal	Size	VG	F	VF	Unc
Ata 8	1876	Brass	—mm	—	—	—	—

As last, but DIEZ / 10. (Eklund 1535)

Rulau	Date	Metal	Size	VG	F	VF	Unc
Ata 9	1876	Brass	—mm	—	—	—	—

As last, but CINCO / 5. (Eklund 1534)

Issues of Bernardo Tornini

Rulau	Date	Metal	Size	VG	F	VF	Unc
Ata 12	(1892)	xx	31mm	7.00	8.00	11.00	—

xx Black vulcanite.
MINAS DEL MORADO / 175688 (mfrs. no.) / 50 C / . CALDERA . Rv: VALE EN MERCADERIAS / 50 C / . BERNARDO TORNINI .

Rulau	Date	Metal	Size	VG	F	VF	Unc
Ata 13	(1892)	xx	30mm	9.00	—	—	—

As last, but ctsp B T on reverse.

Chañaral
CA. INCA DE ORO Y COBRE

Rulau	Date	Metal	Size	VG	F	VF	Unc
Ata 16	ND	++	26mm	—	—	15.00	—

++ Red vulcanite.
Ca. INCA DE ORO Y COBRE / DE / COPIAPO / . +. / . CHAÑARAL . Rv: VALE . / 20 C / .+. / EN MERCA-DERIAS.

Rulau	Date	Metal	Size	VG	F	VF	Unc
Ata 17	ND	**	23mm	—	—	15.00	—

** Black vulcanite.
As last, but 10 C.

David Henkle places these tokens under Inca de Oro (canton or municipality?) in Atacama Province. The company name means: Inca Gold & Copper Co. of Copiapo.

MINERALES DE CHAÑARAL

Rulau	Date	Metal	Size	VG	F	VF	Unc
Ata 20	1877	Copper	—mm	—	—	—	—

MINERALES DE CHAÑARAL / (crossed pick and hammer) / 1877. Rv: VALE EN MERCADERIAS / CINCUENTA / 50 / CENTAVOS / *-*-*. (Ulex 3725; Eklund 1497)

Rulau	Date	Metal	Size	VG	F	VF	Unc
Ata 21	1877	Copper	19mm	—	—	—	—

As last, but DIEZ / 10 / CENTAVOS. (Eklund 1496)

Chañaral had been ceded by Bolivia to Chile in 1866.

Copiapo
FERRO-CARRIL DE COPIAPO

Rulau	Date	Metal	Size	VG	F	VF	EF
Ata 24	(1860's)	xx	Oval 34x25mm	85.00	—	400.	—

xx Black vulcanite.
Locomotive right (the "Copiapo," first locomotive in Chile). Rv: FERRO-CARRIL / AGUA / * DE COPIAPO *. (*TAMS Journal* for Feb. 1972, pg. 16)

Elwin Leslie says this is a receipt for water, not a transport payment, by the Copiapo Railway. Private contractors hauled water to the right of way at first; later water tank cars were used.

The original line, from Caldera to Copiapo (50 miles) opened in 1852. The engine "Copiapo" was built 1850 in Philadelphia. In 1855 the line reached San Antonio, 40 miles south of Copiapo. By 1871 two branch lines were added. In 1895 the government bought the railroad.

MINA TRAVESIA

Rulau	Date	Metal	Size	VG	F	VF	Unc
Ata 26	ND	Copper	32mm	—	8.00	—	—

MINA TRAVESIA / $.1 / . COPIAPO . Rv: VALE EN MERCADERIAS / UN / PESO / -.-.

Huasco
CORNELIO SAAVEDRA

Rulau	Date	Metal	Size	VG	F	VF	Unc
Ata 30	ND	Copper	19mm	—	—	8.00	—

Mining tools in circle. Around: CORNELIO SAAVEDRA / * HUASCO *. Rv: MINA SOCABON / 10 / CENTAVOS (in circle) / * LABRAR *. Plain edge. (Zaika coll.)

BIO BIO PROVINCE

Los Angeles
CLUB DE LOS ANJELES

Rulau	Date	Metal	Size	F	VF	EF	Unc
Bio 1	1889	xx	30.5mm	—	—	18.50	—

xx Black vulcanite.
CLUB DE LOS ANJELES / 151845 (mfr. no.) / (Outline star, in circle) / . 1889. Rv: VEINTE CENTAVOS / 20 (in circle) / . CHILE .

CHILOE PROVINCE

VELMA'S

Rulau	Date	Metal	Size	VG	F	VF	Unc
Che 3	ND	Brass	Scal 19mm	—	—	75.00	—

VELMA'S / (Bearded head left) / CHILO. Rv: Blank. Scarce. (Plante 1992 stocklist, lot 118)

Chiloe (Chilo) is a large island which, with a section of Chilean mainland and many small islands, constitutes Chiloe Province. The capital is the port of Ancud on Chiloe Island.

CONCEPCION PROVINCE

Coronel
MINAS SCHWAGER

Rulau	Date	Metal	Size	VG	F	VF	Unc
Ccp 5	(1892)	**	30.5mm	—	7.50	14.00	20.00

** Red vulcanite.
Crossed pick and sledgehammer above lamp, all in beaded circle. Around: MINAS SCHWAGER / .CORONEL. Rv: 20 (in beaded circle). Around: VEINTE CENTAVOS / * * *. (Eklund 1510; *TAMS Journal* for Dec. 1972, pg. 230)

Rulau	Date	Metal	Size	VG	F	VF	Unc
Ccp 6	(1892)	**	24mm	—	—	10.00	—

As last, but DIEZ CENTAVOS / 10. (Eklund 1509; Zaika coll.)

Rulau	Date	Metal	Size	VG	F	VF	Unc
Ccp 7	(1892)	vv	24mm	—	3.00	6.00	—

vv Black vulcanite.
As last, but CINCO CENTAVOS / 5. (Eklund 1508)

Rulau	Date	Metal	Size	F	VF	EF	Unc
Ccp 9	ND	**	31mm	—	—	10.00	—

Obverse similar to last, but mfr. no. 152 - 507 is divided by the lamp. Rv: Similar to last 20-centavos, from new mold with numerals thin and unshaded. (Harrison coll.)

Rulau	Date	Metal	Size	F	VF	EF	Unc
Ccp 10	(1904)	xx	36mm	—	12.00	15.00	—

TIENDAS / 239344 (mfr. no.) / DE / MINAS / SCHWAGER / .+. / CORONEL. Rv: CARNE / 40 Cts / + / CARNE.

Rulau	Date	Metal	Size	VG	F	VF	Unc
Ccp 12	ND	vv	30.5mm	15.00	17.50	22.50	—

Obverse as last, but ropelike arcs added. Rv: CARNE / UN PESO / CARNE. (Harrison coll.)

Rulau	Date	Metal	Size	F	VF	EF	Unc
Ccp 14	1920	gg	25mm	12.00	15.00	18.00	—

gg Yellow-black-yellow vulcanite.
MINAS SCHWAGER / (crossed mine tools above lamp) / * CORONEL *. Rv: CIRCULACION PRIVADA / 20 C / * 1920 *.

Rulau	Date	Metal	Size	F	VF	EF	Unc
Ccp 15	1920	hh	21.5mm	—	—	7.50	—

hh Green-black-red vulcanite.
As last, but 10 C. (Bill Judd report)

Tiendas = Stores. Circulacion privada = Private circulation (of token coinage.)

About 1860 F. W. Schwager opened his Boca Maule coal mine near the Maule River north of Coronel. At the same time Guillermo Delano opened the important Puchoco Delano coal mines on Coronel Bay. Both mines had undersea shafts, as did most coal mines in the Concepcion Province area. Puchoco Delano was inundated by the sea and abandoned in 1881.

In 1892 Delano and Schwager combined to form the second largest mining enterprise in the Coronel area, La Compania Carbonifera y de Fundacion de Schwager, owners of the Boca Maule, Arenas Blancas and Puchoco Delano mines, and the Schwager Railroad. Only the Lota mining enterprise was larger.

Minas Schwager reopened the flooded Puchoco Delano mine, bypassing the flooded workings and intercepting the coal seam further west.

The very handsome Minas Schwager vulcanite tokens were used to pay workers. These could be exchanged for goods at the company's stores.

Lota
ESTABLECIMIENTO DE LOTA

Rulau	Date	Metal	Size	VG	F	VF	Unc
Ccp 18	ND	ff	40mm	—	—	40.00	—

ff Red-brown vulcanite.
Steamship with sails left, in beaded circle. Around: ESTABLECIMIENTO DE LOTA / (ornament). Rv: UN PESO / $1 (in beaded circle) / * * *. (Eklund 1530; Smith 500E)

Rulau	Date	Metal	Size	VG	F	VF	Unc
Ccp 19	ND	ff	30mm	—	—	15.00	—

As last, but VEINTE CENTAVOS / 20. (Eklund 1529; Smith 500D)

Rulau	Date	Metal	Size	VG	F	VF	Unc
Ccp 20	ND	gg	23mm	—	—	10.00	—

gg Black vulcanite.
As last, but CINCO CENTAVOS / 5 (in circle). (Eklund 1527; Smith 500A)

There are also both dark green and red-brown vulcanite 10-centavo tokens in this issue, worth $12 each in VF. These are coal mine tokens, apparently used also for dock and railway workers. Smith called them transportation tokens, but this seem doubtful.

Rulau	Date	Metal	Size	VG	F	VF	Unc
Ccp 22	ND	Brass	31.5mm	6.00	9.00	12.00	—

Sidwheeler with sails right, in beaded circle. Around: ESTABLECIMIENTO DE LOTA / *. Rv: VEINTE CENTAVOS / 20 (in beaded circle) / * * *. (Eklund 1526; Smith 500H)

Brass tokens denominated 10 and 5-centavos are known, worth 60% as much as the 20-centavos.

Rulau	Date	Metal	Size	VG	F	VF	Unc
Ccp 24	ND	Brass	20mm	—	—	—	—

ESTABLECIMIENTO DE LOTA / C / 10 / *. Rv: DIEZ CENTAVOS / C / 10 / *.

Rulau	Date	Metal	Size	VG	F	VF	Unc
Ccp 25	ND	Brass	19mm	—	—	—	—

As last, but C / 5 and CINCO CENTAVOS.

The coal mine tokens of Establecimiento de Lota were followed by those of its parent, Compania de Lota y Coronel, all part of the giant Cousino coal-copper-shipping-farming empire.

Lota Alto
COMPANIA DE LOTA Y CORONEL

Almacen No. 1

Rulau	Date	Metal	Size	F	VF	EF	Unc
Ccp28	1920	xx	41mm	9.50	12.00	18.50	—

xx Blue-black-blue vulcanite.
COMPANIA DE LOTA Y CORONEL / VALE / POR / 1 KILO / DE / CARNE / * LOTA *. Rv: ALMACEN No. 1 / 1920 (in circle) / * LOTA ALTO *. (*TAMS Journal* for Dec. 1972. pgs. 227-231; Rulau coll.)

Rulau	Date	Metal	Size	VG	F	VF	Unc
Ccp 30	1920	gg	22mm	—	10.00	15.00	—

gg Red-black-red vulcanite.
COMPANIA DE LOTA Y CORONEL / 1 / LITRO / DE / LECHE / . LOTA . Rv: ALMACEN No. 1 / 1920 (in circle) / . LOTA ALTO .

Almacen No. 2

Rulau	Date	Metal	Size	F	VF	EF	Unc
Ccp 32	1920	+ +	41mm	9.50	12.00	18.50	—

+ + Green-black-green vulcanite.
COMPANIA DE LOTA Y CORONEL / VALE / POR / 1 KILO / DE / CARNE / * LOTA *. Rv: ALMACEN No. 2 / 1920 (in circle) / * LOTA ALTO *. (Rulau coll.)

Rulau	Date	Metal	Size	F	VF	EF	Unc
Ccp 33	1920	+ +	31mm	—	—	—	—

As last, but 1/2 KILO.

Rulau	Date	Metal	Size	F	VF	EF	Unc
Ccp 35	1920	+ +	21mm	—	10.00	15.00	—

COMPANIA DE LOTA Y CORONEL /1 / LITRO / DE / LECHE / . LOTA . Rv: ALMACEN No. 2 / 1920 (in circle) / . LOTA ALTO .

A Chilean government decree of 1851 exempted from duty all copper smelted with Chilean coal. A wealthy Portuguese merchant of Valparaiso, Matias Cousino, saw the advantages of this and formed a partnership with Thomas Garland and with Jose Alemparte, owner of the huge Calcura Estate and lessee of coal mining rights in the Lota area.

Compania de Lota y Coronel was founded in 1852 by the partners; it was destined to become the largest and wealthiest coal mine in Chile. Soon after 1852 the Cousino family forced out the partners and took over sole control. Matias Cousino then purchased a copper mine at Carrizalillo near Chañaral, and built his own copper smelting plant at Lota. At its peak the Lota smelter produced 7200 tons of copper ingots per year.

Cousino established his own steamship line, partly to ferry coal and copper outward and to bring copper ores in to Lota Bay. He managed to extinguish the rights of the Rojas family over the coal mines at Puchoco Rojas and Playa Negra on Coronel Bay. Matias Cousino died in 1863 and was succeeded by his son, Luis Cousino and, at Luis' death, by Luis' widow, Doña Isadora Goyenechea de Cousino, who became sole owner.

Doña Isadora was celebrated as "the richest woman in the world." She travelled the world like royalty on her own steamers. The company prospered mightily. It owned 200,000 acres of farmland — the entire Lota, Colcura, Laraquete and Coronel estates in the Lota-Coronel area, and Los Rios estate 50 miles south at Curanilahue in Arauco Province. It built a large copper smelter at Maitenes near Santiago, and built Lota Alto just north of Lota as a "company town" serving its nearby mines at Chambique, Alberto, Gran Carlos and Chiflon Grande.

Doña Isadora de Cousino died in 1898, willing the Lota properties to her six children.

0-0-0-0-0-0-0-0-0-

Coal mine pay in the 19th century was low by comparison to that in the nitrate and copper mines of Chile. In the early Cousino days the wage was 50 to 60 centavos for an 11-hour day (U.S. 30-35 cents). Paydays were irregular and coincided with feast days and national holidays, since Chilean miners celebrated extensively on payday.

In 1972 Elwin Leslie wrote: "Most workers had little thought of saving for the future, and looked forward only to the next payday and its accompanying drinking, gambling and revelry."

The Lota workers, whether coal miners, railway hands or dock workers, were paid in company tokens which could be exchanged for goods at the company's stores. In addition to the daily wage, miners received free housing and coal.

COQUIMBO PROVINCE

La Higuera
MINERAL DE LA HIGUERA

Rulau	Date	Metal	Size	F	VF	EF	Unc
Coq 4	(1891)	vv	41mm	10.00	20.00	25.00	30.00

vv Green-black-green vulcanite.
MINERAL DE LA HIGUERA / VALE / $1 (shaded) / EN / . MERCADERIAS . Rv: Ornate monogram AIJ / 165277 (mfr no). (David Harrison coll.; Rulau coll.)

MAGALLANES PROVINCE

Punta Arenas
CONSTANTINO

Rulau	Date	Metal	Size	VG	F	VF	Unc
Mag 1	ND	Brass	21mm	—	—	75.00	—

CONSTANTINO / PTA. ARENAS / MAGALLANES. Rv: VALE POR / 20 / CTS. / EN MERCADERIAS. (Dick Hanscom report)

HOTEL IMPERIAL

Rulau	Date	Metal	Size	VG	F	VF	Unc
Mag 4	ND	Brass	21mm	—	—	85.00	—

HOTEL IMPERIAL / PUNTA / ARENAS / MAGALLANES. Rv: VALE POR / 20 / CTS. / .EN. / MERCADERIAS.

Rulau	Date	Metal	Size	VG	F	VF	Unc
Mag 5	ND	Brass	21mm	—	—	75.00	—

HOTEL IMPERIAL PTA / ARENAS / *** / MAGALLANES / +. Rv: Similar to last. (*Alaskan Token Collector & Polar Numismatist*)

A. L.

Rulau	Date	Metal	Size	VG	F	VF	Unc
Mag 9	ND	Brass	21mm	—	—	85.00	—

A. L. / PTA ARENAS / MAGALLANES. Rv: VALE POR / 20 / CTS. / EN MERCADERIAS.

Punta Arenas, a busy port on the Strait of Magellan on the South American mainland, is the continent's most southerly city of importance. Its tokens apparently were all struck by the same firm, and competition for them has driven their price upward in the past 10 years.

Tierra del Fuego
S. E. DE TIERRA DEL FUEGO

Rulau	Date	Metal	Size	VG	F	VF	EF
Mag 15	(1895)	++	35mm	—	—	100.	150.

++ Black vulcanite.
.+. / S. E. / DE / TIERRA DEL FUEGO. Rv: . VALE . / $ 1 / EN MERCADERIAS. (*TAMS Journal* for Oct 1971, pgs. 174-175)

Mag 16	(1895)	xx	30mm	—	—	75.00	100.

xx Red Vulcanite. As last, but 50 C.

Also reported are black vulcanite 50 C, and both red and black vulcanite 20 C tokens, each worth $70 in VF.

Sociedad Explotadora de Tierra del Fuego was a sheep ranching concern which operated several estates on the large island at South America's southern tip.

NUBLE PROVINCE

Chillan
TERMAS MINERALES CHILLAN

Rulau	Date	Metal	Size	VG	F	VF	Unc
Nub 3	ND	Brass	23mm	—	7.00	12.00	—
		TERMAS MINERALES / CHILLAN. Rv: VALE VEINTE / 20 / Cts. Plain edge.					
Nub 4	ND	Brass	19mm	—	4.00	8.00	—
		As last, but VALE DIEZ / 10.					

Tokens for a mineral bath.

O'HIGGINS PROVINCE

Sewell
BRADEN COPPER COMPANY

Rulau	Date	Metal	Size	VG	F	VF	Unc
Ohi 3	(1904)	xx	36mm	—	20.00	—	—
		xx Green-black-green vulcanite.					
		BRADEN COPPER COMPANY / VALE / $1 / EN / MERCADERIAS. Rv: VALE UN PESO / BCc monogram (in circle) / * EN MERCADERIAS *. (*TAMS Journal*) for June 1973, pg. 94)					
Ohi 4	(1904)	yy	26mm	15.00	20.00	—	—
		yy Tan-black-green vulcanite.					
		As last, but 20 C and VALE VEINTE CTS.					
Ohi 5	(1904)	rr	26mm	20.00	25.00	—	—
		rr Red vulcanite.					
		As last (20 C).					

Also known as tan-black-tan 20 C and red vulcanite 10 C tokens, worth $18 each in VG-F.

Rulau	Date	Metal	Size	VG	F	VF	Unc
Ohi 6	ND	zz	31.5mm	—	25.00	—	—
		zz Tan-black-tan vulcanite.					
		Similar to last un peso token, but BCc monogram is replaced by separate leters B C C.					

A later issue features a crossed pick and hammer replacing the monogram or initials of earlier issues. All are scarce.

O-O-O-O-O-O-O-O-O

Braden Copper Co. owned El Teniente, a copper mountain near Rancagua south of Santiago, the Chilean capital. It is the largest underground copper mine in the world, and a city, Sewell, sits on its slopes.

Copper had been mined in this area for many years, but owner Juan de Dias Correa lost it in 1890 for failing to pay taxes. Wine magnate Enrique Concha y Toro acquired the property in 1897, but sold out to Americans William Braden and Barton Sewell in 1903.

Braden and Sewell organized Braden Copper Co. as a public company which issued 625,000 preferred and 625,000 common shares. In 1907 they built a railway from Sewell to Rancagua (45 miles), and later recapitalized as Braden Cop-

per Mines Co. with U.S. $10 million. In 1915 Kennecott Copper Corp. of Montana bought 95% of the Braden stock for $57 million, but Braden Copper Mines Co. continued to operate the mines. In 1929 production increased to 176 million pounds of copper.

In 1967 Chile acquired 51% of the Braden shares for $80 million, and in 1970 took over the mines' operation. It said it would complete the nationalization of El Teniente.

Use of token money was restricted by Chile in 1908, requiring issuers to redeem their tokens on demand in cash. This legislation was largely ignored by the mines until the 1920's.

SANTIAGO PROVINCE

CANAL DE S. BERNARDO DE MAYPO

Rulau	Date	Metal	Size	VG	F	VF	Unc
Sgo 1	1821	Copper	27mm	150.	300.	500.	800.
		Fish (?) swimming in canal. Around: CANAL DE (conjoined DE) S. BERNARDO DE (conjoined) MAYPO / *. Rv: View of mountains with volcano, So at upper left and ¼ at upper right — all in central circle. Around: REPUBLICA DE CHILE / . 1821 . Ornamented edge. (Medina pg. CCLXVI; Eklund 1531; KM N21 or KM 1)					

Struck at Santiago Mint, this is a ¼-real token used to pay wages for canal workers. The Maipo River runs through the area. Listed in the Krause-Mishler coin catalog under "necessity coinage."

Santiago (City)
ASOCIACION DE JOYEROS RELOJEROS Y AFINES

Rulau	Date	Metal	Size	F	VF	EF	Unc
Sgo 3	1976	Brass	25mm	—	8.50	—	11.00
		Male bust left. Around: 1ER. DIRECTOR. DE. LA. CASA. DE. MONEDA / □ FRANCISCO. GARCIA. DE. HUIDOBRO □ / So mintmark, Rv: ASOCIACION DE JOYEROS RELOJEROS / Y FINES / FISA / 1870 1976 / So mintmark. Plain edge.					

Struck at the Santiago Mint. Francisco Garcia de Huidobro was the first director of the Santiago Mint.

Asociacion de Joyeros Relojeros y Afines = Association of Jewelers, Watchmakers and Related Trades.

CLUB DE SETIEMBRE

Rulau	Date	Metal	Size	F	VF	EF	Unc
Sgo 4	(1895-1910)	Brass	32mm	6.00	8.00	—	—
		CLUB DE SETIEMBRE / $ 1 $ / . SANTIAGO. Rv: Blank. (Zaika coll.)					
Sgo 5	ND	xx	33.5mm	6.50	9.00	—	—
		As next, but 5 / PESOS. Numbers examined: 3628.					

Rulau	Date	Metal	Size	F	VF	EF	Unc
Sgo 5A	ND	++	33mm	—	6.50	8.00	
		++ Pink vulcanite.					
		CLUB DE SETIEMBRE / (control number incused) / * SANTIAGO *. Rv: 2 / PESOS. Raised rims on each side. Numbers examined: 3410. (Zaika coll.)					

A hoard of this club's gaming tokens came on the market in 1985-86, and another in 1990. Vulcanite tokens of 50 C, $1 and $10 are reported, as well as brass pieces of $5, 50 C and 20 C; all seem common.

ENTRADA AL STA. LUCIA

Rulau	Date	Metal	Size	VG	F	VF	Unc
Sgo 6	ND	Brass	25mm	—	11.00	15.00	—

Castle-like structure on hill, ENTRADA AL above, Sta LUCIA in exergue. Rv: (Small circular wreath) / 20 / CENTAVOS / (rosette), all within laurel border. Plain edge. Rare. (Eklund 1549; Zaika coll.)

Santa Lucia was an amusement park in Santiago ?

METROPOL HOTEL

Rulau	Date	Metal	Size	VG	F	VF	Unc
Sgo 11	ND	CN	21mm	-.-	8.00	—	—

METROPOL HOTEL / -.- / SERVICIO ESMERADO / -.- / SANTIAGO. Rv: VALE / 20 CENTAVOS, / EN, / CONSUMO. Plain edge. (Rulau coll.)

A machine token? Servicio esmerado = Meticulous service.

PARROQUIA DE SAN LAZARO

Rulau	Date	Metal	Size	VG	F	VF	EF
Sgo 20	(1885)	xx	25mm	—	—	—	12.50

xx Black vulcanite.
CONFERENCIAS DE S. VICENTE DE PAUL. / .+. / BONO / .+. Rv: PARROQUIA DE SAN LAZARO / (mfr no) 124309 / . SANTIAGO . (Rulau coll.)

This also occurs in red vulcanite; same prices. Parroquia = Parish. Bono = Voucher.

VINCIT LABOR OMNIA IMPROBA

Rulau	Date	Metal	Size	VG	F	VF	Unc
Sgo 25	ND	xx	40.8mm	—	—	20.00	—

xx Undetermined nickel alloy.
Laureate king's bust right. Around: . VINCIT . LABOR . OMNIA . IMPROBA . Rv: Crowned, pillared Spanish arms. Around: HISPAN . ET . IND . REX . So . B . DE . PLA. Ornamented edge. (Smithsonian coll.; ex-Brand N.Y. sale, ex-Mrs. E. M. Norweb)

The regal portrait is of Carlos IV. BOT. D. PLA. = Button of silver. This imitation 8 reales was supposedly made by a tailor and used as money.

TALCA PROVINCE

Talca
CIA. MOVILIZADORA DE CARGA I PASAJERES

Rulau	Date	Metal	Size	VG	F	VF	Unc
Tca 4	(1900)	Copper	25mm	—	9.00	15.00	—

Five-pointed star separates in its angles: Cia / M / de / C / P. Around: CINCO CENTAVOS / .TALCA. Rv: Cia MOVILIZADORA DE CARGA I PASAJEROS / 5 / CENTAVOS / TALCA. Reeded edge. (Eklund 1564 var.; Smith 720YA)

This company, owned by Messers Forno and Scarfini, provided horsecar service for passengers and cargo.

TARAPACA PROVINCE

Argentina
PEDRO BARGMANN

(Peruvian dominion)

Rulau	Date	Metal	Size	VG	F	VF	Unc
Tpc 1	1869	Copper	25mm	—	—	35.00	—

MAQUINA ARGENTINA / PEDRO / BARGMANN / . 1869 . Rv: SENA POR / DOS PANES. Plain edge. (Fonrobert 10099; Eklund 1596; Leslie 60b). This piece is known ctsp 20.

Rulau	Date	Metal	Size	VG	F	VF	Unc
Tpc 2	1869	Copper	20.5mm	—	—	27.50	—

As last, but UN PAN. (Leslie 60a; Schiaffino 42)

Pan = Mass of nitrate. There is also a cuarto panes token, copper, 30.5mm, rare; it also occurs ctsp 40.

Rulau	Date	Metal	Size	VG	F	VF	Unc
Tpc 4	1869	Copper	25mm	—	—	35.00	—

MAQUINA ARGENTINA / PEDRO / BARGMANN / . 1869 . Rv: SENA POR / DOS REALES. (Fonrobert 10098; Eklund 1595)

R. N. CO. LTD.
(Rosario Nitrate Co. Ltd.)

Rulau	Date	Metal	Size	VG	F	VF	Unc
Tpc 7	ND	++	31mm	—	—	7.75	—

++ Vulcanite; red obverse, blue reverse.
OFICINA ARGENTINA. / $1 (large, shaded) / . R. N. Co. Ltd. Rv: Same as obverse. (Leslie 60j; Chanique 57; Schiaffino 48; Rulau coll.)

Pedro Bargmann was the proprietor of this mining enterprise 1869-71, then Juan Gildemeister, and later the Rosario Nitrate Co. Ltd. All issued tokens for payment of their workers.

Brac
OFICINA BRAC

Rulau	Date	Metal	Size	VG	F	VF	Unc
Tpc 10	ND	Vulcanite *	45.5mm	—	—	6.50	9.50

OFICINA / (circle) + BRAC + (the C carries an accent mark above it). Rv: $2 (large). (L. 99g; Schiaffino 70; Zaffern coll.; Rulau coll.)

* Obverse green, reverse brown.

SABIONCELLO Y SARGO
Oficina Brac

(Peruvian dominion)

Rulau	Date	Metal	Size	VG	F	VF	Unc
Tpc 13	ND	XX	46mm	—	6.00	10.00	—

XX Maroon vulcanite clad to black core.
SABIONCELLO Y SARGO / (empty circle) / . OF .
BRAC . Rv: $2. (Leslie 99f; Schiaffino 69)

Oficina Brac was located at 20° 44' by 69° 40'. Apparently the S. & S. tokens were issued under Peruvian dominion of the area. Vulcanite tokens in 10, 20 and 50 centavos and 1 and 2 pesos are reported.

Camina
THE CAMINA NITRATE CO. LD.

Rulau	Date	Metal	Size	F	VF	EF	Unc
Tpc 17	(1900)	vv	36mm	10.00	15.00	—	—

vv Tan-black-tan vulcanite.
THE CAMINA NITRATE / 222628 / (mfr no) / Co. Ld.
/ +++ / . OFICINA . / CAMINA. Rv: VALE EN MER-
CADERIAS / 1 ? shaded) / UN PESO / . EN PUL-
PERIA . (Leslie 126g; Chanique 121; Schiaffino 113)

Rulau	Date	Metal	Size	F	VF	EF	Unc
Tpc 18	ND	xx	31mm	—	7.50	—	—

xx Red vulcanite.
As last, but 50 / CINCUENTA / CENTAVOS. (Leslie 126e; Schiaf. 111)

Campamento Alianza
OFICINA ALIANZA

Rulau	Date	Metal	Size	VG	F	VF	Unc
Tpc 22	ND	Brass	35mm	4.00	8.00	12.50	30.00

OFICINA ALIANZA / 1 / PULPERIA. Rv: Same as
obverse. Two crescent cutouts, above and below
numeral 1. Plain edge. (Leslie 21g; Chanique 28;
Schiaffino 17)

This is part of an extensive series of metal tokens in brass or cupronickel, from 10 centavos to 2 pesos. Most are common.
Alianza was built in 1872 by Banco Nacional del Peru.

Chiquiquirai
OFICINA LA PATRIA

(Peruvian dominion)

Rulau	Date	Metal	Size	VG	F	VF	Unc
Tpc 25	ND	++	Sq 31mm	—	—	8.00	—

++ Red vulcanite.
OFICINA / LA PATRIA / +*+ within beaded circle.
Ornaments in the square corners. Rv: 20 (large, shaded)
in beaded circle. Ornaments in square corners. (Leslie
387b; Chanique 269; Schiaffino 234)

There are a number of other tokens of this nitrate mine. The mine was located in Chiquiquirai canton, 40 miles from the port of Pisagua. Its proprietors were, successively: Compania Nueva Tamarugal (called New Tamarugal Nitrate Co. Ltd.); Compania Salitrera Rimac, and La Sociedad Salitrera La Perla.

Cocina Canton
COMPANIA SALITRERA PERUANA

(Peruvian dominion)

Rulau	Date	Metal	Size	VG	F	VF	Unc
Tpc 30	1874	Brass	25mm	—	—	—	—

COMPANIA SALITRERA PERUANA / 1874. Rv:
VALE EN LA PULPERIA / 40 CTS. (Schiaffino 340)

Tpc 31	1874	Brass	22mm	—	10.00	25.00	—

As last, but 20 CTS. (Sch. 339)

Tpc 32	1874	Brass	19mm	—	10.00	25.00	—

As last, but 10 CTS. (Sch. 338)

Tpc 34	ND	**	20mm	—	—	—	—

** Black vulcanite.
OFICINA PERUANA / COMPA. COLORADO. Rv:
VALE EN LA PULPERIA / 10 C. EN MERCA-
DERIAS. (Sch. 341)

Located in Cocina canton.

Huantajaya
MINA DESCUBRIDORA

Rulau	Date	Metal	Size	VG	F	VF	Unc
Tpc 37	ND	xx	40mm	—	—	12.00	—

xx Red vulcanite.
MINA DESCUBRIDORA / *+* / UN PESO / 459659
(mfr no) / . HUANTA JAYA. Rv: $1 (large, shaded).

A copper mine? Interestingly, Huantajaya is also the name of a rich silver mining area in Arequipa Dept., Peru. This token, however, is clearly Chilean.

Iquique
CIGARRERIA
"CAPITAN PRAT"

Rulau	Date	Metal	Size	VG	F	VF	Unc
Tpc 40	(1891)	Cardboard *	41mm	—	—	—	25.00

* Black printing on grey cardboard round.
CIGARRERIA "CAPITAN PRAT" / 50 / Centavos / *
IQUIQUE *. Rv: Blank. (Christensen 78)

CIGARRERIA
"LA HABANERA"

Rulau	Date	Metal	Size	VG	F	VF	Unc
Tpc 42	(1891)	Cardboard *	41mm	—	—	—	25.00

* Black printing on bluish cardboard round.
CIGARRERIA "LA HABANERA" / 10 / Centavos / *
IQUIQUE *. Rv: Blank. Printed "reeding". (Christensen 90A)

Cuban cigar store.

CIGARRERIA "LA CENTRAL"

Rulau	Date	Metal	Size	VG	F	VF	AU
Tpc 44	(1891)	Cardboard *	41mm	—	—	—	25.00

CIGARRERIA "LA CENTRAL" / 40 / CENTAVOS /
* IQUIQUE *. Rv: Blank. (Christensen 75)

Cigar store.

DESPACHO
"EL BUEN GUSTO"

Rulau	Date	Metal	Size	VG	F	VF	AU
Tpc 46	(1891)	Cardboard *	41mm	—	—	—	25.00

* Black printing on grey cardboard round.
DESPACHO "EL BUEN GUSTO" / 20 / San Martin,
126. / VEINTE CENTS. / o IQUIQUE o. Rv: Blank.
(Christensen 70; Rulau coll.)

Grocery store.

PULINK

Rulau	Date	Metal	Size	VF	F	VF	Unc
Tpc 48	(1891)	Cardboard *	41mm	—	—	—	25.00

* Black printing on grey cardboard round.
PULINK / 25 / Centavos / * IQUIQUE *. Rv: Blank.
Printed "Reeding." (Christensen 95)

ANDRES TASSARA

Rulau	Date	Metal	Size	VF	F	VF	Unc
Tpc 50	(1891)	Cardboard *	41mm	—	—	—	25.00

* Black printing on grey cardboard round.
ANDRES TASSARA / 20 / Centavos / * IQUIQUE *.
Rv: Blank. (Christensen 98)

UNION BAR

Rulau	Date	Metal	Size	VG	F	VF	Unc
Tpc 52	(1891)	Cardboard *	41mm	4.00	15.00	—	25.00

* Black printing on grey cardboard round.
UNION BAR / 30 / CENTAVOS / - / * EN CONSU-
MACION *. Rv: Blank. Printed "reeding." (Christen-
sen 103)

B. VERDUGO

Rulau	Date	Metal	Size	VG	F	VF	Unc
Tpc 54	(1891)	Cardboard *	41mm	—	—	—	25.00

* Black printing on grey cardboard round.
B. VERDUGO / 50 / Centavos / * IQUIQUE *. Rv:
Blank. (Christensen 106)

ZUELERIA PLAZA PRAT

Rulau	Date	Metal	Size	VG	F	VF	Unc
Tpc 56	(1891)	Cardboard *	41mm	—	—	—	25.00

* Black printing on whitish cardboard round.
ZUELERIA PLAZA PRAT Y ZAPATERIA LA BOTA
VERDE / (diamond) / (diamond) 20 (diamond) / (dia-
mond) / - IQUIQUE -. Rv: Blank. (Christensen 91)

Tpc 57	(1891)	Cardboard *	41mm	—	—	—	25.00

As last, but 10 (centavos). (Christensen 92)

Bootmaker.

CAIDA DE LA DICTADURA

Rulau	Date	Metal	Size	F	VF	EF	Unc
Tpc 59	1891	Gilt/Cop	28.3mm	—	—	22.50	

Crested, supported Chilean arms. Around: CAIDA DE
LA DICTADURA / * 29 AGOSTO 1891 *. Rv:
HONOR / A LA MARINA / I AL / EJERCITO / CON-
STITUCIONAL / CHILE. Plain edge. (Tanenbaum
coll.)

Caida de la dictadura = Downfall of the dictatorship. Honor a la marina i al
ejercito constitucional Chile = Honor to the constitutional navy and army (of)
Chile.

This medalet celebrates the surrender of the presidential troops to the congressional forces in the bitter 1891 civil war.

PRIMERAS VICTIMAS DE LA REVOLUCION

Rulau	Date	Metal	Size	F	VF	EF	Unc
Tpc 60	1891	Bronze	33.3mm	—	—	15.00	—

PRIMERAS VICTIMAS DE LA REVOLUCION / FELIPE PEREYRA / DE LUCENA / - / MANUEL ARTIGAS / * DE LA INDEPENDECIA *. Rv: CUMPLIMIENTO DEL DECRETO / 25 / DE MAYO / DE / 1891 / . DEL 31 DE JULIO DE 1811. Plain edge (Tanenbaum coll.)

La Peña
DUPONT NITRATE COMPANY
Oficina Peña Grande

Rulau	Date	Metal	Size	VG	F	VF	Unc
Tpc 65	ND	CN	29mm	6.50	10.50	13.00	—

20 / CENTAVOS within circular central field surrounded by recessed, denticles circle. Around: DUPONT NITRATE COMPANY / * OFICINA PEÑA GRANDE *. Rv: PAGADERO / SIN / DE SCUENTO. within recessed, denticled circle. Around: VALE PARA LA PULPERIA / ** 20 CTS. **. Plain edge. (Leslie 507d; Schiaffino 335)

OFICINA LA PALMA

Rulau	Date	Metal	Size	VG	F	VF	Unc
Tpc 68	ND	++	31mm	6.00	8.00	—	—

++ Green-black-green vulcanite.
(Ornaments / OFICINA / LA PALMA / (ornaments). Rv: Large 50 (shaded) / 179844 (?, mfr no). (Leslie 384f; Chanique 264; Schiaffino 225)

Two specimens in the Rulau collection have been cancelled by clipping out a semicircular "bite."
This piece also occurs in red vulcanite; same valuations.

Rulau	Date	Metal	Size	VG	F	VF	Unc
Tpc 69	ND	VV	31mm	6.00	8.00	—	—

VV Black-green vulcanite.
As last, but 10 (shaded), no mfr no. (Leslie 384c; Schiaf. 221; Chanique 259)

Oficina La Palma belonged to The New Tamarugal Nitrate Co. Ltd.

THE LONDON NITRATE CO. LTD.
Oficina Santa Laura

(Peruvian dominion)

Rulau	Date	Metal	Size	VG	F	VF	Unc
Tpc 71	ND	CN	35mm	—	—	15.00	—

THE LONDON NITRATE CO. LTD. / OFICINA / SANTA / LAURA. Rv: Large 2. Plain edge. Thick flan. (Leslie 705e; Eklund 2279; Chanique 494A; Schiaffino 509; Rulau coll.)

In La Peña canton, 41 miles from Iquique.

Negreiros
C. O. Y CA.
Establecimiento Agua Santa

Rulau	Date	Metal	Size	VG	F	VF	Unc
Tpc 74	ND	Brass	33mm	—	14.00	—	—

ESTABLECIMIENTO / C O y CA / + AGUA SANTA +. Rv: VALE UN PESO EN MERCADERIAS / UN PESO / $1 (shaded) / *. Plain edge. (Leslie 15e; Schiaffino 11)

Rulau	Date	Metal	Size	VG	F	VF	Unc
Tpc 75	ND	CN	28.5mm	—	9.00	—	—

As last, but VALE CINCUENTA CENTAVOS (etc.) and 50 / CENTAVOS. (Leslie 15d; Schiaf. 10)

Rulau	Date	Metal	Size	VG	F	VF	Unc
Tpc 76	ND	Copper	21mm	—	10.00	—	—

As last, but + 10 + / CENTAVOS. (Eklund 1457; Leslie 15c; Chanique 10; Schiaf. 9)

C. O. y Ca. = Campbell Outram & Co. A series of vulcanite tokens was issued later for this enterprise. Agua Santa = Holy water.

JUNOY & CA.

Rulau	Date	Metal	Size	VG	F	VF	Unc
Tpc 80	ND	xx	30.5mm	—	5.50	10.00	—

xx Green-black-green vulcanite.
JUNOY & Ca. / (ornament) / OFICINA / SAN JORGE / (ornament). Rv: $1 (large). (Leslie 639b & c; Chanique 449; Schiaffino 444)

Oficina San Jorge, 68 miles from Iquique, originally belonged to The San Jorge Nitrate Co. Ltd. Later its owners were: Moldes Canjo y Cia., Junoy y Ca. and, finally J. Zayas y Ca.

OFICINA DEL PROGRESO

Rulau	Date	Metal	Size	F	VF	EF	Unc
Tpc 82	(1892)	xx	40.5mm	—	6.00	8.00	11.00

xx Red vulcanite. OFICINA / 178426 (mfr. no.) / . DEL PROGRESO. Rv: VALE EN PULPERIA / (arc) / $1 (large, shaded). (Leslie 543f; Chanique 389; Schiaffino 360)

There are also red vulcanite 50-centavos, 35mm, $11 in EF, in this series, and both earlier and later vulcanite tokens of this mining enterprise.

Pampa Negra
OFICINA AGUADA

Rulau	Date	Metal	Size	F	VF	EF	Unc
Tpc 83	ND	vv	40mm	6.50	10.00	—	—

vv Red vulcanite.
OFICINA / (empty beaded circle) / . AGUADA . Rv:
VALE UN PESO EN MERCADERIAS / $1 / *+*.
(Leslie 12c; Schiaffino 5)

Issued for Pedro Perfetti's Cia. Salitrera Aguada.

Pisagua
EVARISTO BRANES

(Peruvian dominion)

Rulau	Date	Metal	Size	VG	F	VF	Unc
Tpc 86	(1874-76)	Brass	31mm	—	—	—	—

EVARISTO BRANES / PISAGUA / * SAN FRAN-
CISCO *. Rv: VALE EN LA PULPERIA / 1 / . PESO .
Plain edge. (Ulex 3403; Eklund 1541; Leslie 630c;
Schiaffino 431)

Tpc 87	(1874-76)	Brass	28mm	—	—	—	—

As last, but 4 / . REALES . (Eklund 1540; L. 630b;
Schiaffino 430)

Tpc 88	(1874-76)	Brass	23mm	—	—	—	—

As last, but 2 / . REALES . (L. 630a; Schiaf. 429)

OTTO HARNECKER
Oficina Bearnes

(Peruvian dominion)

Rulau	Date	Metal	Size	VG	F	VF	Unc
Tpc 90	(1878)	Brass	31.5mm	—	—	—	—

* OTTO HARNECKER * / PISAGUA / BEARNES.
Rv: * VALE EN LA PULPERIA * / 10 / CTS. Plain
edge. (Ulex 3403; Eklund 1542; Leslie 87a; Schiaffino
61)

There are also brass 31mm 20 CTS. and brass 31mm 1 SOL tokens in this
issue, all issued about 1878.

OTTO HARNECKER
Sta. Catalina & Bearnes

(Peruvian dominion)

Rulau	Date	Metal	Size	VG	F	VF	Unc
Tpc 92	ND	Brass	32mm	—	—	—	—

OTTO HARNECKER / Sta CATALINA / Y /
BEARNES / * PISAGUA *. Rv: VALE EN LA PUL-
PERIA / 1 / PESO. Plain edge. (Schiaffino 498; Leslie
690a)

San Antonio
THE COLORADO NITRATE
CO. LTD.

Rulau	Date	Metal	Size	F	VF	EF	Unc
Tpc 95	(1906)	++	40.5mm	—	—	8.50	15.00

++ Black vulcanite.
THE COLORADO NITRATE COMPANY Ltd /
289036 (mfr no.) / C B / .+. Rv: 1 (large, shaded). (Leslie 150b; Chanique 155)

Tpc 96	ND	xx	25.5mm	5.00	6.50	8.50	—

xx Tan-black-tan vulcanite.
THE COLORADO NITRATE Co, Ltd / C. B. / +. Rv:
20 C / +.

Tpc 97	ND	&&	Hexag 26mm	—	—	10.00	—

&& Red vulcanite.
Similar to last (20 C). (Leslie 150a; Schiaffino 121)

Tpc 98	ND	vv	21mm	2.00	3.00	6.00	8.00

vv = Deep blue vulcanite.
As last, but 10 C. (Schiaffino 120; Zaffern coll.)

C. B. = Oficina Carmen Bajo (20 degrees 16 minutes S. by 69 degrees 48
minutes W.). Chanique reports a 10-centavos in black vulcanite in hexagonal
format.

OFICINA CALA-CALA

This nitrate mine at San Antonio in Tarapaca Province was one of Chile's
most important. It saw extensive token use over a half century or more, from
several different owners.

Its proprietors which can be traced, in chronological order, include:
Gibbs & Co., issued tokens
Juan Vernal Castro
Eufemia C. de Hidalgo
Lorenzo Perez Roca, issued 1901 and 1905 tokens
Zoila H. de Roca, his widow
Pablo S. Mimbela, issued 1916 tokens

GIBBS & CO.

Rulau	Date	Metal	Size	VG	F	VF	Unc
Tpc 100	ND	xx	36mm	—	8.00	10.00	—

xx Red-black-red vulcanite.
OFICINA / GIBBS & Co. / CALACALA. Rv: $1. (Les-
lie 117b; Schiaffino 89)

Tpc 101	ND	++	26.5mm	—	—	5.00	8.00

++ Green vulcanite on black core.
As last, but 20 C. (Leslie 117a; Chanique 104; Schiaffino 88)

LORENZO PEREZ ROCA

Rulau	Date	Metal	Size	VG	F	VF	Unc
Tpc 104	1901	Aluminum	35mm	—	—	Scarce	—

LORENZO PEREZ ROCA / OFICINA / CALA-CALA
/ 1901 / (tiny) PARIS. Rv: No. descr. available. (Schiaffino 94). Perhaps only a pattern.

Tpc 105	1901	Aluminum Hexag 35mm		—	—	—	—

As last, but $1 on reverse and no PARIS. (Schiaf. 93;
Chanique 108). Chanique reports this is octagonal and
cupronickel.

Rulau	Date	Metal	Size	VG	F	VF	Unc
Tpc 106	1901	Aluminum	Sq 35mm	—	—	15.00	—

As last, but 50 C. (Leslie 117c; Schiaf. 92; Chanique 106). Chanique says this is CN.

Rulau	Date	Metal	Size	VG	F	VF	Unc
Tpc 107	1901	Aluminum	Scal Oval 45x30mm	—	—	15.00	—

As last, but 20 C. (L. 117d; Schiaf. 91; Chan. 105). Chanique says this is CN.

Rulau	Date	Metal	Size	VG	F	VF	Unc
Tpc 108	1901	Aluminum Hexag	30mm	—	—	—	—

As last, but 10 C. (L. 117c; Schiaf. 90; Chan. 102). Chanique says this is CN.

All the well-made 1901 Perez Roca tokens were struck in Paris.

OFICINA CALA-CALA

Rulau	Date	Metal	Size	VG	F	VF	Unc
Tpc 111	(1905)	Aluminum	33m	—	—	Scarce	—

OFICINA CALA-CALA. Rv: 50 C. (Leslie 117g; Schiaffino 95)

P. S. MIMBELA

Rulau	Date	Metal	Size	VG	F	VF	Unc
Tpc 114	ND	Aluminum	36mm	—	9.00	16.00	—

OFICINA / (large signature) P S Mimbela / CALA-CALA. Rv: 100 (shaded). Plain edge. (Leslie 117h; Schiaffino 96; Chanique 111)

Rulau	Date	Metal	Size	VG	F	VF	Unc
Tpc 115	ND	Aluminum	36.5mm	—	8.50	15.00	—

OFICINA / (small signature) P S Mimbela / (tiny) SCHENONE / CALA-CALA. Rv: 100 (shaded). (Leslie 117i)

P. MIMBELA

Rulau	Date	Metal	Size	VG	F	VF	Unc
Tpc 117	1916	CN	32mm	4.00	5.50	10.00	18.00

Young girl's bust left. Small F. RASVMNY incused at lower right. Rv: OFICINA CALA-CALA P. MIMBELA / 1 $ / (tiny triangle, on which is: A. D. & CIA. / . 1916 . / (tiny) SILVAIN GUILLOT PARIS. Plain edge. (Leslie 117n; Schiaffino 100; Rulau coll.)

Rulau	Date	Metal	Size	VG	F	VF	Unc
Tpc 118	1916	CN	27.4mm	4.00	5.00	7.00	11.00

As last, but 50 / CENTAVOS. Plain edge. (Eklund 1479; L. 117-l; Schiaf. 99; Rulau coll.)

Rulau	Date	Metal	Size	VG	F	VF	Unc
Tpc 119	1916	Silver	27.4mm	—	—	Proof	150.

As last (50 centavos). Struck in 2mm thickness as specimen. (Leslie 117m)

Rulau	Date	Metal	Size	VG	F	VF	Unc
Tpc 120	1916	CN	23.5mm	1.50	3.00	5.00	8.00

As last, but 20 / CENTAVOS. (L. 117k; Schiaf. 98)

Rulau	Date	Metal	Size	VG	F	VF	Unc
TPC 121	1916	CN	21.5mm	2.50	4.00	6.00	9.00

As last, but 10 / CENTAVOS. (L. 117j; Schiaf. 97)

This series of tokens was struck by Silvain Guillot of Paris, France. The obverse was designed by F. Rasumny. Some work was done by A. D. & Co., presumably of Paris.

This entire series saw extensive use as coinage both within the company's operations and in neighboring communities. Specimens may be found almost smooth from daily wear.

San Francisco
DOLORES

(Peruvian dominion)

Rulau	Date	Metal	Size	VG	F	VF	Unc
Tpc 124	(1853)	Brass	36mm	—	25.00	55.00	—

(All incused): DOLORES / 1 PESO / (ornament). Rv: Blank. Plain edge. (Eklund 1759; Leslie 224c; Schiaffino 166; Pesant 68)

Rulau	Date	Metal	Size	VG	F	VF	Unc
Tpc 125	(1853)	Brass	33mm	—	—	—	—

As last, but 4 R. (Eklund 1758; Leslie 224b; Schiaffino 165; Pesant 69)

Rulau	Date	Metal	Size	VG	F	VF	Unc
Tpc 126	(1853)	Brass	31mm	—	—	—	—

As last, but 2 R. (Eklund 1757; Leslie 224a; Schiaffino 164; Pesant 70)

Earlier writers attributed these in error to Las Villas or Matanzas provinces, Cuba.

EDUARDO DELANO
Oficina Sacramento

(Peruvian dominion)

Rulau	Date	Metal	Size	VG	F	VF	Unc
Tpc 129	(1872)	Brass	37.5mm	—	—	—	—

OFICINA SACRAMENTO / 100 / o. Rv: EDUARDO DELANO / CIENTO / o. Plain edge. (Leslie 594a; Schiaffino 404)

Delano succeeded Montero Leon as owner (see next entries).

L. MONTERO LEON
Oficina Sacramento
de Zapiga

(Peruvian dominion)

Rulau	Date	Metal	Size	VG	F	VF	Unc
Tpc 131	ND	Copper	37mm	—	—	—	—

OFICINA SACRAMENTO / (ornament) / CIENTO / (ornament) / -*-. Rv: L. MONTERO LEON / (ornament) / 100 / (ornament) / .-*-. Plain edge. (Leslie 594d; Schiaffino 403)

Rulau	Date	Metal	Size	VG	F	VF	Unc
Tpc 132	ND	Copper	24mm	—	—	—	—

As last, but VEINTE and 20. (L. 594c; Schiaf. 402)

Rulau	Date	Metal	Size	VG	F	VF	Unc
Tpc 133	ND	Copper	19mm	—	—	—	—

As last, but DIEZ and 10. (L. 594b; Schiaf. 401)

G. S. Y CA.
(Glavich, Stipovich & Co.)
Oficina Union

Rulau	Date	Metal	Size	VG	F	VF	Unc
Tpc 136	ND	++	26mm	—	—	—	—

++ Black vulcanite.
OFICINA UNION / G. S. y CA. / SAN FRANCISCO. Rv: VALE VEINTE CTS. / 20 C / EN MERCADERIAS. (Leslie 777; Schiaffino 548)

Oficina Union was at 19 degrees 42 minutes by 69 degrees 57 minutes. Cia. Nacional de Salitres La Union succeeded Glavich Stipovich as owners.

CA. N. S. U.
Oficina Union

Rulau	Date	Metal	Size	VG	F	VF	Unc
Tpc 140	ND	vv	30mm	—	—	—	—

vv Red vulcanite.
OFICINA UNION / * / Ca. N. S. U. / (crossed tools) / . SAN FRANCISCO . Rv: VALE CINCUENTA Cts / .*. / 50 C / .*. / . EN MERCADERIAS . (Leslie 777c; Schiaffino 550)

Rulau	Date	Metal	Size	VG	F	VF	Unc
Tpc 141	ND	++	20.5mm	—	—	—	—

++ Black vulcanite.
As last, but evaporation tanks replace the crossed tools, and DIEZ and 10 C replace CINCUENTA and 50 C. (L. 777b; Schiaf. 549)

Ca. N. S. U. = Compania Nacional de Salitres la Union.

Santa Catalina
OFICINA ANGELA

Rulau	Date	Metal	Size	VG	F	VF	Unc
Tpc 144	ND	Brass	--mm	—	—	—	—

OFICINA ANGELA. Rv: $1. (Chanique 43; Schiaffino 33)

| Tpc 145 | ND | Brass | 25mm | — | — | — | — |

As last, but 20. (Chan. 42; Schiaf. 32)

| Tpc 147 | (1882) | xx | 25mm | — | — | — | — |

xx Red vulcanite.
OFICINA / L y P / 99109 (mfr no) / ANGELA. Rv: VALE / 10 C / EN MERCADERIAS. (Leslie 39a; Schiaffino 31)

L y P = Loayza And Pascal.

Soledad
CIA. DE SAL. Y F.C.
DE JUNIN
Oficina San Antonio

Rulau	Date	Metal	Size	VG	F	VF	Unc
Tpc 150	ND	Aluminum	40mm	—	15.00	22.50	32.50

OFICINA SAN ANTONIO CIA DE SAL Y F C DE JUNIN * / PULPERIA. Rv: $2 (large). Plain edge. (Leslie 606c; Schiaffino 416)

| Tpc 151 | ND | Aluminum | 35mm | — | — | 15.00 | 23.00 |

As last, but $1. Plain edge. (Leslie 606b; Schiaf. 415)

Red vulcanite 20-centavo tokens, 30mm, are known.

SOCIEDAD SALITRERA
DE LA PROVIDENCIA

(Peruvian dominion)

Rulau	Date	Metal	Size	VG	F	VF	Unc
Tpc 153	(1874)	xx	Rect 50x31mm	—	—	60.00	—

xx Black vulcanite.
SOCIEDAD SALITRERA / * / DE LA / PROVIDEN-CIA / (ornament). Rv: UN PESO. (Leslie 396c; Schiaffino 242)

This is also issued in Olive vulcanite.

Rulau	Date	Metal	Size	VG	F	VF	Unc
Tpc 155	(1874)	@@	35mm	—	35.00	—	—

@@ Vermilion vulcanite.
SOCIEDAD / * / SALITRERA / DE LA / -.- / PROVI-DENCIA. Rv: CUATRO / REALES. (L. 396b; Schiaffino 241)

| Tpc 156 | (1874) | xx | --mm | — | 35.00 | — | — |

xx Black vulcanite.
As last, but DOS / REALES. (L. 396a; Schiaf. 240)

There is also a Dos Pesos vulcanite token, Leslie 396e, which is rare. Providencia originally was owned by Gil Galte y Ca. and then by Compania Salitrera Providencia.

J. C.
Oficina Nueva Soledad

(Peruvian dominion)

Rulau	Date	Metal	Size	VG	F	VF	Unc
Tpc 159	(1872)	@@	31.5mm	—	—	—	—

@@ Vermilion vulcanite.
OFICINA / J. C. / NUEVA SOLEDAD. Rv: VALE EN LA PULPERIA / 1 / PESO. (Leslie 474a; Schiaffino 294)

J. C. = Juan Cauvi.

Sur Canton
BUENA VENTURA

(Peruvian dominion)

Rulau	Date	Metal	Size	VG	F	VF	Unc
Tpc 162	ND	CN	Rect 32x40.5mm	—	—	22.50	—

BUENA VENTURA / 1 (large) / PULPERIA. Rv: Same as obverse. Plain edge. (Leslie 108d; Schiaffino 77)

The Rulau specimen is "tracked" on each side with incused squiggles, possibly cancellation marks. Scarce. Non-tracked pieces bring $35 in VF.
This enterprise was later known as Buenaventura Syndicate Ltd. The mines are 42 miles fom Iquique.

LAGUNAS
(The Lagunas Nitrate Co.)

Rulau	Date	Metal	Size	VG	F	VF	Unc
Tpc 165	ND	CN	40mm	9.00	13.00	20.00	—

LAGUNAS / 1 / * PULPERIA *. Rv: Same as obverse. Plain edge. (Leslie 363h; Chanique 251; Schiaffino 253)

This token is part of a lengthy series of metallic tokens.

Tambillos
MINAS DEL DOCTOR
AGTN. VERGARA

(Peruvian dominion)

Rulau	Date	Metal	Size	VG	F	VF	Unc
Tpc 170	1877	Brass	28mm	—	12.00	—	—

MINAS DEL DOCTOR AGTn VERGARA / 24 DE SETIEMBRE / (Crossed hammer & pick) / 2 NOVIEMBRE * / * 1877 *. Rv: MINA PABELLON DEL ROSARIO / VEINTE / * 20 * / CENTAVOS / * TAMBILLOS *.

Elwin Leslie located this mine at 21 degrees 21 minutes South, 60 degrees 30 minutes West.

Zapiga
MARCOS CICARELLI
Oficinas Porvenir y Union

Rulau	Date	Metal	Size	F	VF	EF	Unc
Tpc 173	ND	Brass	35.5mm	—	9.00	—	—

MARCOS CICARELLI / OFICINAS / PORVENIR Y UNION / -.-. Rv: CANJE POR MERCADERIAS / $2. (Leslie 537b)

Tpc 174	ND	Brass	30mm	—	9.00	—	—

As last, but $1. (L. 537a; Schiaffino 342; Henry Christensen Oct. 1975 sale, lot 158)

JAZPAMPA BAJO NITRATE
CO. LD.

Rulau	Date	Metal	Size	F	VF	EF	Unc
Tpc 176	ND	xx	31mm	—	9.50	12.50	—

xx Tan-black-tan vulcanite.
$1 (shaded) / 239438 (mfr no) / JAZPAMPA BAJO NITRATE Co. Ld. Rv: ENTREGUESE / MERCADERIAS (on panel) / 236438 (mfr no) / AL PORTADOR. (Leslie 330c; Chanique 227; Schiaffino 193)

Control number is stamped on obverse. Numbers examined: 241 to 9016. This issue is more scarce than prices indicate.

PACCHA

(Peruvian dominion)

Rulau	Date	Metal	Size	VG	F	VF	Unc
Tpc 179	(1853)	Brass		—	—	50.00	—

(All incused): PACCHA / 2 R / (ornament). Rv: Blank. (Leslie 480b; Schiaffino 296)

Tpc 180	(1853)	Brass	28mm	—	—	35.00	—

As last, but 1 R. (Leslie 480a; Schiaffino 295)

NORTH & COMBER
Oficina Paccha

Rulau	Date	Metal	Size	VG	F	VF	Unc
Tpc 182	ND	xx	25mm	—	—	—	—

xx Black Vulcanite.
NORTH & COMBER / + / 20 C / + / . OFICINA PACCHA . Rv: VALE EN LA PULPERIA / + / 20 C / + / . POR MERCADERIAS . (Leslie 480d; Schiaffino 297)

Tpc 183	ND	Vulcanite	--mm	—	—	—	—

As last, but 10 C. (Leslie 480c)

Uncertain
H. C.
Oficina San Lorenzo

(Peruvian dominion)

Rulau	Date	Metal	Size	VG	F	VF	Unc
Tpc 200	1872	Copper	30mm	—	—	—	—

OFICINA SAN LORENZO / H. C. / 1872. Rv: VALE / 100 / PULPERIA. (Schiaffino 461)

Tpc 201	1872	Copper	23mm	—	—	—	—

As last, but 50. (Sch. 460; Leslie 657b)

Tpc 202	1872	Copper	18mm	—	—	—	—

As last, but 10. (Sch. 459; Leslie 657a)

H. C. = Hugeat Caplong. Specimens are known counterstamped ZZ3.

COMPANIA SALITRERA
RIMAC
Oficina Rimac

(Peruvian dominion)

Rulau	Date	Metal	Size	VG	F	VF	Unc
Tpc 205	(1876)	Copper	23mm	—	8.00	14.00	—

COMPANIA SALITRERA / RIMAC. Rv: OFICINA RIMAC / VALE / 40. (Kirtley March 1989 sale, lot 886; Ulex 3412; Schiaffino 389; Eklund 1365)

Salitrera = Nitrate mine. Also issued were copper 20 cent. 23mm (Sch. N/L) and 10 cent., 18mm (Sch. 388), and 100 cent., 30mm (Sch. 391).

GRANJA, DOMINGUEZ
Y LACALLE
Oficina Cruz de Zapiga

(Chilean military rule)

Rulau	Date	Metal	Size	VG	F	VF	Unc
Tpc 208	1881	++	--mm	—	—	—	—

++ Maroon vulcanite.
OFICINA CRUZ DE ZAPIGA / 1881 / GRANJA, DOMINGUEZ Y LACALLE. Rv: VALE VEINTE GRAMOS DE SALITRE. (Leslie 207a; Schiaffino 151)

Rulau	Date	Metal	Size	VG	F	VF	Unc
Tpc 209	1881	xx	30mm	—	—	—	—

xx Tan vulcanite over black core.
OFINCINA / VALE / VEINTE / GRAMOS / DE / SALITRE / CRUZ DE ZAPIGA. Rv: GRANJA / DOMINGUEZ / Y LACALLE / 1881. (Leslie 207b)

Vale veinte gramos de salitre = Worth 20 grams of nitrate (saltpeter).

OFICINA PAN DE AZUCAR

Rulau	Date	Metal	Size	VG	F	VF	Unc
Tpc 212	ND	Brass	35mm	—	11.00	17.50	22.50

OFICINA PAN DE AZUCAR / PULPERIA (in circle) / . *. Rv: $1 (1 is large, shaded). Plain edge. (Chanique 337; Rulau coll.; Leslie 495d)

There is also a tan-black-tan vulcanite $1 token of this issuer, and other denominations in metal. The vulcanite peso fetches $12 in VF.

MO. 1 TIENDA

(Peruvian dominion)

Rulau	Date	Metal	Size	VG	F	VF	Unc
Tpc 215	(1854)	Copper	33mm	—	—	—	—

(All incused): Mo. 1 / 50 C. Rv: TIENDA (in scroll-like indent) / 8 8 / 8. (Leslie 54a)

OFICINA DIEZ DE SEPTIEMBRE

(Peruvian dominion)

Rulau	Date	Metal	Size	VG	F	VF	Unc
Tpc 217	ND	+ +	45.5mm	—	—	16.00	—

+ + Vulcanite; blue obverse, brown reverse, black core.
OFICINA DIEZ DE SEPTIEMBRE / (empty circle) / +. Rv: VALE EN MERCADERIAS / $2 (large, shaded) / +. (Leslie 221d; Schiaffino 162)

SOCIEDAD BENEFICIADORA DE TOCOPILLA

Rulau	Date	Metal	Size	F	VF	EF	Unc
Tpc 220	ND	Vulcanite *	30.5mm	—	—	—	—

* Tan both sides, clad to black center.
SOCIEDAD / .o. / BENEFICIADORA (on panel) / DE / o TOCOPILLA o. Rv: Large 20 C (shaded). (Zaffern coll.)

UGARTE CEVALLOS Y CA.
Oficina San Lorenzo

(Peruvian dominion)

Rulau	Date	Metal	Size	VG	F	VF	Unc
Tpc 225	1875	Copper	23mm	—	—	—	—

OFICINA SAN LORENZO / UGARTE CEVALLOS Y CA. / 1875. Rv: VALE / 20 CS. / EN / PULPERIA. (Schiaffino 463; Leslie 657d)

Rulau	Date	Metal	Size	VG	F	VF	Unc
Tpc 226	1875	Copper	18mm	—	—	25.00	—

As last, but 10 CS. (Sch. 462; Eklund 1384; L. 657c)

Rulau	Date	Metal	Size	VG	F	VF	Unc
Tpc 227	1875	Copper	30mm	—	—	—	—

As last, but 50 CS. (L. & Sch. not listed)

VALPARAISO PROVINCE

Valparaiso
FABRICA DE FICHAS DE GOMA

Rulau	Date	Metal	Size	VG	F	VF	Unc
Vpo 2	1881	+ +	40mm	—	—	150.	—

+ + Red vulcanite.
FABRICA DE FICHAS DE GOMA / ornate monogram GH / + VULCANITE TICKETS +. Rv: IMPRENTA DEL UNIVERSO (in ornate lettering) / .*. / VALE / $1 / EN FICHAS / 1881 / .*. / + VALPARAISO +. V. Rare. (Eklund 1577)

Fabrica de Fichas de Goma = Manufactory of tokens of rubber. Vale $1 en fichas = Value one peso in tokens.
This rare token, known only from the Eklund catalog, was not listed by Leslie or other catalogers. The factory may have been responsible for the production of many of the early Chilean Vulcanite tokens.

AUGUST MOLLER

Rulau	Date	Metal	Size	VG	F	VF	Unc
Vpo 4	ND	+ +	27mm	—	22.50	—	—

+ + Black vulcanite.
AUGUST MOLLER / 20 CTs. / * VALPARAISO *. Rv: Blank.

PARROQUIA DE SAN LUIS

Rulau	Date	Metal	Size	VG	F	VF	EF
Vpo 8	(1880's)	Copper	21mm	—	—	—	20.00

CONFERENCIA DE SAN VICENTE DE PAUL / DE SENORAS / *. Rv: PARROQUIA DE SAN LUIS VALPARAISO / 20 (in beaded circle) / *. Plain edge. (Henkle report)

Parroquia = Parish.

UNATTRIBUTED CHILE

Sagasca
BASSORI DEVESCOVI Y CA.

Rulau	Date	Metal	Size	VG	F	VF	Unc
Chi 2	ND	xx	35mm	—	—	27.50	—

xx Black vulcanite.
BASSORI, DEVESCOVI Y Ca / (empty circle) / .
SAGASCA . Rv: VALE POR MERCADERIAS EN
PULPERIA / $1 (large, shaded) / *.

Rulau	Date	Metal	Size	VG	F	VF	Unc
Chi 3	ND	xx	Oct 36mm	—	—	27.50	—

As last, but octagonal flan. (Chanique 421A)

Vulcanite 20 and 10-centavo tokens are known in this series. Worth $10 each in VF.

CAMARA CHILENA DE LA CONSTRUCCION

Rulau	Date	Metal	Size	VG	F	VF	Unc
Chi 5	ND	Bronze	29mm	—	—	4.00	5.00

Two plumb bobs hang in front of a brick wall. Around:
CAMARA CHILENA / . DE LA CONSTRUCCION .
Rv: CAJA / DE / COMPENSACION / (stamped
numerals) / So. Plain edge. Issued holed. Numbers examined: 17394. (Zaika coll.)

Struck at Santiago Mint for the pay office of the Chilean construction ministry?

CIA. MANUFACTURERA DE PAPELES

Rulau	Date	Metal	Size	F	VF	EF	Unc
Chi 7	ND	Vulcanite *	21.4mm	—	—	7.00	—

* Red, black and green. CIA. MANUFACTURERA DE
PAPELES / PULPERIA between semicircles / . Rv: 10
C#1 / +. (Zaffern coll.)

Rulau	Date	Metal	Size	F	VF	EF	Unc
Chi 8	ND	++	26.5mm	—	—	8.00	—

++ Black vulcanite.
As last, but 20C (Rulau coll.; Zaika coll).

Cia. Manufacturera de Papeles = Papers Mfg. Co.

COMPANIA "CANDELARIA" SALITRERA

Rulau	Date	Metal	Size	VG	F	VF	Unc
Chi 10	(1904)	*	40mm	—	—	8.00	11.50

COMPANIA / (small) 210886 / "CANDELARIA" /
SALITRERA. Rv: $1 (large). (L. 129c; Zaffern coll.)

* Light brown-black-light brown vulcanite.

CONCHA Y TORO

Rulau	Date	Metal	Size	VG	F	VF	EF
Chi 12	ND	Brass	16mm	—	6.50	10.00	—

CONCHA Y TORO / 60 / *. Rv: 6. Plain edge. Crude
work. (Zaika coll.)

Rulau	Date	Metal	Size	VG	F	VF	EF
Chi 13	ND	Brass	16mm	2.50	4.00	6.00	9.00

As last, but 40 and 4. (Tanenbaum coll.; Zaika coll.)

Rulau	Date	Metal	Size	VG	F	VF	EF
Chi 14	ND	Brass	16mm	—	4.00	6.00	—

As last, but 30 and 3.

Rulau	Date	Metal	Size	VG	F	VF	EF
Chi 15	ND	Brass	16mm	—	4.00	6.00	—

As last, but 10 and 1.

These are early wine producing tokens. This issuer later used machine-made tokens bearing the mintmark of the Santiago Mint (So), in denominations of 1, 20, 30, 40, 60 and 80.

D. C. G. S.
Salitre Muelle Sur

Rulau	Date	Metal	Size	VG	F	VF	Unc
Chi 17	ND	Leather	27mm	—	—	55.00	—

Flag flying right, letters D C G S in cross upon it.
Around: SALITRE / 38 / MUELLE SUR. Rv: Blank.
(Schimmel June 1989 sale, lot 377; Rulau coll.)

Schimmel believed that Salitre Muelle Sur (Saltpeter South Dock, or Mole) refers to loading of nitrate on board a ship. Not listed by Leslie or Chanique. A small hoard of 22 pieces was dispersed in 1990.

E. E.

Rulau	Date	Metal	Size	VG	F	VF	Unc
Chi 19	ND	xx	24mm	2.00	—	5.00	—
		xx Red vulcanite.					
		E oo E. Rv: 10 C. (Harrison coll.)					

Found 1990 in a Chilean hoard. By its style it is probably Chile.

F.F.C.C. EN CONSTRUCCION

Rulau	Date	Metal	Size	VG	F	VF	Unc
Chi 21	ND	Brass	23mm	—	—	6.00	—
		F.F.C.C. EN CONSTRUCCION / MR monogram / CHILE. Rv: VALE AL PORTADOR / 20 C. Plain edge. (Zaika coll.)					

Quivolgo
H. SANTA MARIA

Rulau	Date	Metal	Size	VG	F	VF	Unc
Chi 23	ND	Copper	26mm	8.00	—	20.00	—
		QUIVOLGO across center, branches above and below. Rv: H. SANTA MARIA / 20 / * CENTAVOS *. Plain edge. Scarce. (Ulex 3759; Eklund 1543)					
Chi 24	ND	Copper	23mm	—	—	37.50	—
		Similar to last, but 10 / * CENTAVOS *. Plain edge. Rare. (Rulau coll.)					

Probably issued 1850's to 1870's. The 20-centavos seems more available than the 10, yet it has been seen in only five sales lists in the last four years. Hacienda Santa Maria has not been located.

MINES ET USINES DU CHACAY

Rulau	Date	Metal	Size	VG	F	VF	Unc
Chi 26	ND	Copper	26mm	—	—	8.00	—
		Crossed hammers, MINES ET USINES DU CHACAY / * around. Rv: 1 PESO (Eklund 1495)					
Chi 27	ND	Copper	20.5mm	—	—	7.00	—
		As last, but 20 / CENTAVOS. (Zaika coll.)					

The language is French. Copper 10 and 5-centavo tokens (Eklund 1494 and 1493) also were issued.

PARROQUIA DE SANTA ANA

Rulau	Date	Metal	Size	VG	F	VF	EF
Chi 30	(1880's)	Zinc	23mm	—	—	—	50.00
		CONF. SANTA LUISA DE MARILLAC / BONO / (Star). Rv: PARROQUIA DE SANTA ANA / (Rosette) / . Plain edge. (Rulau coll.)					

Parroquia = Parish. Bono = Voucher.

TERMAS DE TOLHUACA

Rulau	Date	Metal	Size	VG	F	VF	Unc
Chi 32	ND	CN	Oct 23mm	—	10.00	—	—
		TERMAS DE TOLHUACA / 10 Cts. / (triangular mint mark). Rv: 10 / Cts. Plain edge. (Zaika coll.; Bernal 117)					

Triangular mint mark is inscribed: "./fc". There is also a 5 Cts. token in CN, Oct 20mm. Also claimed for Colombia.

ALFREDO Y TERESA VALENZUELA

Baptismal Jeton

Rulau	Date	Metal	Size	F	VF	EF	Unc
Chi 35	1888	Copper	18mm	—	—	30.00	—
		Radiant star in circle. Around: ALFREDO Y TERESA VALENZUELA / * PADRINOS *. Rv: (Starburst) / ALICIA CHILD / MARZO / 1888 / (crossed branches). Plain edge. (Rulau coll.)					

Padrinos = Godparents and protectors. Baptismal medalet, or jeton, for a girl baby, Alicia Child, whose godparents were the prominent Valenzuela family. Alicia was born (or baptized) in March, 1888.

Baptismal jetons are seldom encountered by collectors; all are uniformly scarce as few of each would have been struck.

COLOMBIA

TRILLADORA

In Spanish, this normally means "threshing machine." In the coffee districts of Colombia, it has a special meaning, "processing plant."

The businesses called Trilladoras were concentrated mostly in Antioquia, Cundinamarca, Caldas, Valle and Tolima departments, and within these in their capitals — Medellin, Bogota, Manizales etc. Coffee bean selection, weighing, cleaning, baking ovens and other processing took place there.

ANTIOQUIA DEPARTMENT

Caceres
BLANCO

Rulau	Date	Metal	Size	VG	F	VF	Unc
Ant 3	ND	Brass	27.3mm	9.00	15.00	20.00	—

BLANCO / (Cup, snake) / (9 stars)/ (tiny) HADIN A PARIS. Rv: CUARTILLO / (flower) / 9 stars. Plain edge. (Ulex 2814; Bernal 149; Zaika coll.; Eklund 1102)

Rulau	Date	Metal	Size	VG	F	VF	Unc
Ant 4	ND	Brass	27.3mm	—	—	—	—

As last, but ctsp R on reverse. (Bernal 152)

Struck by Hadin in Paris, France. See also Ribon Hermanos under Mompos.

Medellin
MUNICIPIO DE MEDELLIN

Municipios?

Rulau	Date	Metal	Size	F	VF	EF	Unc
Ant 8	ND	Copper	31mm	—	20.00	—	—

MUNICIPIO DE MEDELLIN / TESORERIA. Rv: (Incused number). (Bernal 475-476). Numbers examined: 256, 287, 385, 786.

Rulau	Date	Metal	Size	VG	F	VF	Unc
Ant 9	ND	Brass	36mm	—	6.00	9.00	—

MEDELLIN in scrollwork cartouche across center. Rv: 1 / TAREA / (radiant star). Plain edge. (Clark 233; Bernal N/L)

Ant 8 was used in this manner: City treasurer used these for cashing city checks. Client would deposit his check at a booth and receive a token. When his number was called, he would turn in the token and collect his cash. This procedure ended about 1960.

HARD & RAND INC.

Rulau	Date	Metal	Size	VG	F	VF	Unc
Ant 11	ND	Brass	25mm	—	—	12.00	—

6-pointed star. Around: TRILLIDORA (sic!) BOLIVAR / H. & R. Rv: HARD & RAND, Inc. / (incused number) / MEDELLIN. (Numbers examined: 19, 955) (Bernal 327)

Rulau	Date	Metal	Size	VG	F	VF	Unc
Ant 12	ND	Brass	25mm	—	—	15.00	—

Half moon, TRILLIDORA BOLIVAR / H. & R. Rv: As last. (Numbers examined: 162, 2243.) (Bernal 328)

Rulau	Date	Metal	Size	VG	F	VF	Unc
Ant 13	ND	Brass	25mm	—	—	14.00	—

Shield, TRILLADORA BOLIVAR / H. & R. Rv: As last. (Numbers examined: 2101) (Henkle report)

TRILLADORA LOPEZ V.

Rulau	Date	Metal	Size	VG	F	VF	Unc
Ant 18	ND	Brass	30mm	5.00	8.00	10.00	—

TRILLADORA LOPEZ V. / MEDELLIN - COLOMBIA. Rv: Same as obverse. (Bernal 325)

Trilladora = Coffee processing plant. This was early 20th century.

Rionegro
EDUARDO SANIN

Rulau	Date	Metal	Size	VG	F	VF	Unc
Ant 21	ND	Brass	21mm				

EDUARDO SANIN RIONEGRO. Rv: Blank. (Bernal 455)

Also claimed as Santander Dept.

Santa Barbara
STA. BARBARA

Rulau	Date	Metal	Size	VG	F	VF	Unc
Ant 25	ND	Brass	29mm	—	—	—	—
		Sta BARBARA / 1 / ARROBA. Rv: Blank. (Bernal 316)					
Ant 26	ND	Brass	31.5mm	—	—	—	—
		As last, but 2. (Bernal 317)					

Segovia
SEGOVIA & CO.
La Elvira

Rulau	Date	Metal	Size	VG	F	VF	Unc
Ant 27	ND	Brass	20.3mm	—	—	12.00	—
		Tree. Rv: SEGOVIA & CO. / 10 / . LA ELVIRA . Plain edge. (Bernal 369; Blanton coll.)					

Zaragoza
MEDRANO

Rulau	Date	Metal	Size	VG	F	VF	Unc
Ant 30	(1850's)	Copper	28mm	—	Unique?	—	—
		Sailing ship right. Rv: VALE MITAD/MEDRANO / ctsp script R M in relief within oval depression (Sweeny M6a)					

Possibly issued by a predecessor of Jose D. Medrano, an 1890's general store proprietor of Zaragoza. The only reported piece is in a New York collection.

Uncertain
BERTA ARIAS DE BOTERO
La Sandalia

Rulau	Date	Metal	Size	VG	F	VF	Unc
Ant 40	ND	Copper	22mm	—	—	—	—
		BERTA ARIAS DE BOTERO. Rv: (Eagle carrying a laurel wreath in its beak, on a panel) / LA / SANDA-LIA. (Bernal 144; Blanton coll.)					

These occur counterstamped AB.

LORENT, KELLER & CIA.
Hacienda de Montebello

Rulau	Date	Metal	Size	VG	F	VF	Unc
Ant 45	1885	Copper	17mm	—	—	20.00	—
		HACIENDA DE MONTEBELLO / (Anchor) / .1885. Rv: LORENT, KELLER & CIA. / ¼ REAL. Plain edge. (Bernal 178)					
Ant 46	1885	Copper	18.5mm	—	—	—	—
		As last, but ½ REAL. (Bernal 181)					
Ant 47	1885	Copper	18.5mm	—	—	—	—
		As last, but ctsp GG1 on obverse or reverse. (Bernal 179-180)					
Ant 48	1885	Copper	21mm	—	—	—	—
		As the first token, but 1 REAL. (Bernal (182)					

ATLANTICO DEPARTMENT
Barranquilla (City)
MANUEL ANGULO

Rulau	Date	Metal	Size	VG	F	VF	Unc
Atc 3	(1839-40)	Copper	29mm	40.00	75.00	100.	—
		ESQUINA / DEL / (Cannon left) / VERDE. Rv: VALE MITAD / MANUEL ANGULO / (script MA in oval). Wide dentilated border on each side. Plain edge. (Scott; Bernal 52; Sweeny M3; Ulex 3876; Eklund 1307)					

Some of these tokens were struck over U.S. Hard Times tokens, such as Low 103, the 1836 Robinson piece of Attleboro, Mass. Others are struck on blank planchets, probably later, in the 1850's. Sizes range from 28.1 to 29.4mm.

Esquina del (cannon) Verde = Corner of the Green Cannon. Possibly struck by Scovill Mfg. Co., Waterbury, Conn.

Manuel Angulo was a storekeeper in Barranquilla at the "Corner of the Green Cannon," where Paseo de Bolivar crosses Progreso, and where there still exists a green cannon commemorating a visit by Simon Bolivar in 1830.

J. CHAPMAN

Rulau	Date	Metal	Size	VG	F	VF	Unc
Atc 6	ND	Brass	18mm	15.00	25.00	—	—
		J. CHAPMAN / .*. Rv: + / MITAD / +. Plain edge. (Ulex 3344; Eklund 1258; Bernal 10; Sweeny J1)					
Atc 7	ND	Brass	18mm	—	20.00	—	—
		As last, but ctsp on obverse; TR / TR. (Rulau coll., ex-Bill Judd)					

D. J. DE CASTRO

Rulau	Date	Metal	Size	VG	F	VF	Unc
Atc 9	1858	Copper	19mm	—	30.00	50.00	—
		D. J. DE CASTRO / 1858 / *. Rv: VALE / MITAD / 1858 / *. Plain edge. Rare. (Fonrobert 9117; Eklund 1330; Bernal 53; Sweeny D3)					

The issuer was Diego J. de Castro of Barranquilla, prominent in the 1850's.

H. GANS

Rulau	Date	Metal	Size	VG	F	VF	Unc
Atc 12	ND	Copper	Sq 26mm	—	—	40.00	—
		Colombian arms in ornate circle. Rv: RELOJERIA Y JOYERIA / H. / GANS / (ornament) / * BARRAN-QUILLA *. Plain edge. (Eklund 1099; Paul Bosco Nov. 1985 sale)					

Gans, a watchmaker and jeweler, also issued tokens for Colon in Panama, then a Colombian city. See under Panama.

C. E. GERLEIN

Rulau	Date	Metal	Size	VG	F	VF	Unc
Atc 14	ND	Brass	19mm	—	—	—	—

C. E. GERLEIN. Rv: MITAD. (Scott; Ulex 3345; Eklund 1253; Bernal 5; Sweeny C3)

This is believed to be an error token for Eduardo C. Gerlein. Scarce.

E. C. GERLEIN

Rulau	Date	Metal	Size	VG	F	VF	Unc
Atc 15	(1860's)	Brass	19mm	—	—	—	—

E. C. GERLEIN. Rv: MITAD. (Eklund 1078; Bernal 4; Sweeny E1)

Struck for Eduardo C. Gerlein, a Barranquilla storekeeper of the 1860's. The governor of Bolivar Department for 1889-98 was Eduardo B. Gerlein.

PEDRO LAZA GRAU

Rulau	Date	Metal	Size	VG	F	VF	Unc
Atc 17	ND	Brass	24.2mm	—	—	—	—

-.- / PEDRO / LAZA / GRAU / -.-. Rv: MITAD. Plain edge. Rare. (Bernal 11; Sweeny P1)

Pedro Laza Grau, a prominent merchant of Barranquilla, was president of the Constitutional Assembly of Bolivar Department in 1852.

LLAMAS HS.

Rulau	Date	Metal	Size	VG	F	VF	Unc
Atc 20	ND	Bronze	18mm	—	12.00	—	—

LLAMAS / Hs. Rv: * / MITAD. / *. (MITAD in tall letters) (Bernal 6; Ulex 3345; Sweeny L3a; Eklund 1263). The period after MITAD almost touches raised border.

Rulau	Date	Metal	Size	VG	F	VF	Unc
Atc 21	ND	Bronze	18mm	20.00	—	—	—

As last, but MITAD in small letters. (Bernal 7; Sweeny L3)

Rosendo C. and J. de la C. Llamas were operating a general store in Barranquilla in the 1890's.

PELLET

Rulau	Date	Metal	Size	VG	F	VF	Unc
Atc 24	(1880's)	Copper	18.1mm	—	—	—	—

PELLET. / .+. Rv: + / MITAD. / +. Rare. (Sweeny P2)

A. J. SENIOR

Rulau	Date	Metal	Size	VG	F	VF	Unc
Atc 26	ND	Brass	23mm	—	—	—	—

Arms of Colombia. Rv: A. J. SENIOR MERCANCIAS DE TODAS CLASES . BARRANQUILLA. (Bernal 346)

VENGOECHEA

Rulau	Date	Metal	Size	VG	F	VF	Unc
Atc 28	ND	Copper	18.5mm	—	—	—	—

* / VENGOECHEA / *. Rv: * / MITAD / *. Plain edge. (Fonrobert 9187; Ulex 3346; Eklund 1283 & 1398; Sweeny V2)

Probably issued by Vengoechea & Co., Barranquilla general merchants, before 1878. The spelling has been reported erroneously as Vengeochea.

BOLIVAR DEPARTMENT

Calamar
RAFAEL BALLESTAS

Rulau	Date	Metal	Size	F	VF	Unc	Proof
Bol 2	ND	Brass	24mm	—	—	35.00	50.00

RAFAEL BALLESTAS / (mortar and pestle). Rv: MITAD. (Weyl 3372; Ulex 3344; Eklund 1276; Bernal 17; Rulau coll; Sweeny R1)

Rulau	Date	Metal	Size	F	VF	Unc	Proof
Bol 3	ND	Copper	24mm	—	—	45.00	55.00

Same as last. (Rulau coll.; Sweeny R1a)

Rulau	Date	Metal	Size	F	VF	Unc	Proof
Bol 4	ND	CN	24mm	—	—	50.00	60.00

Same as last. (Behringer coll.; Eklund 1278; Sweeny R1b)

All struck by Scovill Mfg. Co., Waterbury, Conn. The Rulau collection contains two proof specimens in brass and one in copper.

Sweeny concludes these were issued by Rafael Ballestas, a general storekeeper of Calamar in the 1890's. The tokens were issued before 1892.

Mompos
F. DEL CASTILLO DE F.

Rulau	Date	Metal	Size	VG	F	VF	Unc
Bol 20	1870	Brass	30mm	—	—	35.00	—

F. DEL CASTILLO DE F. / (balance scales) / * MOMPOS *. Rv: CENTAVOS / * 2½ * / 1870. (Fonrobert 8214; Bernal 341; Scott; Eklund 1125)

Mompos (Santa Cruz de Mompos) is in northern Bolivar province. Today it has about 11,000 inhabitants. It is situated on the Magdalena River.

RIBON HERMANOS

Rulau	Date	Metal	Size	VG	F	VF	Unc
Bol 22	ND	Brass	30mm	—	30.00	—	—

Serpent coils around branch and Kylix. Around: RIBON HERMANOS / + MOMPOS +. Rv: Flag, on which is a 7-pointed star with RH in circle at its center. Around: 2½ CENTAVOS / (tiny) HADIN A PARIS. Plain edge. (Fonrobert 8215; Bernal 342; Eklund 1126; Scott)

Rulau	Date	Metal	Size	VG	F	VF	Unc
Bol 23	ND	Brass	30mm	—	—	—	—

As last, but resello with '14' ctsp on token (Bernal 343)

An extremely well made and attractive token. The business of the Ribon Brothers must have been good to order their tokens from Paris. Issued before 1878.

Among the people executed in Cartagena on Feb. 24, 1816, we find one Pantaleon German Ribon.

JOSE M. RUIZ

Rulau	Date	Metal	Size	VG	F	VF	Unc
Bol 25	1844	Copper	29mm	—	—	—	—

Sunface in rays. Rv: VALE MITAD / JOSE M. RVIZ / .-. / MOMPOS / 1844. Wide dentilated border on each side. Plain edge. (Scott; Bernal 50; Eklund 1124; Sweeny J8)

It is believed that this Ruiz token, the 1838 Manuel Ma. Pla token of Cartagena, the Velez Matos and Espinosa-Olier pieces and the Manuel Angulo / Esquina del Verde token were all struck in the United States to the order of Colombian merchants by a single American diesinker who utilized old Hard Times tokens as one source of planchets. In those days New Orleans was the port of entry for Cartagena shipments.

Zambrano
CASTRO I CA.

Rulau	Date	Metal	Size	VG	F	VF	Unc
Bol 30	ND	Brass	19mm	—	—	—	—

CASTRO I CA. / ZAMBRANO. Rv: MITAD. (Scott; Eklund 1235; Bernal 3; Sweeny C1)

A.A. DE HOYOS

Rulau	Date	Metal	Size	VG	F	VF	Unc
Bol 32	ND	Copper Oval 23x1 9mm		—	—	—	—

A. A. DE HOYOS / (ornament in oval) / * ZAMBRANO *. Rv: * / MITAD / *. (Scott; Randel coll.; Bernal 56.2; Sweeny A1; Eklund 1234)

J. W. Scott had attributed Zambrano to Venezuela. Struck before 1892.

MIRANDA
Uncertain Location

Rulau	Date	Metal	Size	VG	F	VF	Unc
Bol 40	(1890's)	Brass	18.2mm	—	—	—	—

+ / MIRANDA / +. Rv: + / MITAD / +. Rare. (Sweeny M8)

In the 1890's, merchants named Miranda operated general stores in the Bolivar communities of Carmen and Palmito.

Cartagena (City)
ACUEDUCTO CARTAGENA

Rulau	Date	Metal	Size	VG	F	VF	Unc
Bol 8	1907	Brass	31mm	—	—	—	—

Flan is slotted across center of obverse. Flan is also centrally holed, above the slot. All incused: ACUEDUCTO / 1907 / CARTAGENA. Rv: Ornament made up of crossed serif S's. Plain edge. (Bernal 295)

Payment tally for water?

S. ALANDETI
(Should be Alandete)

Rulau	Date	Metal	Size	F	VF	Unc	Proof
Bol 10	ND	Copper	22.8mm	—	15.00	55.00	100.

* / S. ALANDETI / *. Rv: (Radiant 6-pointed star) / MITAD / (Cock left). Plain edge. (Fonrobert 9181; Ulex 3344; Eklund 1280; Bernal 22; Sweeny S2)

Struck by Scovill Mfg. Co., Waterbury, Conn., before 1878.

Simon Alandete was a soap and candle maker of Cartagena. The Alandete Brothers were well-known merchants. It is believed Alandete refused delivery of the tokens because of the misspelling.

This piece is found in the U.S in mint condition, but is seldom seen in South America. The proofs were probably specimen strikings.

CASINO DEL CARIBE

Rulau	Date	Metal	Size	F	VF	EF	Unc
Bol 12	ND	CN	22.5mm	—	3.00		

Carib Indian woman standing, CASINO DEL CARIBE around. Rv: View of the city, CARTAGENA COLOMBIA above. Plain edge.

Gaming token.

A. MA. MERLANO

Rulau	Date	Metal	Size	VG	F	VF	Unc
Bol 14	1856	Bronze	26mm	—	—	—	—

A. M. MERLANO / 1856. Rv: MITAD. Plain edge. (Eklund 1246; Sweeny A4)

Rulau	Date	Metal	Size	VG	F	VF	Unc
Bol 15	ND	Bronze	24mm	—	—	—	—

(All in Germanic script): A. Ma. / MERLANO. Rv: (Normal block letters): MITAD. (Eklund 1247; Weyl 3378; Sweeny A3)

Both pieces are very rare. The Merlano family businesses were in Cartagena and Morroa in the 19th century. Struck before 1887.

MANUEL MA. PLA

Rulau	Date	Metal	Size	VG	F	VF	Unc
Bol 17	1838	Copper	29mm	50.00	75.00	150.	250.

Three-masted ship at sea. Around: CARTAGENA PLAZA DE LA YERBA 1838. Rv: VALE MITAD / Mauel Ma Pla (this line all in script) / TIENDA / No 11 (this line in script). Plain edge. (Fonrobert 8199; Ulex 2709; Scott; Bernal 51; Sweeny M4a-c; ANS coll.)

This is probably the most famous and most expensive private token issue of Colombia, and it is the earliest yet reported. It is one of Latin America's "classic" tokens, sought by collectors of coins as well as exonumia.

Tienda = Store. His store was located at Number 11 Plaza de la Yerba in the inner walled city of Cartagena facing the port, one of the best commercial locations in the thriving Caribbean seaport.

Most of these tokens were struck over U.S. Hard Times tokens, this fact having been mentioned often in 19th and early 20th century auction catalogs and in Scott's *Copper Coin Catalog* of 1913. It is well documented by Elwin C. Leslie in "Colombia, South America Merchant Tokens struck over United States Hard Times Tokens," appearing in the August 1973 edition of *TAMS Journal*.

The Pla token is known struck over 1841-dated HT tokens, so the die could have been used for a time after 1838 by its American token maker, who has not been identified. However, Low 58, the 1841 token in question, could itself have been struck as early as 1837! (See Russ Rulau's 3rd edition *Hard Times Tokens*.)

Other Colombian tokens which are known to have been struck over Hard Times tokens include the Velez Matos piece; Manuel Angulo - Esquina del Verde token. It is also possible the Jose M. Ruiz 1844 token of Mompos and the Espinosa & Olier tokens could have used HT tokens as planchets, though Leslie had found none by 1973.

Plaza de la Yerba (or Hierba) was a place where grass or hay for animals was sold, thus the name. Today it still exists, and is known as Plaza del Ecuador.

Sweeny concludes the tokens were issued for Tienda (store) number 11, rather than No. 11 Plaza de la Yerba. We do not concur; having eleven or more stores would have been unlikely in the Colombia of that period.

Specimens examined have been struck over these Hard Times tokens: Low 95 and Low 97, Merchants Exchange; Low 58, Webster Credit Current; Low 44, Shipwreck. There is even a report of an overstrike on Low 41, a Bushnell restrike, but we discount this as an error in reporting.

BOYACA DEPARTMENT

Chita
TRUJILLO & CIA.

Rulau	Date	Metal	Size	VG	F	VF	Unc
Boy 5	ND	Bronze	23.5mm	10.00	12.00	15.00	—

TRUJILLO & CIA / * / SALINA / DE / .CHITA. Rv: 1 / ARROBA within ornate cartouches. Tiny RH (?) at bottom. Plain edge. (Bernal 600)

Salina = Salt mine. The arroba was a weight unit equal to about 25.36 pounds, though in Colombia each department set its own standard.

The Chita salt works is mentioned in a 1913 book, "Colombia" by P. J. Eder, published in London.

Paipa and Sotaquira
MANZANO FARMING CO.

Rulau	Date	Metal	Size	VG	F	VF	Unc
Boy 10	1901	Bronze	28.5mm	—	—	30.00	—

MANZANO FARMING CO. / 25 / * COLOMBIA * / 1901. Rv: MANZANO, CARRENO, SOCONSUCA. PAPAYO / Y / SATIVA / SOTAQUIRA Y PAIPA. Plain edge. Scarce. (Bernal 154)

Rulau	Date	Metal	Size	VG	F	VF	Unc
Boy 11	1901	Silv/Bz	28.5mm	—	—	—	—

As last. Comm. (Bernal 153)

Rulau	Date	Metal	Size	VG	F	VF	Unc
Boy 12	1901	Bronze	24.3mm	—	—	30.00	—

As last, but 10. (Bernal 158; Blanton coll.)

This issue occurs with a variety of counterstamps, possibly for use on specific haciendas. These ctsps are reported by Bernal:

CC monogram	Bernal 162
FC monogram	159
BJ monogram	157 & 160
K	155
M.R.P.	156 & 161

Manzano, Carreño and Soconsuca were the partners in the enterprise, which raised papayo (tree bearing papaya fruit) and sativa (other cultivated products). Paipa and Sotaquira are in Tundama Province on the Boyaca River, in Boyaca Dept.

Henkle says all Manzano Farming tokens are also claimed for Puerto Carreño in Vichada Dept!

CALDAS DEPARTMENT

Manizales
CIRCULO DEL COMERCIO

Rulau	Date	Metal	Size	VG	F	VF	Unc
Cal 3	1922	CN	--mm	—	—	—	—

CIRCULO DEL COMERCIO / 1922 (in beaded circle) / * MANIZALES *. Rv: $2oo ORO. Plain edge.

Rulau	Date	Metal	Size	VG	F	VF	Unc
Cal 4	1922	CN	32.5mm	—	—	15.00	—

As last, but $1oo ORO.

Rulau	Date	Metal	Size	VG	F	VF	Unc
Cal 6	1922	CN	Rect 38x19mm	—	—	15.00	—

CIRCULO DEL COMERCIO / 1922 / MANIZALES. Rv: $0.10 ORO. Plain edge. (Bernal 432; Zaika coll.)

These tokens have been claimed for Panama and Philippine Islands. They were struck by Grammes Co., Allentown, Pennsylvania, according to a 1971 report by Robert E. Paige, a former Grammes employee.

CENTRO SOCIAL MANIZALES

Rulau	Date	Metal	Size	VG	F	VF	Unc
Cal 8	1925	CN	42mm	—	—	—	—

CENTRO SOCIAL MANIZALES. RV: 1925 / $200 ORO. (Bernal 422)

This is part of a series of CN tokens: $10, $5, $1 and $0.10, probably struck by Grammes Co. Other sets dated 1935 were struck for Club Manizales and, undated, for Club Antioquia in Manizales.

CAUCA DEPARTMENT

Popayan
F. B. MALO

Rulau	Date	Metal	Size	VG	F	VF	Unc
Cca 6	ND	Bronze	24.2mm	—	—	—	—

(All Gothic lettering): F . B / MALO / -.-. Rv: (Normal block letters): MITAD. Dentilated border on each side. (Bernal 31; Sweeny F1)

Francisco Malo, a Popayan merchant of the 1890's, is credited as the issuer.

TRILLADORA ORDOÑEZ

Rulau	Date	Metal	Size	VG	F	VF	Unc
Cca 9	ND	Copper	23.4mm	—	—	20.00	—

Flying eagle. Rv: TRILLADORA / POPAYAN / ORDOÑEZ. (Bernal 326; Blanton coll.)

CHOCO DEPARTMENT

EMPRESA SAUTATA

Rulau	Date	Metal	Size	VG	F	VF	Unc
Cho 4	ND	Brass	35.2mm	—	7.50	10.00	—

In central circle: EFECTOS / AL / TRADAJADOR. Around: EMPRESA / SAUTATA. Rv: 500 on plain field. Plain edge. (Bernal 379)

Trabajador (worker) is misspelled on this token as Tradajador. Colombian specialist Herman Blanton reports that a variety supposedly exists with the proper spelling, but he was never able to verify this.

Empresa Sautata was a gold mine in the rich Choco gold country, operating in the 20th century. Blanton is uncertain what the "500" stands for, but says this is a miner's work token.

CORDOBA DEPARTMENT

Terr. Lorica
MONTERIA

Rulau	Date	Metal	Size	F	VF	Unc	Proof
Cdb 3	ND	Copper	24mm	—	—	60.00	155.

MONTERIA. Rv: ⅛ / DE REAL. Plain edge. (Eklund 1127; Rulau coll.)

Rulau	Date	Metal	Size	F	VF	Unc	Proof
Cdb 4	ND	Brass	24mm	—	15.00	60.00	—

As last, (Bernal 367; Behringer coll.)

Struck by Scovill Mfg. Co. The Rulau collection specimen of the copper token is in proof, possibly unique. Lorica is on the Sinu River.

COMPANIA DEL SINU

Rulau	Date	Metal	Size	VG	F	VF	Unc
Cdb 7	ND	Brass	13mm	—	—	60.00	—

COMPANIA / DEL / SINU. Rv: VALE QUARTILLO / *. (Scott; Eklund 1157; Bernal 629; ANS coll.)

Rulau	Date	Metal	Size	VG	F	VF	Unc
Cdb 8	ND	Brass	16mm	—	—	40.00	—

As last, but VALE / MEDIO / REAL. (Scott; Eklund 1158)

The Sinu River wends its way to the Pacific Ocean through Cordoba Department.

CUNDINAMARCA DEPARTMENT

Bogota
F. DE G.
(Fondo de Empleados)

Rulau	Date	Metal	Size	VG	F	VF	Unc
Cun 4	ND	CN	23.2mm	—	—	—	—

Liberty head right (modeled on the Colombian 5-centavo coin of 1918-50, KM 199. Rv: F de G (F and G in large, ornate format). Plain edge. (Bernal 113)

F. de G. stands for Fondo de Empleados del Banco de la Republica (Bank of the Republic Employees' Fund). Since it is an issue of the nation's central bank, it may have been struck at the Bogota Mint.

MANUEL QUESADA

Rulau	Date	Metal	Size	VG	F	VF	Unc
Cun 7	ND	Bronze	28mm	—	—	—	—

Shield of Gran Colombia in beaded central circle. Around: MANUEL QUESADA / * ESPANOL *. Rv: 1A CALLE REAL 62-64 / GRAN / SURTIDO / DE VARIAS / MERCANCIAS / (ornament) / * BOGOTA *. Plain edge. (Bernal 482)

Colombia last used the shield of Gran Colombia on coinage in 1837, replacing it with the shield of Nueva Granada. It is not certain that this fact can be used to date this token as an early piece, however.

Fusagasuga
RAFAELITA

Rulau	Date	Metal	Size	VG	F	VF	Unc
Cun 10	1892	Bronze	22mm	—	—	—	—

RAFAELITA / * 1892 * / FUSAGASUGA. Rv: Emblem of La Fortuna. Common. (Bernal 332)

Nilo
BALUNDA

Rulau	Date	Metal	Size	VG	F	VF	Unc
Cun 15	ND	CN	23.4mm	15.00	—	—	—

Within wreath: BALUNDA. Rv: Within wreath: 20 / CENTAVOS / .o. (Bernal 199)

Rulau	Date	Metal	Size	VG	F	VF	Unc
Cun 16	ND	CN	21.2mm	—	—	15.00	—

As last, but 10. (Bernal 195)

Rulau	Date	Metal	Size	VG	F	VF	Unc
Cun 17	ND	CN	19mm	—	—	15.00	—

As last, but 5. (Bernal 193)

Finca Balunda was in Nilo municipio. In 1923, when its proprietor was Jorge Olguin, it had 50,000 coffee trees in production. The tokens are older, however. These tokens are known bearing countersamps: M, C2o or C5o.

GRAU & CA.
Cafetal de San Jose

Rulau	Date	Metal	Size	VG	F	VF	Unc
Cun 30	1901	Bronze	24mm	—	—	15.00	—

CAFETAL DE SAN JOSE / 20 / CUNDIAMARCA / 1901. Rv: GRAU & CA. / (ornament) / * COLOMBIA *. (Bernal 163)

Rulau	Date	Metal	Size	VG	F	VF	Unc
Cun 31	1901	Bronze	Oct 19mm	—	—	15.00	—

As last, but 10. (Bernal 164)

Rulau	Date	Metal	Size	VG	F	VF	Unc
Cun 32	1901	Bronze	19mm	—	—	15.00	—

As last, but 5. (Bernal 165)

LA GUAJIRA DEPARTMENT

Riohacha
A. R. DE A. & CO.

Rulau	Date	Metal	Size	VG	F	VF	Unc
Gja 1	ND	Brass	19.5mm	—	25.00	—	—

¼ / A. R. DE A. & CO. / RIO HACHA. Rv: ¼ / J. A. B. E. / S. JUAN. Plain edge. (Bernal 313; Blanton coll.; Eklund 1138)

CANO DUGANO
MARTINEZ & CA.

Rulau	Date	Metal	Size	VG	F	VF	Unc
Gja 3	1878	Bronze	22mm	—	—	—	—

CANO DUGANO MARTINEZ Y CA / A LA / BUENA FE / — / RIO-HACHA / 1878. / * Rv: (Clasped hands) / UN CUARTILLO. Plain edge. (Bernal 312; Eklund 1137)

A. GONZALEZ CANO Y CIA.

Rulau	Date	Metal	Size	VG	F	VF	Unc
Gja 5	ND	Brass	12-sided 23mm				

Knight's head in helmet right. Rv: A. GONZALEZ CANO Y Cia / RIO HACHA / * CUARTILLO *. (Eklund 1139)

D. P.

Rulau	Date	Metal	Size	VG	F	VF	Unc
Gja 8	ND	Brass	17mm	—	—	15.00	—

D. P. / (two stars). Rv: RIOHACHA / (two stars). Plain edge. (Ulex 2814; Eklund 1140; Bernal 415)

S. P.

Rulau	Date	Metal	Size	VG	F	VF	Unc
Gja 10	ND	Brass	20.5mm	25.00	30.00	40.00	—

S P / RIOHACHA. Rv: UN / CUARTILLO. Plain edge. (Ulex 2814; Scott; Bernal 314; Eklund 1141)

Rulau	Date	Metal	Size	VG	F	VF	Unc
Gja 11	ND	Brass	20.5mm	25.00	30.00	40.00	—

As last, ctsp M M on reverse. (Rulau coll.)

Riohacha (formerly Rio Hacha) is a port city on the Caribbean.

MAGDALENA DEPARTMENT

Santa Marta
CLUB SANTA MARTA

Rulau	Date	Metal	Size	VG	F	VF	Unc
Mag 3	ND	CN	Scal 29mm	—	—	—	—

CLUB SANTA MARTA / 20 CENTAVOS / CAYON & ZUNIGA. Rv: 20. (Bernal 466)

AM DE LA CUADRA

Rulau	Date	Metal	Size	VG	F	VF	Unc
Mag 5	1855	Brass	28mm	—	25.00	35.00	75.00

AM / DE . LA / CUADRA. Rv: UNA / MITAD / 1855. (Fonrobert 8263; Eklund 1098; Bernal 55; Rulau coll.; Sweeny A2; Blanton coll.)

Rulau	Date	Metal	Size	VG	F	VF	Unc
Mag 6	1855	Bronze	28mm	—	—	—	90.00

As last. Specimen strike! (Bernal N/L; Rulau Coll.; Sweeny A2a)

MITAD = Half cuartillo. Struck at Scovill Mfg. Co., Waterbury, Conn. These pieces measure precisely 27.7 to 28mm in Unc. condition, not 26mm as stated by Bernal.

J. MA. GOMEZ

Rulau	Date	Metal	Size	VG	F	VF	Unc
Mag 8	ND	Bronze	18mm	—	—	—	—

J. MA. GOMEZ, Rv: QUARTILLA. (Eklund 1148; 1899 Weyl catalog)

NARIÑO DEPARTMENT

Sandona
MIGUEL CAICEDO A.

Rulau	Date	Metal	Size	VG	F	VF	Unc
Nar 3	ND	Aluminum	25mm	—	—	—	—

MIGUEL CAICEDO A / (ornament) / .PROPRIE-TARIO. Rv: SANDONA / VALE / UN PEON. Plain edge. (Bernal 602-603)

Vale Un Peon = Worth one laborer. The term peon can mean pawn in chess, man in checkers, foot soldier, pedestrian, servile peasant. The expression "vale un peon' is odd; it probably has a colloquial meaning.

Tumaco
F. BENITEZ

Rulau	Date	Metal	Size	VG	F	VF	Unc
Nar 6	1897	Aluminum	22.5mm	—	—	—	15.00

* / F. BENITEZ / (ornament) / TUMACO / 1897. Rv: VALE POR / UN / QUINTAL / DE / TAGUA / (tiny) L. H. MOISE. S.F. Plain edge. (Zaffern coll.; Eklund 2179)

Rulau	Date	Metal	Size	VG	F	VF	Unc
Nar 7	1897	CN	22mm	—	—	25.00	—

As last. (Eklund 2180)

The quintal is a unit of weight. In Colombia it equaled 101.4 pounds, but each Colombian department used its own weight standards.

Tagua = Species of nut.

NORTE DE SANTANDER DEPARTMENT

Cucuta
EL CASINO

Rulau	Date	Metal	Size	VG	F	VF	Unc
NDS 1	ND	Copper	33.5mm	—	—	—	20.00
		EL / CASINO / -.- / CUCUTA. Rv: 2 / F. Plain edge. (Eklund 1424)					
NDS 2	ND	Copper	30mm	—	—	—	—
		As last, but 1 / F. is shown. (Ek. 1423)					
NDS 3	ND	Copper	24mm	—	—	—	10.00
		As last, but ½ / F. (Ek. 1422)					
NDS 4	ND	Copper	20.5mm	—	—	—	—
		As last, but 2½ / Rs. (Ek. 1421)					
NDS 5	ND	Copper	19mm	—	—	—	15.00
		As last, but 1 / R. is shown. (Ek. 1420)					
NDS 6	ND	Copper	18mm	—	—	—	—
		As last, but ½ / R. (Ek. 1419)					
NDS 8	ND	Aluminum	22mm	—	—	—	—
		EL / CASINO / CUCUTA. Rv: 25 / CENTAVOS. (Bernal 462)					

Gaming pieces. R = Real. F = Fuerte (silver peso).

LA INDIA

Rulau	Date	Metal	Size	VG	F	VF	Unc
NDS 11	ND	Aluminum	30.3mm	—	—	—	—
		Indian head left, LA INDIA / * CUCUTA * around. Rv: . 1 . / FUERTE. Plain edge. Rare. (Bernal 391)					

This plantation also issued aluminum 25 centavos (22mm), 10 C. (18mm) and 5 C. (14mm). The fractional tokens are more easily obtained.

El Carmen
RIVES

Rulau	Date	Metal	Size	VG	F	VF	Unc
NDS 15	1872	Brass	18.3mm	—	—	—	—
		R in diamond / SANTANDER / CARMEN. Rv: UNA / MITAD / 1872. Plain edge. (Barredo 783; Sweeny R4)					
NDS 16	1880	Brass	19.4mm	—	—	—	—
		RIVES / SANTANDER / CARMEN. Rv: R-in-diamond / UNA MITAD / 1880. Plain edge. (Bernal 49; Sweeny R5)					

Rives' trade is not known. Santander Dept. in the 1800's included Norte de Santander Dept.

Pamplona
PERALTA Y LAMUS

Rulau	Date	Metal	Size	F	VF	EF	Unc
NDS 20	ND	Copper	18mm	—	—	—	—
		ALMACEN DEL DIA / VALE / ¼ / CUARTILLO / - / FARMACIA PRINCIPAL. Rv: RESPONSABLES / * / PAMPLONA / * / PERALTA & LAMUS. Plain edge. (Bernal 368)					

QUINDIO DEPARTMENT

Armenia
CLUB AMERICA

Rulau	Date	Metal	Size	F	VF	EF	Unc
Qui 1	1925	CN	27.2mm	15.00	—	—	—
		CLUB / -.- / AMERICA / -.- / ARMENIA. Rv: 1925 / 0.10 / ORO. Plain edge. (Bernal 433; Blanton coll.)					

CAFE PALATINO

Rulau	Date	Metal	Size	VG	F	VF	Unc
Qui 20	ND	Brass	20.00	—	—	—	—
		CAFE PALATINO / (two ears of grain). Rv: UN VINO in rectangular cartouche / (ear of grain). (Bernal 234)					
Qui 21	ND	Brass	16mm	—	—	—	—
		Obverse as last. Rv: UN TINTO. (Bernal 232)					

Un vino = One (glass) wine. Un tinto = One demitasse of black coffee.

CLUB PALATINO

Rulau	Date	Metal	Size	VG	F	VF	Unc
Qui 23	ND	Nic/Alum	30mm	—	—	—	—
		Horseshoe. Around: CLUB PALATINO / ARMENIA CALDAS. Rv: 50 / CENTAVOS. (Bernal 439)					

TRILLADORA "LA PERLA"

Rulau	Date	Metal	Size	VG	F	VF	Unc
Qui 26	ND	Bronze	20mm	—	10.00	—	—
		Trilladora / Armenia / "La Perla." Rv: Vale / 1 / Caja. (Bernal 324)					

Trilladora = Coffee processing plant. Caja = Box.

TRILLADORA ROSITA

Rulau	Date	Metal	Size	VG	F	VF	Unc
Qui 29	ND	Copper	21mm	—	—	—	10.00
		Rose, in circle. Around: TRILLADORA ROSITA ARMENIA, CALDAS *. Rv: VALE POR ESCOGER UNA UNIDAD / UNA (on shaded circle) / *. Plain edge. (Zaika coll.)					

Trilladora = Processing plant for coffee.

SAN ANDRES Y PROVIDENCIA DEPARTMENT

San Andres Island
I. H. C.

Rulau	Date	Metal	Size	F	VF	EF	Unc
SAP 4	ND	Nickel	20.5mm	—	—	2.00	3.00

SAN ANDRES ISLA / ½ PESO / I. H. C. Rv: Same as obverse. Plain edge. (Bernal 217; Zaffern coll.)

Rulau	Date	Metal	Size	F	VF	EF	Unc
SAP 5	ND	Bronze	20.5mm	—	—	—	—

Same as last. (Bernal 218)

Rulau	Date	Metal	Size	F	VF	EF	Unc
SAP 6	ND	Nickel	17mm	—	—	2.00	3.00

Similar, but 1 PESO. (Bernal 219)

The island of San Andres is a Colombian possession off the coast of Nicaragua near the U.S.-leased Corn Islands. San Andres, neighboring Providencia island, and the Albuquerque cays together make up the Colombian department of San Andres y Providencia.

The city of San Andres on San Andres I. is the department seat.

I.H.C. = International Hotel Casino. These are gaming tokens.

INGENIO PROVIDENCIA S.A.

Rulau	Date	Metal	Size	F	VF	EF	Unc
SAP 10	ND	Aluminum	32.5mm	—	—	—	—

INGENIO PROVIDENCIA, S.A. / (incuse) 1695. Rv: (incuse) GG. (Bernal 298)

I. E. RUBINSTEIN & SON

Rulau	Date	Metal	Size	VG	F	VF	Unc
SAP 12	ND	CN	16mm	—	50.00	—	—

I. E. RUBINSTEIN & SON / R. C. SAN ANDRES. Rv: VALUE / * 5 * / CENTS. (Bernal 222)

SAN ANDREAS ISLA

Rulau	Date	Metal	Size	F	VF	EF	Unc
SAP 14	ND	Brass	23mm	—	10.00	—	—

SAN ANDREAS ISLA / 3. Rv: Eagle surrounded by 20 stars, V. B. (Bernal 220)

Rulau	Date	Metal	Size	F	VF	EF	Unc
SAP 15	ND	Brass	32mm	—	10.00	—	—

Obverse as last. Rv: Eagle within chain of 50 stars. (Bernal 221)

San Andreas was an earlier name for the island city.

SANTANDER DEPARTMENT

Bucaramanga
D. DE M.
(D. de Martinez)

Rulau	Date	Metal	Size	VG	F	VF	Unc
Snt 3	(1890's)	Bronze	19.4mm	30.00	—	—	—

D de M. Rv: MITAD. (Ulex 3345; Eklund 1254; Bernal 1; Sweeny D2)

Possibly Bucaramanga general store operation. D. Martinez is listed as proprietor of Bucaramanga's principal store in 1897 in *Anuario del Comercio*. Uncertain attribution.

REYES GONZALEZ Y HERMANOS LUISIANA

Rulau	Date	Metal	Size	VG	F	VF	Unc
Snt 9	1888	Bronze	21mm	—	—	—	—

Cow's head, 10 cs— above. Rv: LUISIANA / 1888 / REYES GONZALEZ Y HERMANOS / BUCARA-MANGA. Common. (Bernal 321)

Rulau	Date	Metal	Size	VG	F	VF	Unc
Snt 10	1888	Bronze	23mm	—	—	—	—

As last, but 20. Common. (Bernal 322)

Rulau	Date	Metal	Size	VG	F	VF	Unc
Snt 11	1888	Bronze	23mm	—	—	—	—

As last, but counterstamped C / C. (Bernal 323)

TRINIDAD PARRA DE OROZCO & CIA.

Rulau	Date	Metal	Size	VG	F	VF	Unc
Snt 13	ND	Copper	17.5mm	—	—	10.00	—

TRINIDAD PARRA DE OROZCO & COMPANIA around monogram TP de OC. Rv: . BUCARAMANGA . M/ SANTANDER. (Bernal 60; Sweeny T3)

ULPIANO
VALENZUELA E HIJO
Hacienda de la Luisiana

Rulau	Date	Metal	Size	VG	F	VF	Unc
Snt 16	1869	Copper	20.7mm	—	—	—	—

. ULPIANO VALENZUELA E HIJO. / 1 / BUCARA-
MANGA. Rv: HACIENDA DE LA LUISIANA . / 1 /
1869. Rare. (Fonrobert 8179; Ulex 2814; Eklund 1100;
Scott; Bernal N/L)

Rulau	Date	Metal	Size	VG	F	VF	Unc
Snt 17	1869	Copper	18.5mm	—	—	—	—

As last, but ½ on either side. Rare. (Fonr. 8180)

Bucaramanga is the capital of Santander Department. 1 = One real.

LETANO VALENZUELA E HIJO
Hacienda de la Luisiana

Rulau	Date	Metal	Size	VG	F	VF	Unc
Snt 19	1869	Copper	21mm	—	—	—	—

HACIENDA DE LA LUISIANA / 1869. Resello
incused at center: (2 brand marks ?). Rv: LETANO
VALENZUELA E HIJO / NGA. (Bernal 394)

GEO. VON LENGERKE
Hacienda de Montebello

Rulau	Date	Metal	Size	VG	F	VF	Unc
Snt 22	1865	Copper	20mm	—	—	—	150.

GEO. VON LENGERKE / 1 (in circle) / . BUCARA-
MANGA . Rv: HACIENDA DE MONTEBELLO / 1
(in circle) / . 1865 . Plain edge. (Tanenbaum coll.)

This token is apparently unpublished in all references!

Ocaña
J. R. L.

Rulau	Date	Metal	Size	VG	F	VF	Unc
Snt 25	ND	Brass	23mm	—	—	—	—

J. R. L. / (ornament) / SANTANDER. Rv: -.- / MITAD
/ -.-. (Bernal 48; Sweeny J9)

J. R. L. = Jose R. Lemus, distillery owner of Ocaña, in the 1890's.

Yucal
J. M. A.

Rulau	Date	Metal	Size	VG	F	VF	Unc
Snt 30	1880	Copper	20.4mm	—	—	—	—

J. M. A. / YUCAL. Rv: MITAD / 1880. Plain edge.
(Sweeny J5)

Only 2 specimens are known, each one in private collections in Colombia.
Discovered 1989 by Enrique Bernal, Caracas, Venezuela.

Uncertain
E. R. C.

Rulau	Date	Metal	Size	VG	F	VF	Unc
Snt 40	ND	Brass	23mm	—	—	—	—

E. R. C. / (ornament) / SANTANDER. Rv: + / MITAD
/ +. (Bernal 47; Sweeny E4)

J. J. DE L.

Rulau	Date	Metal	Size	VG	F	VF	Unc
Snt 42	ND	Brass	19.5mm	—	—	—	—

J. J. DE L. Rv: MITAD. (Ulex 3346; Eklund 1259; Bernal 46; Sweeny J4)

R. E.

Rulau	Date	Metal	Size	VG	F	VF	Unc
Snt 50	ND	Brass	22mm	10.00	—	—	—

R. E. / (Star) / SANTANDER. Rv: * / MITAD / *. Plain
edge. (Sweeny R3; Bernal 32; Eklund 1150; Weyl 2698).
Also known with reeded edge (scarce)!

Rulau	Date	Metal	Size	VG	F	VF	Unc
Snt 51	ND	Brass	22mm	—	—	—	—

As last, but resello GJ ctsp on reverse. A variety has the
resello double-impressed. (Bernal 33)

Rulau	Date	Metal	Size	VG	F	VF	Unc
Snt 52	ND	Brass	22mm	—	—	—	—

Similar, but resello GJ and another resello, a boot, ctsp
on reverse. (Bernal 35)

Rulau	Date	Metal	Size	VG	F	VF	Unc
Snt 53	ND	Brass	22mm	—	—	—	—

Similar, but resello J.C.P. in rectangle ctsp on reverse.
(Bernal 36)

Rulau	Date	Metal	Size	VG	F	VF	Unc
Snt 54	ND	Brass	22m	—	—	—	—

Similar, but resello GJ and resello FM ctsp on reverse.
(Bernal 37)

Rulau	Date	Metal	Size	VG	F	VF	Unc
Snt 55	ND	Brass	22mm	—	—	—	—

Similar, but resello, a 4-petal flower, ctsp on obverse.
(Bernal 38)

Rulau	Date	Metal	Size	VG	F	VF	Unc
Snt 56	ND	Brass	22mm	—	—	—	—

Similar. Resello 4-petal flower ctsp on obverse and
resello CJ ctsp on reverse. (Bernal 41)

Sweeny says R.E. possibly Rafael Espinosa, general merchant of Natagaima,
Tolima Dept., which leaves word SANTANDER unexplained. Issued before
1897.

G. & C.

Rulau	Date	Metal	Size	VG	F	VF	Unc
Snt 60	ND	Brass	23mm	—	—	—	—

G. & C. / SANTANDER. Rv: MITAD. (Bernal 44;
Sweeny G1)

Rulau	Date	Metal	Size	VG	F	VF	Unc
Snt 51	ND	Brass	23mm	—	—	—	—

As last, but resello shaped like an arch is ctsp on
obverse. (Bernal 45)

Rulau	Date	Metal	Size	VG	F	VF	Unc
Snt 62	ND	Brass	23mm	—	—	—	—

As last, but ctsp GT monogram (T sideways). (Sweeny
G1b)

SUCRE DEPARTMENT

Corozal
E. P.

Rulau	Date	Metal	Size	VG	F	VF	Unc
Scr 3	ND	Copper	23mm	—	—Unique?		—

E.P. / COROZAL. Rv: A. A. V. / COROZAL. (Bernal 111; Sweeny E3)

E. P. = Ezequiel Perez, 1890's general merchant of Corozal. Token's existence not confirmed.

E. T. B.

Rulau	Date	Metal	Size	VG	F	VF	Unc
Scr 5	ND	Bronze	22.7mm	—	—	—	50.00

E. T. B. / COROZAL. Rv: * / MITAD / *. Plain edge. Rare. (Bernal 56.1; Rulau coll; Eklund 1306; Behringer coll; Sweeny E6)

The Rulau specimen, in Unc., was struck at Scovill Mfg. Co., Waterbury, Conn. It has an interesting provenance, with only four owners since it was struck: Scovill Mfg. Co.; a Scovill employee and his estate; Ralph Behringer, and the author.

These pieces have been examined by a number of experts and variously attributed to British Honduras, Peru and to Panama. There are also Corozals in Honduras and Puerto Rico, but the MITAD style clearly indicates Colombia.

Sincelejo
MA. DE LA C. ECHAVEZ

Rulau	Date	Metal	Size	VG	F	VF	Unc
Scr 8	ND	Brass	24mm	10.00	—	—	—

(Spray) / Ma De La C. / ECHAVEZ / (spray). Rv: MITAD. Plain edge. (Bernal 12; Sweeny M1)

Sweeny pointed out that the May 31, 1984 edition of the Bogota newspaper *El Tiempo* reported the death of Maria del Carmen Echavez in Cartagena. Her grandfather was an Arjona and her husband was a Vergara, both names associated with Mitad tokens.

Sweeny opined that the woman may have been a descendant of the issuer of this token.

I. A. M.

Rulau	Date	Metal	Size	VG	F	VF	Unc
Scr 10	(Before 1897)	Bronze	19.3mm	10.00	—	—	—

(Star) / I A M / (star) / SINCELEJO. Rv: * / MITAD / *. Plain edge. Rare. (Bernal 13; Eklund 1156; Sweeny I1)

TOLIMA DEPARTMENT

Libano
El LIBANO

Rulau	Date	Metal	Size	VG	F	VF	Unc
Tma 1	ND	Bronze	23.4mm	—	—	—	—

EL LIBANO / * 1 * / REAL. Rv: 1. (Bernal 337)

Rulau	Date	Metal	Size	VG	F	VF	Unc
Tma 2	ND	Bronze	21mm	—	—	—	—

As last, but * ½ *. (Bernal 335)

LIBANO COFFEE CO.

Rulau	Date	Metal	Size	VG	F	VF	Unc
Tma 4	ND	Brass	25mm	—	—	—	—

LIBANO COFFEE CO. / UN. Rv: Blank. Plain edge. (Bernal 338)

Rulau	Date	Metal	Size	VG	F	VF	Unc
Tma 5	ND	Brass	25.4mm	—	—	12.00	—

LIBANO COFFEE Co / 2. Rv: Blank. (Blanton coll.)

VALLE DEL CAUCA DEPARTMENT

E. CERRUTI
Buenaventura

Rulau	Date	Metal	Size	F	VF	EF	Unc
VDC 2	1872	+ +	23mm	—	Rare	—	—

+ + Red Vulcanite.
E. CERRUTI . - / BUENAVa / - / 1872. Rv: SEIS / REALES / *. Very rare. (Bernal 393)

Seis Reales = 6 reales, or 6/10 peso in 1872.

During the Colombian Civil War of 1885, Gen. Eliseo Payan confiscated the personal and business holdings of the foreign firm, E. Cerruti & Cia. Cerruti was arrested but later released to men from an Italian warship.

Cerruti later sued the Colombian government and his case became an international cause; he even sought the intercession of U.S. President Cleveland. In part, Cerruti's claims led to the Italian blockade and bombardment of Cartagena under Adm. Candriani in 1890. The matter was finally settled by Colombia paying to Italy the sum of 20,000 pounds sterling, then about $100,000.

Cali
AMERICAN COFFEE CORPORATION

Rulau	Date	Metal	Size	F	VF	EF	Unc
VDC 5	ND	Copper	21mm	3.50	5.00	7.00	9.00

AMERICAN COFFEE CORPORATION / UNA (on shaded circle). Rv: VALE POR ESCOGER UNA UNIDAD / ACC (on triangle, in circle) / *. Plain edge. (Eklund 2307; TAMS Maverick 9831; Bernal 513-514; Zaika coll.)

A.C.C.'s main office was in Cali; it was headquarters for several sites. This token has been claimed for Guatemala and Peru. Varieties exist, all common.
Unidad = Unit.

GRAN CLUB

Rulau	Date	Metal	Size	VG	F	VF	Unc
VDC 7	1907	Rect	29x23mm	—	—	—	—

GRAN CLUB / CALI / 1907. Rv: Large $1. (Bernal 435).

JACOBSON WATCH CO. LTDA.

Rulau	Date	Metal	Size	VG	F	VF	Unc
VDC 9	ND	Copper	34.5mm	—	—	—	—

JACOBSON WATCH CO. LTDA / "CON RELOJES SIEMPRE A LA VANGUARDIA" / APARTADO AEREO 1880 / CALI. Rv: Mulco Orfina Jawaco Oris / RELOJES DE PRECISION / (Roman numerals resembling a watch). (Bernal 627)

UNATTRIBUTED COLOMBIA

A.A.

Rulau	Date	Metal	Size	VG	F	VF	EF
Clb 1	ND	Silver	32mm	—	300.	—	500.

A. A within beaded oval, in relief, ctsp on Spanish-American 4-reales. (Ulex 2818; Duffield 942-943; Fonrobert 8259)

Clb 2	ND	Silver	27mm	—	300.	—	500.

Similar ctsp on Spanish-American 2-reales. (Fonrobert 8260; Ulex 2817; Duffield 941)

This piece in VG realized $310 in the Nov. 1983 Lepczyk sale. Another, in VF, was estimated at $500 in the Sept. 1980 Almanzar sale.

Clb 3	ND	Silver	22.5mm	—	300.	—	500.

Similar ctsp on Spanish-American 1-real. (Fonrobert 8261; Duffield 940; Brunk collection)

Clb 4	ND	Silver	20mm	—	300.	—	—

Similar ctsp on Colombia 1-real coin of 1827-36 type, KM-87. (Smithsonian collection)

These coins are reported with additional counterstamps: M / F on one side, and N in relief within border of dots on opposite side, on a 4-reales (Duffield 942); M in relief within line and dotted square, and the letters W h E, on a 4-reales (Duffield 943); letter B on a 1-real (Duffield 940); and r / MR on the Colombian 1-real coin.
The Colombian real now in the Smithsonian collection fetched $145 in Good condition in the March 1984 Lepczyk sale.
The A.A. mark must exactly match the description on Clb 1 to qualify for this listing!

ALVAREZ Y VEGA

Rulau	Date	Metal	Size	VG	F	VF	Unc
Clb 6	ND	Brass	18.7mm	—	5.00	8.00	—

ALVAREZ Y VEGA / ¼. Rv: UN / CUARTILLO. Plain edge. (Blanton coll.)

ANGELITO

Rulau	Date	Metal	Size	VG	F	VF	Unc
Clb 8	ND	Brass	22.5mm	—	—	—	—

Bust of winged boy, ANGELITO. Rv: Two crossed machetes, ANGELITO. Grooved edge. (Bernal 141)

Clb 9	ND	Brass	22mm	—	—	—	—

As last, but plain edge. (Bernal 140)

HACIENDA DE APOSENTOS

Rulau	Date	Metal	Size	VG	F	VF	Unc
Clb 11	ND	Brass	Oct 29mm	7.00	17.50	—	—

Fouled anchor. Rv: HACIENDA DE APOSENTOS / 20 / *. Plain edge. (Bernal 175; Blanton coll.)

Clb 12	ND	Brass	Oct 26.4mm	—	15.00	—	—

As last, but 10. (Bernal 176; Rulau coll.; Ex-Elman)

Clb 13	ND	Brass	Oct 20mm	—	—	—	—

As last, but 5. (Bernal 177)

B Brand Mark

Rulau	Date	Metal	Size	VG	F	VF	Unc
Clb 15	ND	CN	20mm	—	—	—	—

B-type brand mark ctsp on Colombia 1886 5-centavos, KM-183.2. (Krueger April 1991 sale, lot 1755)

BANCO CAFETERO

Rulau	Date	Metal	Size	VG	F	VF	Unc
Clb 17	ND	CN	30.5mm	—	—	—	—

Banco / Cafetero. Rv: PAGADOR / No (relief) 3 (incuse, on square boss) / 93 (incuse, on rect. boss) — all on crosshatched background.

M. T. BELA

Rulau	Date	Metal	Size	VG	F	VF	Unc
Clb 19	ND	CN	16mm	—	—	—	—

M. T. BELA in high relief ctsp on Ecuador 1909-H ½-centavo coin, KM 57. (Bernal 396)

ESTO DE LA TORRE

Rulau	Date	Metal	Size	VG	F	VF	Unc
Clb 21	ND	Brass	20mm	—	—	19.00	—

(All incused): ESTO DE LA TORRE / N Z. Rv: ½ / CUARTILLO. (Limarc report)

J. G.
Los Micos

Rulau	Date	Metal	Size	VG	F	VF	Unc
Clb 23	ND	Copper	22mm	—	—	—	—

LOS / (Condor in flight) / (Coffee leaf) / MICOS. Rv: (Ornament) / J. G. / (ornament). (Blanton coll.)

PEDRO GARRALDE

Rulau	Date	Metal	Size	VG	F	VF	Unc
Clb 25	ND	Brass	18.4mm	—	10.00	—	—

LA CONFITERIA / . PEDRO GARRALDE . Rv: UN / CUARTILLO. Plain edge. (Blanton coll.)

Namai
MANUEL GOMEZ C.

Rulau	Date	Metal	Size	VG	F	VF	Unc
Clb 27	ND	CN	27.5mm	—	—	—	—

MANUEL GOMEZ C. / (Tree) / NAMAI. Rv: CINCO / ARROBAS. (Bernal 315)

GREEN & GARCIA

Rulau	Date	Metal	Size	VG	F	VF	Unc
Clb 30	ND	CN	26.4mm	—	10.00	—	—

GREEN & GARCIA / 5 / ***. Rv: VALE CINCO REALES / 5 / *. (Bernal 168)

| Clb 31 | ND | CN | 24.5mm | — | 5.00 | — | — |

As last, but DOS REALES / 2 / ***. (Bernal 169)

| Clb 32 | ND | CN | 31.7mm | — | 25.00 | — | — |

As last, but DIEZ REALES / 10 / *****. Ctsp X. (Blanton coll.)

I. S. J.

Rulau	Date	Metal	Size	VG	F	VF	Unc
Clb 34	ND	Copper	30mm	—	—	—	25.00

Two facing cornucopiae on plain field. Rv: I. S. J. within ornate circular border. (Bernal 126)

| Clb 36 | ND | Copper | 22.5mm | — | — | — | 20.00 |

Female bust left. Rv: As last. (Bernal 127)

| Clb 38 | ND | Copper | 20mm | — | — | — | 20.00 |

Flying eagle. Rv: As last. (Bernal 128)

Onaca
KUNHARDT COMPANIA

Rulau	Date	Metal	Size	VG	F	VF	Unc
Clb 41	ND	Brass	24.5mm	—	10.00	—	—

KUNHARDT / -.- / * ONACA * / -.- / COMPANIA. Rv: CENTAVOS / 10 / * ORO *. Plain edge. (Bernal 68)

| Clb 42 | ND | Brass | 28.5mm | — | 10.00 | — | — |

As last, but 25. (Bernal 69)

D. LL.

Rulau	Date	Metal	Size	VG	F	VF	Unc
Clb 44	ND	Brass	19mm	—	—	11.00	—

D. LL / -.- . Rv: 2½ / CENTAVOS. Plain edge. (Bernal 296)

S. G. P.
Hacienda Lincon

Rulau	Date	Metal	Size	VG	F	VF	Unc
Clb 46	ND	Copper	19.5mm	—	—	—	—

HACIENDA LINCON. Rv: S. G. P. Plain edge. (Bernal 416)

PENON & CIE.
Hacienda de Don Diego

Rulau	Date	Metal	Size	VG	F	VF	Unc
Clb 48	ND	Brass	24mm	—	—	—	—

5 / REALES in beaded circle. Around: HACIENDA DE DON DIEGO / * PENON & Cie *. Rv: Same as obverse. Plain edge. (Bernal 355)

| Clb 49 | ND | Brass | Scal 24mm | — | 10.00 | — | — |

As last, but 1 / REAL. (TAMS Maverick 12484)

HACIENDA DE PERIODIAS

Rulau	Date	Metal	Size	VG	F	VF	Unc
Clb 52	ND	Brass	28mm	—	—	—	—
		HACIENDA / DE / PERODIAS. Rv: UNA / TAREA. Plain edge. (Bernal 360)					
Clb 54	ND	Brass	29mm	—	—	—	—
		HACIENDA DE PERODIAS / 5 @ / DE CAFE. Rv: 5-pointed star. Plain edge. (Bernal 359)					

The second type above also occurs with numeral 1 (brass, 23mm), (½ brass, 20mm) and ¼ (CN, 16.8mm)

Dr. Barriga del Diestro (see Bibliography) says that many 19th century Colombian tokens were well struck in foreign countries so as to resist counterfeiting. He refers to some of the better designed pieces as "infalsificables" (non-counterfeitables).

PEDRO B. PLATA
Cafetales Palmita

Rulau	Date	Metal	Size	VG	F	VF	Unc
Clb 56	1897	Bronze	22mm	—	—	—	—
		PEDRO B. PLATA / * 1897 *. Rv: CAFETALES PALMITA / 1. (Bernal 331)					

SOCIEDAD DE
SAN VICENTE DE PAUL

Rulau	Date	Metal	Size	F	VF	EF	Unc
Clb 60	ND	CN	21mm	—	—	—	—
		Virgin and Child. Around: SOCIEDAD DE SAN VICENTE DE PAUL. Rv: -.- / SOPA / DE / SAN VICENTE / -.-. (Bernal 142)					

Rulau	Date	Metal	Size	F	VF	EF	Unc
Clb 61	ND	Aluminum	25.5mm	—	—	—	—
		. SOCIEDAD DE S. VICENTE DE PAUL . / (bust of a saint) / CONF. DE S. ANTONIO. Rv: . SOCIEDAD DE S. VICENTE DE PAUL . / $3 / CONF. DE S. ANTONIO. Plain edge. (Bernal 143)					

Sopa = Soup.
Henkle says Peru!

TERESITA J.B.Q.

Rulau	Date	Metal	Size	VG	F	VF	EF
Clb 63	1900	CN	20mm	—	—	—	—
		TERESITA J. B. Q. / 1900 ctsp on Costa Rica 1-centavo coin of the 1865-74 type, KM 109 or 120. (Bernal 397)					

James Sweeny disputes the attribution to Colombia by Bernal.

TRILLADORA CENTRAL

Rulau	Date	Metal	Size	VG	F	VF	Unc
Clb 65	1929	Copper	23mm	—	10.00	—	—
		TB monogram. Rv: . TRILLADORA . / 19'29 / CENTRAL. (Bernal 329; Blanton coll.)					

Trilladora = Processing plant.

A. A. YANET

Rulau	Date	Metal	Size	VG	F	VF	Unc
Clb 67	ND	Aluminum	24.5mm	—	—	—	—
		A. A. / Yanet / *. Rv: 40 C. Plain edge. (Bernal 116)					

UNATTRIBUTED MITAD TOKENS

The word Mitad means "half," indicating the half of a cuartillo, or one-eighth of a real (1¼ U.S. cents).

A substantial number of Latin American tokens bear this word as an indication of value. There is a class of South American pieces, many struck by Scovill Mfg. Co., Waterbury, Conn., using flans of 18-26 millimeters and very mundane inscriptions, such as the name or initials of a merchant on one side and the word MITAD on the other.

German numismatic activity in the 19th century, good as it was overall in penetrating the mysteries of Latin American tokens, caused today's collectors real problems with these Mitad pieces.

Adolf Weyl, the Berlin cataloger of the giant Fonrobert collection in 1878, placed under Callao, Peru some pieces of this type. Jules Fonrobert acquired most of his pieces directly from traders in Latin America as coin dealers in general did not handle — or even know of — Latin American tokens in those days. It is quite probable that one of Fonrobert's suppliers was located in the port of Callao, and since they were mavericks, it was natural for him to attribute them in that manner.

Thirty years later in 1908, another German cataloger, Adolph Hess of Frankfurt/Main, handled the marvelous Ulex collection sale. Here the problem was compounded. Ulex was an energetic collector who sought out even more sources in Latin America for tokens, probably many of them fellow Germans. (By 1908 Central America and northern South America had acquired a large number of German immigrants who became hacienda owners, merchants and even government officials.)

Hess' Ulex sale catalog listed 47 pieces of the Mitad type which were dumped unceremoniously under Callao because of the assumptions 30 years earlier of Weyl.

As far back as World War I some of these Mitad tokens could verifiably (from their legends) be placed under Colombia rather than Peru. Examples include Manuel Ma. Pla in Cartagena, E. P. in Corozal, Castro i Ca. in Zambrano, etc.

Ole P. Eklund, between 1911 and 1936, assembled a handwritten manuscript of Latin American tokens using his own collection plus that of the American Numismatic Society, and extensive research in American and European auction catalogs. In the 2500-odd listings, Eklund repeated the mistake of placing these Mitad pieces under Callao. Though the Eklund manuscript was never published, it is well known in scholarly numismatic circles and typed copies are plentiful.

Many Mitad pieces are still mavericks today, though that is changing. They are now grouped under Colombia (none came from Callao, Peru) and more is being learned about them. Prof. Enrique Bernal's 1988 Spanish-language catalog of Colombian tokens lists many of them (though he ignored some of the Ulex pieces), without attempting to attribute them to localities.

In February 1991 James Sweeny and Bernal brought out "The MITAD Tokens of Latin America" as a Token and Medal Society project, and this keen work unraveled many Mitad mysteries. Most of the tokens attributed to localities are placed in the northernmost departments of Colombia (such as Atlantico, Magdalena, Bolivar, Norte de Santander, Santander, Sucre etc.).

Their cataloging here in a mass-circulation volume should speed the process of attribution.

S.A.

Rulau	Date	Metal	Size	VG	F	VF	EF
Mit 1	ND	Brass	22.5mm	—	—	—	—

(Star) / S. A. Rv: * / MITAD / *. (Ulex 3344; Bernal 21; Eklund 1279; Sweeny S1)

S. A. = S. Alandeti ? Before 1878.

ARJONA

Rulau	Date	Metal	Size	VG	F	VF	EF
Mit 2	ND	Brass	20.2mm	—	—	—	—

* / ARJONA / *. Rv: * / MITAD / *. Reeded edge. (Ulex 3344; Eklund 1248 & 1251; Bernal 9; Sweeny A5)

Possibly issued before 1908 by Angel M. Arjona, a Barranquilla merchant of the 1870's.

M. ANGULO

Rulau	Date	Metal	Size	VG	F	VF	Unc
Mit 3	ND	Brass	19mm	7.50	12.50	—	—

M. ANGULO. Rv: MITAD. (Ulex 3345; Bernal 8; Eklund 1089; Sweeny M2). There are minor die varieties.

Possibly issued by Manuel G. Angulo, a general merchant in Santa Marta, Magdalena Dept., listed in the 1890's. He was, perhaps, a descendant of Manuel Angulo of Barranquilla (which see). This token must have been issued before 1884.

R. B.

Rulau	Date	Metal	Size	VG	F	VF	Unc
Mit 4	ND	Brass	18mm	—	—	—	30.00

R. B. Rv: MITAD. (Fonrobert 9182; Ulex 3344; Eklund 1275; Bernal 23; Sweeny R2)

Issued before 1878. The Rulau collection contains an Unc. specimen. R. B. = Rafael Ballestas? Struck by Scovill Mfg. Co., Waterbury, Conn.

B.C.
(B. Caceres)

Rulau	Date	Metal	Size	VG	F	VF	Unc
Mit 5	ND	Brass	22.2mm	—	—	15.00	—

(Star) / B. C. Rv: * / MITAD / *. (Ulex 3344; Scott; Bernal 27; Eklund 1252; Sweeny B1)

A die variety measures 22.7mm. These pieces are known ctsp MT, MC or C (Animal). Eklund attributed this to Caceres, which may not be correct.

DAVID BARRAZA

Rulau	Date	Metal	Size	VG	F	VF	Unc
Mit 6	1858	Copper	19mm	—	—	—	—

DAVID BARRAZA / 1858 (ornament). Rv: VALE / MITAD / 1858 / (ornament). Plain edge. Rare. (Eklund 1329; Sweeny D1)

J. H. D.

Rulau	Date	Metal	Size	VG	F	VF	Unc
Mit 7	ND	Brass	19.6mm	—	—	—	—
Mit 8	ND	Brass	19.6mm	6.50	—	—	—

J H D monogram in wreath. Rv: MITAD in large letters. Plain edge. (Eklund 2254; Bernal 24; Sweeny J3)

As last, but MITAD in small letters. (Bernal 25; Sweeny J3a)

M. D.

Rulau	Date	Metal	Size	VG	F	VF	Unc
Mit 10	ND	Copper	22mm	—	—	10.00	—

* / * M D. * / *. Rv: * / MITAD / *. (Ulex 3346; Scott; Eklund 1266; Bernal 56.3; Sweeny M5)

Possibly issued before 1908 by general merchant Moises Diaz of Velez, Santander Dept.

EL PROGRESO

Rulau	Date	Metal	Size	VG	F	VF	EF
Mit 11	(1850's)	Copper	28mm	—	—	—	—

Stylized early locomotive left, EL PROGRESO below. Rv: MITAD in laurel wreath. Plain edge. Weight 4.34 gr. (Sweeny E2; Smithsonian coll.)

Possibly issued by the Barranquilla street railway on Progreso. Only 1 known.

ESPINOSA + OLIER

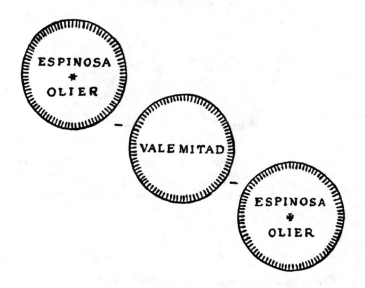

Rulau	Date	Metal	Size	VG	F	VF	EF
Mit 12	(1840's)	Copper	29mm	—	—	—	—

ESPINOSA / + / OLIER. Rv: VALE / MITAD. Wide dentilated border on each side. Plain edge. (Scott; Eklund 1108; Bernal 14; Sweeny E5)

| Mit 13 | (1840's) | Copper | 29mm | — | — | — | — |

ESPINOSA / * / OLIER. Rv: VALE / MITAD. (Leslie report; Sweeny E5a)

Espinosa and Olier ?

M. F.

Rulau	Date	Metal	Size	VG	F	VF	Unc
Mit 14	(1850's)	Brass	26mm	—	—	—	—

(Star) / M. F. / (caduceus) — all in oak wreath. Rv: (Star) / MITAD / (tiny ship left) — all in laurel wreath. Rare. (Eklund 1267; ANS coll.; Sweeny M7)

M. N. J. G.

Rulau	Date	Metal	Size	VG	F	VF	Unc
Mit 15	ND	Brass	19.8mm	—	—	—	—

M N J G. Rv: MITAD. Rare. (Sweeny M9)

J. M. GOMES

Rulau	Date	Metal	Size	VG	F	VF	Unc
Mit 16	ND	Brass	18.1mm	—	—	—	—

J. M. / GOMES. Rv: MITAD. (Ulex 3345; Sweeny J6; Eklund 1260)

| Mit 17 | ND | Copper | 18.1mm | — | — | — | — |

As last, but stars added above and below MITAD. (Sweeny J6a)

S. H.

Rulau	Date	Metal	Size	VG	F	VF	Unc
Mit 18	ND	Copper	22.9mm	—	—	15.00	70.00

(Star) / S. H. Rv: * / MITAD / *. (Fonrobert 9185; Ulex 3345; Eklund 2187; Bernal 20; Sweeny S4). Struck by Heaton Mint, Birmingham, England.

| Mit 19 | ND | Brass | 22.7mm | — | — | — | 55.00 |

Similar to last, but with stippled star. (Struck by Scovill Mfg. Co., Waterbury, Conn.). Plain edge. (Sweeny S4b; Rulau coll.)

Ulex in 1908 said this was issued by S. Herrera. In all, over 50,000 tokens were struck of all types.

James Sweeny (1991) opts for Santiago Hernandez, general merchant of Santa Marta, Magdalena Dept. Sweeny S4 was struck at the Heaton Mint, Birmingham, England, before 1878. There is a minor die variety of this Heaton piece in brass.

HOYER

Rulau	Date	Metal	Size	VG	F	VF	Unc
Mit 20	ND	Brass	18.5mm	—	—	—	—

HOYER. / . (Star) . Rv: + / MITAD / +. Plain edge. (Bernal 2; Sweeny H1)

Possibly issued by Crez Hoyer, storekeeper in Barranquilla, Atlantico Dept. in the 1860-70 period. This token is also known in Copper (Sweeny H1a).

ISLA

Rulau	Date	Metal	Size	VG	F	VF	Unc
Mit 21	ND	Copper	18.5mm	—	—	—	—

ISLA. Rv: MITAD. Plain edge. (Scott; Eklund 1077; Bernal 54; Sweeny I2; Fonrobert 8273)

Probably from Barranquilla. A very scarce token. Isla is a surname. Before 1878.

G. J. & CO.

Rulau	Date	Metal	Size	VG	F	VF	Unc
Mit 22	ND	Brass	20mm	—	10.00	—	—

G. J. & Co. Rv: MITAD. (Ulex 3346; Bernal 29; Eklund 1257; Sweeny G2)

| Mit 23 | ND | Brass | 20mm | — | — | — | — |

As last, but ctsp JJJ on either obverse or reverse. (Bernal 29.1)

Guillermo Jones, hardware merchant of Bucaramanga of the 1890's, could have been the issuer.

LEHMANN

Rulau	Date	Metal	Size	VG	F	VF	Unc
Mit 25	ND	Bronze	--mm	—	—	Ex. rare	—

LEHMANN. Rv: MITAD. (Ulex 3345; Eklund 1262; Sweeny L2)

M. & V.

Rulau	Date	Metal	Size	VG	F	VF	Unc
Mit 28	ND	Copper	23mm	—	—	25.00	35.00

M & V / (Tall cup with stem and spout). Rv: * / MITAD / *. Plain edge. (Eklund 1271; Ulex 3346; Sweeny M12; Rulau coll.)

| Mit 29 | ND | CN | 20mm | — | 75.00 | 100. | — |

Same, struck over U.S. 1858 Flying Eagle cent. (Eklund 1272; Sweeny M12a)

Struck before 1892 by Scovill Mfg. Co., Waterbury, Connecticut.

L. MERLANO

Rulau	Date	Metal	Size	VG	F	VF	Unc
Mit 30	ND	Copper?	24mm	—	—	—	—

L. / MERLANO / (ornate bar). Rv: MITAD. (Eklund 1264, from 1887 or 1899 Weyl listings)

JOSE DE MIER

Rulau	Date	Metal	Size	VG	F	VF	Unc
Mit 31	ND	Copper	28mm	—	—	—	—

JOSE DE MIER / *. Rv: VALE / MITAD / -+-. (Eklund 2257; Sweeny J7)

The name has been reported variously as JOSE D. MER and JOSE D. MER(tens), and the size as 18mm. This piece has not been examined.

One M. J.de Mier operated a distillery in Santa Marta, while one Jose de Mier was located in Barranquilla.

T. N.

Rulau	Date	Metal	Size	VG	F	VF	Unc
Mit 32	ND	Brass	23mm	—	—	—	—

(Star) / T. N. Rv: * / MITAD / *.(Bernal 26; Sweeny T1)

| Mit 33 | ND | Brass | 19.7mm | — | — | — | — |

T. N. Rv: MITAD. (Sweeny T2)

| Mit 34 | ND | Brass | 19.7mm | — | — | — | — |

As last, ctsp BiV. (Sweeny T2a)

M. P.

Rulau	Date	Metal	Size	VG	F	VF	Unc
Mit 35	ND	Copper	23mm	—	—	—	—

M. P. Rv: * / MITAD / *. (Eklund 1268; Sweeny M10)

Possibly issued by M. Posada, Cartagena. Rare.

D. P. R.

Rulau	Date	Metal	Size	VG	F	VF	Unc
Mit 36	(1850's)	Copper	27.6mm	—	—	—	—

D P R. Rv: VALE / MITAD. Plain edge. (Bernal 56.4; Eklund 1255; Tanenbaum coll.); Sweeny D4)

D. R.

Rulau	Date	Metal	Size	VG	F	VF	Unc
Mit 37	ND	Copper	29mm	—	—	—	—

D. R. within thick circular wreath overstruck on reverse of U.S. 1837 Large cent. Rv: VALE / MITAD / RECUERO / (Flower) overstruck on obverse of coin. Thick dentilated border overstruck on each side. Plain edge. Weight 10.485 gr. (Eklund 1188; Stohr R-IV-29; Smithsonian coll.; Sweeny D5a)

| Mit 38 | ND | Copper | 26.7mm | — | — | —Unique? | |

As last, but struck with different dies on thin copper disc. Weight 2.9 grams. (Smithsonian coll; Sweeny D5)

Both above pieces in the Smithsonian Institution collection are in part red Unc. condition.

F. R.
(F. Ramon)

Rulau	Date	Metal	Size	VG	F	VF	Unc
Mit 40	ND	Brass	22.4mm	—	—	25.00	35.00

(Star) / F. R. Rv: * / MITAD / *. Plain edge. Scarce. Star has raised rope border. Struck at Scovill Mfg. Co., Waterbury, Conn. (Sweeny F3a; Rulau coll; Fonrobert 9183)

| Mit 41 | (1879) | Copper | 23mm | — | 15.00 | 18.00 | 22.50 |

Similar to last, but larger. Star has solid raised border. Plain edge. Common. (Ulex 3345; Eklund 1256; Bernal 19; Sweeny F3). Mintage: 22,900 at Heaton Mint, Birmingham, England.

The Scovill striking was earlier; estimated 20,000 pieces. Two specimens in the Rulau collection are impaired brass proofs with wire rims; worth $100 or more each; these were obtained from a Scovill executive's estate.

A surviving order book of the Heaton Mint shows that 22,900 pieces were struck of this type in 1879. These apparently were to replenish the earlier Scovill striking of these tokens.

M. R.

Rulau	Date	Metal	Size	VG	F	VF	Unc
Mit 42	ND	Brass	24mm	—	15.00	18.00	22.50

M R / (Mortar and Pestle). Rv: MITAD. Plain edge. Common. (Fonrobert 9184; Bernal 15; Sweeny M11; Rulau coll.; Eklund 1270; Ulex 3346)

| Mit 43 | ND | Bronze | 24mm | — | — | — | 35.00 |

As last. Specimen striking. (Sweeny M11a)

| Mit 44 | ND | CN | 24mm | — | — | — | 40.00 |

As last, Specimen striking. (Sweeny M11b)

| Mit 45 | ND | Copper | 24mm | — | 20.00 | 23.00 | — |

As the first token, but with resello ctsp: Four petals in X form. Scarcer than the token without resello. (Bernal 16)

Definitely issued before 1878, as it appeared in the giant Fonrobert sale.

Possibly the issues of an apothecary, M. Rojas, for half cuartillo value, as reported by Fonrobert's cataloger, Adolf Weyl. The mitad at this time was worth 1/64 peso, or about U.S. 1.56+ cents.

It was possibly issued by Manuel Romanos, a general storekeeper in the 1890's of Carmen, Bolivar Department, reported by Sweeny.

H. ROSA

Rulau	Date	Metal	Size	VG	F	VF	Unc
Mit 46	ND	Copper	18.2mm	—	—	—	—

H. ROSA. Rv: MITAD. (Sweeny H2)

Possibly from Barranquilla.

SANTANDER

Rulau	Date	Metal	Size	VG	F	VF	Unc
Mit 47	1874	Brass	22.5mm	—	—	20.00	27.50

(Hand holding a torch) / SANTANDER. Rv: (6-pointed star) / MITAD / 1874. Plain edge. (Bernal 42; Scott; Schrotter 73; Rulau coll.; Eklund 1149; Sweeny S3)

| Mit 48 | 1874 | Brass | 22.5mm | | | | |

As last, but resello MO ctsp on reverse. (Bernal 43)

Santander here is believed to be a family name. It is not known who caused this token to be struck, but it was probably made by Scovill, Mfg. Co., Waterbury, Conn.

There is a Santander Department in Colombia, but it seems unlikely that such a geographical expression would appear alone on a token.

P. M. U.

Rulau	Date	Metal	Size	VG	F	VF	Unc
Mit 50	ND	Brass	22.7mm	—	—	25.00	35.00

(Star) / P. M. U. Rv: * / MITAD / *. Plain edge. (Fonrobert 9186; Eklund 1274; Bernal 28; Sweeny P3; Zaffern coll.; Rulau coll.)

P. M. U. = P. M. Urban? Before 1878.

VELEZ MATOS

Rulau	Date	Metal	Size	VG	F	VF	EF
Mit 51	(ca 1835)	Copper	29mm	15.00	40.00	—	—

VELEZ / MATOS. Rv: VALE MITAD across center. Wide dentilated border on each side. (Fonrobert 8272; Eklund 1160; Bernal 56; Sweeny V1)

This token had a value of 1/64 peso, or half a cuartillo, when issued. In fabric it resembles British and American tokens of this period. Specimens are known on thin planchets.

With FAVR hallmarkings

Mit 52	(ca 1836-37)	Copper	29mm	—	—	Rare	—

As last, but with nine separate hallmarkings counterstamped. FAVR incuse within rectangular indent ctsp on obverse, neatly between VELEZ and MATOS. On reverse, the same FAVR mark is impressed twice. Also on reverse, there are two line-groups of three hallmarks below each FAVR mark:

First line: (Ornate A) (Eagle displayed) (t).

Second line: (Crowned leopard head) (Crown / 18) (crowned leopard head).

(Token in Joseph Zaffern collection; Sweeny V1e)

Discovery of the FAVR hallmarkings on the Zaffern specimen permits some conclusions to be made about the Valez Matos token. Authorities had begun to conclude Velez Matos was issued about 1840; this discovery could push the probable issue date back to about 1837.

We may also infer that Velez Matos was a jewelry-silversmith firm with import trade connections with England. One of the marks, the Eagle Displayed, is clearly American, so it may be assumed that someone in Colombia was impressing hallmarks.

Several of the hallmarks are clearly elements used in London, England. The crowned leopard's head was the London guild mark until 1821. The small t = 1834-35 and the ornate A = 1836-37; each is an *exact match* with date-letters published by the London guild of goldsmiths and silversmiths.

Favr (Faur, Favre ?) has not been traced through European silversmith sources. The Crown / 18 is the standard English mark for 18-karat (.750 fine) gold. The hallmarks may be capricious.

A final conclusion: The Velez Matos token may well be the earliest of all Colombian tokens and thus the most important historically. The earliest dated piece has been 1838 which could be a founding date.

M. V.
(M. Veloz ?)

Rulau	Date	Metal	Size	VG	F	VF	Unc
Mit 53	1887	Brass	18mm	—	—	—	—

M V / (Star) / 1887. Rv: (Star) / MITAD / (star). Plain edge. Ulex 3346; Eklund 1273; Bernal 30; Sweeny M13)

VERGARA

Rulau	Date	Metal	Size	F	VF	EF	Unc
Mit 54	ND	Copper	18mm	—	12.50	15.00	27.50

-.- / VERGARA / -.-. Rv: (Clover) / MITAD / (clover). Plain edge. (Eklund 1282; Bernal 56.5; Sweeny V3)

Struck by Scovill Mfg. Co., Waterbury, Conn. The Rulau collection contains four of these pieces in red Unc. condition.

Possibly issued from either Corozal or Santander in Cauca Dept. Could be connected with 1863 coffee token of Francisco Vergara, Eklund 1337.

ECUADOR

GUAYAS PROVINCE

Guayaquil
S. HERNANDEZ & CO.

Rulau	Date	Metal	Size	VG	F	VF	Unc
Gys 5	(1902-10)	Brass	21mm	5.00	7.50	11.00	—

Head of Edward VII of Great Britain right. Around: OBSEQUIO - CIGARRILLOS S. HERNANDEZ & Co-. Rv: Crowned horseman galloping right (similar to TO HANOVER counters of Britain). Around: AMOR EN EL SUENO - LA FLOR DE GUAYAQUIL.

Rulau	Date	Metal	Size	VG	F	VF	Unc
Gys 6	ND	Brass	21mm	5.00	7.50	10.00	—

Liberty head of Chilean type right. Around: As last. Rv: Arms of Chile. Around: As last.

Rulau	Date	Metal	Size	VG	F	VF	Unc
Gys 8	ND	Brass	21mm	—	20.00	—	—

Coin style of Ecuador 2-decimos. Rv: Arms of Ecuador. Around: As last. (Henry Christensen Oct. 1975 sale, lot 215)

These were probably struck in Birmingham for the cigarette makers, S. Hernandez and Co. The tokens have also been claimed for Peru, but La Flor de Guayaquil means The Flower of Guayaquil. These tokens are found in Ecuador. Also examined: Coin types of Peru, Italy, France.

LETECHI HERMANOS

Rulau	Date	Metal	Size	VG	F	VF	Unc
Gys 11	ND	CN	18mm	—	12.50	18.50	—

LETECHI HERMANOS / GUAYAQUIL / *. Rv: Large ¼. Plain edge. (Scott; Eklund 1163)

SANTIAGO LETECHI

Rulau	Date	Metal	Size	VG	F	VF	Unc
Gys 13	ND	Brass	21mm	—	—	15.00	—

SANTIAGO LETECHI / ¼ / (tiny) MASSONET / (rosette). SANTIAGO LETECHI / ¼ / (rosette). Plain edge. (Eklund 2178)

Rulau	Date	Metal	Size	VG	F	VF	Unc
Gys 14	ND	Brass	16mm	—	—	—	—

As last, but ⅛ (real). (Eklund 2177)

These were struck by Massonet in Paris, who also prepared medals for the 1893 World's Columbian Exposition in Chicago.

JOSE GABRIEL PEÑA

Rulau	Date	Metal	Size	VG	F	VF	Unc
Gys 20	1917	Nickel	25mm	—	11.00	—	—

JOSE GABRIEL PEÑA / 1917 / GUAYAQUIL. Rv: HACIENDA GUAYABO / 10 CENTAVOS. (Alcedo Almanzar report in 1971)

LOS RIOS PROVINCE

Babahoyo
A. O. R.
Hacienda Violeta

Rulau	Date	Metal	Size	VG	F	VF	Unc
LRS 1	ND	Brass	31mm	—	—	—	—

HACIENDA / A O R / . VIOLETA . Rv: VALE / 50 / . CENTAVOS . (*TAMS Journal* for Dec. 1986, pg. 188)

A. O. R. = Alfredo O. Reyre.

PICHINCHA PROVINCE

Quito
CASINO COLON

Rulau	Date	Metal	Size	VF	EF	Unc	Proof
Pch 3	ND	Silver	Sq 36mm	—	—	45.00	55.00

Caravel at center. Around: CASINO COLON / 500 / SUCRES / QUITO ECUADOR. Rv: Map at center on which is: 500 / SUCRES. Around: CASINO COLON / QUITO ECUADOR. Intermittently reeded edge. (Zaffern coll.)

This was also issued in Gilt Silver, square, 36mm, worth $20 in EF or $35 in Unc. or $40 Proof. The gross weight of each type is 20.9 grams.

VIDAL DE J. CAMACHO

Rulau	Date	Metal	Size	VG	F	VF	Unc
Pch 10	1896	Aluminum	24mm	—	—	—	—

VIDAL DE J. CAMACHO / QUITO / 1896. Rv: GRAN PELUQUERIA Y PERFUMERIA / SUCRE / 5. Plain edge. (Dale Seppa coll.; Dana Roberts report)

Gran peluqueria y perfumeria = Great hairdressing salon and perfumery.

COLON TERRITORY

Isla San Cristobal
N. C.

Rulau	Date	Metal	Size	VG	F	VF	EF
CLT 1	(1870's)	Lead	Oval 20mm ?	—	—	—	—

Large N C within beaded border. Rv: No descr. available.

This token, valued at 5 centavos, circulated among the Cobos-Monroy workers (see under Manuel J. Cobos). It is not certain what N. C. stands for, but the C. may be Cobos.

A stamped, sole-leather token reportedly preceded the lead token.

NOTE: Territorio de Colon = Galapagos Islands, or Colon Archipelago, 15 large and several hundred small islands lying on the equator 650 miles west of Ecuador (at 89-92 degrees West Longitude).

Here in 1835 Charles Darwin spent several weeks while working out his "Origin of the Species" and theory of evolution.

MANUEL J. COBOS

Rulau	Date	Metal	Size	VG	F	VF	EF
CLT 3	(1889)	Lead	Oval 37x26mm	—	—	1000.	—

M. COBOS. / (ornament) / PROGRESO. Rv: Blank. Apparently unique. (Smithsonian coll.)

CLT 4	(1889)	Lead	Rect 38 x26mm	—	—	1000.	—

As last. Apparently unique. (Smithsonian coll.)

CLT 5	(1889)	Lead	Oct 39.5x27mm	—	—	1000.	—

As last. Apparently unique. (Smithsonian coll.)

CLT 6	(1889)	Copper	Oval 36x23mm ?	—	—	Rare	—

M. COBOS. / 80 c / PROGRESO. Rv: Blank.

CLT 7	(1890's)	Copper	34mm ?	—	—	Scarce	—

INGENIO - PROGRESO / 100 / * CHATAM *. Rv: MANUEL J. COBOS / (cruciform ornament) / *****. Plain edge.

There are also paper notes of Ingenio Progreso in 50-centavo and 1-sucre denominations. About 1904 Juan J. Pino, the newly-appointed territorial chief of the Colon Archipelago, prohibited the circulation of tokens and paper scrip in lieu of federal coinage and paper money.

In 1869 Manuel J. Cobos and Jose Monroy took over the work of clearing and planting San Cristobal (formely Chatham) Island in the Galapagos group. At first their products were sugar cane, Dyer's moss and fish.

In 1870 they carved out a sugar plantation and refinery and by 1878 there were 150 people on the estate. By 1889 Cobos was sole manager and he named the estate Ingenio Progreso. The population grew to 287 in 1889 and 334 in 1893.

In near-slavery conditions, the peons were paid from 8 to 14 reales per week in tokens or scrip issued by Cobos (about 80 cents to $1.40) - for workdays of 13 to 18 hours.

Ecuadorian authorities were made aware of these conditions in early 1904 when, after the murders of Manuel J. Cobos and territorial chief Reina on the plantation, some 85 peasants fled by boat to Tumaco in Colombia.

Leather and rubber tokens of Cobos have been reported. (Research of this series is due to the efforts of Dale Seppa).

ANACARSIS MEDINA

Rulau	Date	Metal	Size	VG	F	VF	Unc
CLT 10	ND	Copper	23mm ?	—		Rare	—

ANACARSIS MEDINA / . CHANDUT . Rv: VEINTE CENTAVOS / 20 / *. Plain edge. (Seppa report)

Galapagos Islands
R.

Rulau	Date	Metal	Size	VG	F	VF	EF
CLT 15	ND	Silver	37mm	—	20.00	—	30.00

R incuse, ctsp on Ecuador 1888 or 1897 1-sucre coin. Reeded edge. For the Galapagos penal colony. There are 15 large islands in the Colon Archipelago, making up Ecuador's lone territory of Colon.

A Doubtful attribution.

R. A.
(Rogelio Alvarado)

Rulau	Date	Metal	Size	VG	F	VF	EF
CLT 17	ND	Silver	37mm	—	90.00	—	125.

Script R A monogram within circle ctsp on Ecuador 1888 - HEATON or 1897 -LIMA 1 sucre, KM 53. Reeded edge.

CLT 18	ND	Silver	30mm	—	75.00	—	115.

Similar ctsp on Ecuador 1884 half-sucre. Reeded edge.

CLT 19	ND	Silver	23mm	—	45.00	—	70.00

Similar ctsp on Ecuador 1889-SANTIAGO or 1895-TF or 1916 2-decimos. Reeded edge.

This counterstamp is also known on Ecuador 18mm 1-decimo silver and on 1893 and 1912 15mm silver ½-decimo coins.

Rogelio Alvarado was supposedly a merchant who used prisoners in a penal colony on the Galapagos Islands in the Pacific, a part of Ecuador. ANACS has declared the 1912 ½-decimo a fake.

UNATTRIBUTED ECUADOR

Puerto de San Jose
R. DE PAIS

Rulau	Date	Metal	Size	VG	F	VF	Unc
Ecu 4	ND	Copper	22mm	—	—	—	—

* R. DE PAIS * / * (in beaded circle) / PUERTO DE SAN JOSE. Rv: 2 / REALES / (ornament). (Ulex 2860; Eklund 1164; ANS collection; Schimmel report)

Also claimed as Guatemala. There is no Puerto de San Jose in Ecuador.

San Jose

Rulau	Date	Metal	Size	VG	F	VF	Unc
Ecu 7	ND	Vulcanite	--mm	—	—	—	—

SAN JOSE. Rv: 2 REALES. (Salbach 1911 sale; Eklund 1165)

RIOS
Hacienda Rios

Rulau	Date	Metal	Size	VG	F	VF	EF
Ecu 11	ND	Copper	36mm	—	—	50.00	—

RIOS in relief within rect. depression ctsp on Great Britain 1797 Cartwheel penny.

Attribution by Dale Seppa, who located these in Ecuador.

YNGENIO ECUADOR

Tokens featuring a palm tree and legend YNGENIO ECUADOR / 1864, issued by M. y J. F. de La Vega in 1-real denomination, copper or brass, 19mm, are NOT from Ecuador, though assigned there by Fonrobert, Eklund and others. These pieces, struck in the United States, are from the Ecuador sugar estate, Camaguey Province, Cuba.

DIRECCION DE BIENESTAR

Rulau	Date	Metal	Size	F	VF	EF	Unc
Ecu 15	1978	Goldine	25mm	—	—	2.50	3.50

Three-masted ship within beaded circle. Rv: ARMADA DEL ECUADOR / DIRECCION / DE / BIENESTAR / 1978. (Dale Seppa coll.)

Armada del Ecuador = Navy of Ecuador. Direccion de Bienestar = Directorate of Welfare.

FALKLAND ISLANDS
(Islas Malvinas)

EAST FALKLAND

Stanley
GLOBE HOTEL

Rulau	Date	Metal	Size	VG	F	VF	Unc
EF 1	ND	Brass	27mm	—	—	85.00	—

GLOBE HOTEL (relief) / 4D (incuse, in circle) / + STANLEY + (relief). Rv: No. descr. available. (Bob Lyall coll.; Dick Hanscom report)

Rulau	Date	Metal	Size	VG	F	VF	Unc
EF 2	ND	Brass	27mm	—	—	100.	—

GLOBE HOTEL / (empty circle) / + STANLEY +. Rv: 3 D in central circle, wreath below. Plain edge. (Bob Lyall coll.)

COMPLIMENTS OF 365

Rulau	Date	Metal	Size	F	VF	EF	Unc
EF 6	ND	Aluminum	32mm	—	—	30.00	40.00

Crowned bust of Queen Elizabeth II right. Rv: WITH COMPLIMENTS OF 365. Scarce. (Carol Plante 1992 stocklist, lot 154)

The "compliments of 365" refers to islanders eating mutton 365 days a year. Sheep raising is a principal activity of the islands' economy. Elizabeth II ascended the throne in 1952.

SOUTH GEORGIA

Grytviken
C A DE P Monogram
(Compania Argentina de Pesca)

Rulau	Date	Metal	Size	VG	F	VF	Unc
SGI 1	(1908-14)	Aluminum	38mm	—	—	75.00	—

Ornate monogram C A DE P / (tiny) C. Y AF. ROSSI. Rv: 5 (large, ornate) / KRONER. Plain edge.

Rulau	Date	Metal	Size	VG	F	VF	Unc
SGI 2	(1908-14)	Aluminum	22m	—	—	60.00	—

As last, but 10 / ORE.

Also reported are aluminum rectangular (32x38mm) 1 KRONE and octagonal (28mm) 50 ORE, at comparable prices.

Compania Argentina de Pesca (Argentine Fish Co.) was a South Georgia-based whaling enterprise owned by Carl Anton Larsen, P. Christophersen, H. H. Schlieper and E. Tornquist, registered in Buenos Aires in 1904. Most workers were Norwegians from Vestfold province, thus the ore and kroner denominations.

Called "monkey money," the tokens went out of use July 1, 1914. They controlled access to alcoholic beverages at Grytviken.

South Georgia is a British colony, a dependency of the Falkland Islands government, some 105 miles long located 900 miles southeast of Port Stanley in the Falklands. Claimed by Argentina, it has been occupied by the British since 1775.

(See Dick Hanscom's "The Whaling Company Tokens of South Georgia Island" in the Sept. 1991 issue of *Coin News* of England.)

The Buenos Aires diesinkers Constante and A.F. Rossi used the C. y AF. ROSSI signature 1899-1921.

FRENCH GUIANA

Cayenne
F. TANON & CIE.

Rulau	Date	Metal	Size	F	VF	EF	Unc
FG 1	ND	**	Oval 24x18mm	—	300.00	400.00	—
		** Nickel-plated zinc. F. TANON & Cie / * CAYENNE *. Rv: 50. Plain edge. (Gadoury-Elie Guyane 1.8)					
FG 2	ND	CN	Oval 24x18mm	—	300.00	400.00	—
		As last, but 30 (centimes). (Gadoury 1.7)					

20 and 10-centime tokens were also issued in CN; same values.

Rulau	Date	Metal	Size	F	VF	EF	Unc
FG 4	ND	Aluminum	Scal 22mm	—	300.00	400.00	—
		Obverse as last. Rv: * / 50 c / *. (Gadoury 1.4)					
FG 5	ND	Aluminum	Scal 22mm	—	300.00	400.00	—
		As last, but 30 c. (Gadoury 1.3)					

20 and 10-centime tokens also were issued in aluminum. All the Tanon and Co. tokens are very rare and were published for the first time in 1990 in Victor Gadoury's catalog (see Bibliography).

A listing in the *Commercial Almanac* for 1913 reveals that G. Clanis and F. Tanon were associated in the import-export and steamboat business in French Guiana. The 1922 edition reported that the firm was now F. Tanon et Cie, with branches in Approuague, Mana, St. Laurent and Sinamary.

In 1922 Tanon et Cie. main office was located in Paris, France, at 7 Rue du Colonel Moll. Specialist Roland Elie considers that the Tanon tokens were in use in the 1918-30 period.

GUYANA

EAST BERBICE

Nieuw Amsterdam
WINKELVEREENIGING

Rulau	Date	Metal	Size	VG	F	VF	Unc
Gyn 5	ND	Brass	—mm	—	—	—	—
		WINKELVEREENIGING Nw AMSTERDAM / H. U. Z. Rv: 1 GULDEN. (Eklund 1731)					
Gyn 6	ND	Brass	—mm	—	—	—	—
		As last, but 25 CENT. (Eklund 1730)					

There are also brass 5 and 1-cent tokens of this type reported by Ole P. Eklund.

Eklund's listing, taken from the Schulman 1911 catalog, attributed these pieces to New Amsterdam in East Berbice, British Guiana, but David Henkle prefers Nieuw Amsterdam in Commewijne, Surinam, which is a port city across the estuary from Paramaribo.

Henkle notes that the cent-gulden system was introduced by the British only in 1828, possibly after these tokens' issuance. Scholten does not list them in his catalog; he may have doubted their American origin.

The Surinam Nieuw Amsterdam was known as Kroonenberg at least until World War II.

EAST DEMERARA

Georgetown
MIDDLEMASS BROTHERS & CO.

Rulau	Date	Metal	Size	VG	F	VF	Unc
Gyn 12	ND	Brass	24.5mm	45.00	100.00	250.00	—
		GEORGETOWN / MIDDLEMASS / BROTHERS & CO / DEMERARA. Rv: Same as obverse. Weight 4.38 grams. (Pridmore 63; Byrne 1365; British Museum coll.)					

The issuer has not been traced. Issued before 1870.

TRADE & NAVIGATION 1838
(Balgarnie)

Rulau	Date	Metal	Size	F	VF	EF	Unc
Gyn 14	1838	Copper	33mm	9.00	22.50	65.00	80.00
		Female with caduceus and laurel spray seated on a bale left. TRADE & NAVIGATION / 1838 around. Rv: PURE COPPER PREFERABLE TO PAPER. / ONE / STIVER. Plain edge. Weight 15.42 grams. (Pridmore 60; Byrne 1363; Fonrobert 7880; Scott)					

Issued by Balgarnie, a Scottish dry goods dealer in Water Street, Georgetown. Several die varieties exist. Two differing obverse dies were used, one with a somewhat larger female (as pictured on the next token below). All were struck in England.

Rulau	Date	Metal	Size	F	VF	EF	Unc
Gyn 16	1838	Copper	33.5mm	—	20.00	35.00	50.00
		Obverse as last (larger female variety). Rv: Laureate draped male bust left (George IV ?), PURE COPPER PREFERABLE TO PAPER, around. Plain edge. (Pridmore 61; Byrne 1364)					

Muling struck in England. About 1880 a hoard of this muled token was uncovered in County Tyrone, Ireland in a bog, and was turned over to authorities.

B. G. WHARF

Rulau	Date	Metal	Size	VG	F	VF	Unc
Gyn 18	ND	Brass	35.5mm	—	F	100.	—

(All incused): B. G. / WHARF & / S/S / LABOR. Rv: P 178. Plain edge. Issued holed. (Byrne 1366)

Bob Lyall doubts this is a Guyana token.

ESSEQUIBO

ANNANDALE

Rulau	Date	Metal	Size	VG	F	VF	Unc
Gyn 21	1842	Lead	24mm	—	—	500.	—

ANNANDALE ESSEQUIBO / * / BITT / 1842. Rv: Blank. Plain edge. (Pridmore 62; ANS collection; Eklund 2104; Lyall 110)

Bitt = 4 pence. Yet Fred Pridmore opines that this is a work tally representing payment for a service. Annandale sugar plantation was on the coast, 11 miles southeast of Georgetown. Only 1 piece known.

Pomeroon
PICKERSGILL SAW MILLS LTD.

Rulau	Date	Metal	Size	VG	F	VF	Unc
Gyn 25	(1904-16)	Brass	38mm	—	—	215.	—

PICKERSGILL SAW MILLS LTD. / (starburst) / POMEROON / -.- / BRITISH GUIANA. Rv: GOOD FOR / 1oo / IN MERCHANDISE. Plain edge. (Byrne 1367; Lyall 117)

Rulau	Date	Metal	Size	VG	F	VF	Unc
Gyn 26	(1904-16)	Brass	30.5mm	—	—	250.	—

As last, but 50 (cents). (Byrne 1368)

Rulau	Date	Metal	Size	VG	F	VF	Unc
Gyn 27	(1904-16)	Brass	27mm	—	—	400.	—

As last, but 25. (Byrne 1369)

The Pomeroon is a river in Essequibo. The mill was at Pickersgill village, as was the company store.

UNATTRIBUTED GUYANA

T. ROE

Rulau	Date	Metal	Size	VG	F	VF	Unc
Gyn 40	ND	Copper	34mm	20.00	—	35.00	—

T. ROE / 178 ctsp on Demerara & Essequibo 1813 1-stuiver, KM-10. Engrailed edge.

Tool check or identification tag?

E. UNITT

Rulau	Date	Metal	Size	VG	F	VF	Unc
Gyn 42	ND	Copper	34mm	20.00	—	35.00	—

E. UNITT ctsp on Essequibo & Demerara 1813 1-stuiver, KM-10. (Stanley Steinberg sale of Oct. 1990, lot 31)

PARAGUAY

Special Note on Paraguay: This country's tokens are less well known, and more scarce, than any other Latin American nation's private currency. We are especially grateful for assistance to: Carlos A. Pusineri Scala, long-time director of Asuncion's House of Independence Museum; Numismatica Independencia SRL of Asuncion, and George Lill III, Chicago, Ill.

Rulau	Date	Metal	Size	VG	F	VF	Unc
Boq 4	1924	Brass	24.4mm	—	—	—	—

SOCIEDAD FORESTAL DE PUERTO GUARANI . / (ornament) / 1924 / (ornament). Rv: ½ / KILO / (word scratched out) / .o. Beaded border on each side.

Boq 5	1924	Brass	24.4mm	—	—	—	—

Obverse similar to last. Rv: 1 (large, shaded) / LITRO / - DE - / LECHE.

Boq 6	1924	Brass	24.4mm	—	—	—	—

Obverse as last. Rv: ½ / LITRO / - DE - / LECHE.

Boq 8	1925	Aluminum	45.3mm	—	—	—	—

SOCIEDAD FORESTAL DE PUERTO GUARANI * / (ornament) / 1925 / (ornament). Rv: 25 (large, shaded) / KILOS / CARNE. Ornate border on each side.

Boq 10	1930	Aluminum	27mm	—	—	—	—

SOCIEDAD FORESTAL DE PUERTO GUARANI . / (ornament) / 1930 / (ornament). Rv: 1 (large, shaded) / KILO / CARNE / .o. Beaded border on each side.

Leche = Milk. Carne = Meat. Sociedad forestal = Forest corporation. All pieces are rare.

ALTO PARANA DEPARTMENT

HOTEL-CASINO P. P. STROESSNER
Puerto Presidente Stroessner

Rulau	Date	Metal	Size	VG	F	VF	Unc
AP 4	ND	Svd/Br	24mm	—	—	18.00	—

HOTEL-CASINO / 25 / P. P. STROESSNER. Rv: Same as obverse. Plain edge.

AP 5	ND	Svd/Br	18mm	—	—	5.00	—

As last, but 5.

AP 6	ND	Svd/Br	21mm	—	—	15.00	—

As last (5), but spelling STPOESSNER. Error.

Also claimed without evidence as Vietnam and Brazil. The port city was renamed La Ciudad del Este after Stroessner's removal.

ASUNCION DEPARTMENT

Asuncion
HOTEL-CASINO
ITA-ENRAMADA

Rulau	Date	Metal	Size	F	VF	EF	Unc
Asu 6	ND	Svd/BR	21mm	12.00	—	—	—

HOTEL-CASINO / 10 / ITA-ENRAMADA. Rv: Same as obverse. Plain edge. There are 3 die varieties. (Rulau coll.)

Asu 7	ND	Svd/BR	21mm	12.00	—	—	—

As last, but 5. (Bernal 419)

Gaming machine tokens. Also claimed without evidence for Brazil, Chile and Colombia.

BOQUERON DEPARTMENT

Puerto Guarani
SOCIEDAD FORESTAL

Puerto Pinasco
P.

Rulau	Date	Metal	Size	VG	F	VF	Unc
Boq 12	ND	Copper	21.5mm	—	—	10.00	—

P. Rv: VALE / 20 / CENTAVOS / EN COMERCIO. Dentilated border on each side.

Modern token distributed by International Products Corp., 29 Broadway, New York City, for use in Puerto Pinasco, Paraguay.

Puerto Sastre
CAMPOS Y QUEBRACHALES

Rulau	Date	Metal	Size	VG	F	VF	Unc
Boq 14	ND	Aluminum	35.3mm	—	—	—	—

CAMPOS Y QUEBRACHALES / FABRICA / - DE - / TANINO / . PUERTO SASTRE . Rv: 1 (large, shaded) / KILO. Ctsp L in reverse field.

Rulau	Date	Metal	Size	VG	F	VF	Unc
Boq 15	ND	Aluminum	35.4mm	—	—	—	—

CAMPOS / -Y- / QUEBRACHALES / -.- / PUERTO SASTRE. Rv: 1 (large, shaded) / KILO / (tiny) A. N. BARES (E is retrograde). Ctsp 8 in reverse field.

Rulau	Date	Metal	Size	VG	F	VF	Unc
Boq 17	ND	Aluminum	38.8mm	—	—	—	—

CAMPOS Y QUEBRACHALES / FABRICA / - DE - / TANINO / . PUERTO SASTRE . Rv: 2 (large, shaded) / KILOS. Along lower right rim: (tiny) E. BARES.

This was a tannin producing facility headquartered at Puerto Sastre in Boqueron Dept. Its branch operation at Puerto Mihanovich in neighboring Olimpo Dept. also issued tokens in kilo denominations.

Paraguay won the Chaco War of 1932-35 and afterward organized the newly-won Bolivian territory into Boqueron and Olimpo Departments, and extended the boundaries of Presidente Hayes Department northward. There had been Chaco agreements between Bolivia and Paraguay in 1913, 1915 and 1928-29, but the Chaco was not definitively assigned to Paraguay until 1935.

Thus these tokens may be post-1935 in provenance.

CONCEPCION DEPARTMENT
Puerto Max
QUEBRACHALES FUSIONADOS

Rulau	Date	Metal	Size	VG	F	VF	Unc
Ccn 5	ND	Brass	39.3mm	—	—	—	—

Logo of concentric circles. Around: SOCIEDAD ANONIMA / * QUEBRACHALES FUSIONADOS *. Rv: PUERTO MAX / -.- / VALE DE ALMACEN / .-. / SF. monogram 10.

Rulau	Date	Metal	Size	VG	F	VF	Unc
Ccn 6	ND	Brass	34.2mm	—	—	—	—

As last, but 5.

Rulau	Date	Metal	Size	VG	F	VF	Unc
Ccn 7	ND	Brass	30.4mm	—	—	—	—
Ccn 8	ND	Brass	24mm	—	—	—	—

As last, but 1.
As last, but 0.50.

OLIMPO DEPARTMENT

Puerto Mihanovich
CAMPOS Y QUEBRACHALES

Rulau	Date	Metal	Size	VG	F	VF	Unc
Olm 7	ND	Aluminum	35.5mm	12.50	20.00	—	—

CAMPOS Y QUEBRACHALES / FABRICA / - DE - /
TANINO / . PUERTO SASTRE . Rv: PUERTO N.
MIHANOVICH / 1 (large, shaded) / . KILO . Along
lower right rim: (tiny) MAIPU 270.

Rulau	Date	Metal	Size	VG	F	VF	Unc
Olm 8	ND	Aluminum	40.4mm	—	—	Rare	—

As last, but 2 (large, shaded) / KILOS.

This tannin producing facility was a branch of the Puerto Sastre firm, which also issued tokens in Boqueron Dept. Tokens were probably issued after 1935 (see Campos y Quebrachales under Boqueron Dept.)

SAN PEDRO DEPARTMENT

Itacurubi del Rosario
OBRAJE ITACURUBI

Rulau	Date	Metal	Size	VG	F	VF	Unc
SPD 3	1912	CN	20.1mm	—	—	—	—

OBRAJE ITACURUBI / PARAGUAY / J. H. A. BOX.
Rv: 1912 / 0.50 (shaded) / CENTAVOS. Plain edge.

Also reported in Brass.

UNATTRIBUTED PARAGUAY

C. A.

Rulau	Date	Metal	Size	VG	F	VF	EF
Par 1	ND	Copper	36mm	—	—	65.00	—

C A ctsp on Paraguay 1870 4-centesimos, KM-4.1.
(ANS coll.)

A hacienda token, according to the ANS ticket.

C-A-1

Rulau	Date	Metal	Size	VG	F	VF	EF
Par 3	ND	Copper	36mm	15.00	—	—	—

C-A-1 ctsp on Paraguay 1870 4-centesimos, KM-4.1.

C. M. C.

Rulau	Date	Metal	Size	VG	F	VF	Unc
Par 5	ND	Brass	22.5mm	—	3.50	—	—

C M C / 1 / CARNE. Rv: Blank.

Tentative attribution. Acquired in Paraguay.

San Antonio
I. P. C.

Rulau	Date	Metal	Size	VG	F	VF	Unc
Par 7	ND	xx	32mm	—	—	Scarce	—

xx Black fiber.
   (All incused): I P C / 2 Ks. / SAN ANTONIO. Rv:
Blank. (George Lill coll.)

Rulau	Date	Metal	Size	VG	F	VF	Unc
Par 8	ND	**	32mm	—	—	Scarce	—

** Dark blue fiber.
   As last, but 1 K. (George Lill coll.)

CAFE NACIONAL

Rulau	Date	Metal	Size	VG	F	VF	Unc
Par 10	ND	CN	24.2mm	—	—	—	—

(All incused): CAFE NACIONAL / 20 / - J.R. -. Rv: Blank.

Rulau	Date	Metal	Size	VG	F	VF	Unc
Par 11	ND	CN	27mm	—	—	—	—

(All incused): CAFE NACIONAL / 50 / - J.R. -. Rv: Blank.

These tokens were hole-cancelled after their use ended. Uncancelled tokens are scarce.

Rulau	Date	Metal	Size	VG	F	VF	Unc
Par 13	ND	Aluminum	23.8mm	—	—	—	—

CN monogram. Rv: 10. Beaded border on each side.

COVTINO

Rulau	Date	Metal	Size	VG	F	VF	EF
Par 16	ND	Copper	25.5mm	—	—	150.00	—

.*. / (Radiant Sunface); amid the rays is: C-O-V-T-I-N-O-*-*-*, all in octagonal frame, ctsp on worn, clipped copper coin. (Fonrobert 10201; Ekund 1633)

Counterstamped before 1878.

C. E.
(Centro Español)

Rulau	Date	Metal	Size	VG	F	VF	Unc
Par 19	ND	Aluminum	Rect 25.3x15.4mm	—	—	—	—

2 0 c /Ctsp C. E. Rv: Blank. Raised rim.

Rulau	Date	Metal	Size	VG	F	VF	Unc
Par 20	ND	CN	27mm	—	—	—	—

(Ornament) / 7 0 c- / (ornament). Ctsp C -- E. Rv: Blank. Plain edge.

Puerto Galileo
ESTANCIAS Y QUEBRACHALES

Rulau	Date	Metal	Size	VG	F	VF	Unc
Par 25	ND	Copper	34mm	—	—	—	—

ESTANCIAS / Y / QUEBRACHALES / (ornament) / PUERTO GALILEO. Rv: 2 (large, shaded). Plain edge.

Rulau	Date	Metal	Size	VG	F	VF	Unc
Par 26	ND	Copper	30.8mm	—	—	—	—

As last, but 1 (large, shaded).

Rulau	Date	Metal	Size	VG	F	VF	Unc
Par 27	ND	Copper	26mm	—	—	25.00	—

As last, but 0.50 (large, shaded).

Quebracho is a tropical hardwood tree. Estancias Y Quebrachales = Ranches and forests.
Campos Y Quebrachales = Fields and forests.

LA GUARDIA NACIONAL

Rulau	Date	Metal	Size	VG	F	VF	Unc
Par 33	1901	Brass	26.5mm	—	25.00	—	—

Soldier standing, facing. Around: ORGANIZACION DE LA GUARDIA NACIONAL / * 1a. CIRCUN-SCRIPCION *. Rv: Paraguayan shield in laurel wreath. Around: REPUBLICA DEL PARAGUAY / * 25 DE NOVIEMBRE 1901 *. Plain edge. Issued with loop.

These medals, which are scarce, were originally issued with a silver wash. Specialist George Lill says he saw about 10 of them in the decade of the 1980's in South America.

Parac
A. P. M.
(Atilio Peña Machain)

Rulau	Date	Metal	Size	VG	F	VF	Unc
Par 46	ND	Aluminum	$$	—	—	—	—

$$ Diamond-shaped, 37.7x27.7mm.
As last, but 2.

Rulau	Date	Metal	Size	VG	F	VF	Unc
Par 36	ND	Copper	26.2mm	—	—	Rare	—

A. P. y M. above Liberty cap on pole, wreath below. Rv: PARAC / VALE / ¼. Plain edge. (ANS coll.)

Rulau	Date	Metal	Size	VG	F	VF	Unc
Par 37	ND	Copper	20mm	—	—	Rare	—

A. P. M. above Liberty cap on pole, wreath below. Rv: PARAC / VALE / ⅛. Plain edge.

Values given are one-quarter and one-eighth real. Paraguay abandoned the peso-real system for decimalization in 1870, thus these tokens predate 1870. They are among Paraguay's earliest and rarest private currency tokens.

Rulau	Date	Metal	Size	VG	F	VF	Unc
Par 47	ND	Aluminum	XX	—	—	—	—

XX Diamod-shaped, 29.5x23.7mm.
As last, but 1 divides K1 -- 1o.

Rulau	Date	Metal	Size	VG	F	VF	Unc
Par 50	ND	Aluminum	25.3mm	—	—	—	—

Triangular logo as on above tokens, surrounded by legend in outer triangle: INTERNACIONAL / COMPANIA / DE PRODUCTOS. Rv: 2 (large, shaded) / KILOS / (small) / A. N. BARES.

MERCADO INCLAN

Rulau	Date	Metal	Size	VG	F	VF	Unc
Par 39	ND	Aluminum	20.5mm	—	8.00	—	—

MERCADO / + INCLAN +. Rv: SUCESION / + UGO +. Plain edge.

Acquired in Paraguay; tentative attribution. Dr. Pusineri Scala says it is not Paraguayan.

IP Monogram
(Internacional Compania de Productos)

Rulau	Date	Metal	Size	VG	F	VF	Unc
Par 42	ND	Aluminum	Hexag 27.5x34.5mm	—	—	10.00	—

IP monogram within triangle. Rv: 2 (large, shaded) / Kgs. (George Lill collection)

Rulau	Date	Metal	Size	VG	F	VF	Unc
Par 43	ND	Aluminum	Hexag 22x26.5mm	—	—	10.00	—

As last, but 1 / Kg.

Collected in Paraguay. Kgs = Kilograms.

Rulau	Date	Metal	Size	VG	F	VF	Unc
Par 44	ND	Aluminum	&&	—	—	—	—

&& Diamond-shaped, 38x 31mm.
Obverse as last. Rv: 5 (large, shaded) divides Ki -- los.

L P Monogram
(Luis Patri)

Rulau	Date	Metal	Size	VG	F	VF	Unc
Par 52	ND	Copper	21.7mm	—	—	—	—

Ornate LP monogram. Rv: VALE / * 0.20 * / EN CONSUMO.

Rulau	Date	Metal	Size	VG	F	VF	Unc
Par 54	ND	Brass	21mm	—	—	—	—

Ornate LP monogram / (tiny) A. BARES. Rv: VALE / * 0.20 * / EN CONSUMO.

PARAGUAY LAND CATTLE CO.

Rulau	Date	Metal	Size	VG	F	VF	Unc
Par 60	1912	Brass	38mm	—	—	100.00	—

Large PLC monogram at center. PARAGUAY LAND CATTLE Co. / . 1912 . around. Rv: Large numeral 100 on shaded central disc. Plain edge.

Rulau	Date	Metal	Size	VG	F	VF	Unc
Par 61	1912	Brass	34.3mm	—	—	100.	—

As last, but 50.

| Par 62 | 1912 | Copper | 31mm | — | 30.00 | 45.00 | — |

As last, but 20. (Jerry Schimmel report)

| Par 63 | 1912 | Brass | 26mm | — | — | 55.00 | — |

As last, but 10. (ANS coll.)

| Par 64 | 1912 | Copper | 21mm | — | 40.00 | — | — |

As last, but 5.

This token series may have been struck in England.

Puerto Maria QUEBRACHALES FUSIONADOS

Rulau	Date	Metal	Size	VG	F	VF	Unc
Par 66	ND	Brass	30.4mm	—	—	—	—

Logo of concentric circles. Around: SOCIEDAD ANONIMA / * "QUEBRACHALES FUSIONADOS" *. Rv: PUERTO MARIA / -.- / VALE DE ALMACEN / .-. / FS. monogram 1.

| Par 67 | ND | Brass | 25.8mm | — | — | — | — |

Obverse as last. Rv: VALE DE ALMACEN / $0.50 / * PUERTO MARIA *.

Quebrachales Fusionados Sociedad Anonima = Merged (Hardwood) Forests Inc. Almacen = Grocery.

A similar set of tokens was issued for the organization's operations at Puerto Max.

RECUERDO DE PRISONEROS TUCUMAN

Rulau	Date	Metal	Size	VG	F	VF	Unc
Par 70	1925	CN	22mm	—	—	—	—

(All engraved): REPUBLICA DEL PARAGUAY. Rv: RECUERDO DE PRISONEROS TUCUMAN 1/IX/1925. Engraved on 1935 token type, Herz 210. (ANS coll.)

Tucuman is in Argentina.

PERU

ANCASH DEPARTMENT

Santa
DIONISIO DERTEANO
Hacienda Puente

Rulau	Date	Metal	Size	VG	F	VF	Unc
Anc 1	1878	CN	26mm	—	10.00	15.00	20.00

Sheaf of wheat. Around: HACIENDA PUENTE / 1878 / SANTA. Rv: Within wreath: VALE / 20 / CENTAVOS. Below: DIONISIO DERTEANO. Plain edge. (Ulex 3408; Schrötter 85; Scott; Eklund 1387; Schiaffino 589)

Rulau	Date	Metal	Size	VG	F	VF	Unc
Anc 2	1878	CN	24mm	—	5.00	8.00	15.00

As last, but 10 / CENTAVOS. (Eklund 1386; Schiaf. 588)

Rulau	Date	Metal	Size	VG	F	VF	Unc
Anc 3	1878	CN	18mm	—	10.00	16.00	20.00

As last, but 5 / CENTAVOS. (Ulex 3408; Eklund 1385; Schiaf. 587)

This issue has always been fairly available. There were three complete sets of these tokens in the 1908 Ulex sale in Berlin. Von Schrötter attributed these tokens in error to Mexico.

For more information on this issue, see the *TAMS Journal* for Dec. 1986, page 188.

APURIMAC DEPARTMENT

Abancay
L. LETONA
Hacienda Pachachaca

Rulau	Date	Metal	Size	VG	F	VF	Unc
Apu 5	ND	Brass	30mm	—	—	20.00	—

HACIENDA / * / L. LETONA / * / PACHACHACA. Rv: VALE POR / 4 / REALES. Plain edge. (Ulex 3396; Schiaffino 650; Eklund 1354)

Rulau	Date	Metal	Size	VG	F	VF	Unc
Apu 6	ND	Brass	27mm	—	—	—	—

As last, but 2 / REALES. Rare. (Schiaf. 649)

Rulau	Date	Metal	Size	VG	F	VF	Unc
Apu 7	ND	Brass	23mm	—	—	—	—

As last, but 1 / REAL. Scarce. (Schiaf. 648)

Rulau	Date	Metal	Size	VG	F	VF	Unc
Apu 9	ND	Bronze	23mm	—	8.50	12.50	—

HACIENDA / * / L. LETONA / * / PACHACHACA. Rv: VALE POR * / ¼ / AGUARDIENTE. (Eklund 1355; Schiaf. 651; Kirtley March 1989 sale, lot 890)

Rulau	Date	Metal	Size	VG	F	VF	Unc
Apu 11	ND	Bronze	27mm	—	—	12.50	—

As last, but 1 / ARROBA AGUARDIENTE. (Eklund 1356; Schiaf. 652)

Rulau	Date	Metal	Size	VG	F	VF	Unc
Apu 12	ND	Bronze	30mm	—	—	12.50	—

As last, but 1 QUINTAL / AGUARDIENTE. (Schiaf. 653; Eklund 1357)

Aguardiente is a raw, sugar-based brandy. The fraction ¼ on the Aguardiente token above stands for ¼ quintal, or 25.36 pounds avoirdupois.

The quintal is a measure of weight. In Peru it was 101.43 pounds avoirdupois. In other Latin American nations the quintal was a bit less, 101.4 pounds. In Brazil it was 129.54 pounds.

The arroba is a liquid measure equal in Peru to 6.7 gallons; the word arroba can also mean a measure of weight of 25.36 pounds, or precisely the same as the ¼ quintal.

For more information on this hacienda, see "Las Fichas Hacendarias de Pachachaca y San Gabriel" by Ernesto Melgar in *Revista de la Sociedad Numismatica del Peru* for 1978. Dr. Lazaro Letona owned both Pachachaca and San Gabriel haciendas.

A Brief History of Pachachaca

Doña Leonor de Costilla y Gallinato donated the sugar cane plantation of Pachachaca to the Jesuit Order in colonial times. Situated in Pachachaca valley in the Province of Abancay (Apurimac Department, this hacienda was the most extensive and wealthiest of the Jesuits' highland properties. In 1767 it was valued at 227,319 pesos.

The high levels of production achieved by the Society of Jesus were not maintained by the royal administration after it had been confiscated from the order, and it passed into the hands of the republic in ruinous condition. The republican regime sold Pachachaca to the Argentinian citizen Bartolome Arroz.

The senior Arroz was succeeded by his son Antonio Arroz, but he died in Europe, leaving Pachachaca to his widow. The widow remarried a doctor from El Salvador, Lazaro Letona, and the Letonas worked the plantation.

In 1887 Letona was so successful that he acquired most of the valley of Pachachaca and was the richest landowner in Abancay. He operated the haciendas of Pachachaca, San Gabriel and Illanga. The first two plantations issued tokens with Letona's name on them.

A Peruvian law in 1878 required the withdrawal of tokens that would substitute for official coinage. It is possible that those denominated in reales were issued prior to 1878 and those in arrobas or quintals after that time as an evasion. But there are contemporary accounts (from about 1865) noting that Indian workers were paid in aguardiente (raw brandy), which the arroba-quintal tokens measured.

L. LETONA
Hacienda San Gabriel

Rulau	Date	Metal	Size	VG	F	VF	Unc
Apu 14	ND	Brass	30mm	—	—	—	—

L. LETONA / HACIENDA SAN GABRIEL. Rv: VALE POR / 4 / REALES. Rare. (Schiaffino 670)

Rulau	Date	Metal	Size	VG	F	VF	Unc
Apu 15	ND	Brass	27mm	—	—	—	—

As last, but 2 / REALES. (Schiaf. 669)

Rulau	Date	Metal	Size	VG	F	VF	Unc
Apu 16	ND	Brass	23mm	—	—	—	—

As last, but 1 / REAL. (Schiaf. 668)

Rulau	Date	Metal	Size	VG	F	VF	Unc
Apu 18	ND	Bronze	30mm	—	8.00	12.00	—

As last, but VALE POR / 1 QUINTAL / AGUARDIENTE. (Schiaf. 673; Kirtley March 1989 sale, lot 883)

Rulau	Date	Metal	Size	VG	F	VF	Unc
Apu 19	ND	Bronze	27mm	—	—	—	—

As last, but 1 ARROBA / AGUARDIENTE. (Schiaf. 672)

Rulau	Date	Metal	Size	VG	F	VF	Unc
Apu 20	ND	Bronze	23mm	—	—	12.00	—

As last, but ¼ / AGUARDIENTE. (Schiaf. 671)

For an explanation of this series of Lazaro Letona, see under Hacienda Pachachaca in this reference.

AREQUIPA DEPARTMENT

Arequipa
FERRO CARRIL DE MOLLENDO

Rulau	Date	Metal	Size	F	VF	EF	Unc
Aqp 1	1871	Silver	23.3mm	—	—	50.00	60.00

Locomotive (of steam type 2-6-0) right in central circle. Around: FERRO CARRIL DE MOLLENDO A AREQUIPA. Rv: DECRETADO / EN / 30 DE ABRIL DE / 1868 / INAUGURO SE / EN 1o ENERO DE / 1871. Plain edge. Weight 5.1 grams. (Fonrobert 9246; Christensen Apr. 1976 sale, lot 1709; Dick Grinolds coll.)

Rulau	Date	Metal	Size	F	VF	EF	Unc
Aqp 2	1871	Copper	23.3mm	—	—	—	28.00

As last.

Issued to honor the opening of the railway from Mollendo, a port city on the Pacific south of Arequipa, to the department capital some 60 miles inland. The railroad was authorized in 1868 and inaugurated Jan. 1, 1871.

M. FORGA

Rulau	Date	Metal	Size	VG	F	VF	Unc
Aqp 4	ND	Bronze	24mm	—	—	35.00	60.00

Misti volcano. Rv: * M. FORGA * / 20 C / AREQUIPA. (Scott; Eklund 1237; Schiaffino 754)

Rulau	Date	Metal	Size	VG	F	VF	Unc
Aqp 5	ND	Bronze	21mm	—	—	25.00	—

As last, but 10 C. (Schiaf. 753)

Arequipa is located at the foot of Misti volcano. In his 1913 *Copper Coin Catalog*, John W. Scott referred to this mountain as "Crater Misti."
The 10-centavo token is known counterstamped 5 (worth $20 in VF).

JOSE M. OSORIA

Rulau	Date	Metal	Size	VG	F	VF	Unc
Aqp 10	1862	Brass	20mm	—	—	17.50	—

Flower. Around: AREQUIPA / (ornaments). Rv: JOSE . M. OSORIA / 1 (in beaded circle) / +1862.+ (Eklund 1238; Schiaffino 743)

Rulau	Date	Metal	Size	VG	F	VF	Unc
Aqp 12	ND	Copper	20mm	8.00	—	17.50	—

Obverse similar to last. Rv: * / MEDIO / REAL in palm and laurel wreath. (Eklund 1239; Schiaffino 945)

Schiaffino spelled the surname Osorio, but the ANS specimen of Eklund 1238 clearly states Osoria.

Camana
HACIENDA PUCCHUM

Rulau	Date	Metal	Size	VG	F	VF	Unc
Aqp 15	ND	Aluminum	21mm	—	—	6.00	8.50

HACIENDA PUCCHUM / CAMANA. Rv: VALE POR MERCADERIAS / 10. (Schiaffino 666). May also exist in Brass.

Rulau	Date	Metal	Size	VG	F	VF	Unc
Aqp 16	ND	Aluminum	18mm	—	—	6.00	8.50

As last, but 5. (Schiaf. 665)

Huantajaya
MINA SAN BARTOLO

Rulau	Date	Metal	Size	VG	F	VF	Unc
Aqp 19	ND	++	26mm	—	22.50	35.00	—

++ Red vulcanite.
MINA SAN BARTOLO / (Star of David in circle) / . HUANTAJAYA . Rv: VALE VEINTE Cts / EN / MERCADERIAS / 20 C / ANTONIO VALDES C. (Ulex 3382; Eklund 1312)

A silver mine.

AYACUCHO DEPARTMENT

Ayacucho
ROMERIAS ESPAÑOLAS

Rulau	Date	Metal	Size	F	VF	EF	Unc
Aya 2	1896	Gilt/Bz	Oct 28.2mm	—	—	10.00	15.00

Crowned, mantled Spanish royal arms. Rv: ROMERIAS ESPAÑOLAS / 2 / FEBRERO / 1896 / * AYACUCHO *. Plain edge. Looped for suspension. (Rulau coll., ex-Barinaga)

Romerias Españolas = Spanish festivals of fellowship.

344

CALLAO CONSTITUTIONAL PROVINCE

Callao (City)
BILLAR DE LOS AMIGOS

Rulau	Date	Metal	Size	VG	F	VF	Unc
Cal 1	ND	Copper	30mm	4.00	9.00	—	—

BILLAR de los AMIGOS / 1 SOL (in circle) / . callao. Rv: J.M.Y.CA. (Ulex 3342; Schiaffino 875)

Rulau	Date	Metal	Size	VG	F	VF	Unc
Cal 2	ND	Copper	30mm	—	—	—	—

As last, but ctsp with a Star. (Schiaffino 875a)

Billar de los Amigos = Billiards of the Friends.

CALLAO CLUB

Rulau	Date	Metal	Size	VG	F	VF	Unc
Cal 4	1867	CN	30mm	—	15.00	30.00	60.00

THE CLUB / CALLAO / * FOUNDED 1867 *. Rv: FIVE / REALES. (Schiaffino 901)

Rulau	Date	Metal	Size	VG	F	VF	Unc
Cal 5	1867	CN	24mm	—	—	30.00	—

As last, but TWO / REALES. (Schiaf. 899)

Rulau	Date	Metal	Size	VG	F	VF	Unc
Cal 6	1867	CN	Oval 27x18mm	—	—	30.00	—

As last, but shape of flan changes. (Schiaf. 900, *TAMS Journal for Oct. 1971*, page 191; Eklund 1293)

Rulau	Date	Metal	Size	VG	F	VF	Unc
Cal 7	1867	CN	20mm	—	—	20.00	50.00

As last, but ONE / REAL. (Schiaf. 897; Eklund 1292)

Rulau	Date	Metal	Size	VG	F	VF	Unc
Cal 8	1867	CN	Oval 24x15mm	—	—	30.00	—

As last, but shape of flan changes. (Schiaf. 898; TAMS Maverick 3393)

Supposedly a brothel.

CHOCOLATERIA J. DEVOTO

Rulau	Date	Metal	Size	VG	F	VF	Unc
Cal 11	1863	Brass	20mm	—	—	25.00	—

CHOCOLATERIA J. DEVOTO / 1 divides RE--AL / * 1863 *. Rv: DULCERIA / (star in circle) / ----CALLAO----. (Schiaffino 847)

COLVILLE & CO.

Rulau	Date	Metal	Size	VG	F	VF	Unc
Cal 13	ND	Copper	20mm	—	18.00	25.00	—

Defiant eagle stands left. Around: LIBRERIA AMERICANA. Rv: COLVILLE & Co / UN REAL / CALLAO. Plain edge. (Eklund 1284; Schiaffino 789)

Libreria Americana = American bookstore.

FONDA DE ROMA

Rulau	Date	Metal	Size	VG	F	VF	Unc
Cal 15	ND	Copper	20mm	—	18.00	25.00	32.50

FONDA DE ROMA / (eagle). Rv: UN / REAL. (Schiaffino 849; Eklund 2309)

Rulau	Date	Metal	Size	VG	F	VF	Unc
Cal 16	ND	Copper	20mm	—	18.00	25.00	32.50

As last, but MEDIO / REAL. (Sch. 848)

Fonda de Roma = Rome Inn.

HOTEL YTALIANO

Rulau	Date	Metal	Size	VG	F	VF	Unc
Cal 19	1863	Brass	20mm	—	—	30.00	35.00

Crowned female; 5-pointed star. Around: HOTEL YTALIANO. Rv: CALLAO / 1 (large) / 1863. (Fonrobert 9196; Eklund 1285; Ulex 3343; Schiaffino 885)

In an article published in 1970 in *Revista de la Sociedad Numismatica del Peru* entitled "Las Fichas Peruanas," Luis de Aliaga refers to aluminum tokens of this hotel in 1 and 10-centimo denominations bearing the date 1863. Since aluminum did not become available commercially for use in tokens before about 1891, this must indicate a founding date.

Fonrobert reported the brass 1863 token in 1878 with full description; for some reason Jose Antonio Schiaffino in his 1984 catalog of Peruvian tokens did not mention it.

A "10" denomination token in brass is reported.

Rulau	Date	Metal	Size	VG	F	VF	Unc
Cal 21	1863 *	Aluminum	--mm	—	—	—	—

HOTEL YTALIANO. 1863. Rv: 10 CENTIMOS. (Schiaffino 886)

Rulau	Date	Metal	Size	VG	F	VF	Unc
Cal 22	1863 *	Aluminum	--mm	—	—	—	—

As last, but 1 CENTIMO. (Sch. 885)

* Not issued before 1890.

SCHMIDT'S SALOON

Rulau	Date	Metal	Size	VG	F	VF	Unc
Cal 27	(ca 1860)	Brass	20mm	12.00	18.50	26.00	35.00

Bottle between two glasses atop a board (bar counter), a corkscrew left is below. All within a circular laurel wreath. Rv: SCHMIDTs SALOON / 1 / REAL / * CALLAO *. Plain edge. (Eklund 1291; Schiaffino 868; Rulau Coll; Ulex 3343)

This is a handsome token, one of the classic tokens of South America, probably struck in the United States. By its style it must date from about 1860. It resembles the workmanship on U.S. Civil War tokens, but the obverse die is one that has not been used in any other country of which we are aware.

CUZCO DEPARTMENT

Quillabamba
M. P. C.
(Mariano Pancorvo Carrasco)

Rulau	Date	Metal	Size	VG	F	VF	Unc
Cuz 7	ND	CN	19mm	—	—	—	—

M. P. C. Rv: REPRESENTA / 1/ REAL. (Schiaffino 645)

Rulau	Date	Metal	Size	VG	F	VF	Unc
Cuz 8	ND	CN	15mm	—	—	—	—

As last, but ½ / REAL. (Schiaf. 744)

Numismatist Ernesto Melgar discovered these tokens were issued by the hacienda of Mariano Pancorvo Carrasco near Quillabamba.

These tokens have been claimed for Bolivia.

B.L.
(Benjamin Latorre)
Hacienda Maranura

Rulau	Date	Metal	Size	VG	F	VF	Unc
Cuz 11	ND	CN	21mm	—	—	—	—

MARANURA / B. L. Rv: REPRESENTA / DOS / REALES. (Schiaffino 643; Ulex 2675)

Quillabamba is located on the Vilcanota River. Ulex had placed this token under Venezuela.

ICA DEPARTMENT

Chincha Island
QUMLIN

Rulau	Date	Metal	Size	VG	F	VF	Unc
Ica 1	ND	Brass	19mm	—	60.00	135.	

ISLA DE CHINCHA / (Flower) / QUMLIN. Rv: UN / REAL within wreath. (Ulex 3351; Eklund 1301; Schiaffino 925). Also known in Copper.

Rulau	Date	Metal	Size	VG	F	VF	Unc
Ica 2	ND	Brass	19mm	—	—	—	—

As last, but MEDIO / REAL above branches. (Smith Peru 560B; Schiaf. 924)

Rulau	Date	Metal	Size	VG	F	VF	Unc
Ica 3	ND	Brass	19mm	—	—	60.00	—

Similar to last, but no branches. (Scott; Eklund 1300)

Rulau	Date	Metal	Size	VG	F	VF	Unc
Ica 5	1889	Copper	30mm	—	—	125.	200.

ISLAS DE CHINCHA / (Star) / (ornaments). Rv: VALE VEINTE CENTAVOS / 20 / . 1889 . (Eklund 1302; Schiaf. 921)

Rulau	Date	Metal	Size	VG	F	VF	Unc
Ica 6	ND	Copper	32mm	40.00	—	75.00	—

Obverse as last. Rv: Empty space within center of two concentric circles. (Schiaf. 926)

Kenneth Smith considers the Medio Real token of Qumlin a transportation piece, used to pay ferry boat fee from Pisco to Chincha island. Peruvian numismatist Luis de Aliaga considers the 1889-dated token as paying the fare between the port of Pisco and the island of Chincha.

There is another set of tokens for the Chincha Islands issued by Jose Oleviera in brass in 20mm size in denominations of Un Real and Medio Real (Schiaffino 922-923)

The pieces listed above are somewhat anomalous; either they are or are not transportation tokens. Smith (*Catalogue of Wold Transportation Tokens and Passes*) recognized only one of them as such, and Aliaga another. Since the Qumlin pieces are among Peru's classic tokens, issued before decimalization of the currency in 1863, it was thought best to include the series.

Chincha
UNA TAREA - 1850

Rulau	Date	Metal	Size	VG	F	VF	Unc
Ica 9	1850	Bronze	30mm	—	10.00	18.00	—

+ AGOSTO 31 DE 1850 around floreate device. Rv: UNA / TAREA within wreath. Plain edge. (Schiaffino 564)

Rulau	Date	Metal	Size	VG	F	VF	Unc
Ica 10	1850	Copper	30mm	—	10.00	25.00	—

As last. (Schiaf. 565)

Peruvian exonumist Luis de Aliaga attributed this issue to the haciendas of San Jose and San Rejis.

For later tokens of these haciendas, see under Monasi y Bueno and under Carrillo de Albornoz.

J. M. MONASI Y BUENO
Haciendas de San Jose y San Rejis

Rulau	Date	Metal	Size	VG	F	VF	Unc
Ica 12	1876	Copper	30mm	—	—	10.00	—

HACIENDAS DE SAN JOSE Y SAN REGIS / 1876 / +. Rv: J. M. MONASI Y BUENO / VALE / 50 / -.-. (Schiaffino 575)

Rulau	Date	Metal	Size	VG	F	VF	Unc
Ica 13	1876	Copper	23mm	—	—	10.00	—

As last, but 20. (Schiaf. 574)

Rulau	Date	Metal	Size	VG	F	VF	Unc
Ica 14	1876	Copper	18mm	—	—	10.00	—

As last, but 10. (Schiaf. 573)

JULIO CARRILLO DE ALBORNOZ
Haciendas de S. Jose y S. Rejis

Rulau	Date	Metal	Size	VG	F	VF	Unc
Ica 16	ND	Copper	30mm	—	—	—	—

HACIENDAS DE SAN JOSE Y SAN REJIS / (large ornament). Rv: JULIO CARRILLO DE ALBORNOZ/ VALE / 40, Cg. (Schiaffino 676)

Rulau	Date	Metal	Size	VG	F	VF	Unc
Ica 17	ND	Copper	23mm	—	—	—	—

As last, but 20 C. (Schiaf. 675)

Rulau	Date	Metal	Size	VG	F	VF	Unc
Ica 18	ND	Copper	19mm	—	—	—	—

As last, but 10 C. (Schiaf. 674)

P.S.
(Paz Soldan)

Rulau	Date	Metal	Size	VG	F	VF	Unc
Ica 21	ND	Silver	36mm	—	—	Scarce	125.

P. S. monogram. Rv: 5 / PESETAS. (Schiaffino 663)

Rulau	Date	Metal	Size	VG	F	VF	Unc
Ica 22	ND	CN	36mm	—	—	45.00	—

As last. (Sch. 664)

The P. S. used on these pieces is the sign of the Paz Soldan family, proprietors of Hacienda Juan de Arona, in Chincha, Ica Dept.

Palpa
E. H. & CA.
Hacienda Santa Isabel de Lacra

Rulau	Date	Metal	Size	VG	F	VF	Unc
Ica 26	ND	Copper	25mm	—	—	30.00	—

DIEZ / LACRA. Rv: 10 C. / E. H. & Ca. (Schiaffino 621a)

Peruvian exonumist Luis de Aliaga showed that these tokens circulated in Hacienda Santa Isabel de Lacra.

Pisco
CASIMIRO DUENAS

Rulau	Date	Metal	Size	VG	F	VF	Unc
Ica 28	1863	Copper	20mm	—	—	25.00	—

Rosette in circle of leaves. Around: CASIMIRO DUENAS PISCO / * 1863 *. Rv: UN / REAL (in laurel wreath). (Schiaffino 745; Eklund 2154)

Rulau	Date	Metal	Size	VG	F	VF	Unc
Ica 29	1863	Brass	20mm	—	—	20.00	—

As last, but ½ / REAL. (Schiaf. 744)

Quebrada Cuprifera
FELIX MASSARDO Y CA.

Rulau	Date	Metal	Size	VG	F	VF	Unc
Ica 31	1878	Copper	30mm	—	—	15.00	—

FELIX MASSARDO Y Ca. / 1878 (in circle) / *. Rv: MINERAL CINCO CRUZES / 50 (in circle) / *. (Ulex 3725; Eklund 1501; Schiaffino 701)

Rulau	Date	Metal	Size	VG	F	VF	Unc
Ica 32	1878	Copper	24.5mm	5.00	8.50	12.50	—

As last, but 20. (Eklund 1500; Schiaf. 700)

Rulau	Date	Metal	Size	VG	F	VF	Unc
Ica 33	1878	Copper	19.5mm	4.00	—	12.50	—

As last, but 10. (Ek. 1499; Schiaf. 699)

San Juan Bautista
MINA NARDUCCI

Rulau	Date	Metal	Size	VG	F	VF	Unc
Ica 36	ND	Copper	38mm	—	—	40.00	—

Radiant sunface. Rv: MINA NARDUCCI / 1 SOL / . YCA . (Schiaffino 717)

Rulau	Date	Metal	Size	VG	F	VF	Unc
Ica 37	ND	Copper	30mm	—	—	30.00	—

Obverse as last. Rv: MINA NARDUCCI / 50 / C / + / . YCA . (Schiaf. 716)

Rulau	Date	Metal	Size	VG	F	VF	Unc
Ica 38	ND	Copper	24mm	—	30.00	45.00	—

As last, but 20. (Eklund 1407)

MINAS DE CANZA

		Metal	Size	VG	F	VF	Unc
Ica 40	1879	Copper	24.5mm	—	10.00	20.00	—

MINAS DE CANZA / -.- / 1879 / -.- / * YCA *. Rv: 20 / -.- / -* DE *- / -.- / FEBRERO. (Schiaffino 703)

		Metal	Size	VG	F	VF	Unc
Ica 41	1879	Copper	20mm	—	10.00	20.00	—

As last, but 10. (Schiaf. 702)

These tokens occur ctsp P, and are worth about the same thus. "Yca" is an old form of "Ica."

LA LIBERTAD DEPARTMENT

Trujillo
CENTENARIO DE LA INDEPENDENCIA

Rulau	Date	Metal	Size	F	VF	EF	Unc
Lbt 4	1920	Silver	17.5mm	—	12.50	—	20.00

Winged griffin rampant, K shield on its breast. Around: CENTARIO DE LA INDEPENDENCIA / ... Rv: 29 DE DICIEMBRE / TRUJILLO / PERU / + 1820 - 1920 +. Plain edge. (Rulau coll.)

What is described as a griffin could be a winged llama.

C. D. GLYNN Y HNO.

Rulau	Date	Metal	Size	F	VF	EF	Unc
Lbt 6	ND	Copper	--mm	—	—	—	—

C. D. GLYNN Y HNO. Rv: ½ R. (Scott)

HOTEL DEL COMERCIO

Rulau	Date	Metal	Size	VG	F	VF	Unc
Lbt 7	ND	Copper	20mm	—	—	Scarce	—

Fowl on patter. Around: HOTEL DEL COMERCIO / TRUJILLO / (ornament). Rv: Within circular wreath: * / MEDIO (straight) / REAL. Plain edge. (Henkle N/L; ANS coll.)

Lbt 8	ND	Copper	20mm	—	—	Scarce	—

Obverse as last. Rv: On plain field: MEDIO (curved) / REAL. Plain edge. (Eklund 1392; Schiaffino 890)

The latter token occurs ctsp Crown on reverse.

RESTAURANT DE PARIS

Rulau	Date	Metal	Size	VG	F	VF	Unc
Lbt 9	ND	Copper	20mm	—	—	25.00	—

RESTAURANT DE PARIS / (fowl on platter) / (ornament). Rv: MEDIO / REAL. (Schiaffino 858; Eklund 1394)

LUIS G. ALBRECHT
Hacienda Casagrande

Location Uncertain

Rulau	Date	Metal	Size	VG	F	VF	Unc
Lbt 15	ND	++	24mm	—	—	—	35.00

++ Black vulcanite.
VALE DIEZ CENTAVOS / HACIENDA / CASA-GRANDE amid lines, pearls and rays / . LUIS G. ALBRECHT. Rv: VALE DIEZ CENTAVOS / 10 / CENTAVOS / L. G. A. (Schrotter 86; Schiaffino 605)

Lbt 16	ND	**	19mm	—	—	—	35.00

** Orange vulcanite.
As last, but CINCO CENTAVOS. (Schiaffino 604)

Also issued were black vulcanite 20 centavos, 28mm; orange vulcanite 30 centavos, 30mm, and black vulcanite 50 centavos, 35mm. (Schiaffino 606-608).

L. G. A.
(Luis G. Albrecht)

Rulau	Date	Metal	Size	F	VF	EF	Unc
Lbt 18	ND	Gold	34mm	—	—	Rare	—

EMPRESA AGRICOLA CHICAMA LTDA. / L. G. A. Rv: 50 (incuse). Plain edge. (Schiaffino 625)

Lbt 19	ND	Silver	34mm	—	—	Scarce	—

As last, but 35 incused on reverse. Plain edge. (Schiaf. 624)

Lbt 20	ND	Silver	34mm	—	—	Scarce	—

As last, but 25 incused on reverse. (Schiaf. 623)

Peruvian exonumist Luis de Aliaga considers these to be medals for long service as a worker for this agricultural enterprise. The numerals represent years of service rendered.

The Chicama River flows through La Libertad Department to the Pacific Ocean. There is a port city, Puerto Chicama, also in La Libertad Dept.

LIMA DEPARTMENT

Cañete
ENRIQUE SWAYNE

Rulau	Date	Metal	Size	VG	F	VF	Unc
Lim 3	(1870)	Copper	24mm	10.00	15.00	22.50	—

Radiant sunface. Around: PAGADERO EN / CAN-ETE. Rv: HACIENDAS DE / 2 / ENRIQUE SWAYNE. Plain edge. (Ulex 3347; Eklund 1296; Schiaffino 682)

Lim 4	(1870)	Copper	19.5mm	5.00	10.00	18.00	—

Radiant sunface. Around: HACIENDAS DE / . ENRI-QUE SWAYNE. Rv: PAGADERO EN / 1 / CANETE. Plain edge. (Scott; Schiaffino 681)

Rulau	Date	Metal		Size	VG	F	VF	Unc
Lim 5	(1870)	Copper		18mm	3.50	6.00	15.00	—

As last, but ½. (Schiaffino 680; Scott; Guttag 3917; Eklund 1294)

Rulau	Date	Metal	Size	VG	F	VF	Unc
Lim 6	(1870)	Nickel	18mm	—	—	—	275.

As last (½). Pattern? Also reported in silver.

The 2-centavo token was struck at the Lima Mint on blanks for the 2-centavo coin of Peru, KM-188.1. (Research by Henry Christensen).

Regarding Lim 3: Don Guillermo Swayne y Mendoza, a grandson of Enrique Swayne, stated in his *Mis Antepasadas* that the 2-centavo token, of the same size and weight as the national coin of that era, circulated side by side with the coin of the realm in Lima. He says he saw many of them in his youth.

Regarding Lim 6: Guillermo Swayne said he possessed one of these in either nickel or silver; he did not know which. Our contributor Dale Seppa opines that it was probably a pattern struck in nickel by a supplier in an attempt to get an order for nickel coinage, which was then new.

Enrique Swayne also issued paper scrip. See "El Billete de 10 Centavos de Enrique Swayne" by Jaime Otero M. in *Numismatica*, journal of La Sociedad Numismatica del Peru.

Chorrillos
ESCUELA DE APLICACIONES

Rulau	Date	Metal	Size	VG	F	VF	Unc
Lim 9	1898	Copper	23mm	—	—	6.00	—

ESCUELA DE APLICACIONES / CANTINA / COR-RILLOS / 24 ABRIL 1898 / M. A. B. Y. CA. Rv: 20. (Schiaffino 819)

Rulau	Date	Metal	Size	VG	F	VF	Unc
Lim 10	1898	Copper	18mm	—	—	6.00	—

As last, but 10. (Sch. 818)

Huacho
DONAYRE Y COMPANIA

Rulau	Date	Metal	Size	VG	F	VF	Unc
Lim 14	1863	Brass	20mm	—	—	35.00	—

DONAYRE Y COMPANIA / 1863 / HUACHO. Rv: UN / REAL. (Schiaffino 745)

Rulau	Date	Metal	Size	VG	F	VF	Unc
Lim 15	1863	Brass	20mm	—	—	35.00	—

As last, but MEDIO / REAL. (Sch. 734)

HACIENDA CHACACA

Rulau	Date	Metal	Size	VG	F	VF	Unc
Lim 17	1878	CN	30mm	—	—	25.00	—

HACIENDA CHACACA / HUACHO / (cane?) / 1878. Rv: VALE POR / 40 / CENTAVOS. (Schiaffino 586; Eklund 1311)

MUELLE DEL HUACHO

Rulau	Date	Metal	Size	F	VF	EF	Unc
Lim 18	1901	Brass	23mm	—	—	12.50	—

* PADRINO * / (small wreath) / EXMO. SOR. / PRE-SIDENTE / DE LA / REPUBLICA / -- / EDUARDO L. DE ROMAÑA. Rv: Within circular wreath: INAU-GURACION / DEL / MUELLE / DE / HUACHO / -.- / *MARZO DE 1901 *. Plain edge. (Rulau coll.)

Medalet honors the inauguration of the Huacho dock, whose patron was President de Romaña, in March, 1901. The president was a force in opening the Cerro de Pasco mining region to foreign investors.

PRO MARINA

Rulau	Date	Metal	Size	F	VF	EF	Unc
Lim 19	1916	Silver	--mm	—	—	—	40.00

PRO MARINA 20 CENT. Issued by Huacho city council July 28, 1916. Issued holed. (Hudson April 1990 sale, lot 832)

Huaral
GRANADINO
Jesus del Valle

Rulau	Date	Metal	Size	VG	F	VF	Unc
Lim 21	1892	CN	38mm	10.00	14.00	25.00	35.00

Sun rising above three mountains. Around: * GRANA-DINO * / JESUS DEL VALLE 1892. Rv: VALE / 1 (large) / **** SOL ****. Dentilated border on each side. (Eklund 1109; Schiaffino 593)

Rulau	Date	Metal	Size	VG	F	VF	Unc
Lim 22	1892	CN	30mm	—	10.00	—	25.00

Obverse as last, Rv: VALE / 50 / * CENTAVOS *. (Eklund 2388; Schiaf. 592)

Rulau	Date	Metal	Size	VG	F	VF	Unc
Lim 23	1892	CN	24mm	4.00	7.00	12.00	—

As last, but 20. (Schiaf. 591)

Rulau	Date	Metal	Size	VG	F	VF	Unc
Lim 24	1892	CN	18mm	—	5.00	9.00	14.00

As last, but 10. (Schiaf. 590)

GRANADINO
Pasamayo

Rulau	Date	Metal	Size	VG	F	VF	Unc
Lim 26	1892	CN	38mm	—	—	17.00	—

Sun rising above three mountains. Around: * GRANA-DINO * / PASAMAYO 1892. Rv: VALE / 1 (large) / **** SOL ****. (Schiaffino 597)

Rulau	Date	Metal	Size	VG	F	VF	Unc
Lim 27	1892	CN	30mm	—	—	15.00	—

Obverse as last. Rv: VALE / 50 / * CENTAVOS *. (Schiaf. 596)

Rulau	Date	Metal	Size	VG	F	VF	Unc
Lim 28	1892	CN	24mm	—	6.50	10.00	—

As last, but 20. (Schiaf. 595)

Rulau	Date	Metal	Size	VG	F	VF	Unc
Lim 29	1892	CN	18mm	4.00	6.50	10.00	—

As last, but 10. (Schiaf. 594)

In 1983, LIMARC described this as a cotton estate.

Rimac
AGUAS DEL RIMAC

Rulau	Date	Metal	Size	VG	F	VF	Unc
Lim 31	1873	Copper	30mm	—	—	35.00	—

AGUAS DEL RIMAC / (Star) / * 1873 *. Rv: Cantina / ....*.... / VALE / 100. Plain edge. (Schiaffino 817)

Rulau	Date	Metal	Size	VG	F	VF	Unc
Lim 32	1873	Copper	30mm	—	—	—	—

As last, but VALE / 40. (Sch. 816)

Rulau	Date	Metal	Size	VG	F	VF	Unc
Lim 33	1873	Copper	23mm	—	—	—	—

As last, but VALE / 20. (Sch. 815)

Rulau	Date	Metal	Size	VG	F	VF	Unc
Lim 34	1873	Copper	18mm	—	10.00	—	—

As last, but VALE / 10. (Sch. 814; Ulex 3413; Eklund 1361)

Aguas del Rimac Cantina = Waters of Rimac tavern.

V.S.
(Vicente Silva)

Rulau	Date	Metal	Size	VG	F	VF	Unc
Lim 35	(Before 1880)	Brass	32mm				

V S monogram. Rv: Description not available; no value shown. (Schiaffino 697-698). Also issued in Copper.

Silva was an owner of haciendas in Lima Department before the War of the Pacific.

Lima (City)
ANTIGUA BOTICA FRANCESA

Rulau	Date	Metal	Size	VG	F	VF	Unc
Lim 40	ND	Brass	22mm	—	6.00	8.00	12.00

Snake coiled around palm tree, E. D. incused below. Rv: * ANTIGUA BOTICA FRANCESA * / UN / REAL / LIMA. (Ulex 3298; Eklund 1323; Schiaffino 785)

Rulau	Date	Metal	Size	VG	F	VF	Unc
Lim 41	ND	Brass	18mm	—	—	5.00	10.00

As last, but MEDIO / REAL. (Eklund 1322; Schiaf. 784)

These tokens are not round, but polygonal. The 1 R. is 24-sided and the ½ R. 25-sided.

ARBOCCO HS. Y CIA.

Rulau	Date	Metal	Size	F	VF	EF	Unc
Lim 54	ND	Bronze	22mm				9.00

ARBOCCO Hs. Y CIA. / (factory building) / CIGARILLOS / LIMA. Rv: Coat of arms of Imperial Germany, ALEMANIA below. Plain edge. (Ulex 3298; Schiaffino 955)

Rulau	Date	Metal	Size	F	VF	EF	Unc
Lim 44	ND	Aluminum	22mm	—	—	—	8.00

As last, (Schiaffino 956)

The above store cards of the tobacco factory of Arbocco Hermanos & Compania is part of a lengthy series. On each token is displayed the coat of arms of a different nation. All tokens are in bronze in either 22 or 20mm sizes, or aluminum 22mm. The shields shown are those of the nation as it existed at the turn of the 20th century.

The nations represented include: Argentina, Belgium, Bolivia, Brazil, Colombia, Costa Rica, Cuba, Chile, Ecuador, Spain, United States, Greece, Guatemala, Haiti, Honduras, Great Britain, Italy, Japan, Mexico, Monaco, Montenegro, Paraguay, Persia, Peru, Portugal, Russia, Sweden-Norway, Santo Domingo, Switzerland, Turkey, Uruguay and Venezuela. A similar token shows the large initials R F and word Francia for France.

PETER BACIGALUPI

Rulau	Date	Metal	Size	VG	F	VF	Unc
Lim 47	1888	Copper	23mm		—	25.00	—

Crossed bottles and champagne glass. Around: LIMA DE JUNIO / 1888. Rv: YNAUGURACION / DEL / NUEVO SALON / PARRINELLO / CALLE DE LAS MANTIS / No. 2 / PADRINO / PETER BACIGALUPI. (Zaika coll.)

CAPELLA HELADOS

Rulau	Date	Metal	Size	VG	F	VF	Unc
Lim 49	ND	CN/Br	23mm	—	—	15.00	25.00

Dish of ice cream in roped circle. Around: HELADOS / * CAPELLA *. Rv: VALE / 20 cs. / -.- in beaded circle. Around: (Ornament) / PORTAL DE ESCRIBANOS. (Eklund 2294)

Portal de escribanos = Notaries entrance. Helados = Ice creams. Schiaffino reports this token in aluminum, possibly in error. Observed pieces are nickel-plated brass.

CAFE DEL TELEGRAFO

Rulau	Date	Metal	Size	VF	F	VF	Unc
Lim 48	ND	Copper	20mm	—	—	80.00	100.

Crescent moonface left in beaded circle. Around: CAFE DEL TELEGRAFO / *. Rv: * / MEDIO / REAL within wreath. Plain edge. Rare. (Eklund 1326; Schiaffino 807; ANS coll.)

Quite similar moonface tokens were issued by Cafe del Teatro.

CASA DE MONEDA

Rulau	Date	Metal	Size	F	VF	EF	Unc
Lim 50	1873	Copper	23mm	—	—	Rare	—

Gothic script C. S. in beaded circle. Around: CASA DE MONEDA / (quatrefoil). Rv: (Ornament) / LIMA 1873 / (ornament). Plain edge. (Eklund 1327; ANS coll.)

Rulau	Date	Metal	Size	F	VF	EF	Unc
Lim 50A	1873	Copper	18mm	7.00	—	—	—

As last, but smaller.

Rulau	Date	Metal	Size	F	VF	EF	Unc
Lim 51	1878	Copper	18mm	9.00	—	—	—

As last, but 1878. (Limarc report)

All used at the Lima Mint, possibly as passes, or possibly as small change in the canteen.

CHACARILLA

Rulau	Date	Metal	Size	F	VF	EF	Unc
Lim 53	(1870)	Brass	20mm	—	—	15.00	—

* CHACARILLA * / (Bunch of grapes). Rv: Within laural wreath: UN / REAL. Plain edge. (Schiaffino 768; ANS coll.)

FETE NATIONALE

Rulau	Date	Metal	Size	F	VF	EF	Unc
Lim 55	1920	Silver	23.3mm	—	15.00	—	25.00

Liberty head in Phrygian cap right, within palm and oak wreath. Tiny J R at lower left. Rv: FETE / NATIONALE / 14 / JUILLET / * 1920 * / -. LIMA .- / PEROU -- all within ornamental border. Plain edge. Issued holed. (Rulau coll.)

Issued by the French colony in Lima. July 14 is Bastille Day.

FIESTA DEL ARBOL

Rulau	Date	Metal	Size	F	VF	EF	Unc
Lim 57	1909	Silver	30mm	—	—	—	30.00

Man and woman plant tree, small J R under the ground. Around: FIESTA DEL ARBOL / ESCUELAS FISCALES (Festival of the Tree, financial schools). Rv: 13-line inscription; last line reads: + LIMA 31 DE JULIO DE 1909 +. Plain edge. (Rulau coll.; Louis Hudson Apr. 1990 sale, lot 819)

GABAR Y DEHORS

Rulau	Date	Metal	Size	VG	F	VF	Unc
Lim 60	ND	Copper	30mm	—	15.00	—	—

GABAR Y DEHORS / CALLE DE MERCADERES * / (ornament) / 189 / (ornament) / (ornaments). Rv: COMPLET / -.- / No. (numeral stamped incuse. Examined: 6). (Schiaffino 796)

| Lim 61 | ND | Copper | 23mm | — | 15.00 | — | — |

Obverse as last. Rv: COUPE / -.- / No. (numeral stamped incuse. Examined: 3, 4, 5). (Schiaffino 793-795)

Rulau	Date	Metal	Size	VG	F	VF	Unc
Lim 62	ND	Copper	18mm	—	15.00	—	—

Obverse as last. Rv: BARBE / No. (numeral stamped incuse. Examined: 2). (Schiaffino 792)

Gabar and Dehors were French barbers, and they lettered their tokens in French. Complet = Complete. Coupe = Haircut. Barbe = Shave. The discs may have been a system of keeping their patrons waiting in order for service.

HERNANDEZ Y BUMILLER

Rulau	Date	Metal	Size	F	VF	EF	Unc
Lim 69	(1890's?)	Aluminum	22mm	—	—	16.00	20.00

Ornate 8-pointed star, HERNANDEZ Y BUMILLER / . around. Rv: Shield of arms above wreath, PARAGUAY below. Plain edge. (Schiaffino 1014 var.; ANS coll.)

Schiaffino catalogs as numbers 1014 thru 1018 the shield reverses of China, Ecuador, Persia, Russia and Switzerland. Henkle adds those of Dominican Rep. (San Domingo), Montenegro, Peru and Venezuela. Other national shields may exist.

The issuer was a cigarette manufacturing company.

GOLDEN BALL HOTEL

NOTE: the "ball" described in this series is a dotted globe, the heraldic method of showing a golden ball.

Rulau	Date	Metal	Size	VG	F	VF	Unc
Lim 64	1862	Copper	20mm	—	10.00	25.00	—

BOLA DE ORO / (Ball) / 1862. Rv: Within laurel wreath: UN / REAL. (Ulex 3237; Eklund 1342; Schiaffino 883). This token also is known in Gilt Copper and in Brass.

| Lim 65 | ND | Copper | 20mm | 3.00 | 8.00 | 20.00 | — |

GOLDEN BALL HOTEL / (Ball) / bola / * DE ORO *. Within laurel wreath: MEDIO / REAL. (Ulex 3237; Eklund 1340; Scott; Schiaffino 884a; TAMS Maverick 12048)

| Lim 66 | ND | Copper | 20mm | — | 12.50 | — | — |

GOLDEN BALL HOTEL / (Large ball on ornate shield) / . BOLA DE ORO . Rv: Within laurel wreath: * / MEDIO / REAL. (Eklund 1341)

| Lim 67 | ND | Copper | 20mm | — | 12.50 | — | — |

As last, but small ball on ornate shield. (Eklund 1341a)

Records indicate that the Golden Ball Hotel (Hotel Bola de Oro) was owned in 1860 by Marchand and Maroux at Mercaderes 7.

HOTEL AMERICANO

Rulau	Date	Metal	Size	VG	F	VF	Unc
Lim 70	(1860)	Copper	20mm	14.00	22.50	30.00	60.00

Eagle displayed, U.S. shield on its breast. Above: HOTEL AMERICANO. Rv: MEDIO / REAL within wreath. Plain edge. (Ulex 3298; F. 8993; Schiaffino 888; Eklund 1338)

This is one of Peru's "classic" tokens. It was struck in the United States for J. Grelland y Cia at Espaderes 14.

HOTEL FRANCES

Rulau	Date	Metal	Size	VG	F	VF	Unc
Lim 72	(1860)	Copper	20mm	—	—	30.00	—

* PEDRO MAURY * / UN / REAL. Rv: * HOTEL FRANCES - * / (French imperial eagle). Plain edge. (Fonrobert 8994; Schiaffino 893; Eklund 1343)

The hotel was at Bodegones 153 about 1860.

GRAN HOTEL MAURY

Rulau	Date	Metal	Size	VG	F	VF	Unc
Lim 74	ND	Aluminum	23mm	—	—	10.00	20.00

GRAN HOTEL MAURY / VISCONTI Y VELAS-QUEZ. Rv: 10 CENTAVOS. (Schiaffino 894)

| Lim 75 | ND | CN | 19mm | — | — | 10.00 | 20.00 |

HOTEL MAURY / LIMA. Rv: No description available. (Sch. 895)

For other tokens of Visconti y Velasquez, successors to Pedro Maury, see under Confiteria Maury and Restaurant del Parque Zoologico, both in Lima.

CONFITERIA MAURY

Rulau	Date	Metal	Size	VG	F	VF	Unc
Lim 77	ND	**	36mm	—	—	—	—

** Maroon vulcanite.
CONFITERIA MAURY / LIMA / VISCONTI Y VELASQUEZ. Rv: USO INTERNO / 1. (Schiaffino 833)

| Lim 78 | ND | ++ | 33mm | — | — | — | — |

++ Green vulcanite.
As last, but 50. (Sch. 832)

| Lim 79 | ND | && | 34mm | — | — | — | — |

&& Red vulcanite.
As last, but 20. (Sch. 831)

Uso interno = Internal use.

PABELLON NACL.

Rulau	Date	Metal	Size	F	VF	EF	Unc
Lim 85	1840	Silver	32mm	—	—	150.	—

Flag-mantled Peruvian arms, with oval wreath as crest, over trumpets, swords, bell, cannonballs etc. Rv: LA / MONEDA / EN HONOR / AL PABELLON / NACI. AGo. 27. / DE 1840. / (Rosette). (Hudson May 1991 sale, lot 514)

La moneda en honor al pabellon nacional Agosto 27 de 1840 = The coin in honor to the national colors, August 27, 1840. Probably struck at Lima Mint, this is a 4-real proclamation piece.

RESTAURANT DEL PARQUE ZOOLOGICO

Rulau	Date	Metal	Size	VG	F	VF	Unc
Lim 90	ND	Aluminum	Oct 23mm	—	—	—	—

RESTAURANT DEL PARQUE ZOOLOGICO / LIMA / VISCONTI Y VELASQUEZ. Rv: 10 C. Plain edge. (Schiaffino 859)

JUILLET 14
(French issues in Peru)

Rulau	Date	Metal	Size	F	VF	EF	Unc
Lim 94	1886	Silver	23mm	—	—	—	20.00

Allegorical Liberty head (as on early Liberia patterns). JUILLET 14, 1886. Issued holed for suspension from red-white-blue ribbon. Weight 5.3 grams. (Hudson April 1990 sale, lot 822)

| Lim 95 | 1892 | Silver | 23mm | — | — | — | 20.00 |

Republique Francaise shield. Rv: Six-line French inscription. JUILLET 14, 1892. Issue holed. Weight 5.4 grams. (Hudson lot 823)

| Lim 96 | 1895 | Silver | Oct 25mm | — | — | — | 20.00 |

Allegorical Liberty head, flags in background. Rv: Five-line French inscription. JUILLET 14, 1895. Issued holed. Weight 7.3 grams. (Hudson lot 824)

| Lim 97 | 1897 | Silver | Hexag 25mm | — | — | — | 20.00 |

Allegorical Liberty head left. JUILLET 14, 1897. Issued holed. Weight 6.8 grams. (Hudson lots 825-826)

LA PROVIDENCIA SOCIEDAD

Rulau	Date	Metal	Size	VG	F	VF	Unc
Lim 100	1862	CN	19mm	—	3.50	6.00	19.00

Caduceus between two cornucopiae. Rv: :LA PRVIDENCIA SOCIEDAD: / 1 / REAL / FUNDADA 1862 / GENERAL DEL PERU. Reeded edge. (Ulex 3236; Eklund 1347; Schiaffino 783)

| Lim 101 | 1862 | CN | 19mm | — | 4.50 | 9.00 | 25.00 |

As last, but MEDIO / REAL. Reeded edge. (Fonrobert 9127; Ulex 3235; Eklund 1346; Schiaffino 782)

| Lim 103 | 1862 | Brass | 20mm | — | 12.00 | 20.00 | — |

Caduceus between two cornucopiae, oak branches on either side. Rv: * LA PROVIDENCIA SOCIEDAD * / * / UN REAL / FUNDADA 1862 / GENERAL DEL PERU. Reeded edge. (Eklund 1348; Schiaf. 781)

| Lim 104 | 1862 | Brass | 20mm | 4.00 | 7.00 | 10.00 | — |

As last, but MEDIO / REAL. Reeded edge. (Schiaf. 780)

The cupronickel and brass issues are from completely different dies. The CN issues are more plentiful in the marketplace.

La Providencia Sociedad General del Peru was a bank, and its token issues enjoyed wide circulation in Lima and elsewhere, being accepted as ordinary coins. The last republican coinage in the real and half-real denominations came in 1861 (Krause-Mishler numbers 181 and 180), and these were replaced with the decimal system dinero (10 centavos) and half-dinero in 1863, KM numbers 190 and 189 respectively.

The bank was founded in 1862, and the first issues, in CN, may have appeared the same year to help fill the gap between reales and dineros. Old habits die hard with the public, and the decimal system found tough going early on.

The bank, Peru's first private bank, also issued paper money in peso denominations dated 1863, and in sol denominations dated 1864. The bank changed its name to El Banco La Providencia and issued sol-denomination notes dated 1867-1877.

NICOLAS MACCERA Y CIA.

Rulau	Date	Metal	Size	VG	F	VF	Unc
Lim 110	ND	Brass	23mm	—	—	10.00	—

Dish of ice cream in beaded circle. Around: HELA-
DERIA DE FILIPINAS / * LIMA *. Rv: NICOLAS
MACCERA Y CIA. / 10 (in circle) *****. Plain edge.
(Schiaffino 852)

Rulau	Date	Metal	Size	VG	F	VF	Unc
Lim 111	ND	Brass	23mm	—	—	10.00	—

As last, but 5. (Schiaf. 851)

Heladeria de Filipinas = Philippine ice cream parlor.

MORINS HOTEL

Rulau	Date	Metal	Size	VG	F	VF	Unc
Lim 113	1859	Copper	20mm	9.50	13.00	20.00	55.00

MORINS HOTEL / (Building) / LIMA. Rv: * BANOS
TIBIOS * / 1 (large and ornate / * 1859 *. Plain edge.
(Fonrobert 9121; Ulex 3230; Eklund 1345; Rulau coll.;
Schiaffino 880a)

Rulau	Date	Metal	Size	VG	F	VF	Unc
Lim 114	1859	Copper	20mm	9.50	13.00	20.00	55.00

As last, but + 1859 + (crosses in place of rosettes).
(Schiaf. 880b; Rulau coll.)

Rulau	Date	Metal	Size	VG	F	VF	Unc
Lim 115	(1859)	Copper	20mm	—	—	35.00	65.00

As last, but no date. (Schiaf. 882)

Rulau	Date	Metal	Size	VG	F	VF	Unc
Lim 116	1859	Lead	20mm	—	—	80.00	—

Similar to Lim 114 (+ 1859 +). (Schiaf. 881)

There are varieties of the obverse with large letters and small letters on
MORINS HOTEL. Owners were Courejoles y Lopez y Cia at Portal de Escro-
banas 128 in 1860.

Baños Tibios = Lukewarm baths. These tokens were good for one bath at the
hotel. All struck by Scovill Mfg. Co., Waterbury, Conn.

This is one of the "classic" tokens of Peru, known and collected for well over a
century. It can be located in lesser conditions but is quite scarce in Unc.

PERFUMERIA DE GUILLON

Rulau	Date	Metal	Size	VG	F	VF	Unc
Lim 118	ND	Aluminum	28mm	—	—	12.00	16.00

Queen Victoria young head right. Around: PERFUM-
ERIA DE GUILLON / * LIMA *. Rv: POLVOS / DE /
HELICONIA. (Bergsoe 1732; Eklund 1349; Schiaffino
1020)

Located at Calle de Mercaderias 189, according to Luis de Aliaga. This is the
same address given on the tokens of Gabar y Dehors of Lima, which see.

Tokens with the same Queen Victoria obverse, all in aluminum, 28mm, same
values, also occur with these reverse legends: POLVOS / DE / KALYDORINA;
POLVOS / DE / MAGNOLIA; POLVOS / DE / TERCIOPELINA; POLVOS /
DE FLORES DE LA PLATA. All are perfume fragrances of the Guillon firm,
which was headquartered in France; note the following token:

Rulau	Date	Metal	Size	VG	F	VF	Unc
Lim 120	ND	Aluminum	28mm	—	—	12.00	—

Young head of Queen Victoria right. Around: PARFU-
MERIE DE GUILLON / * PARIS *. Rv: No descr.
available. (Schimmel report)

This token, clearly destined for Guillon's French clients, could have been used
among the large French community in Lima as well.

2da FERIA INTERNACIONAL DEL PACIFICO

Rulau	Date	Metal	Size	F	VF	EF	Unc
Lim 125	1961	Nic-Brass	33mm	—	—	—	9.00

Stylized woman (logo of the fair), LIMA 1961 around.
Below: (tiny) Pareja (script) LME monogram. Rv: Four
pennants amid three interlocking circles at top. Below:
12/29 / OCT. 1961 / 2da FERIA / INTERNACIO /
NAL / DEL PACIFICO / LIMA - PERU. Plain edge.
(Zaffern & Rulau colls.)

Commemorates the Second International Trade Fair of the Pacific, held at
Lima Oct. 12-29, 1961. The medalet was designed by Pareja, engraver at the
mint, and struck at the government's Lima Mint (LME monogram mintmark).
The medalet is attractive.

TRAMWAYS DE LIMA

Rulau	Date	Metal	Size	VG	F	VF	Unc
Lim 130	1878	Silver	37mm	—	—	30.00	40.00

Tramcar. TRAMWAYS / DE LIMA around. Rv:
Inscription. 1878. Plain edge. Weight 24.9 grams.
(Mayaux 442; Ulex 3269)

Designed by E. Gris. Commemorates the opening of the Lima Tramways system.

There are 19th century tramways tokens of Lima dated 1877 in hard rubber
and 1884 in copper, from this same system. However, transportation tokens are
not listed in this catalog.

LORETO DEPARTMENT

Iquitos
A.REATEGUI

Rulau	Date	Metal	Size	VG	F	VF	Unc
Lor 6	ND	Brass	31mm	—	—	5.00	7.50

A. REATEGUI / IQUITOS. Rv: FICHA PARA
HACER FUNCIONAR LAS MAQUINAS. Plain edge.
(Schiaffino 879)

Ficha para (etc.) = Token for working the machines. Amusement token, modern.

MADRE DE DIOS DEPARTMENT

Paucartambo
PAUCARTAMBO RUBBER CO. LTD.

Rulau	Date	Metal	Size	F	VF	EF	Unc
MDD 3	ND	**	30mm	—	20.00	—	—

** Cream-black-cream vulcanite.
THE PAUCARTAMBO RUBBER CO. LTD. / PAU-CARTAMBO, MADRE DE DIOS, CR. Rv: VALE POR DIEZ LIBRAS DE ORO EN MERCADERIAS SEGUN CONVENIO. (Schiaffino 690)

Rulau	Date	Metal	Size	F	VF	EF	Unc
MDD 4	ND	**	25mm	—	20.00	—	—

As last, but CINCO LIBRAS. (Schiaf. 689)

Rulau	Date	Metal	Size	F	VF	EF	Unc
MDD 5	ND	**	22mm	—	20.00	—	—

As last, but UNA LIBRA. (Schiaf. 688)

This plantation also issued black vulcanite 2 and 1-sol tokens, and red vulcanite 50 and 20-centavo pieces of similar design. They are worth about 10 percent less than the libra denominations above.

PIURA DEPARTMENT

Piura
POLS PETIT Y CA.

Rulau	Date	Metal	Size	VG	F	VF	Unc
Piu 5	ND	Brass	Oct 24mm	—	—	—	—

POLS PETIT Y CA. PIURA. ½ REAL. (U. 3406)

PUNO DEPARTMENT

W. H. CHRISTY
Empressa Titicaca

Rulau	Date	Metal	Size	VG	F	VF	Unc
Pun 3	1889	CN	21mm	—	—	15.00	—

EMPRESA TITICACA / W. H. CHRISTY / 1889. Rv: VALOR / 10 / CENTAVOS / EN MERCADERIAS. (Schiaffino 738)

Rulau	Date	Metal	Size	VG	F	VF	Unc
Pun 4	1889	xx	36mm	—	—	9.00	—

xx Black vulcanite.
141725 (mfr. no.) / W. H. CHRISTY / 1889 / *+*. Rv: EMPRESA TITICACA / (arc) / VALOR / 20 / CENTAVOS / EN / MERCADERIAS.

Rulau	Date	Metal	Size	VG	F	VF	Unc
Pun 5	1889	xx	30mm	—	—	9.00	—

As last, but 10 / CENTAVOS.

Black vulcanite 5 and 1-centavo tokens are known. These pieces have been claimed for Chile and Bolivia.

TACNA DEPARTMENT

Tacna
ANTONIO BERTELON

Rulau	Date	Metal	Size	VG	F	VF	Unc
Tac 1	ND	Copper	18mm	—	—	25.00	50.00

ANTONIO BERTELON / TACNA. Rv: VALE / UN / CUARTILLO. (Ulex 3417; Schiaffino N/L; Eklund 1560; Neumann 22492)

Rulau	Date	Metal	Size	VG	F	VF	Unc
Tac 2	ND	Copper	15mm	—	—	25.00	50.00

As last, but VALE / MITAD / DE UN / CUARTILLO. (Schiaf. 749; Eklund 1559; Neumann 22493)

Tacna was under Chilean occupation 1879-1929. Issued before 1862.

CLUB DE LA UNION

Rulau	Date	Metal	Size	VG	F	VF	Unc
Tac 5	ND	Copper	27mm	—	—	15.00	—

CLUB DE LA UNION / TACNA. Rv: DOS / REALES. (Schiaffino 910; Neumann 22494; Eklund 1562)

Rulau	Date	Metal	Size	VG	F	VF	Unc
Tac 6	ND	Copper	21mm	—	—	15.00	—

As last, but UN / REAL. (Ulex 3417; Schiaf. 909)

Rulau	Date	Metal	Size	VG	F	VF	Unc
Tac 7	ND	Copper	17mm				

As last, but MEDIO / REAL. (Schiaf. 908)

Rulau	Date	Metal	Size	F	VF	EF	Unc
Tac 9	ND	**	40mm				

** Green vulcanite.
CLUB DE LA UNION / TACNA. Rv: Large $1. (Schiaf. 913)

Rulau	Date	Metal	Size	F	VF	EF	Unc
Tac 10	ND	++	30mm	—	—	—	—

++ Yellow vulcanite.
As last, but 20 C. (Schiaf. 912)

Rulau	Date	Metal	Size	F	VF	EF	Unc
Tac 11	ND	xx	25mm	—	—	—	—

xx Red vulcanite.
As last, but 10 C. (Schiaf. 911)

HRI. GRANJEAN Y CIA.

Rulau	Date	Metal	Size	VG	F	VF	Unc
Tac 13	ND	Brass	27mm	—	—	—	—

Hri-GRANJEAN Y Cia- / DE FABRICA / COS. MALO / RELOJERO / TACNA. Rv: MEDALLA DE HONOR / RELOJERIA / AL RELOX DE CRISTAL. (Eklund 1563; Schiaffino 1026)

UNATTRIBUTED PERU

P. BASSINO
Restaurant Trocadero

Rulau	Date	Metal	Size	VG	F	VF	Unc
Per 3	ND	Bronze	24mm	—	—	—	—

RESTAURANT TROCADERO / P. BASSINO. Rv: 20 CTVS. (Schiaffino 862)

| Per 4 | ND | Bronze | 21mm | — | — | — | — |

As last, but 10 CTVS. (Sch. 861)

J. B.
Hacienda de Chancayllo

Rulau	Date	Metal	Size	VG	F	VF	Unc
Per 6	1872	Copper	30mm	—	—	25.00	—

HACIENDA DE CHANCAYLLO / (View of mountains and buildings). Rv: JULIO DE 1872 / 10 / * J. B. * (Eklund 1498; Schiaffino 568)

| Per 7 | 1872 | Copper | 23mm | — | — | — | — |

As last, but 5. (Schiaf. 567)

J. B. = Jose Balta.

BOTADA AL AGUA
San Roman Family

Rulau	Date	Metal	Size	F	VF	EF	Unc
Per 9	1891	Silver	Oval 25 x 20mm	—	—	17.50	—

Crew in rowing scull. Around: BOTADA AL AGUA / CHALUPA CAPITANIA No. 1 / MAYO 18 DE 1891. Rv: PADRINOS / CORONEL PREFECTO / MANUEL / SAN ROMAN / SENORITA / MARIA JOSEFA SAN ROMAN. Plain edge. (Zaika coll.)

Botada al agua = Water launching? Reverse inscription translates: Patron Col. Prefect Manuel San Roman, Miss Maria Josefa San Roman. A medal.

COLISEO DE GALLOS
LA PAMPILLA

Rulau	Date	Metal	Size	VG	F	VF	Unc
Per 17	ND	Bronze	23mm	—	2.50	—	—

* COLISEO DE GALLOS * / $.2 / -.- / LA PAMPILLA. Rv: Circular laurel wreath. (Schiaffino 876)

ENTRADA AL TEATRO

Rulau	Date	Metal	Size	VG	F	VF	Unc
Per 19	ND	Copper	32mm	—	—	—	—

ENTRADA AL TEATRO. Rv: Theatrical symbols. (Schiaffino 877; Eklund 1786)

Entrada al Teatro = Admittance to the theater.

FONDOS PRO-
MONUMENTOS GRAU

Rulau	Date	Metal	Size	VG	F	VF	Unc
Per 21	1935	Bronze	19.5mm	—	—	8.00	10.00

Peru arms in wreath, FONDOS PRO—MONUMENTOS GRAU around. Rv: 8 DE OCTUBRE. DE 1935 / 20 CENTAVOS / ORO. Plain edge. (Brunk Coll.; Schiaffino 1058)

A civic fund-raising token. Struck at Lima Mint. Similar 1935 tokens for the Armament Fund are worth $6 in Unc.

J.

Rulau	Date	Metal	Size	VG	F	VF	Unc
Per 24	ND	CN	21mm	—	—	3.50	5.00

Large J. Rv: VALE UN / REAL / EN / COMERCIO. Denticled border on each side. Plain edge. (Zaffern coll.)

The token was in an envelope marked Peru and Junin.

J. M. & CO.

Rulau	Date	Metal	Size	VG	F	VF	Unc
Per 26	(?)	Silver	18mm	—	—	50.00	—

J M & CO / (Crossed hammer and pick) ctsp on Peru 1880 silver 10-centavos. (Brunk not listed)

JOSE M. MEJIA
Salon del Loro

Rulau	Date	Metal	Size	VG	F	VF	Unc
Per 28	1887	Copper	35mm	—	—	—	—

SALON DEL LORO / JOSE M. MEJIA / ENERO 1887. Rv: SERVICIO EXCLUSIVO DEL INTERIOR DEL ESTABLTO. No. 500. (Schiaffino 864a)

| Per 29 | (1887) | Copper | 35mm | — | — | — | — |

Obverse blank. Rv: As last. (Sch. 864b)

| Per 30 | 1887 | Copper | 24mm | — | — | — | — |

Obverse as the first token above. Rv: SERVICIO EXCLUSIVO DEL INTERIOR DEL ESTABLTO, NO. 200. (Sch. 863a)

| Per 31 | (1887) | Copper | 24mm | — | — | — | — |

Obverse blank. Rv: As last. (Sch. 863b)

Salon del Lora = Parrot Salon.

MIRANDA Y COSTER
Almacen de Santo Domingo

Rulau	Date	Metal	Size	VG	F	VF	Unc
Per 33	1860	Copper	18mm	—	—	35.00	—

Shield of arms at center. Around: ALMACEN DE Sto DOMINGO *. Rv: MIRANDA Y COSTER / 1 / REAL / 1860. Plain edge. Weight 2.55 grams. (Byrne 1154; Schiaffino 774)

Almacen = Grocery.

PUCARA

Rulau	Date	Metal	Size	VG	F	VF	Unc
Per 35	1861	Copper	20mm	—	—	35.00	—

PUCARA /1861. Rv: MEDIO / REAL. (Schiaffino 566)

This was a hacienda.

SALINA SAN BLAS

Rulau	Date	Metal	Size	VG	F	VF	Unc
Per 38	ND	CN	30mm	—	—	15.00	—

SALINA SAN BLAS / (Factory building). Rv: 40. (Schiaffino 727)

| Per 39 | ND | CN | 24mm | — | — | 11.00 | — |

As last, but 20. (Schiaf. 725; Zaika coll.)

| Per 40 | ND | CN | 21mm | — | — | 20.00 | — |

As last, but 10. (Schiaf. 723)

Salina San Blas was reportedly a salt mine which also produced borax. This series also occurs struck in Brass.

SOCIETE DES INCAS

Rulau	Date	Metal	Size	VG	F	VF	Unc
Per 42	1840	Silver	22mm	—	—	—	—

Pelican. SOCIETE - DES INCAS. Rv: Sun. VALENCI-ENNES. Weight 3.6 grams. (Ulex 3421)

French issue for Peru?

TAMBO

Rulau	Date	Metal	Size	VG	F	VF	EF
Per 44	(1)816	Silver?	16mm	—	—	Rare	—

Crossed sabers over a wreath / TAMBO / o / 29 DE (DE in monogram) JUN. 816. Rv: Button shank at center. Used as a button. (ANS coll.)

(Brand Mark)

Rulau	Date	Metal	Size	VG	F	VF	Unc
Per 45	(?)	Bronze	19mm	—	—	15.00	—

Brand mark ctsp on Great Britain 1910 farthing, KM792.

According to specialist Georg Förster, Ludwigshafen, Germany, these pieces are frequently found in Peru.

SURINAM

IETTON HOLLANDAIS

Rulau	Date	Metal	Size	VG	F	VF	EF
Sur 1	ND	Tin	24mm	—	—	70.00	—

Classical head left within two concentric circles, the inner roped and the outer plain. Around: IETTON HOLLANDAIS / (three rosettes). Rv: Supported arms. Plain edge. Weight 3.65 grams. (Scholten 1444; Byrne 1393; Ulex 2611)

SOCIETEIT VAN SURINAME

Rulau	Date	Metal	Size	F	VF	EF	Unc
Sur 3	1764	Gilt/Cop	20mm	—	—	150.	400.

Budding bush separates 17 -- 64, ground with grass below. Rv: SOCIETEIT / VAN / SURINAME (Surinam Company). Plain Edge. Weight 1.7 grams. (Scholten 1437; Byrne 1391-92)

Most authorities consider the above piece to be a legal tender coin rather than a currency token, as they do the doits and multiple doits of 1679 featuring a parrot, illustrated below.

TB VB

Rulau	Date	Metal	Size	VG	F	VF	EF
Sur 5	ND	CN	33.2mm	—	—	500.	—

Tree separates TB -- VB, in relief, within shield-shaped depression, ctsp on blank cuni planchet. Ctsp incuse to right of shield is large numeral 48. Rv: Blank. Plain edge. (HOL 13990; Rulau Coll., ex-Randel, Holland)

The only reported specimen of this unpublished token was purchased in Netherlands in 1991 and resold in Chicago on March 10, 1991. The 48 may indicate stuivers. Also claimed for Berbice in British Guiana, for Dutch East Indies, and for Curacao.

Prior to 1815 the daalder (Spanish dollar) equaled 48 stuivers, but cupronickel alloys were not in common use that early. Stivers were in use until 1839 in British Guiana (Essequibo & Demerara).

H. DE LA FUENTE

Rulau	Date	Metal	Size	VG	F	VF	Unc
Sur 9	ND	Brass	23mm	—	—	—	—

H. DE LA FUENTE - WAGEN-VRACHT. Rv: Blank. (Eklund 1732; Weyl 2362; Scholten 1445)

C. L. P.

Rulau	Date	Metal	Size	VG	F	VF	EF
Sur 11	ND	Copper	30mm	—	75.00	—	—

C L P in relief within outline depression ctsp on France 1789 1-sol.

In 1982, dealer Carol Plante attributed this to the Howard Gibbs collection sold by Hans M. F. Schulman. The attribution may be in error, or this could be a fantasy piece.

PLANTAGE MARIENBURG

Rulau	Date	Metal	Size	G	VG	F	EF
Sur 15	(1890-1910)	Brass	Rect 21x19mm	—	50.00	75.00	125

PLANTAGE / 10 CENT / MARIENBURG. Rv: Large incused Z. Plain edge. (Byrne 236)

Rulau	Date	Metal	Size	G	VG	F	EF
Sur 16	(1890-1910)	Brass	Rect 22x20mm	—	50.00	85.00	150.

As last, but 25 CENT. Rv: Large incused M. Plain edge. (Byrne 237)

Rulau	Date	Metal	Size	G	VG	F	EF
Sur 17	(1890-1910)	Brass	Rect 22x20mm	—	—	125.	175.

As last, but blank reverse.

These tokens have been claimed by Curacao.

Paramaribo
SURINAM TORARICA HOTEL

Rulau	Date	Metal	Size	VF	EF	Unc	Proof
Sur 20	(1971-72)	Silver	39mm	—	—	30.00	35.00

Hotel building, sunrise behind. Around: VIJTIG SURINAM GUILDEN / SURINAM (on panel) / TORARICA (on panel) / HOTEL CASINO (on panel) / . VIJFTIG SURINAM GUILDEN . Rv: Numeral 50 on each of four card suits arranged cruciform on background of 12 concentric circles. Tiny FM monogram at bottom. Intermittently reeded edge. (Zaffern coll.)

Struck by Franklin Mint. These pieces are known struck in gilt silver.

URUGUAY

ARTIGAS DEPARTMENT

Cuaro
JOSE ARTOLA

Rulau	Date	Metal	Size	VG	F	VF	Unc
Art 5	ND	Brass	31mm	—	—	10.00	—

JOSE ARTOLA / (brand mark) / CUARO. Rv: 50 (large shaded) / (tiny) ORZALI B. Y C. Plain edge.

Art 6	ND	Brass	28.5mm	—	—	6.00	—

As last, but 10, and no maker's name. Plain edge.

Art 7	ND	Brass	24mm	—	—	9.00	—

As last, but 1. Plain edge. (Rulau coll.)

Struck by Orzali Bellagamba & Co., Buenos Aires, in the 1890-1905 period.

LARRAUNDARRA

Rulau	Date	Metal	Size	VG	F	VF	Unc
Art 9	ND	Copper	34mm	—	—	25.00	—

Ram left on ground, head turned toward viewer. Rv: * LARRAUNDARRA * / 50 / CUARO. Plain edge. (Zaika coll.)

Art 10	ND	Copper	28mm	—	12.50	20.00	—

As last, but 10. Plain edge. (Rulau coll.)

Rulau	Date	Metal	Size	VG	F	VF	Unc
Art 11	ND	Copper	23.5mm	—	—	9.00	16.00	—

As last, but 1. (Rulau coll.)

The Rulau collection contains 4 pieces of the 10 and 13 of the 1. All hoard pieces which surfaced in April 1990 were purchased.

CANELONES DEPARTMENT

Tala
TALA

Rulau	Date	Metal	Size	VG	F	VF	Unc
Can 5	ND	Copper	22mm	—	—	10.00	—

Brand mark. Rv: TALA. Plain edge.

CERRO LARGO DEPARTMENT

Melo
CENTRO UNION OBRERO

Rulau	Date	Metal	Size	VG	F	VF	Unc
CL 5	ND	CN	26mm	—	—	7.00	—

CENTRO UNION OBRERO / MELO (in beaded circle) . Rv: 10 / CENTESIMOS (on ribbon across numeral). Plain edge.

CL 6	ND	CN	18mm	—	—	10.00	22.00

As last, but 2. This has also been reported in 27mm size.

CL 7	ND	CN	25mm	—	—	10.00	—

As last, but 1.

CLUB UNION

Rulau	Date	Metal	Size	VG	F	VF	Unc
CL 9	ND	CN	30mm	—	—	12.50	—

CLUB UNION / 50 / CENTESIMOS (on ribbon across numeral) / MELO / (tiny TAMMARO. Rv: Blank. Plain edge.

CL 10	ND	CN	25mm	—	—	10.00	—

As last, but 20.

CL 11	ND	CN	22mm	—	—	10.00	17.50

As last, but 10.

COLONIA DEPARTMENT

Carmelo
VILLEGAS HS.

Rulau	Date	Metal	Size	VG	F	VF	Unc
Cln 8	ND	Brass	23mm	—	—	6.00	10.00	—

VIÑEDO / VILLEGAS HS. / (ornament) / * CARMELO (R. O.) *. Rv: 10 (shaded) / (tiny) BELLAGAMBA Y ROSSI. Plain edge. (Rulau coll.)

The Rulau collection contains 10 specimens. Struck by Bellagamba & Rossi, Buenos Aires, founded in 1899.
Viñedo = Vineyard.

Juan L. Lacaze
EMPRESA PUERTO SAUCE Y FELIZ FRESONE LDA.

Rulau	Date	Metal	Size	VG	F	VF	Unc
Cln 11	ND	Brass	36mm	—	8.00	15.00	25.00

EMPRESA / PUERTO SAUCE / . Y . / FELIZ FRE-SONE / Lda. Rv: Large 50 (outline). Plain edge.

Rulau	Date	Metal	Size	VG	F	VF	Unc
Cln 12	ND	Brass	28mm	—	—	—	—

As last, but 10.

Kenneth Smith suggested in the Nov. 1976 *Fare Box* that these might be for transportation. Puerto Sauce is the port area in Juan L. Lacaze.

Miguelete
RIVER PLATE ESTANCIA CO. LD.

Rulau	Date	Metal	Size	VG	F	VF	Unc
Cln 15	ND	Brass	22.5mm	—	—	20.00	—

(Triquetra) / MIGUELETE. Rv: * RIVER PLATE * / 1 / ESTANCIA Co Ld. Reeded edge.

This token has been assigned erroneously to Chile.

Uncertain
CONSTANTINO F. CANDELA

Rulau	Date	Metal	Size	VG	F	VF	Unc
Cln 20	ND	Brass	22mm	—	—	20.00	—

CANTERA / "GREEN" / DE / CONSTANTINO / F. CANDELA. Rv: 10 / (tiny) CONST ROSSI / URU-GUAY. DEP . COLONIA. Plain edge.

Struck by Contante Rossi, Buenos Aires.

CERRO DEL PICHINANGO

Rulau	Date	Metal	Size	VG	F	VF	Unc
Cln 25	ND	Brass	22.5mm	8.50	15.00	35.00	50.00

CERRO DEL PICHINANGO / B. Rv: DEPto DE LA COLONIA / (Golden Fleece). Reeded edge. (Fonrobert 10179; Eklund 1622; Rulau coll.)

No value stated, but worth 10 centesimos. Cerro = Hill.

MALDONADO DEPARTMENT

Punta del Este
CAMARA DE TURISMO

Rulau	Date	Metal	Size	F	VF	EF	Unc
Mal 10	ND	Silver	36mm	—	18.00	30.00	—

Crowned shield of arms, tiny TAMMARO below. Around: PUNTA DEL ESTE / * URUGUAY *. Rv: Aerial view of peninsula and island, small TAMMARO at upper right. Below: *** CAMARA DE TURISMO DE PUNTA DEL ESTE ***. PLATA incused on plain edge. (Rulau coll.)

Promotional token of the Chamber of Tourism of Punta del Este, southeasternmost point in Uruguay at the entrance to the wide estuary of the Rio de La Plata.

San Carlos
RIVER PLATE ESTANCIA CO. LD.

Rulau	Date	Metal	Size	F	VF	EF	Unc
Mal 20	ND	Brass	22.5mm	—	8.00	12.00	—

(Maltese cross) / SAN CARLOS. Rv: * RIVER PLATE * / 1 / ESTANCIA Co Ld. Reeded edge.

MINAS DEPARTMENT

Zapican
M. LARRANDABURU

Rulau	Date	Metal	Size	VG	F	VF	Unc
Mns 6	ND	CN	31mm	—	—	11.00	—

* M. LARRANDABURU * / ZAPICAN - DEP. MINAS / ctsp 20. Rv: Blank. Plain edge.

MONTEVIDEO DEPARTMENT

Carrasco
HOTEL-CASINO MUNICIPAL

Rulau	Date	Metal	Size	VG	F	VF	Unc
Mtv 5	ND	Aluminum	22mm	—	—	9.00	—

HOTEL-CASINO MUNICIPAL / CARRASCO. Rv: 5 CENTESIMOS.

Colon
BERNER HILLJE Y WILKINS

Rulau	Date	Metal	Size	VG	F	VF	Unc
Mtv 9	ND	CN	27mm	—	8.00	—	—

INTERNACIONAL RESTAURANT / 10 / COLON / ... Rv: BERNER, HILLJE, Y WILKINS / 10 / ... Plain edge.

Mtv 10	ND	CN	22mm	—	6.00	—	—

As last, but 2.

Montevideo (City)
JUAN ANTONIO BIA & CIA.

Rulau	Date	Metal	Size	VG	F	VF	Unc
Mtv 30	ND	Aluminum	25mm	8.00	—	—	—

JUAN ANTONIO BIA & Cia / OBSEQUIO / DEL JABON / COLON. Rv: VALE POR / 50 CENTESI-MOS / EN MERCADERIAS. (Seppa Nov. 1990 sale, lot 217)

Mtv 31	ND	Aluminum	25mm	—	6.00	—	—

As last, but 5.

Soap tokens. Obsequio del Jabon Colon = Compliments of Columbus Soap.

BUCKINGHAM PARK

Rulau	Date	Metal	Size	VG	F	VF	Unc
Mtv 33	ND	Brass	21mm	—	6.00	8.50	—

BUCKINGHAM PARK / 10 / CENTESIMOS / -.- / MONTEVIDEO. Rv; VALIDO / POR / 10 CENTESI-MOS / PARA LAS / DIVERSIONES Y JUEGOS / DEL / BUCKINGHAM PARK / -.- / MONTEVIDEO. Plain edge. (Rulau coll.)

Mtv 34	ND	Brass	17mm	—	7.00	15.00	—

Obverse as last, but 5. Rv: Same as obverse. Plain edge. (Zaika coll.)

Good for rides and games in Buckingham Park, an amusement park in Montevideo. Scarce.

CERVECERIA URUGUAYA

Rulau	Date	Metal	Size	VG	F	VF	Unc
Mtv 37	ND	Brass	27.5mm	—	4.00	7.00	—

CERVECERIA URUGUAYA / 5 (in circle) / . MON-TEVIDEO . Rv: VALE / (bar) / CINCO / (bar) / CHOPP. Plain edge.

Mtv 38	ND	Brass	22mm	—	6.00	9.00	—

As last, but UN / (bar) / CHOPP.

Cerveceria Uruguaya = Uruguayan Brewery. Chopp = Glass, or half pint (from German "schoppen").

Mtv 40	ND	Aluminum	28mm	5.00	—	—	—

CERVECERIA URUGUAYA Sdad Ama / MONTE-VIDEO (in beaded circle) / ... / (tiny) TAMMARO. Rv: VALE POR / 1 (on shaded, beaded circle) / . BARRIL VACIO. Two varieties. Plain edge.

Mtv 41	ND	Aluminum	28mm	5.00	—	—	—

As last, but 2 ctsp over numeral 1.

Barril vacio = Empty barrel.

Rulau	Date	Metal	Size	VG	F	VF	Unc
Mtv 42	ND	Aluminum	Sq 27mm	—	5.00	10.00	—

CERVECERIAS / DEL / URUGUAY on radiant field. Rv: VALE POR / 1 / BARRIL VACIO on radiant field.

COCINA ECONOMICA

Rulau	Date	Metal	Size	VG	F	VF	Unc
Mtv 44	ND	Aluminum	22mm	—	—	8.00	—

COCINA ECONOMICA / CERRITO 740 / MONTE-VIDEO. RV: 2 CENTESIMOS.

CONFITERIA AMERICANA

Rulau	Date	Metal	Size	VG	F	VF	Unc
Mtv 46	ND	Brass	26mm	—	5.00	—	—

CONFITERIA AMERICANA / 20 (in beaded circle) / . MONTEVIDEO . Rv: 20. Plain edge.

Mtv 47	ND	Brass	23mm	—	5.00	—	—

As last, but 5.

Mtv 48	ND	Brass	21mm	—	—	7.50	—

As last, but 2.

Mtv 49	ND	Aluminum	21.5mm	—	—	5.00	—

Similar to last (2 centesimos).

HIJOS DE A RUBIO

Rulau	Date	Metal	Size	VG	F	VF	Unc
Mtv 55	ND	Zinc	30mm	—	5.00	—	—

HIJOS DE A. RUBIO / 20 (in beaded circle) / * MON-TEVIDEO * / ctsp P D. Rv: Blank. (Zaika coll.)

MONTEVIDEO

Rulau	Date	Metal	Size	VG	F	VF	Unc
Mtv 60	ND	Brass	23mm	—	5.00	—	—

MONTEVIDEO / URUGUAY. Rv: VALE EN / 5 cts / COMERCIO. Plain edge.

Seemingly a general-purpose trade token.

MONUMENTO AL XX SETTEMBRE

Rulau	Date	Metal	Size	VG	F	VF	Unc
Mtv 62	1896	Brass	25.8mm	—	—	—	10.00

Radiant star atop tall, thin monument. Around: MON-UMENTO AL XX SETTEMBRE / MDCCCLXX. Rv: (Star) / INAUGURAZIONE / XX SETTEMBRE / MDCCCXCVI / - / MONTEVIDEO. Plain edge. Issued with loop. (Rulau coll.)

REPUBLICA PARVENSE

Rulau	Date	Metal	Size	VG	F	VF	Unc
Mtv 70	(1890's)	Aluminum	32.5mm	—	—	32.00	—

Capped Liberty head left. Around: REPUBLICA PARVENSE / o P.D.M.Q. 1878 o. Rv: PESO on scroll across large numeral 1. Plain edge. (Christensen March 1973 sale, lot 2752; ANS coll.)

This was a gambling token for an exclusive Montevideo men's club. The date 1878 is probably the club's founding date.

SDAD. AMA. CERVECERIA MONTEVIDEANA

Rulau	Date	Metal	Size	VG	F	VF	Unc
Mtv 75	ND	Brass	Oct 25.5mm	—	5.00	—	—

Sdad Ama CERVECERIA MONTEVIDEANA / C (Staff) M on 6-pointed star / ... Rv: VALE POR / 1 (in beaded circle) / . BARRIL VACIO . Plain edge.

Mtv 77	ND	Brass	24.5mm	—	5.00	—	—

CERVECERIA MONTEVIDEANA / - / MONTEVIDEO / - / . SOCIEDAD ANONIMA . Rv: 971 (incused). Plain edge.

Cerveceria = Brewery. Barril vacio = Empty barrel.

SOCIETE FRANCAISE DE SECOURS MUTUELS

Rulau	Date	Metal	Size	VG	F	VF	Unc
Mtv 79	1888	Bronze	23.8mm	—	—	—	10.00

"LA PATRIE" / (rosette) / SOCIETE / FRANCAISE / -DE- / SECOURS MUTUELS / -1o- / ANNIVERSAIRE. Rv: FETE DE CHARITE / (radiant star) / 1888 / (ornament) / MONTEVIDEO / (ornament) / (wreath). Plain edge. Issued with loop. (Rulau coll.)

TALLER DE GRABADOS, TIPOGRAFIA

Rulau	Date	Metal	Size	F	VF	EF	Unc
Mtv 81	(1890's)	Silver	26mm	—	—	—	25.00

Minerva bust left in oval of stars. Around (in two concentric circles): TALLER DE GRABADOS, TIPOGRAFIA Y ESTEREOTIPIA DE FX. FABREGUETTES / LA MINERVA / * CALLE SARANDI . 203 * / * MONTEVIDEO *. Rv: Uruguay shield of arms. Around: REPUBLICA ORIENTAL DE URUGUAY / ***. Plain edge. (Rosa 1489)

Store card of an engraving and printing firm. This may also have been struck in iron.

SANTIAGO TELLECHEA

Rulau	Date	Metal	Size	F	VF	EF	Unc
Mtv 85	ND	Aluminum	35mm	—	—	7.00	—

SANTIAGO TELLECHEA / 50 (in beaded circle) / . MONTEVIDEO . Rv: ESTABLECIMIENTO / . DE GANADERIA . In beaded central circle is a counterstamped brand mark. Reeded edge.

Mtv 86	ND	Aluminum	25mm	—	—	5.00	—

As last, but 1. No brand mark on reverse. Reeded edge.

Probably struck by Tammaro in the 1890's.

LORENZO ZABALETA

Rulau	Date	Metal	Size	VG	F	VF	Unc
Mtv 90	ND	Brass	22mm	9.00	—	27.00	—

Arms of Uruguay. Around: LORENZO ZABALETA / * MONTEVIDEO *. Rv: Crossed anchors. Around: BAZAR LA ESPERANZA CALLE 25 DE MAYO No 146 AL 152 * / (Crossed anchors). Reeded edge.

PAYSANDU DEPARTMENT
PAYSANDU CIA.

Rulau	Date	Metal	Size	VG	F	VF	Unc
Pay 6	ND	Copper	38mm	—	—	—	—

PAYSANDU CIA. DEL URUGUAY * / O ctsp on obverse of Uruguay 1857-D 40-centesimos, KM 10. Rv: VALABLE / EN / 10 / PESOS ctsp on opposite side of the coin. (Wes Scharlow coll.)

ROMERIAS ESPANOLAS

Rulau	Date	Metal	Size	F	VF	EF	Unc
Pay 9	1908	Svd/Br	Irreg 32mm	—	—	12.50	16.00

Seated guitarist at left plays as man and woman perform folk dance; tiny HORTA Y Cia at lower right. Rv: ROMERIAS / ESPANOLAS / - 1908 - / PAYSANDU. Issued holed. (Don Bailey coll.)

Romerias Españolas = Spanish festivals of fellowship. A number of such festivals issued medallic tokens in South America in the 1890-1910 period. Struck by Horta & Co. in Buenos Aires, Argentina.

RIO NEGRO DEPARTMENT

Fray Bentos
LIEBIG'S EXTRACT OF MEAT CO. LTD.

Rulau	Date	Metal	Size	VG	F	VF	Unc
RN 1	--	--	--mm	—	—	—	—

No description available. (Eklund ms.)

SALTO DEPARTMENT

Salto
NICOLAS NOBLE

Rulau	Date	Metal	Size	VG	F	VF	Unc
Sto 10	ND	Copper	Oct 33mm	—	8.00	—	—

NICOLAS NOBLE / SALTO in circular format ctsp at center of stock token lettered: MARCA DEL ESTABLECIMIENTO. Rv: 50 / R. O. DEL URUGUAY.

| Sto 11 | ND | Copper | Oct 30mm | — | 5.00 | — | — |

As last, but 25. (Zaika coll.)

ESTABLECIMIENTO BALNEO—TERAPICO

Rulau	Date	Metal	Size	VG	F	VF	Unc
Sto 20	ND	Aluminum	33mm	—	—	—	—

DOCTOR JURKOWSKI. ESTABLECIMIENTO BALNEO-TERAPICO. Monogram. 2 PESOS. (Eklund 1631)

Rulau	Date	Metal	Size	VG	F	VF	Unc
Sto 21	ND	Aluminum	33mm	—	—	—	—
		As last, but 1½ PESOS. (Eklund 1630)					
Sto 22	ND	Aluminum	27mm	—	—	—	—
		As last, but 1 PESO. (Eklund 1629)					
Sto 23	ND	Aluminum	27mm	—	—	—	—
		As last, but 50 CENTESIMOS. (Eklund 1628)					

SAN JOSE DEPARTMENT

San Jose
JOSE B. PORTELA

Rulau	Date	Metal	Size	VG	F	VF	Unc
SJ 6	ND	Brass	35mm	—	8.50	15.00	—

Cattle brand in beaded circle. Around: ESTANCIA DE JOSE B. PORTELA / . SAN JOSE . Rv: Large shaded 50 in beaded circle. Around: REPUBLICA ORIENTAL DEL URUGUAY / ... / (tiny) TAMMARO. Plain edge. (*TAMS Journal* for Dec. 1986, pg. 188; Zaffern coll.)

| SJ 7 | ND | Brass | 22mm | — | 15.00 | 22.50 | — |

As last, but 1 (centesimo). Scarce. (Rulau coll.)

Estancia = Plantation. This is an Uruguayan and southern South American expression equivalent to hacienda, finca, fazenda, rancho etc.

Schimmel opines that Portela's estancia was near the departmental seat at San Jose de Mayo. It was a cattle ranch.

Tokens in 25 and 10-centesimo denominations, 31.5 and 27mm, are worth $7.50 in VF.

UNATTRIBUTED URUGUAY

Ay (brand)

Rulau	Date	Metal	Size	VG	F	VF	Unc
Uru 1	ND	Aluminum	22mm	—	9.00	18.00	—

Ay monogram brand (incused). Rv: Large shaded 1 (in relief). Plain edge. Scarce. (Rulau coll., ex-Warmus; Zaika coll.)

1 = One centesimo

| Uru 2 | ND | Aluminum | 25mm | — | — | 18.00 | — |

Similar, but 5. (Zaika coll.)

D.

Rulau	Date	Metal	Size	VG	F	VF	Unc
Uru 4	ND	Silver	25mm	—	—	25.00	—

Large incuse D ctsp on Uruguay 1877-A (Paris Mint) 20-centesimos, K-M 15. Reeded edge. (Rulau coll.)

San Fernando
RAMON ERRO

Rulau	Date	Metal	Size	VG	F	VF	Unc
Uru 5	(1890's)	Brass	21.5mm	—	—	—	—

Arrow-type brand mark. Around: RAMON ERRO / * SAN FERNANDO *. Rv: 1 (large, shaded) / (tiny) ORZALIBYC.

Ozali Bellagamba & Co. of Buenos Aires struck these tokens circa 1894-99.

ESTABLECIMIENTO DE GANADERIA

Rulau	Date	Metal	Size	VG	F	VF	Unc
Uru 7	ND	Aluminum	36mm	—	—	5.00	—

ESTABLECIMIENTO DE GANADERIA / (beaded circle) / (small crescent moonface left). Rv: REPUBLICA ORIENTAL DEL URUGUAY / 50 in beaded circle / *. Reeded edge. (Eklund 1621)

Uru 8	ND	Aluminum	30mm	6.00	—	—	—

As last, but 25. Reeded edge. (Eklund 1620 & 2282)

Uru 9	ND	Aluminum	31mm	—	—	5.00	—

As last, but 20. Reeded edge.

Uru 10	ND	Aluminum	26mm	—	—	7.00	10.00

As last, but 10. Reeded edge. (Eklund 1619)

Uru 11	ND	Aluminum	26mm	—	—	9.00	—

As last (10), but ctsp PJU in the beaded circle.

Uru 12	ND	Zinc	26.5mm	—	—	9.50	—

As last (10), but struck on zinc planchet. Reeded edge. (Rulau coll.)

Uru 13	ND	Aluminum	23mm	—	7.00	11.00	—

As last, but 1 (centesimo). Reeded edge. (Eklund 1618 & 2281; Grinolds report; Rulau coll.)

Uru 14	ND	Aluminum	23mm	—	7.00	11.00	—

As last (1), but ctsp PJU in the beaded circle. Reeded edge. (Rulau coll.)

Establecimiento de Ganaderia = Cattle breeding enterprise. These were stock tokens for Uruguayan estancias; one was included in Weyl's catalog in 1899.

This series exists in many varieties, with or without a number of counterstamps. Counterstamps seen include: LI; O; XX; ornate Y; VA; YP; 3; U H: balloon brand mark; PJU; A G; JV; 5mm semicircle; EO monogram; L; triangle in circle. It is believed each mark was for a different estancia, utilizing the brand mark or owner's initials.

Tokens usually occur in aluminum, but these are known in brass, zinc and cupronickel. All were struck, apparently, by Tammaro of Montevideo.

The PJU counterstamps may be connected with D. Percontino e Hijos, which see.

ESTANCIA CERRO DEL BOMBERO

Rulau	Date	Metal	Size	VG	F	VF	Unc
Uru 16	ND	Brass	22mm	—	5.00	—	—

ESTANCIA / (brand mark in beaded circle) / . CERRO DEL BOMBERO . Rv: REPUBLICA ORIENTAL DEL URUGUAY / 1 (shaded, in beaded circle) / ... / (tiny) TAMMARO. Plain edge.

Uru 17	ND	Brass	27.5mm	—	15.00	—	—

As last, but 10. Plain edge.

ESTANCIA LAS CONCHILLAS

Rulau	Date	Metal	Size	VG	F	VF	Unc
Uru 19	ND	Brass	29mm	—	—	2.00	5.00

(All incused): W brand mark / 25 / ESTANCIA LAS CONCHILLAS. Rv: Blank. Centrally holed flan. Plain edge. (Ur-46e; Zaika coll.)

Uru 20	ND	Brass	26mm	—	—	2.00	5.00

As last, but 10. (Ur-45c; Zaika coll.)

Uru 21	ND	Brass	22.5mm	—	—	3.00	6.00

(All incused): W brand mark / 1. Rv: Blank. Centrally holed flan. Plain edge. (Ur-46a)

ESTANCIA "LA VERDE"

Rulau	Date	Metal	Size	VG	F	VF	Unc
Uru 23	ND	Copper	20mm	—	—	—	—

* / ESTANCIA / "LA VERDE" / *. Rv: 3 within frame. (Eklund 1626; Schrotter 79a & b)

Also issued in Brass. 3 = 3 centesimos.

Timote
ESTANCIA SAN PEDRO

Rulau	Date	Metal	Size	VG	F	VF	Unc
Uru 25	ND	Copper	21m	5.00	—	—	—

ESTANCIA SAN PEDRO / B / - TIMOTE -. Rv: 1. Plain edge.

Uru 26	ND	Brass	33mm	8.50	—	14.00	—

Obverse and reverse 21mm dies as above, stamped on larger planchet. Obverse also ctsp beneath die: S P / 50. Plain edge. These occur with thick and thin planchets. (A variety of this contains a diecutting error PEDPO - VF $20) (Zaika coll.)

ESTANZUELA

Rulau	Date	Metal	Size	VG	F	VF	Unc
Uru 28	ND	Brass	23mm	—	5.00	7.00	—

ESTANZUELA / (brand mark). Rv: 1 (shaded). Reeded edge. (Rulau coll.)

A small hoard of 15 pieces was seen in Florida in 1990.

MANUEL V. GARCIA

Rulau	Date	Metal	Size	VG	F	VF	Unc
Uru 35	1906	Brass	34mm	—	—	10.00	—

Bell, in outline form (probably the estate's brand mark). Rv: MANUEL V. GARCIA / 50 (shaded) / . 1906 . Plain edge.

Uru 36	1906	Brass	30mm	—	—	9.00	—

As last, but 10.

Uru 37	1906	Brass	24mm	—	—	7.00	—

As last, but 1.

G. S. L. (?)

ḩSL

Rulau	Date	Metal	Size	VG	F	EF	EF
Uru 38	ND	Copper	32mm	—	—	150.00	

LAS CABRAS / G S L (?) script, all within round frame, ctsp on worn copper coin. (Fonrobert 10202; Eklund 1634)

Rulau	Date	Metal	Size	VG	F	EF	EF
Uru 39	ND	Copper	38mm	—	—	150.00	

Same ctsp on lager worn coin. Rv: Partly illegible ctsp; . . .ELLAS. (Fonrobert 10203).

Adolf Weyl thought the monogram read T S G. It resembles H S L. It is reproduced above.

The name Las Cabras can mean The Goats or The Clouds. In Sept. 1970, Comet Coin Co. stated the counterstamp was for the plantation of Juan Jose Gandarillas. Since Fonrobert knew it, it must have been applied before 1878.

There is a Las Cabras on the Rapel River in chile, in O'Higgins Province.

ENRIQUE MACENTYRE
Estancia Santa Margarita

Rulau	Date	Metal	Size	VG	F	EF	Unc
Uru 40	ND	Brass	25mm	—	—	4.00	—

ESTANCIA SANTA MARGARITA / (brand mark in beaded circle) / . ENRIQUE MAC-ENTYRE . Rv: Blank. Plain edge. (Zaika coll.)

San Juan
MAFFEI & CIA.

Rulau	Date	Metal	Size	VG	F	VF	Unc
Uru 42	1900	Brass	26mm	—	9.00	—	—

MAFFEI & CIA. / SAN JUAN - MUELLES / 1900. Rv: 10 / CENTESIMOS. Plain edge.

Muelles = Docks, quays.

D. PERCONTINO E HIJOS

Rulau	Date	Metal	Size	VG	F	VF	Unc
Uru 47	ND	Zinc	35mm	—	6.00	—	—

D. PERCONTINO E HIJOS / 50 (in beaded circle) / *. Rv: ESTABLECIMIENTO DE GANADERIA / ctsp PJU (in beaded circle). Reeded edge. (Ur-5de)

Rulau	Date	Metal	Size	VG	F	VF	Unc
Uru 48	ND	Aluminum	23mm	—	5.00	—	—

Similar to last, but 1, and crescent stop on reverse. Reeded edge. (Ur-5ff; Zaika coll.)

See PJU counterstamps also under ESTABLECIMIENTO DE GANADERIA listings in Uruguay.

DORIMEL U. PEREIRA
Estancia El Pedernal

Rulau	Date	Metal	Size	VG	F	VF	Unc
Uru 50	ND	Brass	22.5mm	—	5.00		

Cross above DORIMEL U. PEREIRA, all in beaded circle. Around: ESTABLECIMIENTO GANADERO / "EL PEDERNAL". Rv: 1 (shaded, in beaded circle). Around: REPUBLICA ORIENTAL DEL URUGUAY / ... / (tiny) TAMMARO. Plain edge. (Ur-50)

FEDERICO PERQUER
Estancia del Ombu

Rulau	Date	Metal	Size	VG	F	VF	Unc
Uru 52	ND	Brass	38mm	—	18.00	25.00	

Large tree. Around: ESTANCIA DEL OMBU/BANDA ORIENTAL. Rv: Sheep standing left. Above: FEDERICO PERQUER / Co (incuse). (Eklund 1624)

Rulau	Date	Metal	Size	VG	F	VF	Unc
Uru 54	ND	Copper	22mm	—	10.00		

OMBU / (brand mark). Rv: Desc. not available.

The ombu is a species of tree.

Los Altos
RIVER PLATE
ESTANCIA CO. LD.

Rulau	Date	Metal	Size	VG	F	VF	Unc
Uru 60	ND	Brass	22.5mm	—	10.00		

Circle-on-cross brand mark (enameled red) / LOS ALTOS. Rv: * RIVER PLATE * / 50 / ESTANCIA Co Ld. Reeded edge.

J. S.
Estancia de Las Saladas

Rulau	Date	Metal	Size	VG	F	VF	Unc
Uru 63	ND	Brass	33mm	—	—	—	—

ESTANCIA DE LAS SALADAS / (Anchor with Tau) separates J -- S. Rv: VALE / POR 50. Reeded edge. (F. 10181; Eklund 1625)

Estancia = Estate or Ranch. Worth 50 centesimos.

SARANDI Y TUSAINCO

Rulau	Date	Metal	Size	VG	F	VF	Unc
Uru 65	ND	Aluminum	34mm	6.00	11.00	20.00	—

Uruguayan arms, ESTADO ORIENTAL DE URUGUAY around. Rv: SARANDI / Y TUSAINCO / * (button shank) * / RINCON DE LAS / GALLINAS. (Fauver pgs. 80-81)

Also known in aluminum, 38mm; brass, and brass 38mm. Buttons.

SUARES HOS.

5

Rulau	Date	Metal	Size	VG	F	EF	Unc
Uru 67	ND	Copper	30mm	—	25.00	—	—

SUARES - Hos ctsp on Uruguay 1869-A 2-centesimos, KM-12. Scarce.

JOSE LUIS UGARTEMENDIA E HIJOS
Estancia La Concepcion

Rulau	Date	Metal	Size	VG	F	VF	Unc
Uru 70	ND	Brass	36mm	—	—	20.00	—

Brand mark in beaded circle. Around: JOSE LUIS UGARTEMENDIA E HIJOS / . Ecia LA CONCEPCION . Rv: REPUBLICA ORIENTAL DEL URUGUAY / 5 (shaded) / (tiny) TAMMARO. Plain edge.

Alcedo Almanzar reports a specimen counterstamped incuse 6 / TC.

Rulau	Date	Metal	Size	VG	F	VF	Unc
Uru 85	ND	CN	35.3mm	—	4.00	7.00	—

Large 5 (shaded) in circle of beads. Rv: Smaller 5 (14mm, shaded) in circle of denticles. Plain edge. (Ur-81; Rulau coll; Grinolds Aug. 1989 sale, lot 715)

Z

Rulau	Date	Metal	Size	VG	F	VF	Unc
Uru 80	ND	Zinc	29mm	—	4.00	—	—

Z within double circle. Rv: 40. Reeded edge. (Ur-60g)

Rulau	Date	Metal	Size	VG	F	VF	Unc
Uru 81	ND	Zinc	24mm	—	4.00	—	—

Z within single circle. Rv: 20. Reeded edge. (Ur-60d)

Rulau	Date	Metal	Size	VG	F	VF	Unc
Uru 82	ND	Zinc	20mm	—	4.00	—	—

Z on plain field. Rv: 1. Reeded edge. (Ur-60a)

Attributed to Uruguay by Central Carolina Exchange, Greensboro, N.C., which assigned the Ur numbers.

1

Rulau	Date	Metal	Size	VG	F	VF	Unc
Uru 87	ND	Aluminum	21mm	—	—	—	3.50

Large 1 (shaded) on plain field. Rv: Blank. Thick plain raised rim on each side. Plain edge. (Ur-84a; Rulau coll.; Grinolds Aug. 1989 sale, lot 716)

MISCELLANEOUS PRIVATE COUNTERSTAMPS

Uru 100 **B. DEL T.S.**   on Uruguay copper 1869 4-centesimos, 34mm, KM-13

Uru 101 **C.P.F.**   on Uruguay silver 1920 20-centavos, 25mm, reeded edge, Km-24

Uru 102 **O**   on Uruguay copper 1869-H 1-centesimo, 25.5mm, KM-11

Uru 103 **Y**   on Uruguay copper 1857-D 20-centesimos, 34mm, KM-9

Uru104 **Y in diamond**   on Uruguay cupronickel 1936-A 2-centesimos, KM-20

Uru 105 **20**   on Uruguay copper 1869 2-centesimos, 29mm, KM-12

Uru 106 **30**   on Uruguay silver 1943-So 50-centesimos, 24mm, reeded edge, KM-31

NOTE: All above pieces bring prices of $7.50 to $20 each with clear counterstamp. If identified, they could bring much more.

VENEZUELA

ARAGUA STATE
Cagua
HACIENDA VILLEGAS

Rulau	Date	Metal	Size	VG	F	VF	Unc
Ara 3	ND	Scal	—mm	—	—	—	—

HACIENDA / "VILLEGAS" / TURMERO. Rv: No descr. available.

The plantation was founded in Colonial times by Don Juan de Villegas near the town of Cagua. In 1855 its stone mansion was built by the mason Francisco Revenga. It produced fruits, beans and indigo.

Its beans and indigo took a bronze medal at the 1889 Paris Universal Exposition. In the 20th century it belonged to Federico de La Madriz, from whom it passed to the National Agrarian Institute.

El Consejo
POLICARPO MOSQUERA
La Cruz Yngenio

Rulau	Date	Metal	Size	VG	F	VF	Unc
Ara 4	ND	Brass	26mm	—	—	125.	200.

HACIENDA YNGENIO / LA / (Greek cross between sugar canes). Rv: POLICARPO MOSQUERA / 3 REALES (in beaded circle) / (rosette). Plain edge. (Eklund 2137; Guttag coll.)

Rulau	Date	Metal	Size	VG	F	VF	Unc
Ara 5	ND	Brass	24mm	—	—	125.	—

As last, but 2 REALES. (Eklund 2136)

| Ara 6 | ND | Brass | 21mm | — | — | 125. | — |

As last, but 1 REAL. (Eklund 2299)

| Ara 7 | ND | Brass | 18mm | — | — | 125. | — |

As last, but 1/2 REAL. (Eklund 2135)

Guaica
CARVALLO Y ARVELO

Rulau	Date	Metal	Size	VG	F	VF	Unc
Ara 8	ND	Brass	28mm	—	—	—	—

CARVALLO Y ARVELO / GUAICA / *. Rv: 1 / REAL. Plain edge. (Ulex 3379; Eklund 1310)

| Ara 9 | ND | Brass | 24mm | — | — | — | — |

As last, but 1/2 / REAL. (Stohr FG-5)

| Ara 10 | ND | Brass | 21mm | — | — | — | — |

As last, but 1/4 / REAL. (Ulex 3379; Eklund 1308 & 1161; Stohr FG-6)

Ulex had assigned these in error to Peru.

La Victoria
FEDERICO BRICEÑO LEON

Rulau	Date	Metal	Size	VG	F	VF	Unc
Ara 15	1887	CN	24mm	—	30.00	60.00	75.00

CONSIGNACION GENERAL DE FRUTOS / FEDERICO / BRICENO / LEON / . VICTORIA . Rv: HONNI SOIT QUI MAL Y PENSE / 2 / REALES / * !887 *. (Eklund 1232; Rulau coll.)

| Ara 16 | 1887 | CN | 18mm | — | 30.00 | 70.00 | 85.00 |

Similar, but 1 / REAL / 1887.

Honi Soit Qui Mal y Pense (Evil to him who evil thinks) = The motto of the British Order of the Garter.

These tokens occur ctsp B for Belen, wife of Dr. German Freites; S for Hacienda El Socorro, a Briceno Leon holding, and M F A for Miguel, Federico and Andres, Briceño's sons.

Palomas
E. & P.
(Eraso & Pereira)

Rulau	Date	Metal	Size	VG	F	VF	Unc
Ara 20	ND	Brass	Oct 34mm	25.00	35.00	65.00	—

(Dove flying left) / PALOMAS / E & P. Rv: Large 4. Reverse ctsp with two keyhole brand marks. Rare. (Eklund 1132)

| Ara 21 | ND | Brass | Oct 29mm | — | 50.00 | 100. | — |

As last, but 2. (Eklund 1131; Scott)

| Ara 22 | ND | Brass | Oct 22mm | 20.00 | 30.00 | 80.00 | — |

As last, but 1. (Eklund 1130; Zaika coll.)

E & P = Enrique Eraso and Balbino Pereira, the owners.

Garriga reports ten different tokens, including oval ones "rolled" from octagonal pieces. J. W. Scott 70 years ago auctioned the 4-reales above at $24 in EF-AU, and an AU 2-reales at $75, both princely sums for tokens!

Some tokens are found with the 'P' of E & P obliterated; issued by Eraso after he bought out Pereira. The hacienda was at an elevation of 872 to 924 meters above sea level. Much later the hacienda was sold to Tomas Duarte P. and Jorge Herrera Uslar.

La Fila de Palomas
J. L.
Hacienda Palomas-Carmen

Rulau	Date	Metal	Size	VG	F	VF	Unc
Ana 25	ND	Brass	Oct 33mm	—	—	30.00	—

PALOMAS. CARMEN. / J. L. (in beaded circle) / ***.
Rv: 4. (Eklund 1136; Stohr FP-3)

Rulau	Date	Metal	Size	VG	F	VF	Unc
Ara 26	ND	Brass	Oct 32mm	—	—	—	—

As last, but 2. (Eklund 1135)

Rulau	Date	Metal	Size	VG	F	VF	Unc
Ara 27	ND	Brass	Oct 31mm	—	—	—	—

As last, but 1. (Eklund 1134)

Rulau	Date	Metal	Size	VG	F	VF	Unc
Ara 28	ND	Brass	Oct 16mm	—	—	—	—

As last, but 1/4. (Eklund 1133)

This estate was south of San Casimiro, near La Fila de Palomas and Carmen de Cura. The Rio Caisita is nearby. Garriga reports three denominations of these tokens, struck by the same maker who prepared the E&P Palomas tokens.

PALOMAS

Rulau	Date	Metal	Size	VG	F	VF	Unc
Ara 30	ND	Brass	24mm	—	15.00	40.00	—

(All incused): PALOMAS. (curved) / (ornament). Rv: 1 (tall, thin). Plain edge. (Schimmel report; Stohr FP-7)

San Sebastian
EL NICUAL

Rulau	Date	Metal	Size	VG	F	VF	Unc
Ara 35	(?)	Brass	27.5mm	—	—	50.00	—

RAMON JSAAC CARCANO / (ornament) / . EL NICUAL . Rv: 2 REALES.

Isaac Carcano issued tokens for Hacienda El Nicual, located in San Sebastian district, Aragua, on the Rio Arriba, 39 miles N.E. of El Chino hacienda and 2.5 miles east of Hacienda Cataure. El Nicual was devoted to cocoa and sugar cane production.

El Nicual is singular in Venezuela as the site for a modern peasant movement for land reform, which in 1959 became known as Frente por el Derecho al Trabajo y al Pan (Front for the Right to Work and to Bread).

Villa de Cura
BALTAZAR GONZALEZ Y.
Hacienda Amapola

Rulau	Date	Metal	Size	VG	F	VF	Unc
Ara 40	(1890-92)	Brass	24mm	—	—	—	—

Cow standing right within circle. Around: HACIENDA / AMAPOLA. Rv: BALTAZAR GONZALEZ Y. / 2 REALES (in beaded circle) / BOLIVIA. Plain edge. (Stohr FA-11)

Rulau	Date	Metal	Size	VG	F	VF	Unc
Ara 42	(1890-92)	Brass	18.5mm	—	55.00	75.00	—

As last, but 1/2 REAL. (Eklund 1411; Stohr FA-12)

Villa de Cura was renamed Bolivia during the 1890-92 period, according to Garriga. A 1-real token ctsp A L is reported but not confirmed.

HERNANDEZ HERMANOS
Pedernales

Rulau	Date	Metal	Size	VG	F	VF	Unc
Ara 48	1897	CN	29mm?	—	—	—	—

(All incused): 2 (Large tree) R / 1897. Rv: HERNANDEZ HERMANOS / . PEDERNALES . (Stohr FP-10)

Rulau	Date	Metal	Size	VG	F	VF	Unc
Ara 49	1897	CN	25mm	—	75.00	110.	—

As last, but 1 R.

Rulau	Date	Metal	Size	VG	F	VF	Unc
Ara 50	1902	CN	29mm	—	70.00	115.	—

As next, but 2 R. (Landaeta pg. 33; Stohr FP-9; Garriga pg. 81)

Rulau	Date	Metal	Size	VG	F	VF	Unc
Ara 51	1902	CN	24mm	—	75.00	110.	—

(All incused— 1/2 (Smaller tree) R / 1902. Rv: HERNANDEZ HERMANOS / . PEDERNALES. Plain edge. Rare. (Rulau coll.; ex-Socias Lopez; Stohr FP-12)

Landaeta, Garriga and Stohr all attribute these tokens to Hacienda Pedernales at Villa de Cura in Aragua State. There is a port city of Pedernales in Delta Amacuro State. We follow David Henkle and the Venezuelan authorities in placing these pieces under Aragua State. All pieces are quite rare and desirable.

GEN. JOAQUIN CRESPO

In 1889 the president of Venezuela, Gen. Joaquin Crespo issued a beautiful series of tokens made of vulcanite, with a different color for each denomination. These tokens were used in the numerous haciendas of Gen. Crespo in Aragua and Guarico States (south of Caracas). All are scarce.

BOLIVAR STATE
Ciudad Bolivar
VALLEE & CA.

Rulau	Date	Metal	Size	VG	F	VF	Unc
Blv 10	ND	CN	23mm	—	—	—	—

VALLEE & Ca. / (Lily) / (9 stars in arc) / CIUDAD / - / BOLIVAR. Rv: VALE / (Shell) UN (Shell) / - CUARTILLO -. (Guttag coll.; Eklund 1412)

Ciudad Bolivar is a port on the Orinoco River. Originally called Angostura, it is the birthplace of Venezuelan independence (1819).

Yuruary
F. ALVARADO & CA.

Rulau	Date	Metal	Size	VG	F	VF	Unc
Blv 20	ND	Brass	Hexag 34x39mm	—	—	—	—

F. ALVARADO & Ca. 5 BOLIVAR. (1899 Weyl catalog; Eklund 1579)

Rulau	Date	Metal	Size	VG	F	VF	Unc
Blv 21	ND	CN	Hexag	—	—	—	—

As last, but 2 1/2. (Scott; Eklund 1578)

The Yuruari River flows north through Bolivar State, from near El Dorado to El Callao.

CARABOBO STATE

Aguascalientes
JUSTINA E. DE ALVARADO
Hacienda Aguacaliente

Rulau	Date	Metal	Size	VG	F	VF	Unc
Cbo 1	1905	Brass	27.5mm	—	—	20.00	—

Coffee mill? Around: HACIENDA AGUACALIENTE / -1905-. Ctsp P. Rv: Numeral 2 in wreath at center. Around: JUSTINA E. DE ALVARADO / DOS REALES. Plain edge. (Rulau coll.; Stohr FA-4)

Stohr says Aguascalientes in Carabobo State. Also ¼, ½, 1 and 4-reales.

Chirgua
M. G. PINGEL

Rulau	Date	Metal	Size	F	VF	EF	Unc
Cbo 2	1904	Brass	25mm	—	65.00	75.00	—

Capital C's back-to-back amid ornaments. Rv: M. G. PINGEL / 2 / REALES / . CHIRGUA 1904. Plain edge. (Rulau coll.)

Cbo 3	1904	Brass	21.3mm	—	—	55.00	—

As last, but 1 / REAL.

Cbo 4	1904	Brass	19.5mm	—	—	65.00	—

As last, but 1/2 / REAL.

The Chirigua River forms the boundary between Guarico and Cojedes States. Eklund listed a 4-reales as number 2084, 29mm, rare. Garriga mentions an 8-reales, 32mm.

El Pao
RAMONA R. DE CORONEL

Rulau	Date	Metal	Size	VG	F	VF	Unc
Cbo 5	1859	Brass	21mm	60.00	70.00	—	—

Bull charging left within beaded circle. Around: RAMONA R. DE. CORONEL / - LAGUAMITA -. Rv: F. ESTEBAN CORONEL / VALE / 1/4 / REAL / - 1859 -. (Ulex 2675; Eklund 1198; Stohr FL-23)

Guacara
HACIENDA VIGIRIMA

Rulau	Date	Metal	Size	VG	F	VF	Unc
Cbo 7	ND	—	—	—	—	—	45.00

HACIENDA VIGIRIMA / VALE /. 8 REALES. Rv: Blank. Crude. (Garriga report)

This coffee estate had its token made locally. The hacienda was in an area in which stone petroglyphs are found, carved by the valley Indians' predecessors.

In 1889 the Gastelurema Brothers won a gold medal at the Paris Universal Exposition for their Vigirima coffee beans.

Guigue
ADMINISTRACION TROMPILLO

Rulau	Date	Metal	Size	VG	F	VF	Unc
Cbo 10	ND	Copper	35.5mm	—	15.00	25.00	45.00

ADMINISTRACION / 2 / BOLIVARES / - TROMPILLO -. Rv: Blank. Plain edge. (Rulau coll., ex-Charles Wyatt)

Cbo 11	ND	Copper	26mm	—	7.00	20.00	35.00

As last, but 50 / CENTIMOS. (Stohr FT-14)

Cbo 12	ND	Copper	19.5mm	—	10.00	20.00	30.00

As last, but 25 / CENTIMOS. (Stohr FT-15)

Hacienda El Trompillo was the largest of the multiple landholdings of General Gomez in 1920, near the town of Guigue in Carabobo State. It produced sugar, paper, pulp, brandy, wheat bread, coconut oil, tobacco, cassava, melons, starch, tartar oil, chocolate, etc.

Other denominations are known. (See *TAMS Journal* for Dec. 1986, pgs. 188-189.) Trompillo = (literally) "Little top."

Las Trincheras
LA UNION

Rulau	Date	Metal	Size	VG	F	VF	Unc
Cbo 15	ND	Leather	Rect	—	—	—	—

LA UNION DE BRANGER Y MARTINEZ.

These leather tokens were reissued in solid metal, says Garriga.

Ernesto Branger in the 1895-1905 period established the cotton plantations of Aguacaliente and Palmarito, eventually uniting them under the name La Union. Martinez was his partner in the venture.

Branger Industries today produces textiles, vegetable oils, etc. Las Trincheras is the site of radioactive hot springs.

Montalban
HERMANOS MUÑOZ

Rulau	Date	Metal	Size	VG	F	VF	Unc
Cbo 18	1864	Brass	18mm	—	15.00	40.00	70.00

Cock standing left. Around: HERMANOS MUÑOZ / . MONTALBAN . Rv: Between branches: VALE / 1/4 / 1864. Plain edge. (Scott; Stohr Fm 27; Rulau coll.; Louis Hudson April 1990 sale, lot 861; Zaika coll.)

This is one of the classic rarities among Latin American tokens, missing from many collections but known and sought after for more than a century. It occurs ctsp 1/8 or 1/2.

Batavia
MUNOZ HERMANOS

Rulau	Date	Metal	Size	VG	F	VF	Unc
Cbo 20	ND	Brass	32mm	—	—	—	—

MUNOZ HERMANOS / BATAVIA. Rv: 2 CUAR-
TILLAS. (Bernal 320)

| Cbo 21 | ND | Brass | 25.5mm | — | — | — | — |

As last, but 1 CUARTILLA. (Bernal 319)

| Cbo 22 | ND | Brass | 20mm | — | — | — | — |

As last, but 1/2 CUARTILLA. (Bernal 318)

Montalban
ANDRES PEREZ

Rulau	Date	Metal	Size	VG	F	VF	Unc
Cbo 24	1857	Brass	18mm	—	33.00	60.00	80.00

Rooster left. Around: ANDRES PEREZ / MONTAL-
BAN. Rv: VALE / 1/4 / 1857 between sprays. Plain
edge. (Fonrobert 8027; Eklund 1207; Storer FM 32;
Rulau coll.)

Struck by Scovill Mfg. Co., Waterbury, Conn.

JOSE ANTONIO LANDAETA
Hacienda Montero

Rulau	Date	Metal	Size	VG	F	VF	Unc
Cbo 26	1865	CN	27mm	—	—	—	—

Balance scales. Around: JOSE ANTONIO LAN-
DAETA / MONTERO. Rv: Within laurel wreath:
VALE / 1/2 / 1865. (Ulex 1721; Eklund 408)

| Cbo 27 | 1865 | CN | 20.5mm | — | — | — | — |

As last, but 1/4 R. (Fonrobert 6932; U. 1721; Eklund
407)

Ulex in 1908 reported the latter piece above as 23mm. Sugar plantation.

Puerto Cabello
S. DE. AGREDA, JOVE & CO.

Rulau	Date	Metal	Size	VG	F	VF	Unc
Cbo 30	ND	Copper	Oval	—	—	—	—

S. DE AGREDA, JOVE & Co. / * PTO-CABELLO *.
Rv: 1/4 REAL. Ctsp M.G.

| Cbo 31 | ND | — | Oval | — | — | — | — |

As last, but ctsp G. G. (Garriga report)

Agreda Jove & Co. was an import-export commission house. In 1820 a predecessor firm had been known as J. M. Perez & G. Jove. These may be the oldest
tokens of Venezuela.

GADEA Y SANDREA

Rulau	Date	Metal	Size	VG	F	VF	Unc
Cbo 33	1855	Brass	18mm	—	50.00	90.00	—

Pointer dog walking left. GADEA Y SANDREA /
PUERTO CABELLO around. Rv: VALE / - 1/4 - /
1855. (Ulex 2675; Eklund 1213)

| Cbo 34 | 1856 | Brass | 18mm | — | 35.00 | 45.00 | — |

Similar to last, but 1856. (Eklund 1214)

POLLY & CIA.

Rulau	Date	Metal	Size	VG	F	VF	Unc
Cbo 40	1857	Brass	18mm	—	—	80.00	—

Two fish, the upper facing left and the lower right.
Around: POLLY & Cia / * PUERTO CABELLO *. Rv:
VALE / - 1/4 - / 1857. (Eklund 1215; Stohr FP-21)

| Cbo 41 | 1857 | Brass | 20mm | — | — | 100. | — |

As last, but 1/2. (Eklund 1216)

Valencia
GUILLERMA HEYDEN Y CA.

Rulau	Date	Metal	Size	VG	F	VF	Unc
Cbo 50	ND	Brass	22mm	—	—	—	—

GUILLERMA HEYDEN Y CA / 1/2. Rv: Blank. (1899
Weyl catalog; Eklund 1227)

Guillerma = Guillermina. Also struck in copper.

| Cbo 52 | ND | Copper | 22mm | — | — | — | — |

A glass. 1/2 REAL. Inscription. (1899 Weyl catalog;
Eklund 1230)

| Cbo 53 | ND | Copper | 22mm | — | — | — | — |

ALMACEN DE QUINCALLA Y ARMAS * / GUIL-
LERMA / HEYDEN y Ca / -.- / VALENCIA. Rv:
CALLE DE LA LIBERTAD / 1/8 / REAL (in oak
wreath) *. (Eklund 1229; Stohr FH-3)

The Heyden tokens need physical examination. Struck in Germany?

CARLOS SANCHES G.
Hacienda Cascabel

Rulau	Date	Metal	Size	VG	F	VF	Unc
Cbo 55	ND	Brass	21mm	25.00	—	—	—

HACIENDA - CASCABEL / 1/2 / *. Rv: CARLOS
SANCHES G. / -.- / VALENCIA / -.- / *. Plain edge.
(Eklund 2404)

COJEDES STATE

Carabobo
ANTONIO PIMENTEL
Hacienda Altamira

Rulau	Date	Metal	Size	VG	F	VF	Unc
Coj 12	(1904)	WM	—mm	—	—	—	—

HACIENDAS / - / ANTONIO / PIMENTEL (name in script) / - / DE CAFE. Rv: HACIENDA DE CAFE / 4 / REALES / * ALTAMIRA *. (Ulex 2646; Stohr F-55)

Rulau	Date	Metal	Size	VG	F	VF	Unc
Coj 13	(1904)	Brass	—mm	—	—	—	—

As last, but 2 REALES.

1904-dated tokens in almud denominations were also issued.

DELTA AMACURO STATE

Pedernales
ORINOCO ASPHALT CO.

Rulau	Date	Metal	Size	VG	F	VF	Unc
DA 5	ND	Aluminum	30mm	—	—	—	—

ORINOCO ASPHALT CO. / 50 C. (in circle) / * PEDERNALES *. (Stohr FP-13; Landaeta pg. 33)

Garriga says there are five denominations known, including an alum. 30mm 20-centimo piece. Pedernales is a port city on the Gulf of Paria.

DISTRITO FEDERAL

Fila de Mariches
CARIMAO

Rulau	Date	Metal	Size	VG	F	VF	Unc
DF 1	ND	CN	24.5mm	—	—	50.00	100.

Indian walking left, a sack over his shoulder. CARIMAO below. Rv: 2 / ALMUD. Plain edge. (Eklund 1746; Garriga pg. 73; Ulex 2675)

Rulau	Date	Metal	Size	VG	F	VF	Unc
DF 2	ND	CN	20mm	—	—	50.00	75.00

As last, but 1 / ALMUD. (Eklund 1745)

Rulau	Date	Metal	Size	VG	F	VF	Unc
DF 3	ND	CN	18mm	—	—	50.00	75.00

As last, but 1/2 / ALMUD. (Eklund 1744)

Ulex in 1908 reported a copper token.

J. M. PADRON
Hacienda Guanasna

Rulau	Date	Metal	Size	VG	F	VF	Unc
DF 5	ND	Brass	Oct 24mm	—	—	—	35.00

J M / PADRON / 2. Rv: GUANASNA / 2. Plain edge. (Eklund 1781; Pesant 114; Stohr FG-14; Garriga pg. 47; Randel coll.)

Rulau	Date	Metal	Size	VG	F	VF	Unc
DF 6	ND	Brass	Oct 22mm	—	—	—	35.00

As last, but 1 (real). (Eklund 1780; Pesant 115; Landaeta pg. 33)

Rulau	Date	Metal	Size	VG	F	VF	Unc
DF 7	ND	Brass	Oct 20mm	—	—	—	25.00

As last, but 1/2. (Eklund 1779; Pesant 116; Randel coll.)

This series had been claimed, erroneously, for Cuba. Garriga made a positive identification, however, to Venezuela. (Fila de Mariches in Caracas State).

Hacienda Guanasna was called at times Hacienda Alto del Rodeo or Hacienda Altos de Padron, after its owner, J. M. Padron. It is located south of the urban area of Turumo, near the Quebrada Guanasna. The site appears on property maps with the name Altos de Padron.

Gorgias R. Garriga interviewed a descendant of the hacienda's owner who possesses a complete series of the tokens issued, which had been professionally made in, Garriga says, copper. The set in the William Randel collection, however, is made of brass and quite rare.

Guaracarumbo
FEDERICO N. A. HELLMUND
Hacienda de Guaracarumbo

Rulau	Date	Metal	Size	VG	F	VF	Unc
DF 8	ND	CN	32mm	—	—	125.	—

HACIENDA DE GUARACARUMBO * / DOS / MEDIDAS. Rv: FEDERICO N. A. HELLMUND / 2 (in beaded circle). Plain edge. (Eklund 2401)

Rulau	Date	Metal	Size	VG	F	VF	Unc
DF 9	ND	CN	28mm	—	—	—	—

As last, but UNA / MEDIDA and 1. (Eklund 2400)

Rulau	Date	Metal	Size	VG	F	VF	Unc
DF 10	ND	CN	24mm	—	—	—	—

As last, but MEDIA / MEDIDA and 1/2. (Eklund 2399)

Rulau	Date	Metal	Size	VG	F	VF	Unc
DF 11	ND	CN	18mm	—	—	85.00	—

As last, but UN / CUARTO DE / MEDIDA and 1/4. (Eklund 2398)

Guaracarumbo hacienda was located near Caracas. Medida = Measure.

San Sebastian
RAMON GONZALEZ ESPINOSA
Hacienda El Altar - La Caridad

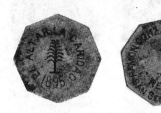

Rulau	Date	Metal	Size	VG	F	VF	Unc
DF 20	1895	CN	Oct 23mm	—	—	—	—
		(All devices and lettering incused): Plant. Around: EL ALTAR / LA CARIDAD / 1895. Rv: RAMON GONZALEZ ESPINOSA / 1 / REAL / SAN SEBASTIAN. (Eklund 944)					
DF 21	1895	CN	Oct 19mm	—	—	—	—
		As last, but 1/2 . (Eklund 943)					

These have been claimed for Guatemala.
Garriga reports that Gonzalez issued six cupronickel tokens up to 4 reales for this cattle raising estate in San Sebastian de los Reyes valley near Caracas.

Caracas (City)
F. T. DE ALDREY

Rulau	Date	Metal	Size	VG	F	VF	Unc
DF 30	ND	Silver	—mm	—	—	—	—
		F. T. DE ALDREY. CARACAS. 1 R. (Ulex 2670)					

B. BONFANTE & CO.

Rulau	Date	Metal	Size	F	VF	EF	Unc
DF 33	(1850's)	CN	22mm	—	50.00	100.	175.
		B. BONFANTE & CO. / DOS / REALES . o..+..o. Rv: CAFE / ESPAGNOL / CARACAS. Reeded edge. (Fonrobert 8016; Eklund 1185)					

Rulau	Date	Metal	Size	F	VF	EF	Unc
DF 34	(1850's)	CN	18.5mm	—	40.00	60.00	125.
		As last, but UN / REAL. Reeded edge. Thick and thin planchet varieties are known. (Eklund 1184; Zaffern coll.; Rulau coll.)					

Rulau	Date	Metal	Size	F	VF	EF	Unc
DF 35	(1850's)	CN	15.5mm	—	25.00	55.00	100.
		As last, but MEDIO / REAL. (Fonrobert 8019; Ulex 2670; Eklund 1183)					

A 1/4-real token of this issuer is also reported. Garriga believed these were gaming tokens.

P. MARQUEZ

Rulau	Date	Metal	Size	VG	F	VF	EF
DF 40	ND	Copper	23mm	—	—	70.00	—
		1/2 R / P. MARQUEZ / CARACAS ctsp on 1818 Caracas cuartillo, Craig-2. (Brunk 52965)					
DF 42	ND	Copper	23mm	—	—	70.00	—
		1 R / P. MARQUEZ / CARACAS ctsp on 1821 Caracas cuartillo, Craig-2. (Brunk 52970)					

J. A. C. MOLLER Y CA.

Rulau	Date	Metal	Size	VG	F	VF	Unc
DF 44	(1850-76)	Copper	22mm	—	—	30.00	—
		ALMACEN DE QUINCALLA Y ARMAS * / J. A. C. / MOLLER Y CA. / -.- / CARACAS. Rv: CALLE DE LAS LEYES DES PATRIAS No 50 * / 1/2 / REAL. Plain edge. (Eklund 1186)					
DF 45	ND	Copper	21.5mm	—	—	80.00	—
		As last, but 1/8 (real). (Ulex 2670; Eklund 1187)					

D. R.

Rulau	Date	Metal	Size	VG	F	VF	Unc
DF 50	ND	Copper	29mm	—	—	80.00	—
		D.R. in laurel wreath ctsp on U.S. 1837 Large cent. Rv: VALE / MITAD / RECUERO ctsp on other side of coin. (1899 Weyl catalog; Eklund 1188)					

CARACAS PRIVATE COUNTERSTAMPS

Rulau	Date	Metal	Size	VG	F	VF	EF
DF 60	ND	Copper	23mm	—	—	—	—
		Caracas Royalist 1/4-real coin of 1818 (Craig 2) ctsp with monogram resembling: 5 r m within rect. indent on obverse. (Zaffern coll.)					
DF 61	ND	Copper	23mm	—	—	—	—
		Caracas Royalist 1818 1/4-real ctsp: N. (Eklund 2390)					
DF 62	ND	Copper	23mm	—	—	35.00	—
		Caracas Royalist 1818 or 1821 1/4-real ctsp: 1 C / P P. (Duffield 1245; Eklund 2391; Brunk 53450). See NOTES below.					
DF 63	ND	Copper	29mm	—	—	—	—
		Thin blank copper flan ctsp: P P / 2. (Eklund 2392)					
DF 64	ND	Copper	26mm	—	—	—	—
		Worn Copper coin ctsp: GP tall monogram (Eklund 2393)					
DF 65	ND	Copper	22mm	—	—	—	—
		Venezuela 1896 12 1/2-centimo coin (KM 28) ctsp: GP tall monogram. (Eklund 2394)					
DF 66	ND	Copper	23mm	—	25.00	—	—
		1/2 P. ctsp on Caracas Royalist 1/4-real, Craig 2. (Brunk 53430)					
DF 67	ND	Copper	23mm	—	25.00	—	—
		Similar to last, but 1 P. (Brunk 53435)					
DF 68	ND	Copper	23mm	—	25.00	—	—
		Similar to last, but 5 P. (Brunk 53440)					
DF 69	ND	Copper	23mm	—	35.00	—	—
		"Arabic script" within rectangular frame ctsp on Caracas Royalist 1817 1/4-real, Craig 2. (Brunk 55100)					

Rulau	Date	Metal	Size	VG	F	VF	EF
DF 71	ND	Copper	23mm	—	15.00	—	—

1/2 R / JMR ctsp on Caracas Royalist 1/4-real, Craig 2. R = Real. (Brunk 52440)

Rulau	Date	Metal	Size	VG	F	VF	EF
DF 72	ND	Copper	23mm	—	15.00	—	—

As last, but 1 R. (Brunk 52441)

Rulau	Date	Metal	Size	VG	F	VF	EF
DF 73	ND	Copper	23mm	—	15.00	—	—

As last, but 2 R. (Brunk 52442)

Rulau	Date	Metal	Size	VG	F	VF	EF
DF 74	ND	Copper	23mm	—	35.00	—	90.00

As last, but 4 R. (Brunk 52444)

Rulau	Date	Metal	Size	VG	F	VF	EF
DF 75	ND	Copper	23mm	—	15.00	—	—

As last, but 5 R / JMR. (Brunk 52445)

Rulau	Date	Metal	Size	VG	F	VF	EF
DF 77	ND	Silver	13mm	—	—	—	—

C. M. ctsp on Venezuela 1830 silver cuartillo, Craig 34. (Garriga report)

Rulau	Date	Metal	Size	VG	F	VF	EF
DF 79	(ca 1830)	Copper	23mm	13.50	—	—	—

F F O ctsp on Caracas Royalist 1813, 1814 or 1816 1/4-real, Craig 2. (Garriga report; 1991 Louis Hudson sale)

Rulau	Date	Metal	Size	VG	F	VF	EF
DF 80	(ca 1830)	Copper	23mm	17.50	—	—	—

F O ctsp on Caracas Royalist 1817 1/4-real, Craig 2.

Rulau	Date	Metal	Size	VG	F	VF	EF
DF 82	ND	Copper	23mm	—	—	—	—

8 Rls ctsp on Caracas Royalist 1/4-real, Craig 2. Dates examined: 1814, 1816, 1817, 1818, 1821. (Garriga report)

Rulau	Date	Metal	Size	VG	F	VF	EF
DF 85	ND	CN	22mm	—	—	—	—

1 / BOLIVAR ctsp on Venezuela 1896 12 1/2-centimo coin, KM-28. (Eklund 2395)

Rulau	Date	Metal	Size	VG	F	VF	EF
DF 86	ND	Brass	23mm	—	—	—	—

1 / J M ctsp on thin blank brass flan. (Eklund 2396)

Rulau	Date	Metal	Size	VG	F	VF	EF
DF 88	ND	Brass	24mm	—	—	—	—

Monogram script JOF (?) ctsp on Bolivia 2-reales token of Hacienda Amapola. (Eklund 2397)

Rulau	Date	Metal	Size	VG	F	VF	EF
DF 90	ND	CN	19mm	—	15.00	—	—

F F D ctsp on Venezuela 5-centimos of 1896 type, KM-27. (Brunk report.)

Rulau	Date	Metal	Size	VG	F	VF	EF
DF91	ND	CN	22.5mm	—	15.00	—	—

Similar ctsp on Venezuela 12 1/2-centimos of 1896 type, KM-28. (Brunk report)

Rulau	Date	Metal	Size	VG	F	VF	EF
DF 92	ND	CN	22.5mm	—	15.00	—	—

J B A / UN / R ctsp on Venezuela 12½-centimos of 1896, KM-28. (Stohr report)

Rulau	Date	Metal	Size	VG	F	VF	EF
DF 93	ND	CN	19mm	—	10.00	—	—

J M C V ctsp on Venezuela 5-centimos of 1925, KM-27. (Stohr report)

NOTES: KM = Krause-Mishler numbers, the same as Yeoman numbers for the Venezuelan coins involved.

1 C / P P; In 1919, a U.S. consular official reported seeing 40 or more of the 1 C / P P counterstamps in one lot in Venezuela. He surmised the 1C meant "one centavo" and these were used after decimalization in 1876, on a hacienda or mercantile establishment.

LARA STATE

Barquisimeto
PEDRO SEEKATZ

Rulau	Date	Metal	Size	VG	F	VF	Unc
Lar 3	ND	Bronze	22mm	—	—	—	—

CALLE DEL COMERCIO / PEDRO / SEEKATZ / * EN BARQUISIMETO *. Rv: Within wreath: 1/4 / REAL. Around: VALE UN CUARTO DE REAL / + EN EL GRAN BAZAR +. (Fonrobert 7971; Eklund 1170; Scott; Stohr FS-32)

Struck in Germany.

Campo Elias
CALDERON BRUZUAL

Rulau	Date	Metal	Size	VG	F	VF	Unc
Lar 6	ND	Aluminum	33mm	20.00	40.00	75.00	—

CALDERON / (rising sun) / * BRUZUAL *. Rv: COMERCIO / 4 / * REALES *. (Louis Hudson 1991 sale; Stohr FB-9)

There are also 1/2, 1 and 2-real aluminum tokens in this issue, valued at $60. each in VF.

Duaca
M / S e H
(Hacienda Moroturito of Segura e Hijos)

Rulau	Date	Metal	Size	VG	F	VF	Unc
Lar 9	(1890's)	Aluminum	34.5mm	—	—	60.00	75.00

(All incused): M / S. e. H / 3 / ALMUD CAFE. Rv: Blank. Plain edge. (Rulau coll.)

Rulau	Date	Metal	Size	VG	F	VF	Unc
Lar 11	(1890's)	Aluminum	26mm	—	—	60.00	75.00

As last, but 1/2 / ALMUD CAFE.

Rulau	Date	Metal	Size	VG	F	VF	Unc
Lar 12	(1890's)	Aluminum	22.5mm	—	—	60.00	75.00

As last, but 1/4 / ALMUD CAFE.

The aluminum tokens are well made. They occur in conditions of EF and Unc. in the numismatic marketplace, which may be unissued remainders.

Hacienda Moroturito also issued locally-made copper tokens earlier; these uniface 23.5mm pieces read S e H / 3 and bring $90 in Fine.

MIRANDA STATE

Dos Caminos
HACIENDA
" SANTA CECILIA"

Rulau	Date	Metal	Size	VG	F	VF	Unc
Mir 6	ND	Brass	25mm	—	—	—	—

HACIENDA " SANTA CECILIA" / (ornament) / DOS CAMINOS. Rv: VALE POR. / 1/2 / REAL / EN MER-CANCIAS. (Guttag coll.; Eklund 2170)

This hacienda issued five token denominations in brass, ranging from 21 to 25mm in diameter. Two are round, two octagonal, and one Maltese cross-shaped.

Paz Castillo
S. PACHECO
Hacienda La Concepcion

Rulau	Date	Metal	Size	VG	F	VF	Unc
Mir 12	ND	CN	Oct 28mm	—	—	—	—

S. PACHECO / + REALES +. Rv: LA CONCEPCION / 2 / (ornament). (Eklund 2297; Garriga report)

Rulau	Date	Metal	Size	VG	F	VF	Unc
Mir 14	ND	CN	Oct 20mm	—	—	—	—

S. PACHECO / 1 / + REAL +. Rv: LA CONCEPCION / (empty field) / (ornament). (Eklund 2296)

Rulau	Date	Metal	Size	VG	F	VF	Unc
Mir 15	ND	CN	Oct 17mm	—	—	—	—

As last, but 1/2. (Eklund 2295)

Coffee estate with a mill and sheller. It was not irrigated, according to Carlos M. Rosales, quoted by Garriga.

H. L. C. A.
Hacienda La Candelaria

Rulau	Date	Metal	Size	VG	F	VF	EF
Mir 20	ND	Brass	22mm	—	—	85.00	95.00

(All incused): A / H C / L. Rv: Intaglio of obverse. Thin flan. Plain edge. Rare. (Rulau coll., ex-Socias Lopez; Carol Plante April 1992 list, lot 592)

Socias Lopez states this was for Hacienda La Candelaria and represented 2 reales. It is quite rare in any condition. Candelaria is now believed to be in Aragua State.

LA HACIENDA CALIFORNIA

Rulau	Date	Metal	Size	VG	F	VF	Unc
Mir 21	ND	CN	34mm	—	—	—	—
		As next, but 5.					
Mir 22	ND	CN	30mm	—	—	—	—

GARANTIZADO / POR / LA HACIENDA / (ornate bar) / CALIFORNIA. Rv: VALE / 2 / REALES. (Eklund 83; Stohr FL-2; Garriga pg. 88)

Rulau	Date	Metal	Size	VG	F	VF	Unc
Mir 23	ND	CN	21mm	—	—	—	—

As last, but 1 / REAL. (Eklund 2193; Bernal 353)

Sugar estate.

Ocumare del Tuy
1798

Rulau	Date	Metal	Size	VG	F	VF	EF
Mir 8	1798	Copper	50mm	—	60.00	—	125.

M D C C X C V I I I - circular fashion around a small palm tree. Rv: Numeral 50 at center, four small palm trees around it in cross form. Plain edge. Weight 111.57 grams. (Christensen July 7, 1978 sale, lot 543; Garriga pg. 81)

Identified in the Christensen sale only as a possible Caribbean coin or weight. It fetched $37.50 against no estimate by the cataloger, who was puzzled over its attribution.

Garriga attributes this piece to Hacienda Piñango at Ocumare del Tuy in Miranda State. The date 1798 could be a founding date for the hacienda; otherwise this would be the earliest dated Venezuelan token.

SUCRE STATE
Araya Peninsula
F.

Rulau	Date	Metal	Size	VG	F	VF	Unc
Suc 1	ND	Copper	Oct 30mm	—	15.00	—	—

(All incused): 1/2 / F / (defaced letters) — within border of 8 rosettes. Rv: Blank. Plain edge. Thick flan. (Eklund 2389)

A similar token was attributed to Maracaibo by Rosales.

H.
(Salinas de Araya)

Rulau	Date	Metal	Size	VG	F	VF	Unc
Suc 3	ND	Copper	—mm	—	—	—	—
		H / (numeral).					
Suc 4	ND	Aluminum	—mm	—	—	—	—
		As last.					

The discoverer Niño found the salt pans in 1499 on the Araya Peninsula. The salt pans became a state monopoly in the 1800's, and these tokens were issued by the administrator of the monopoly, who received a third of the salt mined as his fee.

The Salinas de Araya have been an inexhaustible source of sea salt since 1835, when their exploitation began. Slavery was abolished in Venezuela in 1854. These tokens probably emanate from the salt pans' life in the latter 19th century.

Carupano
LEON SANTELIZ
Hacienda Aguaclara

Rulau	Date	Metal	Size	VG	F	VF	Unc
Suc 8	1905	Aluminum Scal	—mm	—	—	—	—

HACIENDA "AGUA-CLARA" / L. S. / . AGUA-CLARA. (Garriga report)

Leon Santeliz, a Frenchman, settled near Carupano, establishing Aguaclara about 1880. He married Margarita Sisco Flex, a Corsican immigrant. One of his sons, Ramon Santeliz, became the famed Carupanian poet, and other descendants are active in agriculture and finance.

His 1905 scalloped aluminum token series consists of five denominations, all made in Europe.

The account books of this hacienda still exist.

TUNAPUI

Rulau	Date	Metal	Size	VG	F	VF	Unc
Suc 10	(1890's)	Copper Scal	23mm	—	—	—	—

J. FRANCESCHI & Cia / 1 F. / * TUNAPUI *. Rv: 1 F.

This plantation was owned by the Franceschi family. A number of copper token types in franco denominations were issued, in various shapes, says Garriga. These were struck in France.

Rio Caribe
A VALDIVIESO

Rulau	Date	Metal	Size	VG	F	VF	Unc
Suc 20	(1920's)	Lead	30mm	—	—	—	—

A. VALDIVIESO / = ½ =. Rv: Blank. (Garriga report)

Agustin Valdivieso owned this cocoa plantation, Hacienda Bohordal.

TACHIRA STATE

San Cristobal
BOTICA ALEMANA

Rulau	Date	Metal	Size	VG	F	VF	Unc
Tch 4	ND	Bronze	15mm	—	—	—	—

BOTICA ALEMANA / 1 / PALITO. Rv: Blank. (Bernal 333)

Rulau	Date	Metal	Size	VG	F	VF	Unc
Tch 5	ND	Bronze	36mm	—	—	—	—

As last, but 10 / PALITOS. (Bernal 334)

Botica Alemana = German drugstore. Proprietors were Vandisell-Rhode.

Palito was a dry measure, one-half of an almud and equal to 2 cuartillas or 40 libras. In coffee measuring, one "palito grande" equaled 2 sacos, while one "palito chiquito" equaled 1 saco.

Some authorities say this is Zulia State.

ESTADO TACHIRA

Rulau	Date	Metal	Size	VG	F	VF	Unc
Tch 8	1872	Brass	21mm	—	—	—	—

ESTADO TACHIRA / (8-pointed star) / 1872. Rv: SAN CRISTOBAL / 2 / R. (F. 8030; Ulex 2675; Eklund 1217)

Rulau	Date	Metal	Size	VG	F	VF	Unc
Tch 9	1872	Brass	21mm	—	—	—	—

ESTADO TACHIRA 1872 * / (8-pointed star). Rv: SAN CRISTOBAL R / 2 / *. (F. 8031; Eklund 1218)

SUAREZ HERMANOS

Rulau	Date	Metal	Size	VG	F	VF	Unc
Tch 15	ND	Aluminum	26mm	—	—	65.00	—

GARANTIZADO / POR LAS / HACIENDAS / DE / SUAREZ HERMANOS. Rv: VALE / * 1/2 * / PALITO. Plain edge. (Rulau coll.)

Rulau	Date	Metal	Size	VG	F	VF	Unc
Tch 16	ND	Aluminum	—mm	—	—	65.00	—

As last, but * 1/4 *. (Louis Hudson Apr. 1990 sale, lot 859)

There is also a 1-palito in the set. Only about 20 sets are known.

YARACUY STATE

Cocorote
J. B. HELLYER

Rulau	Date	Metal	Size	VG	F	VF	Unc
Ycy 3	1858	Copper	24.5mm	—	—	45.00	120.

* J. B. HELLYER * / UN / REAL / 1858. Rv: EMPRESA / (arms) / DEL YARACUY. (Fonrobert 8037; Ulex 2675; Eklund 1233)

Arms include an alligator on ground.

SAN PEDRO

Rulau	Date	Metal	Size	VG	F	VF	Unc
Ycy 8	1906	—	—mm	—	—	—	—

SAN PEDRO. 2 REALES. Issued holed.

Rulau	Date	Metal	Size	VG	F	VF	Unc
Ycy 9	ND	—	—mm	—	—	—	—

As last, but 1 REAL. Scalloped flan?

Lizarraga Brothers issued these tokens for Hacienda San Pedro. In 1833, Jose Manuel Lizarraga was established at "Hacienda La Lagunetica. Altos de San Pedro."

Guama
JUAN F. COLMENARES

Rulau	Date	Metal	Size	VG	F	VF	Unc
Ycy 13	ND	Copper	18mm	—	—	75.00	—

JUAN F. COLMENARES. 1/4 R. Rv: Blank (Eklund 1195)

Rulau	Date	Metal	Size	VG	F	VF	Unc
Ycy 14	1873	Brass	20mm				

Branch with coffee berries. Around: JUAN F. COLMENARES / * GUAMA *. Rv: VALE 1/2 (between branches) / 1873. (Eklund 1197). Also known in copper.

Rulau	Date	Metal	Size	VG	F	VF	Unc
Ycy 15	1873	Copper	18mm				

As last, but 1/4. (Eklund 1196)

FRANCISCO R. LAGUNA

Rulau	Date	Metal	Size	VG	F	VF	Unc
Ycy 17	ND	Brass	25mm	—	—	90.00	—

FRANCISCO R. LAGUNA / 2 / REALES / . GUAMA . Rv: No description. (Stohr N/L; Louis Hudson 1991 sale)

ATO. I. MIRALLES
Hacienda Aracal

Rulau	Date	Metal	Size	VG	F	VF	Unc
Ycy 19	ND	Copper	27.5mm	25.00	70.00	—	—

Ato I MIRALLES / 4 / REALES / * GUAMA *. Rv: HACIENDA ARACAL / 4 / REALES / * CAFE *. Plain edge. (Rulau coll., ex-Socias Lopez)

Rulau	Date	Metal	Size	VG	F	VF	Unc
Ycy 20	ND	Copper	24.5mm	—	65.00	—	—

As last, but 2 / REALES. Plain edge.

These tokens are quite rare. Specimens in the Rulau collection were dug up with metal detectors and are corroded and pitted. Copper ½ and ⅛-real tokens fetch $35 up in Fine.

Urachiche
ZENON ANTICH

Rulau	Date	Metal	Size	VG	F	VF	Unc
Ycy 25	1858	Copper	18mm	—	60.00	90.00	—

Ceiba tree. ZENON ANTICH / * URACHICHE *. Rv: 1/2 / REAL / 1858. (Scott; 1899 Weyl catalog; Eklund 1226; Stohr FU-1)

Rulau	Date	Metal	Size	VG	F	VF	Unc
Ycy 26	1858	Copper	16mm	—	—	—	—

As last, but 1/4. (Eklund 1225)

This hacienda raised sugar cane and bananas.

ZULIA STATE
La Concepcion
EUSEBIO COLMENARES

Rulau	Date	Metal	Size	VG	F	VF	Unc
Zul 5	ND	Brass	23mm	—	—	—	—

LA / (star-shaped ornament) / (branch) / CONCEPCION / (branch). Rv: Large 1. (Eklund 2402)

Rulau	Date	Metal	Size	VG	F	VF	Unc
Zul 6	ND	Brass	—mm	—	—	—	—

As last, but 1/2 (real).

Rulau	Date	Metal	Size	VG	F	VF	Unc
Zul 7	ND	Brass	—mm	—	—	—	—

As last, but 1/4 (real). (Dave Roberts report)

San Rafael
J. M. VILLANUEVA SAMPAYO

Rulau	Date	Metal	Size	VG	F	VF	Unc
Zul 11	1894	CN	28mm	—	40.00	65.00	—

(All incused): J. M. VILLANUEVA SAMPAYO / 1894 / SAN RAFAEL. Rv: VALE / 2 / REALES. Plain edge. (Eklund 2403)

Rulau	Date	Metal	Size	VG	F	VF	Unc
Zul 12	1894	CN	23mm	15.00	30.00	—	—

As last, but 1 / REAL.

Rulau	Date	Metal	Size	VG	F	VF	Unc
Zul 13	1894	CN	17mm	—	—	—	—

As last, but 1/4 / REAL. (Bernal 351)

Santa Rita
J. M. VILLANUEVA SAMPAYO

Rulau	Date	Metal	Size	VG	F	VF	EF
Zul 15	1894	CN	28mm	—	40.00	—	—

(All incused): J. M. VILLANUEVA SAMPAYO / 1894 / SANTA RITA. Rv: VALE / 2 / REALES. Crudely reeded edge. (Rulau coll.; Stohr FS-25)

The edge seems to have been reeded by hand, by either knife or file cuts all around.

Both Santa Rita and San Rafael, the other locale of Villanueva tokens, are on the shores of Lake Maracaibo. Santa Rita may be in Santa Teresa municipio.

IRON MINES COMPANY OF VENEZUELA

Rulau	Date	Metal	Size	F	VF	EF	Unc
Zul 20	ND	Copper	Sq 38mm	—	—	35.00	55.00

FICHA / IRON MINES COMPANY / OF VENE-ZUELA. Rv: Blank. Plain edge. (Rulau coll.)

Rulau	Date	Metal	Size	F	VF	EF	Unc
Zul 21	ND	Aluminum	Sq 38mm	—	—	35.00	55.00

As last. (Rulau coll.)

According to numismatist Juan Socias Lopez of Caracas, this was an American company.

Extensive iron ore deposits were discovered in the 1940's in Bolivar and Delta Amacuro states, near Cerro Bolivar, called the "iron mountain," and the new (1961) city of Santo Tome de Guayana. American interests were active in their exploitation.

Rulau	Date	Metal	Size	F	VF	EF	Unc
Zul 24	ND	Brass	38mm	—	—	60.00	—

Obverse as last, on round planchet; last line curved. Rv: SE RECAUDAN 5 BOLIVARES / DEL TRABAJA-DOR EN / CALIDAD DE DEPOSITO / PARA GARANTIZAR / QUE EL DEVOLVERA / ESTA FICHA / AL TERMINAR SU EMPLEO / CON ESTA COMPANIA. Plain edge. (Smithsonian coll.)

UNATTRIBUTED VENEZUELA

Caño-Seco
J. V. A.
(Juan Vicente Arciniega)

Rulau	Date	Metal	Size	VG	F	VF	Unc
Ven 1	ND	Brass	29mm	—	—	—	—

J. V. A. HACIENDA CAÑO-SECO. 2 R. (Ulex 2645; Eklund 1174)

Ven 2	ND	Brass	24mm	—	—	—	—

As last, but 1 R. (Eklund 1173; Ulex 2645)

Ulex also reported 1/2 and 1/4 real tokens of this issuer in 1908.

Tamaya
J. R. ACUÑA

Rulau	Date	Metal	Size	VG	F	VF	Unc
Ven 4	ND	Brass	30mm	—	—	—	—

* J. R. ACUÑA * / (5-pointed star) / TAMAYA. Rv: * CINCUENTA CENTAVOS MERCADERIAS * / 50. (Fonrobert 8033; Ulex 2675; Eklund 1224)

Ven 5	ND	Brass	24mm	—	—	—	85.00

As last, but VEINTE and 20. (F. 8034)

Ven 6	ND	Brass	19.5mm	—	—	—	—

As last, but DIEZ and 10. (F. 8035)

Ven 7	ND	Brass	16mm	—	—	—	—

As last, but CINCO and 5. (F. 8036; Eklund 1221)

5 = Half Real. 10 = Real. 20 = 2 Reales. 50 = 5 Reales. Mercaderias = Merchandise.

APTIS

Rulau	Date	Metal	Size	VG	F	VF	Unc
Ven 14	ND	Silver	18mm	—	—	Rare	—

APTIS across field. Rv: ACOLOGIA (curved). (1899 Weyl catalog; Eklund 1168; Stohr FA-1)

Ven 16	ND	Copper	18mm	—	—	—	—

As last.

These tokens represented one real.

ATANASIO BELLO
Hacienda Araguata

Rulau	Date	Metal	Size	VG	F	VF	Unc
Ven 18	1867	Copper	17mm	—	—	—	•

ATANASIO / BELLO / ARAGNATA. Rv: Ape seated on a tree limb. Around: VALE 1/4 REAL/ 1867. (Ulex 2644)

Ven 19	1867	Copper	20mm	20.00	35.00	—	—

As last, but 1/2. (Eklund 1169). Also occurs in brass.

Ven 20	1867	Silver	20mm	—	—	—	—

As last. (Eklund 1169; Stohr FA-17)

Araguato = Ape (*Alouatta ursina*). The name on the token was misspelled ARAGNATA instead of ARAGUATA, the name of the hacienda.

CONCESION JESURUN

Rulau	Date	Metal	Size	VG	F	VF	Unc
Ven 29	ND	Brass	Oct 33mm	—	—	100.	200.

CONCESION / -.- / JESURUN. Rv: VALE / 1 / PESO. (Eklund 1455; Stohr FC-33). The peso equaled 10 reales.

Rulau	Date	Metal	Size	VG	F	VF	Unc
Ven 30	ND	Brass	Oct 28mm	—	—	—	—

(Quatrefoil) / CONCESION / -.- / JESURUN / (quatrefoil). Rv: VALE / 1 / BOLIVAR. (Eklund 1454; Stohr FC-34). The bolivar equaled two reales.

Rulau	Date	Metal	Size	VG	F	VF	Unc
Ven 31	ND	Brass	Oct 24mm	—	25.00	75.00	—

As last, but 1 / REAL. (Eklund 1453; Byrne T-10)

The Jesurun (or Jesurum) family was Jewish in origin, established in Venezuela in the early 1800's in La Guaira and other places, and related to the Jesuruns of Curacao (who were also token issuers). One Dr. A. Jesurum was Venezuelan consul in Panama in 1890.

Dr. Garriga was unable over a long period to find what — and where — "Concesion Jesurun" was.

It would be easy to conclude that the tokens were issued before 1876, when the new centavo-venezolano monetary system was introduced. But the real persisted on tokens long after it was replaced as an official coin — real-denomination tokens exist with dates like 1894, 1902, 1904, 1905, 1906.

EL COJO

Rulau	Date	Metal	Size	VG	F	VF	Unc
Ven 36	1876	Copper	26mm	—	—	—	—

EL COJO / 1876 ctsp on Venezuela 1862-HEATON centavo, Yeoman-7. Weight 7.5 grams. Engrailed edge. (Eklund 1193)

Garriga reports struck tokens of El Cojo made by Tomaron in Paris.

EL PORVENIR

Rulau	Date	Metal	Size	VG	F	VF	Unc
Ven 38	ND	Aluminum	25mm	—	—	27.50	—

(All incuse): = / EL / PORVENIR / . Rv: DOS / REALES. (Louis Hudson 1991 sale)

F. G.
(Florencio Gimenez)
Hacienda La Fortuna

Rulau	Date	Metal	Size	VG	F	VF	EF
Ven 44	(1830-40)	Copper	14mm	—	—	—	—

Script F. G. Rv: 1 / REAL. (Garriga report; Stohr FF-4)

In "valley of Quibor," says Garriga. Believed to be Lara State.

San Antonio
LUIS GARZARO

Rulau	Date	Metal	Size	VG	F	VF	EF
Ven 46	ND	CN	18mm	—	—	35.00	—

LUIS GARZARO / SAN ANTONIO ctsp on Venezuela 1-centavo of 1876-77 type, KM-25. (Brunk 51760)

Rulau	Date	Metal	Size	VG	F	VF	EF
Ven 47	ND	CN	22mm	—	—	35.00	—

Similar ctsp on Venezuela 2 1/2-centavos of 1876-77 type, KM 26.

GOMEZ HERMANOS
Hacienda Turumo

Rulau	Date	Metal	Size	VG	F	VF	Unc
Ven 49	ND	CN	27.5mm	—	—	27.50	50.00

Clasped hands. Around: GOMEZ HERMANOS / *. Rv: HACIENDA TURUMO / 4 Rs- / *. Plain edge. (Rulau coll.; Zaika coll.)

Rulau	Date	Metal	Size	VG	F	VF	Unc
Ven 50	ND	CN	23.2mm	—	—	25.00	45.00

As last, but 2 Rs-.

Rulau	Date	Metal	Size	VG	F	VF	Unc
Ven 51	ND	CN	19mm	—	—	20.00	—

As last, but 1 R.

Rulau	Date	Metal	Size	VG	F	VF	Unc
Ven 52	ND	CN	17mm	—	—	20.00	—

As last, but 1/2 R. (Rulau coll.)

Zaika reports this set in brass! Believed to be in Miranda State.

FRANCISCO GOMEZ GALVIZ
Hacienda de Campo Alegre

Rulau	Date	Metal	Size	VG	F	VF	Unc
Ven 54	1890	CN	26mm	—	—	—	—

ss Variously reported as 21 to 25 mm.
FCO. GOMEZ GALVIS / 1890. Rv: HACIENDA-DE-CAMPO-ALEGRE / 10 / *. (Garriga pg. 89; Stohr Fe-9)

Rulau	Date	Metal	Size	VG	F	VF	Unc
Ven 55	1890	CN	21mm	—	—	—	—

FRANCISCO GOMEZ GALVIZ / 1890. Rv: HACIENDA-DE-CAMPO-ALEGRE / 5 / *. (Bernal 414; Garriga pg. 89)

Bernal says the 5-centavo token seems to be struck over a Colombia 1886 5-centavo coin, KM-183. Believed to be in Caracas district.

Cocotero
J. L. GORRONDONA

Rulau	Date	Metal	Size	VG	F	VF	Unc
Ven 57	ND	Brass	18.4mm	—	32.50	60.00	100.

Tree on ground. COCOTERO above. Rv: 1/2 / . REAL . / J. L. GORRONDONA. Beaded border on each side. Plain edge. (Rulau coll.)

Rulau collection contains two EF specimens. 1 and ¼-real tokens were also issued; same prices.

MANUEL MARIA GONZALEZ

Rulau	Date	Metal	Size	VG	F	VF	Unc
Ven 59	ND	Aluminum	30mm	—	9.50	12.50	—

MANUEL MARIA GONZALEZ / 3 (large) / . HACIENDA COCOTERO. Plain edge. (Garriga pg. 80)

Gonzalez apparently was a successor owner of Hacienda Cocotero to Gorrondona. Aluminum 1 and 1/2 tokens are known.

ARVELO LAPATO AUSTRIA

Rulau	Date	Metal	Size	VG	F	VF	Unc
Ven 63	ND	Brass	21mm	—	25.00	50.00	90.00

ARVELO / LAPATO / AUSTRIA. Rv: Within wreath: 1/4 / REAL. Plain edge. (Zaika coll.; Eklund 52)

There was a farm owner named Arvelo Zapata Austria, Socias Lopez reports.

HERMANOS LIZARRAGA

Rulau	Date	Metal	Size	VG	F	VF	EF
Ven 69	1906	Brass	27.5mm	35.00	45.00	80.00	—

HERMANOS LIZARRAGA / . JBOA 1906. Rv: Large numeral 2. Excessively rare.

Socias Lopez states for 2 reales. Lizarraga Brothers also issued tokens for Hacienda San Pedro, which see. Possibly Yaracuy State.

T. O.
Hacienda de Montelimar

Rulau	Date	Metal	Size	VG	F	VF	Unc
Ven 80	ND	Brass	20.5mm	—	—	60.00	100.

HACa DE MONTELIMAR * / T. O. (large. Rv: Large 2. (Fonrobert 8028; Ulex 2675; Eklund 1212)

Rulau	Date	Metal	Size	VG	F	VF	Unc
Ven 81	ND	Brass	19.5mm	—	—	—	—

As last, but large 1 on reverse. (Eklund 1211; Fonrobert 8029)

ISIDRO OLIVARES
El Oasis

Rulau	Date	Metal	Size	VG	F	VF	Unc
Ven 83	ND	Copper	19mm	—	—	—	—

ISIDRO OLIVARES. EL OASIS. (Weyl; Eklund 1194; Stohr FE-11). Also in brass.

MANUEL PALACIOS VEGAS
Hacienda Quebrada Honda

Rulau	Date	Metal	Size	VG	F	VF	Unc
Ven 88	1891	Nic/Bs	Oct 19mm	—	—	75.00	—

MANUEL PALACIOS VEGAS / (Tree) / o 1891 o. Rv: (All incused): . HACIENDA . / QUEBRADA HONDA / 1/2 ALMUD / CAFE. (Bernal 352)

Probably Hacienda Quebrada Honda of Manuel Palacio Vegas in Quebrada Honda, Caracas district. Or possibly a hacienda of the same name in the Fila de Mariches area. Possibly Miranda State.

RIVERO Y COLMENARES

Rulau	Date	Metal	Size	VG	F	VF	Unc
Ven 100	ND	Brass	19mm	—	—	—	—

SAN JOSE / RIVERO Y COLMENARES. Rv: 1 REAL. (Stohr FS-4)

SAN CARLO

Rulau	Date	Metal	Size	VG	F	VF	Unc
Ven 102	ND	Copper	27mm	—	40.00	75.00	125.

-. * .- / SANCARLO / -. * .-. Rv: (Ornament) / * 1 (large, in beaded circle) * / (ornament). Plain edge. (Eklund 2166)

Rulau	Date	Metal	Size	VG	F	VF	Unc
Ven 103	ND	Copper	27mm	—	—	60.00	—

As last, but 3/4. (Eklund 2319)

Rulau	Date	Metal	Size	VG	F	VF	Unc
Ven 104	ND	Copper	27mm	—	—	—	Rare

As last, but 1/2. (ANS coll.)

Sena
A. S.

Rulau	Date	Metal	Size	VG	F	VF	Unc
Ven 105	ND	Brass	15.5mm	—	10.00	—	—

SENA. / A. S. / 1/2 REAL. Rv: Blank. (Fonrobert 8032; Eklund 1219; Stohr FA-24)

| Ven 106 | ND | Brass | 18mm | — | 10.00 | — | — |

As last, but 1. (Eklund 1220; Stohr FA-24)

F. & A. YAGUA

Rulau	Date	Metal	Size	VG	F	VF	EF
Ven 110	ND	CN	19mm	—	15.00	—	—

F & A / YAGUA / 1/2 ctsp on Venezuela 1896 5-centimos, KM-27. (Stohr 89; Brunk 54980)

ZEREGA

Rulau	Date	Metal	Size	VG	F	VF	Unc
Ven 115	1869	Copper	23mm	—	—	—	—

Tree on ground. Around: EL TRABAJO RECOMPENSA. Rv: ZEREGA / 2 / REALES / -.....- 1869-.....- (F. 7461; Ulex 2208; Eklund 980)

| Ven 116 | 1869 | Copper | 18.5mm | — | — | — | — |

As last, but 1 / REAL. (Fonrobert 7462)

| Ven 117 | 1869 | Copper | 15mm | — | — | — | — |

As last, but 1/2 / REAL. (F. 7463; Eklund 982)

El Trabajo Recompensa = Work Pays. Obviously a motto intended to spur the laborers in the workplace. The 2-reales also has been reported in cupronickel.

Attributed by Fonrobert and Ulex to Honduras in error.

MAVERICK TOKENS

In this section we have gathered those items which are probably Latin American but which we have been unable to assign to any particular nation. Footnotes carry such information as is known to us.

Users of this catalog with information on maverick pieces may report this to: Russell Rulau, Krause Publications, Iola, WI 54990.

C. A.

Rulau	Date	Metal	Size	VG	F	VF	Unc
Mav 1	ND	Aluminum	28mm	—	—	5.00	—

C A (large, shaded) in beaded circle. Rv: VALE / * UNO * / FLOR. Plain edge.

Vale uno flor = worth one flower.

HERCULANO AFRE

Rulau	Date	Metal	Size	F	VF	EF	Unc
Mav 3	ND	Gilt/Cop	21mm	—	15.00	—	—

Indian head left. LIBERTAD on headband. Rv: HERCULANO AFRE / (compass and square) / (ornament). Plain edge. Thick (2.5mm) flan. (Rulau coll., ex-Elman)

A Masonic item.

ANEUROL
Struck ca 1971

Rulau	Date	Metal	Size	F	VF	EF	Unc
Mav 5	1778	Brass	37mm	—	—	—	12.00

Imitation of obverse of 1778 Spanish-American gold doubloon of Carlos III. Rv: MAS VALE TRANQUILIDAD QUE ORO / Aneurol / Lacer (script, in triangle). Plain edge. Thick flan. (*World Coins* for Nov. 1972, pg. 1510)

Mas vale tranquilidad que oro = Tranquility (is) worth more than gold.
A well made, solid-metal store card.

ARENAS CIA. LTDA.

Rulau	Date	Metal	Size	F	VF	EF	Unc
Mav 7	ND	xx	Oct 19.5mm	—	10.00	—	—

xx Red Vulcanite. Within circle: ARENAS CIA. LTDA. Rv: Within circle: T. Wide raised border on each side. (David Harrison coll.)

This token was found in a 4,000-piece hoard of Chile vulcanite pieces in 1990. It may be Chilean.

T. J. BEAUCHAMP
Belfate

Rulau	Date	Metal	Size	VG	F	VF	Unc
Mav 9	ND	Brass	23mm	—	—	—	—

T. J. BEAUCHAMP / 1/2 / REAL / BELFATE. Rv: Blank. Plain edge. (Zaika coll.)

J. BOGDANICH

Rulau	Date	Metal	Size	VG	F	VF	Unc
Mav 11	ND	Brass	21mm	—	—	—	—

J. BOGDANICH. Rv: VALE / 20 / CENTAVOS. (Zaika coll.)

CRISTO

Rulau	Date	Metal	Size	VG	F	VF	EF
Mav 16	ND	Copper	38mm	—	—	—	—

Cross against pebbled field. Rv: 10 in (wreath?) / C R I S T O. Thick flan. (ANS coll.)

This token is in the ANS/Mexican cabinet. It may well be Mexican, from the 1790-1820 period.

CABALLEROS DE DIMAS-ALANG

Rulau	Date	Metal	Size	F	VF	EF	Unc
Mav 13	1941	CN	31mm	—	—	9.50	—

D in star outline between balance scales, square on book below. Around: CABALLEROS DE DIMAS-ALANG / (rosette) 1941 (rosette). Rv: Blank. Plain edge. (Rulau coll.)

Possibly Philippines?

CONF. SANTA LUISA DE MARILLAC
Parroquia de Santa Ana

Rulau	Date	Metal	Size	VG	F	VF	Unc
Mav 15	ND	Zinc	22.5mm	—	—	—	27.50

CONF. SANTA LUISA DE MARILLAC / BONO / *. Rv: PARROQUIA DE SANTA ANA / (rosette) / . Plain edge.

Bono = Voucher. Parroquia = Parish (or parish church). Conf. = (possibly) Confraternidad (Fellowship). Probably Chile.

CUYAMACA CLUB

Rulau	Date	Metal	Size	F	VF	EF	Unc
Mav 17	ND	Bronze	Rect 28.2by 7.7mm	—	—	5.00	—

(All incused): Cuyamaca Club in script. Rv: Blank. Planchet has cut corners. Possibly a nameplate rather than a token.

EN MERCANCIA

Rulau	Date	Metal	Size	VG	F	VF	Unc
Mav 19	ND	Brass	24mm				

VALE / 20 CTS / EN MERCANCIA. Rv: Monogram B?? (Pipher Oct. 1987 sale, lot 2555)

EN MERCANCIA = In merchandise.

Crowned F

Rulau	Date	Metal	Size	VG	F	VF	EF
Mav 21	ND	Copper	41mm	—	—	75.00	

Crown above large serif F ctsp on England 1797 cartwheel twopence, KM 619. (Rulau coll.)

Found in Jamaica in 1951.

J. J. G.

Rulau	Date	Metal	Size	VG	F	VF	EF
Mav 22	ND	Copper	37mm	—	—	—	—

Within dentilated-border circular frame: Script J J G (?). Inscription around illegible except LAS .... N. Rv: Blank. (ANS coll.)

HERMANN

Rulau	Date	Metal	Size	VG	F	VF	Unc
Mav 23	ND	Brass	21mm	—	—	—	—

HERMANN / (outline star). Rv: Same as obverse. Plain edge.

H. F. J.

Rulau	Date	Metal	Size	F	VF	EF	Unc
Mav 25	ND	Brass	31mm	—	—	5.00	—

(Ornament) / H F J . (ornament). Rv: 50. Plain edge. (Zaffern coll.)

Zaffern suggests Fajardo municipio in Puerto Rico, but we cannot confirm.

LAVAMATICAS LA FUENTE

Rulau	Date	Metal	Size	VG	F	VF	Unc
Mav 27	ND	Brass	Oval				
			24x17.5mm	—	—	5.00	—

(All incuse): III / LAVAMATICAS / LA FUENTE / iii.
Rv: Blank. Plain edge. The oval planchet has straight
sides top and bottom. (Rulau coll.)

Lavamaticas la fuente = Automatic washing fountain (?). The word lavamaticas is an invented term.

FERMIN MICHEL

Rulau	Date	Metal	Size	VG	F	VF	Unc
Mav 29	ND	Aluminum	19mm	—	—	5.00	—

FERMIN MICHEL / 5 (shaded) / -.-. Rv: *.* / 5
(shaded) / *.*. Plain edge.

MINERAL DE PUPACYA

Rulau	Date	Metal	Size	F	VF	EF	Unc
Mav 30	1855	GS	26mm	—	—	200.	

MINERAL DE / To. Vs. / (rosette) PUPACYA
(rosette). Rv: VALE 2 REALES / AÑO / . DE 1855.
Plain edge. (ANS coll.)

A. MONTAUTTI & CIA.

Rulau	Date	Metal	Size	VG	F	VF	Unc
Mav 31	ND	Brass	27.5mm	—	—	35.00	—

A. MONTAUTTI & Cia / 20 (in beaded circle) / *
CENTAVOS *. Rv: Blank, but beaded border. Plain
edge. (Tanenbaum coll.)

ONE CENT

Rulau	Date	Metal	Size	VG	F	VF	EF
Mav 33	ND	Copper	26mm	—	25.00	—	—

ONE / CENT ctsp on worn-smooth indecipherable
coin. Serif letters are from individual letter punches.
(Rulau coll.).

Found in Jamaica in 1951.

T. ORLA BIALEGO

Rulau	Date	Metal	Size	F	VF	EF	Unc
Mav 35	ND	Aluminum	25mm	—	—	—	—

Eagle displayed, head turned right. Around: T. ORLA
(tilda over the L) BIALEGO / 154 / (ornaments). Rv:
Blank. Beaded border on each side. Plain edge. (Tanenbaum coll.)

C. P.

Rulau	Date	Metal	Size	VG	F	VF	EF
Mav 36	ND	Copper	31mm	—	—	—	—

C P in relief within rect. depression ctsp seven times (4
obv., 3 rev.) on France 1774 sol, Craig 73. (ANS coll.)

Present-day ANS staff cannot say why this piece was attributed to Mexico by
earlier curators. It does not appear "Mexican" at all.

The hallmark (if it is that) matches no known American, French, British or
other European silversmith punch. Under the circumstances, we place it under
Mavericks for now.

E. C. P.

Rulau	Date	Metal	Size	VG	F	VF	Unc
Mav 37	ND	Brass	22mm	—	—	6.00	—

(All incused): 0.10 / ECP monogram (?). Rv: Blank.
Plain edge. (Brunk coll.)

PONCHE TELLO

Rulau	Date	Metal	Size	VG	F	VF	Unc
Mav 39	1901	Brass	21.3mm	—		F	30.00

Veiled head of Queen Victoria left. PONCHE TELLO around. Rv: St. George and the dragon. 1901 in exergue. Plain edge. (Brunk coll.)

Imitation British gold sovereign. It is possible this is not Latin American.

PRINCESS CRUISES

Rulau	Date	Metal	Size	VF	EF	Unc	Proof
Mav 41	ND	CN	37mm	—	—	5.00	—

Modern cruiseliner half right. Below: ISLAND PRINCESS / PACIFIC PRINCESS / SUN PRINCESS. Rv: Princess / (wavy logo) / Cruises (tiny) R-in-circle. Plain edge.

R (and) Brand-mark

Rulau	Date	Metal	Size	VG	F	VF	EF
Mav 42	ND	Copper	23mm	—			

(Aztec doll) / (Brand mark) / R. Rv: ICO (C retrograde) / G-type brand mark / 2 lines of 13 I's each. (ANS coll.)

DR. R.

Rulau	Date	Metal	Size	VG	F	VF	Unc
Mav 43	ND	Brass	21.5mm	—	—	—	—

CALLE DE LA AGUSTINAS / DR. R. Rv: VALE / UN / BANO. Plain edge. (Zaika coll.)

Vale un bano = worth one bath.

ROYAL CARIBBEAN'S LABADEE

Rulau	Date	Metal	Size	F	VF	EF	Unc
Mav 45	ND	Gold/Bs	Irreg				
			30mm	—	—	—	5.00

LABADEE across crested shield. Rv: Stylized trident-and-anchor. Around: ROYAL CARIBBEAN'S / LABADEE. Weight 10 grams. (Fred Borgmann report)

Modern gambling token.

I.A.S.

Enlarged to show detail

Rulau	Date	Metal	Size	VG	F	VF	EF
Mav 46	ND	Copper	28.5mm	—	—	35.00	

Script I A S in relief within rectangular depression ctsp on U.S. 1802 Large cent. Weight 10.75 grams.

This counterstamp has been attributed to Kingston in Jamaica and to St. Vincent Island. It may be Latin American, but we are aware of no evidence. It matches no known U.S. stamp, either.

S. JOSE

Rulau	Date	Metal	Size	VG	F	VF	EF
Mav 47	ND	Silver?	Irreg				
			36.3mm	—	20.00	—	—

S. JOSE in relief within oval pebbled depression ctsp five times on irregularly round planchet. Rv: Blank. Plain edge, pierced by flan cracks. (Rulau coll.; ex-Bill Judd)

The planchet may have been made by hammering flat both sides of a coin. S. Jose may stand for San Jose.

SAVIO

Rulau	Date	Metal	Size	VG	F	VF	Unc
Mav 49	ND	Brass	21.7mm	—	—	5.00	—

(All incused): SAVIO. Rv: 10 C. Plain edge.

T. V. I.

Rulau	Date	Metal	Size	VF	F	Unc	Proof
Mav 51	ND	CN	34mm	—	—	11.00	—

T. V. I. / (outline Indian head left) / (tiny) USM monogram / $1.00. Rv: Same as obverse, but no USM. Plain edge. Thick flan. (Rulau coll.)

Casino token.

C. P. T.

Rulau	Date	Metal	Size	VG	F	VF	Unc
Mav 53	ND	Brass	16mm	—	—	15.00	—

C. P. T. Rv: 1. (Rulau coll.; R. B. White coll.)

Probably made at Scovill Mfg. Co.

TACATAC

Rulau	Date	Metal	Size	VG	F	VF	Unc
Mav 55	ND	Brass	29mm	—	—	5.00	—

TACATAC amid tulips and leaves. Rv: Ball in wreath of coffee branches. Plain edge. (Zaika coll.)

TENQUEL

Rulau	Date	Metal	Size	F	VF	EF	Unc
Mav 57	ND	Brass	29mm	—	—	15.00	—

(All incused): TENQUEL / UN / REAL. Rv: Blank. Plain edge. (Brunk coll.)

TRIGGER

Rulau	Date	Metal	Size	VG	F	VF	Unc
Mav 59	ND	Bronze	16mm	—	—	—	—

TRIGGER. Rv: ES VALIDO POR / UNA / MONTADA. Plain edge (Zaika coll.)

Una montada = A ride?

TRABAJO

Rulau	Date	Metal	Size	VG	F	VF	EF
Mav 61	ND	Copper	27.5mm	—	—	Rare	—

TRABAJO in relief within 18x3.5mm rectangular depression ctsp on 1851 London Crystal Palace medalet, Taylor's Architectural Medals 166dd, Brown's BHM 2469. (James W. Allen coll.)

Trabajo = work. A previous owner believed this was a Mexico or Caribbean hacienda counterstamp applied to available coppers to indicate one day's labor.

UBI

Rulau	Date	Metal	Size	VG	F	VF	Unc
Mav 63	ND	Copper		+ +	—	100.	

+ + Heart-shaped flan, 15x21mm. Ubi/N. Rv: Blank. (Fonrobert 10199).

Argentina ?

V. M. & S. CO.

Rulau	Date	Metal	Size	VG	F	VF	Unc
Mav 65	ND	Aluminum	Oval 30x50 mm	—	—	—	—

V. M & S. Co. / 10 / DIEZ LITROS MAIZ. Rv: Blank. Pellet border on each side. (Eklund 2183)

VALE UN CIGARRO

Rulau	Date	Metal	Size	VG	F	VF	Unc
Mav 67	ND	Brass	25mm	—	—	3.00	—

VALE UN CIGARRO / 5 (within spherical ornament) / CTVOS. Rv: Same as obverse. Plain edge. (Randel coll.)

EZEQUIEL VALVERDE

Rulau	Date	Metal	Size	VG	F	VF	Unc
Mav 69	ND	Brass	20mm	—	—	—	—

EZEQUIEL VALVERDE / (8-pointed star). Rv: Ls. / (two coffee trees) / ctsp B. (Zaika coll.)

FREDERICO VERLINGE

Struck 1855

Rulau	Date	Metal	Size	F	VF	EF	Unc
Mav 71	5855 *	Bronze	30mm	—	—	—	12.50

AOR: I: FREDERICO VERLINGE, AUG: L: C: PERF: AMIZ: / BENE- / MERENTIUM / PRAEMIUM / A: DAV: L: 5852. Rv: AUG: E RESP: L: FIDELIDADE. / J: A: X: M: / HEROISMO / 5855 / -*-. Plain edge. (Rulau coll.)

* The year-date 5855 given to this medalet is a Masonic date. A.L. 5855 equates with A.D. 1855 in the Christian calendar. Masonic dates may be converted to Christian Era dates by the subtraction of the number 4000.
  Probably Argentina.

VILA, PORTILLA Y CA.

Rulau	Date	Metal	Size	VG	F	VF	Unc
Mav 72	ND	CN	19.5mm	—	—	27.50	—

VILA, PORTILLA Y Ca. / CABEZA / DE / QUESO / *.
Rv: UN / CUARTILLO within circular wreath.

Rulau	Date	Metal	Size	VG	F	VF	Unc
Mav 72A	ND	Brass	19mm	—	—	—	—

As last. (Eklund 1926)

Both Roberto Pesant and Ray Byrnes had attributed Vila to Cuba. The attribution to Bolivia is denied by experts.
Cabeza de queso = (Literally) Head of cheese.

J. VILA Y CA.

Rulau	Date	Metal	Size	VG	F	VF	Unc
Mav 72C	ND	CN	19.5mm	—	—	22.00	—

J. VILA Y Ca / CABEZA / DE / QUESO / - TRINI-
DAD -. Rv: UN / CUARTILLO in circular wreath.
(Pesant 434; Byrne 1193)

Roberto Pesant says his own attribution to Trinidad, Las Villas Province, Cuba, is doubtful. This has also been claimed for Trinidad & Tobago and Bolivia.

VIRGEN MARIA

Rulau	Date	Metal	Size	F	VF	EF	Unc
Mav 73	1882	Brass	30.5mm	—	6.50	—	—

Virgin and child. Around: VIRGEN MARIA / *
SALUD DE LOS ENFERMOS *. Rv: Church. Around:
INAUGURADA EN 10 DE ABRIL DE / * 1882 *.
Plain edge. (Rulau coll.)

VISTA NIEVE

Rulau	Date	Metal	Size	F	VF	EF	Unc
Mav 75	ND	Aluminum	32.3mm	—	—	—	5.00

VISTA / 50 / NIEVE. Rv: Same as obverse. Reeded
edge. (Rulau coll.)

Vista Nieve = Snow view. The reeding is crude, while the fabric of the token is modern.

JUAN VIÑAS
Rose Mount Estates Ltd.

Rulau	Date	Metal	Size	VG	F	VF	Unc
Mav 72	ND	Brass	26mm	—	—	—	—

ROSE MOUNT ESTATES Ltd / 25 / CENTIMES / *
JUAN VIÑAS *. Rv: Blank.,(Bob Lyall coll.)

Possibly French West Indies or Haiti.

10 CENTAVOS

Rulau	Date	Matel	Size	F	VF	EF	Unc
Mav 76	ND	Brass	17mm	—	—	2.50	—

CENTAVOS / 10 (on shaded circle) / + CENTAVOS +.
Rv: Open-top wreath surrounds empty space. Plain
edge. Weight 1.88 grams. (Zaffern coll.)

(Castle)

Rulau	Date	Metal	Size	F	VF	EF	Unc
Mav 80	ND	Copper	19mm	—	—	—	30.00

Turreted castle. Rv: Blank. Plain edge. (Rulau coll.)

Struck by Scovill Mfg. Co., Waterbury, Conn., circa 1860-1880.

GLOSSARY OF TERMS
FOR
LATIN AMERICAN TOKENS

Acequia	Ditch, irrigation canal
Acueducto	Acqueduct
Admitido	Admitted
Agua	Water
Agua gaseosa	Soda water
Aguardiente	Raw brandy
Almacen	Grocery store
Almud	Dry measure. In Cuba, the almud equaled 8.3 lbs. of coffee berries
Arroba	A unit of weight. It varies:
	Argentina 25.32 lbs. avoirdupois
	Brazil 32.379 lbs.
	Colombia each dept set standard
	Guatemala 25.35 lbs.
	Honduras 25.36 lbs.
	Mexico 25.367 lbs.
	Peru 25.36 lbs.
Arroba	A unite of liquid measure. It varies
	Peru 6.7 imperial gals.
	Spain 4.262 gals. (wine)
	Spain 3.319 gals. (other)
Aurifera	Gold mining
Avenida	Avenue
Baño	Bath
Baño Tibio	Warm bath
Barraca	Rubber plantation (Bolivia)
Barril d'Agoa	Barrel of water (Brazil)
Barrio	(Ward, Precinct, Quarter
Bebida	Drink
Bica	Water spout (Brazil)
Billar	Billiards
Billarcitos	Pocket billiards
Bodega	Winery (Argentina)
Bodeguero	Grocer
Bola	Ball
Botica	Drugstore
Boticario	Druggist, Apothecary
Bronce	Brass (usually); also bronze
Cabra	Goat, cloud
Cabreria	Goat stable
Cafe	Cafe, bar, coffee
Cafetal	Coffee plantation
Caja	Box
Cajon	Box
Calle	Street
Callejon	Alley
Calzada	Causeway
Cambio	Money exchange
Campana	Bell
Campesino	Peasant
Campo	Field
Caña	(Sugar) cane
Canal	Canal
Canjeable	Exchangeable
Cantina	Saloon, bar
Caporal	Foreman
Carbon	Charcoal
Carbonifera	Coal mining
Carne	Meat
Carniceria	Butcher shop
Caretada	Load
Carreteria	Stage line
Catorce Grande	"Big 14" familes of El Salvador
Caza	The hunt
Central	Sugar processing center (Cuba)
Cerro	Hill
Cervecia	Brewery
Chapa	Metal identity tag for workers (Puerto Rico)
Chocoloteria	Chocolate factory
Cigarreria	Cigar store
Cigarillo	Cigarette
Ciudad	City
Claco	Early form of Tlaco (⅛ real)
Cobre	Copper
Coliseo	Coliseum
Comercio	Commerce
Comercios	Trades, businesses
Comprobante	Voucher
Confiteria	Cafe, small restaurant
Contramarca	Countermark
Contraseña	Check, token
Contratista	Contractor
Copa	Cup
Corte	Cutting
Cortes de Cafe	Cuttings of coffee
Cortijo	Farm, farmhouse
Cosecha	Harvest
Cuartel	Quarter
Cuartilla	¼ real
Cuartillo	¼ real
Despacho	Office
Despensa	Pantry, larder
Dia	Day
Diligencia	Stagecoach
Dinero Efectivo	Cash
Dueñas	Owners
Efectos	Goods
El Portador Trabajo	The bearer has worked
Empresa	Enterprise
Engenho	Sugar mill (Brazil)
Entrada	Admission ticket of entry
Entregado	Delivered (sometimes Entreg'o)
Equivalente	Equivalent
Escribano	Notary
Escuela	School
Esquina	Corner
Establecimiento	Establishment
Estancia	Farm estate (southern So. America)
Estanco	Monopoly store (esp. for tobacco)
Faena	Day's work
Faina	Overtime work
Fanega	Dry measure (15 bushels, Mexico) (12 almudes, Cuba)
Farmacia	Drugstore
Fazenda	Large ranch, estate (Brazil)
Feria	Fair
Ferreteria	Hardware store
Ferrocarril	Railroad
Ficha	Token, check
Ficha Convencional	Contractual token
Finca	Plantation, farm
Fonda	Inn
Fondo	Fund
Fornecimento	Merchandise (Brazil)
Fuerte	A silver peso
Ganadera	Cattle ranch
Grabador	Engraver
Granja	Farm, grange
Gremio	Guild, union
Gremio de Panaderos	Guild of bakers
Hacienda	Large ranch, estate
Heladeria	Ice cream shop
Helado	Ice cream
Henequen	Hemp, sisal
Hermanos	Brothers
Hipodromo	Hippodrome
Ingenio	Sugar mill (and plantation)
Ingenio de Azucar	Sugar mill
Jabon	Soap
Jardin	Garden
Jornal (pl. Jornales)	Day's work
Joyeria	Jewelry store
Joyero	Jeweler
Juego	Game
Jugador	Player
Latifundista	Large landowner
Leche	Milk
Lecheria	Dairy
Leña	Firewood
Libreria	Bookstore
Limpia Cafetal	Honorable coffee estate
Loro	Parrot
Madera	Wood
Mais or Maiz	Corn
Mecate Chapeo	Area of 400 square meters cleared and cleaned of weeds
Medio	Half
Mercaderias	Merchandise
Mercado	Market
Merced	Grace, mercy

Merceria	Notions store
Mina	Mine
Mineral	Mine operation
Ministerio	Ministry
Mitad	Half. As used on Colombian tokens, it indicates ½ cuartillo, or ⅛ real. As used in Chile, it indicates a base metal or leather token of the 1700's.
Muelle	Dock, mole
Municipalidad	Municipality
Municipio	City
Municipio	Municipal token
Nomina	Roll, roster
Obrero	Worker
Octavo	⅛ real
Oficina	Branch (in Chile: Mine site)
Padrino	Godfather, patron
Padrinos	Godparents
Pagadero	Pay
Pagadero sin desuento	Pay without discount
Palo de tinte	Dye wood
Pan	Bread
Pan	Mass of nitrate
Panaderia	Bakery
Parque	Park
Parque Zoologico	Zoo
Pastor	Shepherd
Peluqueria	Barber shop
Pencas	Leaves (esp. of henequen)
Peon	Laborer
Perfumeria	Perfumery
Pescaria	Fish market (Brazil)
Pieza	Piece
Plantacion	Plantation
Plantio	Plantation, vegetable field
Plaza	Square, plaza
Plazuela	Small square
Poblacion	Town, population
Pochuta	City in Guatemala (NOT a denomination!!)
Portador	Bearer
Pueblo	Village, people
Puente	Bridge
Pulperia	General store
Pulque	Fermented maguey juice
Pulquera	Maker of pulque
Pulqueria	Pulque tavern
Punzonada	Counterstamped
Quebrachales	(Hardwood) forests
Quebracho	A hardwood tree (So. America)
Quintal	A unit of weight. It varies: Brazil 129.54 lbs. avoir. Guatemala 101.4 lbs. Honduras 101.4 lbs. Peru 101.43 lbs. Uruguay 101.4 lbs.
Rabiblancos	"White Birds"—The 20 leading families of Panama

Racion	Ration, portion
Ranchero	Rancher
Rancho	Ranch
Real (pl. Reales)	Basic unit of currency in Spanish America, ⅛ of peso or dollar
Recuerdo	Souvenir
Reis	Portuguese currency units, originally the equal of the Spanish real
Relojeria	Watchmaker's shop
Relojero	Watchmaker
Resello	Revalidation counterstamp
Ril (pl. Riles)	Real token (Puerto Rico)
Romeria	Festival of fellowship
Salina	Salt mine
Salitre	Nitrate (saltpeter)
Salitrera	Nitrate mine, or bed
Seña	Check (metal token)
Sociedad	Society
Sociedad Anonima	Incorporated (approximately)
Sociedad Forestal	Forest corporation
Sopa	Soup
Tabacal	Tobacco plantation
Tabaquero	Tobacconist
Tagua	Species of nut
Tambo	Traveler's resting place
Tanino	Tannin
Tanteo	Trial, test
Tarea	Task
Termas Minerales	Mineral Baths
Tienda	Store
Tienda Mixta	General store (Cuba: company store)
Tinto	Red wine, or demitasse of coffee
Tlaco	Token (⅛ real)
Tlaco de Madera	Wood token (⅛ real)
Trabajo	Labor
Trabajador	Worker
Trilladora	Coffee processing plant
Troquelado	Counterstamped
Tumbador	Forest clearer
Uso interno	Internal use
Uzina	Sugar plantation (Brazil)
Vale	Worth
Vale	Scrip in paper or cardboard
Vale por	Good for
Valle	Valley, Vale
Vaqueria	Dairy
Vaqueta	Cowhide, calfskin
Vidro	Watch crystal
Villa	City
Vino	Wine
Viveres	Provisions
Yngenio	Sugar mill (and plantation)
Zapateria	Shoe store
Zueleria	Bootmaker's store

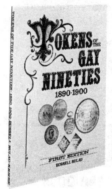
389

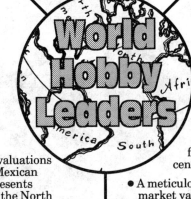

MASTER INDEX
and
Latin American Token Finder

PERIODICALS FOR THE HOBBYIST

☐ **Bank Note Reporter**

The only independently-produced publication devoted to U.S. and world paper money, scrip and related fiscal paper.
$29.95 per year

(Non-U.S. addresses surface rate, $40.25. Canada & Mexico, $46.25)

☐ **Numismatic News**

Weekly tabloid for the serious collector, featuring the Coin Market value guide and the hobby's only full-time Washington D.C., Bureau.
$27.95 per year

(Non-U.S. addresses surface rate, $79.95. Canada & Mexico, $99.00)

☐ **Coins**

Monthly focusing on interests for both the beginning and veteran collector. Informative features and a U.S. coins value guide.
$19.95 per year

(Non-U.S. addresses surface rate, $30.25. Canada, Mexico, $38.95)

☐ **Coin Prices**

The only periodical providing comprehensive value listings of all U.S. coins every issue. Bi-Monthly.
$16.95 per year

(Non-U.S. addresses surface rate, $22.00. Canada & Mexico, $25.25)

☐ **World Coin News**

Newspaper devoted exclusively to World Coins. Keep collectors on top of this hoby with news of international events and information-packed columns.
$24.95 per year

(Non-U.S. addresses surface rate, $47.25. Canada, Mexico, $60.00)

To subscribe, check appropriate boxes and send payment with this form to:

Krause Publications
700 E. State St., Iola, WI 54990-0001

( ) Check (To Krause Publications)

( ) MasterCard/VISA

Name _____

Address _____

City _____

State _____ Zip _____

Acct. No. _____

Exp. Date: Mo. _____ Yr. _____

Signature _____

Phone No. _____

NOTES

NOTES

NOTES

NOTES